CHAM[illegible]
GUIDE T[illegible]
LEGAL PROFESSION

Student Edition 2000

Caroline Walker
Editor

Chambers & Partners Publishing
Saville House, 23 Long Lane, London EC1A 9HL
Tel: (020) 7606 1300

Published by Chambers & Partners Publishing
(a division of Orbach & Chambers Ltd)
Saville House, 23 Long Lane, London EC1A 9HL
Tel: (020) 7606 1300 Fax: (020) 7600 3191

Chambers & Partners Legal Recruitment: (020) 7606 8844

ISBN: 0 85514-302-9

Publisher: *Michael Chambers*

Managing Editor: *Reena SenGupta*

Editor: *Caroline Walker*

Editorial Assistant: *Harriet Merry*

A-Z Co-ordinator: *Al Baker*

Researchers: *Anna Williams, Sheena Lee, Jon Kingham, James Baxter, William Salamone, James Rossiter, Lloyd Pearson*

Production Team: *John Buck, Laurie Griggs, Mitchell Amihod*

Business Development Manager: *Brad Sirott*

Business Development Team: *Richard Ramsey, Neil Murphy, Samantha Atkins*

Database Manager: *Derek Wright*

Printed in England by: *Polestar Wheatons Limited*

Acknowledgements:
Our thanks to the Chambers & Partners' Directory team 1999-2000 for the use of their research; to the Chambers & Partners' Recruitment consultants for their knowledge of the profession; and to the students, trainees, pupils, lawyers and academic personnel who assisted our journalists and researchers.

COMPILING THE STUDENT EDITION

The main purpose of the Student Edition of the Chambers Guide to the Legal Profession is to help students find a suitable firm or set of chambers in which to train. It also provides an introduction to the principal specialist practice areas and the firms and sets which specialise in them.

The book is compiled using three sources:

1. the research and rankings of law firms and barristers' chambers contained in the Chambers Guide to the Legal Profession 1999-2000.

2. hundreds of interviews with students, trainees, pupils, solicitors, barristers, graduate recruitment professionals and other relevant individuals.

3. information provided by consultants from Chambers and Partners Legal Recruitment Consultancy.

Stars awarded to firms and sets in the 'Specialist Practice Areas' and 'Top recommendations' set out in 'The True Picture' follow the rankings in the directory. These are based on research by a team of 12 full time researchers over a period of six months. In 1999 more than 6000 telephone interviews were conducted with individual practitioners and clients, each one lasting an average of 30 minutes.

HOW TO USE THE STUDENT EDITION

The desired practice area can be used to locate the top recommended firms or sets. They can then be cross-referenced in the True Picture and in the A-Z section for further detailed information. Alternatively, a particular firm can be looked up in 'The True Picture' or the A-Z, its main or best practice areas identified and more information on its work types obtained from 'Specialist Practice Areas.'

The student book should be used in conjunction with the Chambers Guide to the Legal Profession 1999-2000. This carries detailed information on every practice area in which the top UK firms are recommended. This is extremely useful for completing application forms and for interview preparation.

CONTENTS

TRAINING AS A SOLICITOR

Introduction

Applying

The Training Contract

After Training

Specialist Practice Areas

Training as a Solicitor

Applying

TIMETABLE FOR 2000-2002

LAW STUDENTS

Penultimate Year

October 1999-February 2000:	Compile information about law firms. Obtain firm brochures. Attend presentations and law fairs on campus.
January - March 2000*:	Apply for open days and vacation schemes.
Spring - Summer 2000:**	Attend vacation schemes. Apply to law firms for training contracts for 2002. Apply for a place on the LPC.

Final Year

September - December 2000:	Attend interviews for training contracts for 2002.

Post Graduation

September 2001:	Commence LPC.
July 2002:	Finish LPC.
September 2002:	Commence training contract (first intake).
March 2003:	Commence training contract (second intake).
September 2004:	Qualify as a solicitor (first intake).
March 2005:	Qualify as a solicitor (second intake).

* It is important to check closing dates for each firm as these will vary. Many close in January or February. Some firms will only accept applications for vacation schemes from penultimate year students whether law or non-law. See pages 18-20 for further information.

** It is important to check closing dates for each firm. Many firms will not accept applications after the summer. A few firms accept applications into the Autumn or even into the following year. Some firms require very early applications from non-law graduates. See pages 22-27 for further information.

*** Some firms may interview earlier or later than these dates.

TIMETABLE FOR 2000-2002

NON-LAW STUDENTS

Penultimate Year

October 1999-February 2000:	Compile information about law firms. Obtain firm brochures. Attend presentations and law fairs on campus.
January - March 2000*:	Apply for open days and vacation schemes.
June - August 2000:	Attend vacation schemes.

Final Year

October 2000-February 2001:	Compile information about law firms. Obtain firm brochures. Attend presentations and law fairs on campus. Apply for training contracts to those firms with unusually early closing dates.
November 2000:	Apply for a place on the CPE course.
January - March 2001*:	Apply for open days and vacation schemes.
January - Autumn 2001:**	Apply to law firms for training contracts for 2003.
September - December 2001*:**	Attend interviews for training contracts for 2003.

Post Graduation

June - August 2001:	Attend vacation schemes and interviews for training contracts for 2003. Apply for a place on the LPC if your CPE institution does not guarantee you a place.
September 2001:	Commence CPE.
July 2002:	Finish CPE.
September 2002:	Commence LPC.
July 2003:	Finish LPC.
September 2003:	Commence training contract (first intake).
March 2004:	Commence training contract (second intake).
September 2005:	Qualify as a solicitor (first intake).
March 2006:	Qualify as a solicitor (second intake).

LAW SOCIETY GUIDE TO RECRUITING TRAINEES

Law Society accreditation

Your firm must be authorised by the Law Society to take trainees. Otherwise your training contract will not be recognised, and you will not be able to practise.

Accreditation criteria

Your trainee principal must have held five consecutive practising certificates and must be UK qualified.

There must be one partner for every two trainees at the firm.

The Law Society's guide to recruiting trainees

The Law Society's guide is summarised below. Any breaches of this guide should be notified to the Law Society in Redditch.

Employers

Employers will not interview for trainee posts before 1st September in the student's final undergraduate year. Students shall not be required to apply earlier than 31 July at the end of their penultimate year. No offer to any student who has done a vacation placement shall be made before 1st September in the student's final year.

Students will be told at interview if there are further selection stages to go through. They will also be told the likely date by which an offer of employment will be made. An offer of employment will not be withdrawn before the time for acceptance has expired.

The employer will write to interviewees within two weeks telling them of the outcome of the interview or confirming that the outcome is still to be determined. All offers must be made in writing.

Time limits for accepting an offer of a training contract must not expire before 1st November in the student's final year (or in the CPE year). In any case, the time period for accepting must never be less than three weeks from the date the offer is sent. If the training contract is not due to start within a year, it is not good practice to set a time limit on the offer.

Employers will consider sympathetically a request to extend the time limit, provided a good reason is given.

Employers will not discriminate directly or indirectly on the grounds of race, religion or sex.

Employers providing financial assistance to trainees in relation to undergraduate or post-graduate studies will explain in writing the terms on which such assistance is offered at the time of the offer of a training contract is made. The above rules governing time limits for accepting an offer of a training contract apply equally to an offer of financial assistance.

Students

Students will respond to offers promptly and not later than three weeks after receipt of the offer (unless the offer is for a contract beginning more than a year later, in which case there is no fixed time limit).

Students will not accumulate offers. Two is the maximum number to be held at any one time. Others (old or new) must be rejected.

An acceptance must be in writing. All other outstanding offers and invitations to interviews must be rejected and no further applications made.

WRITING A CV

It is vital that you present yourself well in your CV or on the firm's standard application form. When deciding whether to interview candidates, most employers will spend only a few minutes (or even seconds) considering each CV or form, so a well drafted document is essential.

There is no one formula for writing a CV, but there are guidelines you should follow. Adhere to these principles and you won't be criticised for the way in which you present yourself.

- Limit your CV to two or three pages at most. US style one-page documents work well as a summary but need supporting documentation and this might not be the best approach given that many firms receive thousands of applications. Think about how best you are going to use your few moments of the recruiter's attention.

- Clarity and presentation are everything. The pages of your CV are your chance to impress on the firm that you have the ability to communicate well. It's not just what you have to say it's how you say it. Choose a clear font and use good quality white or cream paper. It may sound like a basic point, but if there are typographical errors or if it is poorly printed it not only looks bad, it indicates that either you don't care or you simply can't get it right.

- You're not designing a Christmas card. Stay clear of borders, graphics and swirly fonts. As well as making a CV difficult to read, it just comes across as a gimmick.

- The lay out should be self-evident to the reader. If it is chronological then stick to this approach throughout. The reader shouldn't have to work too hard at figuring out your structure. At a glance they should know exactly where they will find a specific piece of information.

- Think carefully about what is relevant. The things that most impress you about yourself may be of very little relevance to the reader. If you're mad keen on surfing, then of course feel free to mention it as a hobby and perhaps also mention if you have been involved in a Surfers against Sewage environmental awareness campaign. However, this sort of information belongs towards the end of the CV in a brief section about your interests. Do not give top billing to the fact that you won the under sixteen long board competition at Fistral Beach six years ago. You're applying for a legal training contract not a lifeguard's job.

- Work out what sort of information will be of most relevance to the firm. Chat with family and friends and maybe even someone who works at the firm. Generally, people will be very willing to help you. Read the firm's brochure and recruitment materials. These often contain useful hints as to the type of information they would wish to see in a CV.

- There's a big difference between an honest CV and one that contains outright lies. Somewhere in the middle is the CV that has embellished certain aspects of your experience. Don't be tempted to give false information, such as academic grades. You merely lay yourself open to being caught out and no-one would criticise an employer for withdrawing an offer of employment in such circumstances. Similarly, don't be tempted to portray yourself as someone you are not. If you sang in the chorus line of the sixth form panto just the once, don't sell yourself as a chorister. The partner who interviews you may wish to discuss Bach in detail. Whilst he won't care that you can't sing, he will care that you tried to deceive him.

- If you have held any posts of responsibility then do mention them. Recruiters like to see this sort of information as it indicates that you have initiative. Involvement in a variety of activities shows that you are a well-rounded person.

- When you have finished drafting your CV, read through it. Is it you? If you don't recognise the person whose life has been summarised on those sheets of paper then take another look at it and figure out what's gone wrong. A bureau can prepare your CV for you but will they capture the essence of who you are? Accept the fact that just as some firms will not appeal to you, you will not appeal to some firms. If the CV can target the firms with which you will have a mutual attraction then the task of selecting your training contract will be made all the easier.

Here are some key 'Don'ts':

- Don't attach a photograph. Recruiters will simply wonder why you have done so.
- Don't bind your CV. It may stand out for the wrong reasons - the one that is difficult to photocopy/scan/fit into an envelope.
- Don't leave gaps in your academic/job history. State when travelling, unemployed or taking a career break etc.
- Don't fall into the trap of using worn-out old clichés such as 'a highly motivated team player with excellent communication skills.' By saying this you say nothing. Demonstrate by example in your CV.
- Don't assume that your interests or your religious/moral/social concerns will be shared by the recruiters. Don't define yourself by them.
- Don't feel obliged to indicate your marital status or ethnic background on your CV. It is unlawful for an employer to base their decision to offer you a job based on sex, race or disability. You should question why an employer asks you about whether or not you are married with children. Legitimate requests for ethnic or cultural background information, details of disability and sex are often included with standard application forms and these should state specifically that the information sought is for statistical monitoring purposes to ensure that a firm is adhering to an equal opportunities policy. These requests will ideally be on a separate form and should be removed from the main application before short-listing candidates for interview.

Many of the above points will apply equally to the completion of a standard application form. In addition, recruiters have told us about the following points:

- Don't send in a messy form. Unbelievably, some do get returned crumpled or bearing coffee rings or with ink stains all over them.
- Excessive crossings out or miles of correction fluid don't impress one little bit. Using more than one pen to complete the form is really off-putting. Always make a copy of the form and complete the copy first. Once you are satisfied with your responses to the questions, take your time in reproducing them onto the original.
- Some sections of the application form have enormous significance; the firms will look closely at the sections which tell them about the sort of person you are. It's make or break on these sections, so get them right. Questions are designed to enable you to illustrate whether or not you have the qualities that make a good solicitor. These questions will differ from form to form and it is the very fact that they differ which you should be aware of. Don't have a standard response that you set down on each firm's application form. Andrew Looney, Graduate Recruitment officer at Eversheds points out that so many people simply don't read questions closely enough, missing the fact that there might be two or three separate issues in the one question. Applicants need to spot how many points need to be addressed in the answer and to ensure that they cover all of them.
- When asked why you chose the firm, don't fall into the trap of regurgitating the messages in the recruitment brochure. If you do, it will be painfully obvious to the recruiters; they wrote the brochure and the last thing they want to see is a chewed up version of their own words. "Tell us why it is that you want to work at the firm" says Andrew Looney. "Why did you choose us? Did you meet people at a recruitment fair or did you do research in the legal directories and conclude we were the right sort of firm for you?"

INTERVIEW TECHNIQUE

You can never prepare fully for an interview. Don't be alarmed by that statement; all it says is that every interview will be different and you can't second guess how a particular one will go. This shouldn't worry you too much - really! Concentrate on preparing to the extent possible and try not to let anxiety ruin the day. Just do your best and be yourself; nobody can expect any more from you. Forget words like 'performance', you're not auditioning for a role in a play. Concentrate on demonstrating your suitability for the job and impressing upon the interviewer the type of person you are.

The very fact that you have been called for interview means that you're off to a cracking start. They like you on paper already. The interview is your chance to enhance their appreciation of what you have to offer. That chance starts from the moment you walk through the door of the building. It may sound trite, but Chambers and Partners Recruitment consultants confirm that the golden rule of 'first impressions count' really does hold true. The tone of an interview can be set within the first few seconds.

If this is the first time you have hunted for a serious job then you may find the following tips of use. If you have come from a different career, read through them to refresh your memory.

- Make sure that your appearance is smart and that your nails, hair, shoes and clothes are clean. Even if you normally wouldn't be seen dead out of your seventies retro-styled wardrobe, be realistic about what you're aiming to achieve on the day of the interview. Wacky ties or socks, clothing that reveals your tattoo from Borneo or non-cultural facial jewellery are going to raise some serious questions about your ability or willingness to conform to established business norms. Is it worth jeopardising a job offer over wearing blue nailpolish for the day? The interviewer is going to look at you with a view to how presentable you'll be to the organisation's clients.

- How many times have you heard claims that only a minority of what is communicated between people comes through the spoken word? It is true - body language is key. Practice giving a firm handshake, think about your posture when you sit so as to avoid nervous perching or an off-putting slouch. Don't feel embarrassed to meet someone's gaze, although we're not advocating a psychotic stare!

- It's OK to smile and you never know, you might even find yourself sharing a laugh with the interviewer at some point. This however is not an encouragement for you to crack jokes - save that for Jongleurs. The good interview is characterised by the parties finding common ground and establishing some sort of rapport. We can't tell you how to produce this at will, it's chemistry, but just remember that every interview you attend holds the potential for you and the interviewer to 'click'. Where there are a number of interviewers just try to remind yourself, from time to time, to acknowledge the presence of all of them. A short glance here and there, directing your answers to all members of a panel instead of just one will maximise your chance of engaging with the panel as a whole.

- If you come across nervously, the interviewer may feel that its just a bit too much like hard work communicating with you. At the same time, guard against coming over as arrogant or a 'know-it-all.' Believe us when we say that you will only know a fraction of what they do about their business.

- The important thing to display is an understanding of the basic profile of the firm or set and to indicate your enthusiasm to become involved in what they do. The latter will be fairly easy if you have a genuine interest in their business. As to the former, the value of good research will become apparent to you at interview. There are a number of sources available to you so do make good use of them – others will. Look on-line for the organisation's website. Read through as many of their brochures as possible, they will invariably produce client-oriented material covering different practice areas or developments on the law. You never know, you may strike it lucky and end up discussing how the firm is advising clients on new disability discrimination law with the interviewing partner, who just happens to be from the firm's employment unit. If you have an interest in a particular practice area, make sure you have some idea of the type of clients that the firm acts for in that area. There's a huge amount of information available in The Chambers Guide to the Legal Profession. From that you can gain an understanding of where a firm or set sits in relation to its competitors in any particular area of law, you can find out the identity of some of its key clients and which have been amongst the most significant recent deals and cases. As well as finding out factual information as to the size of teams and the identity of key lawyers from this publication you may also get a feel for the style of a team. But remember, you are not expected to know everything, it is more important that they recognise genuine interest in their work.

- You will be asked to talk about yourself, so have a think about what you might say. If that means sitting down and writing a list of strengths and weaknesses, then do it by all means but leave them at home. Always try and have examples of things you have done or been involved with rather than crowing about personal attributes. If you have worked in a legal advice centre whilst a student, this will automatically tell the interviewer that you are someone who has started to develop communication and advisory skills. If you play team sports or belong to a group of some sort this indicates that you're not a loner and can work with people as part of a team. Involvement in extra-curricular activities implies that you are well-rounded and have a variety of skills to offer. Don't overstate your interests and involvement though, if you can't follow through it could be embarrassing at best and at worst it will put off the interviewer.

- Analyse your thoughts on certain topics. Why are you drawn to the law? What do you feel are your strongest and weakest points. What have you most enjoyed about your law/non-law undergraduate degree? Don't prepare a script as this could make your answers sound as wooden as a stick or perhaps Keanu Reeves in Bram Stoker's Dracula. Do, however, sit down with someone - your Dad, your Granny, your tutor and chat to them about these topics. Don't make that first formal interview a dry run.

- Finally, be positive - it's the ace in your hand!

Psychometric testing sounds a bit daunting, but if this is part of the screening process don't be put off. It's never going to be of more significance than the interview itself or your credentials on paper. There's nothing to prevent you asking the recruitment personnel to indicate what format any testing will take. There's also nothing to prevent you from asking who is likely to be interviewing you.

VACATION SCHEMES

A vacation placement could be the best interview you'll ever get. Maybe this is why those one, two or three week slots are so keenly fought over. There are more training contracts available than vacation placements and many students do a number of placements which leaves other students without any direct experience other than what they can organise for themselves with, perhaps, smaller local firms. The value of this latter experience should not be under-estimated. Even if you want to work for a commercial firm, nobody is going to criticise you for having sought experience in a smaller firm.

Law Society guidelines state that no interviews may take place or offers of training contracts be made until 1st September in the student's final year of undergraduate study. In other words, the vacation scheme cannot result in a job offer. However, it is not unheard of for a student to find that the training contract interview becomes merely a formality if they have had a good placement with the firm. At the very least it will provide another internal assessment which will be taken into account by the interviewing panel.

What can you expect from a vacation scheme? At some firms they are stage-managed to the nth degree. In go the fresh-faced and enthusiastic students and, ideally, at the end of the placement out they come slightly squeezed into the firm mould. At some firms, no expense is spared; social functions, trips to City institutions and the courts are laid on. While both sides are selling, it is the students who feel 'wooed.'

A common approach is for a firm to locate students in a different department for each week of the scheme. A current trainee may be assigned as a 'minder.' The student will usually sit with a qualified lawyer, sometimes a trainee, occasionally in a room with other students. The firm will aim to give you a flavour of the work in each department and will let you help out on matters, giving you manageable tasks. The extent to which you really can get involved is sometimes surprising. Some students are taken along to client meetings. A summer student at a City firm told us that on two occasions he worked all night with a corporate team on the completion of a deal. As it was a novelty, this sold him on the firm and on corporate law.

Others who had experienced more than one scheme were able to make comparisons between firms and told us that they were unimpressed by some. At the very least, a disappointing vacation scheme can help you decide that you don't want to train with a firm. The magic of doing a vacation placement is that for a couple of weeks you can not only observe how people work, but how they get on with each other. The firm with which you ultimately choose to train ought to be offering you an attractive working environment. You will spend a considerable amount of your waking hours with the people at the firm and as such you need to be certain that the atmosphere is right for you. If you can't stand the idea of working in a traditional, stuffy atmosphere then use the vacation scheme to figure out whether a firm falls into that category or whether the chemistry between you and the firm is right.

With some firms paying students more than £200 a week for the placement, it's a serious business. If you are intending to participate - and absolutely every trainee we spoke to recommended this - then be sufficiently well-organised to get your applications in on time. Be prepared for an interview which might be as rigorous as a training contract interview.

A word of warning. It might not be the brightest idea to fill your Easter and Summer vacations with one scheme after another. This is also an important time for you to pursue your non-professional aspirations. If you want to travel then make sure you fit it in. If you have a desire to be involved in a project outside of the law then do it. If an opportunity for interesting work outside of the law crops up then take it. Many recruitment partners are more impressed by those who have a range of life experiences to talk about at interview. All work and no play....

▶

Vacation Scheme information at a glance

Firm Name	Places for 2000	Duration	Remuneration (per week)	Closing Date
Addleshaw Booth & Co	40	2 wks.	£125	25 Feb. 2000
Allen & Overy	90	3 wks.	£200	31 Jan. 2000
Ashurst Morris Crisp	45-50	3 wks.	£200(1999)	29 Feb. 2000
Baker & McKenzie	30	3 wks	£250	31 Jan. 2000
Barlow Lyde & Gilbert	50	2 wks.	£175	28 Feb.
Berg & Co	yes	1-2 wks		End June 2000
S J Berwin & Co	60	2 wks.	£200	1 Mar. 2000
Berwin Leighton	-	1 wk		29 Feb. 2000
Bevan Ashford	75			
Bindman & Partners	2	3 wks		30 April 2000
Bird & Bird	12	3 wks.	£160	Mar. 2000
Blake Lapthorn	15	1 wk	unpaid	end Mar. 2000
Boodle Hatfield	10	2 wks	£90	1 June 2000
Bristows	36	Summer - 2 wks., Christmas /Easter - 1 wk	£200	Christmas - 15/11; Easter/Summer - 29/2.
Burges Salmon	30	2 wks.	£125	25 Feb. 2000
Cadwalader, Wickersham & Taft	6	4 wks (3 in London and 1 in New York)	£225	18 Feb. 2000
Capsticks	yes	2 wks.		31 Mar. 2000
Cartwrights	18	1 wk		28 Feb. 2000
Clifford Chance	80		£200 pw	11 Feb. 2000
Clyde & Co	64	1 day;	travel expenses	28 Feb. 2000.
CMS Cameron McKenna	55	2 wks.	£200	11 Feb. 2000
Davenport Lyons	10	2-3 wks.	£150	none fixed.
Dawson & Co	2	2 wks.	£150	28 Feb. 2000
Dibb Lupton Alsop	180	1 wk.	£175 London, £125 regions	28 Feb. 2000
Dickinson Dees	20	1 wk	£50	28 Feb. 2000
D J Freeman	16	3 wks.	£150	14 Mar. 2000
Donne Mileham & Haddock	limited number	1-2 wks.	£100	31 Mar. 2000
Edge Ellison	75	2 wks.	£100 Midlands £120 London	11 Feb. 2000
Eversheds	120	2 wks.	regional variations	31 Jan. 2000
Farrer & Co	18	2 wks. at Easter, 3 wks. in summer	£190 p.w	31 Jan. 2000
Fenners	10	2 wks.	competitive rates	30 April 2000
Freshfields	100	2 wks.	£450 (total)	14 Feb. 2000
Garretts	60	3 wks.	£100-£175 (1999)	n/a
Gouldens	Summer (law): 35: Easter (non law): 7 Xmas (non-law): 14	2 wks.	£225	Summer/Easter: 28 Feb. Xmas: 30 Oct
Halliwell Landau	25	2 wks.	£100	31 Mar. 2000
Hammond Suddards	35	3 wks.	£220 (London), £170 pw (Leeds and Manchester)	29 Feb. 2000
Herbert Smith	90	1x1 wk;	£200	Mid-Feb.

Vacation Scheme information at a glance (cont.)

Firm Name	Places for 2000	Duration	Remuneration (per week)	Closing Date
		1x2 wks.; 3x3 wks.		
Hewitson Becke + Shaw	a few	1-2 wks..		
Holman Fenwick & Willan	12	2 wks. Dates: 26 June - 7 July/ 17 July - 28 July	£200	14 Feb.
Holmes Hardingham		1-2 wks.	£250	May 2000
Ince & Co	16	2 wks.	£200	18 Feb. 2000
Irwin Mitchell	30	2 wks.	£75	1 Mar. 2000
Knight & Sons				31 Oct. for Christmas 28 Feb. for Easter 30 April for Summer
Landwell (formerly Arnheim Tite & Lewis)	up to 20	2 wks		25 Feb. 2000
Lawrence Graham	20-24	2	£200	28 Feb. 2000
Lawrence Tucketts	8+			
Laytons	6	1 wk		Mar. 2000
Leigh, Day &Co	varies	2-6 wks.	£150	no official date
Lester Aldridge	8	2 wks.	£60 pw	31 Mar. 2000
Linklaters	80	Christmas - 2 wks. Easter - 2 wks.. Summer - 4 wks.	£200	
Lovells	80	2-3 wks.	£200	19/2/00 for Easter and Summer, 10/11/00 for Christmas
Macfarlanes	40	2 wks.	£200	29 Feb. 2000
Martineau Johnson	60	1 day		25 Feb. 2000
Masons	35 (London), 5 (Manchester)	2 wks.	£175 London, £125 - Manchester	12 Feb. 1999
Mills & Reeve	25	2 wks.	£100	1 Mar. 2000
Mishcon de Reya	8	4 wks.	£150	28 April 2000
Morgan Cole	25	5 wks.		end April 2000
Nabarro Nathanson	available	3 wks.		25 Feb. 2000
Nicholson Graham & Jones	8	2 wks.	£180	
Norton Rose	45 Summer, 15 Christmas	Summer: 3 wks., Christmas: 2 wks.	£200	25 Feb. 2000 for Summer, 3 Nov. 2000 for Christmas.
Olswang	20	3 wks.	£150	31 Jan. 2000
Osborne Clarke	20	1 wk	£80	26 Feb. 2000
Paisner & Co	10	4 wks.	£150	30 April 2000
Pannone & Partners	20	1 wk	0	10 Mar. 2000
Penningtons	Some summer vacation places			31 May 2000.
Pinsent Curtis	140	1 wk		28 Feb. 2000
Radcliffes	10	2 wks.	£130	31 Mar. 2000

Vacation Scheme information at a glance (cont.)

Firm Name	Places for 2000	Duration	Remuneration	Closing Date
Reynolds Porter Chamberlain	12	2 wks.	£175	29 Feb. 2000
Richards Butler	45	2 wks.	£200	31 Mar. 2000
Rowe & Maw	25	2 wks.	£200	29 Feb. 2000
Shadbolt & Co	6	2 wks.	£120	17 Mar. 2000
Shoosmiths	25	2 wks.	£120	29 Feb. 2000
Simmons & Simmons	30	2 wks.	£200	25 Feb. 2000
Sinclair Roche & Temperley	12	2 wks.	£160	28 Feb. 2000
Slaughter and May	60	2 wks.	£225	18 Feb. 2000
Speechly Bircham	8	3 wks.	£160	end Feb. 2000
Stephenson Harwood	21	2 wks.	£175	18 Feb. 2000
Taylor Joynson Garrett	30	2 wks.	£200	25 Feb. 2000
Taylor Vinters	Places available	1 wk		
Taylor Walton	2-3	up to 4 wks.	agreed with trainee	30 April 2000
Theodore Goddard	20	2 wks.	£200	end Feb. 2000
Titmuss Sainer Dechert	8	10 July to 21 July	£190	25 Feb. 2000.
Travers Smith Braithwaite	45	3 wks.	£200	end Mar. 2000
Trowers & Hamlins	25-30	3 wks.	£175	31 Jan. (Easter); 1 Mar. (Summer)
Walker Morris	30-40	1 wk	£100	28 Feb. 2000
Warner Cranston	12	2 wks.	£400	31 Mar. 2000.
Watson, Farley & Williams	30	2 wks.	£200	31 Mar. 2000
Wedlake Bell	4	3 wks.	£150	end Feb. 2000
Weightmans	6	2 wks		31 Mar. 2000
White & Case LLP	20	2 wks.	£250	end Feb. 2000
Wilde Sapte	75	1 wk	£160	17 Mar. 2000
Withers	16	Easter (3 wks.), summer (3 wks.)	£130	18 Feb. 2000
Wragge & Co	Easter 2000: 20 places Summer 2000: 48 places	1 wk 2 wks.	£125 £125	11 Feb. 2000

The table represents the top 50 firms by size plus firms with an A-Z entry. Some information has been summarised. Gaps and omissions show that full information has not been supplied.
See A-Z section for further details.

THE SELECTION PROCESS

Ten years ago a third year student at Birmingham University did a summer placement with a top five City firm. She liked the firm and they liked her. Without a single interview or assessment they offered her a job. In 1990, this was not particularly unusual.

Now, however, it's a different story. Students applying for training contracts are likely to face an assault course of group exercises, written tests and day-long assessments before they secure a job.

A typical assessment day consists of a couple of written tests, a number of group exercises, a couple of interviews and perhaps a presentation to a group. One student told us of her "nightmarish" experience at a large City firm. She and three others were given a group exercise where they had to imagine they were stranded in the desert. They were given fifteen items to rank in order of importance to their survival. The exercise lasted half an hour and a recruitment officer closely observed the whole process. What she found particularly difficult was the awkward behaviour of everyone in the group. Nobody seemed to know what was expected of them and the individuals ranged from being over-assertive to quiet and difficult.

A very different group exercise at another City firm involved a more business-like situation. Twelve candidates were divided into two groups and asked to advise on the purchase of two factories. One had union problems, but solid financial backing, the other had a different set of problems. Again the group was observed and again, our student found the experience quite "tense". She must have performed well though because she was offered a job. When asked why she thought she was successful at one firm and not at the other, she said it had a lot to do with the nature of the group. She felt more comfortable with the second set of people and also with the task. So, it was partly down to chance. However, she also felt more prepared second time round and realised it was better just to be herself. What can a candidate in their first selection round learn from this?

The most obvious answer is to be yourself and you will find the right firm for you. Bob Llewellin, training director with Burges Salmon, says: "It's important not to be a pushover - say something, but it doesn't help to be bombastic." If your arguments aren't accepted by the group don't worry - you might have been asked to argue an unwinnable case. Firms are looking for how good a team player you are - do you listen, can you compromise, do you keep an eye on the time and on details such as budget? You should also remember that firms are looking for all kinds of people - the more measured, thoughtful type as well as the outgoing team leader.

Away from the group exercises, there will often be written tests. These vary from advising on a contract, to rewriting a complex document in simple English to answering multiple choice personality questions. Firms place varying emphasis on the different exercises; for some the interview is crucial while for others, the group exercises are of primary importance. If it is possible to find out in advance (from current trainees perhaps) then this might be advantageous.

The selection and recruitment process is, in many firms a polished, highly professional procedure and the City firms, in particular, waste no time in letting successful and unsuccessful applicants know. In many cases, candidates hear the next day. With the benefit of hindsight, most of our interviewees said they enjoyed their assessments and "the day will almost certainly end with a drinks party" - but don't relax too much - you're probably being assessed there too!

▶

Selection information at a glance

Firm Name	Method of Application	Selection Procedure	Required Degree
Addleshaw Booth & Co	Application form	Interview, assessment day	2:1
Allen & Overy	Application form	Assessment centre	2:1
Anthony Gold, Lerman & Muirhead	Handwritten letter and/or application form	One interview	2:1
Ashurst Morris Crisp	Handwritten / typed letter + CV	Interview with 2 partners	n/a
Baker & McKenzie	Letter + application form	Short oral and written presentation, interview with 2 partners, meeting with a trainee	2:1
Barlow Lyde & Gilbert	Application form		
Beachcroft Wansbroughs	Application form + CV	Assessment Centre & one interview with partners	
Beale and Company	CV + covering letter (typed or handwritten) + SAE	2 interviews with partners	2:1
Berg & Co	Letter + CV	2 interviews with partners and written test	2:1
S J Berwin & Co	Handwritten letter + CV	Interview (early September)	2:1
Berwin Leighton	Application form	Assessment centre + partner interview	2:1
Bevan Ashford	Application form + covering letter		2:1
Biddle	2 page CV + covering letter	1 interview	2:1
Bindman & Partners	CV + Covering letter	2 interviews and written tests	
Bircham & Co.	CV + handwritten letter	2 interviews	2:1
Bird & Bird	Application form	First Interview and Second Interview	2:1
Blake Lapthorn	Application form (on website) + CV	Interview with Partners, including giving a presentation plus group exercise	2.1 2.1
Bond Pearce	Application form, handwritten letter, CV + photo	Interviews and selection day	2:1
Boodle Hatfield	Application form + photo	1 interview with 2 partners	1st or 2.1
Boyes Turner & Burrows	CV + covering letter	2 interviews	2:2
Bristows	Application form	2 individual interviews	2.1 (Preferred)
Burges Salmon	Application form + covering letter	Penultimate year of law degree or final year of non-law degree, apply for open days and vacation placements.	2:1
Cadwalader, Wickersham & Taft	CV + handwritten letter	2 interviews	2:1
Capsticks	Application form + CV	Candidates are encouraged to participate in the firm's summer placement scheme. Final selection by interview with Training Principal and other partners.	2:1+
Cartwrights	Application form	Interviews and aptitude tests	2:1

Selection information at a glance (cont.)

Firm Name	Method of Application	Selection Procedure	Required Degree
Charles Russell	Application form + handwritten letter	Assessment days to include our interview and other exercises designed to assess identified performance criteria	2:1
Cleary, Gottlieb, Steen & Hamilton	CV + covering letter	2 interviews	2.1
Clifford Chance	Application form	First interview with partner and senior assistant, followed by assessment day and interview	2:1
Clyde & Co	Application form + covering letter	Individual interview with recruitment officer, followed by interview with two partners	2:1
CMS Cameron McKenna	Application form.	Two-stage selection procedure. Initial interview followed by assessment centre.	2:1
Cobbetts	Application form + handwritten letter	Six half day assessments	2:2
Coudert Brothers	Letter and CV	2 interviews with partners	2:1
Cripps Harries Hall	Application form (on website) + handwritten letter	1 interview with Managing Partner and Personnel Manager	2.1
Cumberland Ellis Peirs	CV + handwritten letter (adding reference to 'Chambers')	Two interviews with partners	2:1
Davenport Lyons	CV + covering letter	Interviews	2:1
Davies Arnold Cooper	Application form	Open days and individual interviews	2:1 capability
Davies Wallis Foyster	Handwritten letter + CV or DWF application form	Two interviews with partners	2:1 preferred
Dawson & Co	CV + handwritten letter	2 interviews with partners + oral test	2:1
Denton Hall	Application form + handwritten letter	Interview	2:1
Dibb Lupton Alsop	Application form	First interview, assessment afternoon including second interview with 2 partners	2:1
Dickinson Dees	Application form + handwritten letter	Interview	2:1
D J Freeman	Application form	Interview	2:1
Donne Mileham & Haddock	CV + covering letter		2:1
Edge Ellison	Application form (on website)	Selection day, including group exercises and interview	2:1
Eversheds	Application form + handwritten letter to London address	Selection days include group and written exercises plus interview.	2:1
Farrer & Co	Application form + covering letter	Interviews with Graduate Recruitment Manager and Partners	2:1

Selection information at a glance (cont.)

Firm Name	Method of Application	Selection Procedure	Required Degree
Fenners	CV + handwritten letter	2 interviews with partners.	2:1
Field Fisher Waterhouse	Application form + covering letter	Interview	2:1
Finers Stephens Innocent	CV + covering letter	2 interviews with 2 Partners usually including one of the Training Partners	2:1
Freshfields	Application form	1 interview with 2 partners	2:1
Garretts	Application form / CV + covering letter	1 hour interview in London, second interview held in regional office of choice	2:1
Goodman Derrick	CV + covering letter	2 interviews	2:1+
Gouldens	CV + covering letter	2 interviews with partners	2.1
Halliwell Landau	CV + application form	Open days/summer placements	2:1
Hammond Suddards	Application form	Interview x 2	2:1
Harbottle & Lewis	CV + covering letter	Interview	2:1
Harvey Ingram Owston	CV + application form		
Hempsons	Application form + covering letter.	2 interviews. Second interviews held in London.	
Herbert Smith	Application form	Interview	2:2
Hewitson Becke + Shaw	Application form	Interview	2:1+
Holman Fenwick & Willan	Typed CV + handwritten letter	Two interviews with partners	2:1
Holmes Hardingham	CV + covering letter	2 interviews	2:1
Howes Percival	Application form + covering letter	Assessment centres including second interview with training principal and partner	2:1
Ince & Co	CV + Typed/handwritten letter	Interview with 2 partners from Recruitment Committee and a written test	2:1
Irwin Mitchell	Application form	Assessment centres and interviews are held in late August / early September. Successful candidates invited to second interview with 2 partners.	n/a
Jeffrey Green Russell	CV + covering letter	Room will be made available for exceptional candidates.	
Kennedys	CV, application form + handwritten letter	Minimum of one interview with two Partners and Director of Personnel	
Knight & Sons	Hand-written application + CV		2:1
Landwell	Firm's application form	Interview and written test	2:1
Lawrence Graham	Application form	Interview and written exercise	2:1
Lawrence Tucketts	Application form	Assessment Day	n/a
Laytons	Application form	2 interviews	2:1+
Le Brasseur J Tickle	Letter + CV	2 interviews	
Lee Bolton & Lee	Letter + CV	Panel interview	2:1
Leigh, Day & Co	Application form + CV	Interview	
Lester Aldridge	Letter, CV + application form	Interview by a panel of partners	2:1

Selection information at a glance (cont.)

Firm Name	Method of Application	Selection Procedure	Required Degree
Lewis Silkin	Covering letter + CV	Assessment day, including an interview with two partners and an analytical exercise.	2:1
Linklaters	Application form	2 Interviews (same day)	2:1
Lovells	Application form	Assessment day: interview, group exercise, critical reasoning test	2:1+
Mace & Jones	Handwritten letter + typed CV	Interview with partners	2:1
Macfarlanes	Application form + letter	Interview and practical assessment	2:1
Martineau Johnson	Application form	Assessment centre - half day	2:1
Masons	Application form	Assessment day followed by an interview	2:1
May, May & Merrimans	Letter + CV	Interview	2.1
Mayer, Brown & Platt	CV + covering letter	Two interviews with partners, associates and often a current trainee	High 2:1
McCormicks	Letter + CV	Minimum of one interview with Training Partner	2:1
McDermott, Will & Emery	Hand-written letter + CV		
Mills & Reeve	Application form	A 2:1 degree in any discipline Computer skill required.	2:1
Mishcon de Reya	Application form	Assessment Day and Interview	2:1
Morgan Cole	Application form (applications for London should be addressed to the Oxford office)	Assessment Centre and interview	2:1
Nabarro Nathanson	Application form	Interview and assessment day	2:1
Nicholson Graham & Jones	Application form	Interview and assessment	2:1
Norton Rose	Application form	Interview and group exercise	2:1
Olswang	Application form	Interview	2:1
Orchard	Application form	Two interviews	2:1
Osborne Clarke	Application form	Individual interviews and group exercises.	2:1
Paisner & Co	Handwritten letter + CV	CV and interview	2:1
Palser Grossman	CV + covering letter	2 Interviews - the first with a mixed panel and the final interview with partners	2:1 preferred
Pannone & Partners	Application form + CV	Individual interview. Second interview comprises a tour of the firm and informal lunch	2:1
Payne Hicks Beach	Handwritten letter + CV	Interview	2:1
Penningtons	Handwritten letter, CV + application form	1 interview with a partner and director of studies	2:1
Pinsent Curtis	Application form	Assessment centre including interview	2:1

Selection information at a glance (cont.)

Firm Name	Method of Application	Selection Procedure	Required Degree
Pritchard Englefield	Application form	1 interview, in September	generally 2:1
Radcliffes	CV and covering letter or EAF	2 Interviews with partners	2:1
Reynolds Porter Chamberlain	Handwritten letter + application form	Assessment Days held in September	2.1
Richards Butler	Application form	1 interview	n/a
Rowe & Maw	Application form	Selection workshops including an interview and a business exercise	2:1
Russell Jones & Walker	Application form		2:1
Russell-Cooke, Potter & Chapman	Application form	First and second interviews.	2:1
Salans Hertzfeld & Heilbronn HRK	Handwritten letter + CV	2 interviews with partners	2:1
Shadbolt & Co	Handwritten letter + CV	Interview(s)	2:1
Sharpe Pritchard	Letter + CV	Interview with Senior Partner	
Sheridans	Letter + CV	2 interviews	2:1
Shoosmiths	Application form	Assessment centre - one day	2:1
Sidley & Austin	Covering letter + application form	Interview(s)	2:1
Simmons & Simmons	Application form, CV + covering letter	Assessment day: document exercise, interview and written excercise	2:1
Sinclair Roche & Temperley	CV + covering letter	Interview	2:1
Slaughter and May	Covering letter + CV	Interview	Good 2:1 ability
Speechly Bircham	Application form	Interview	2:1
Steele & Co	Handwritten letter + CV	Interview	2:1
Stephenson Harwood	Application form	Interview with 2 partners	2:1
Tarlo Lyons	Letter + CV	2 Interviews with partners	2:1
Taylor Joynson Garrett	Application form	2 interviews, 1 with a partner.	2:1
Taylor Vinters	Application form	1 interview with 2 partners	2:2
Taylor Walton	CV + covering letter	First and second interview with opportunity to meet other partners	2:1+
Teacher Stern Selby	Letter + application form	2 interviews	2:1
Theodore Goddard	Application form	Initial interview followed by second interview	2:1+
Titmuss Sainer Dechert	Letter + application form	1 interview with at least 2 partners	2:1 capability
Travers Smith Braithwaite	Handwritten letter + CV	Interviews	2:1
Trowers & Hamlins	Letter, application form and CV	Interview(s), essay and practical test	2:1+
Walker Morris	Application form + covering letter	Telephone and face to face interviews	2:1
Warner Cranston	Application form + covering letter	Assessment Day: 2 interviews, aptitude test and presentation.	2:1

Selection information at a glance (cont.)

Firm Name	Method of Application	Selection Procedure	Required Degree
Watson, Farley & Williams	Handwritten letter + application form	Interview and assessment	2:1 (preferred)
Wedlake Bell	CV + covering letter	Interviews in September	2:1
Weightmans	Handwritten letter + application form	Interview, short presentation and practical group exercise	
Weil, Gotshal & Manges	Letter + CV	Interview, short presentation and and practical group exercise	2:1
White & Case LLP	Covering letter + CV	Interview	2:1
Whitehead Monckton	Application form + handwritten letter + full CV	Interviews (in December of year of application)	
Wiggin & Co	Letter + CV	2 interviews	2:1
Wilde Sapte	Application form (available from February 2000)	Interviews and testing. Details to be confirmed in February	2:1
Withers	Application form	2 interviews	2:1
Withy King	Application form (on website) + recent photo		
Wragge & Co	Application form	Assessment day and interview	2:1 (preferred)

The table represents the top 50 firms by size plus firms with an A-Z entry. Some information has been summarised. Gaps and omissions show that full information has not been supplied.
See A-Z section for further details.

CANDIDATE PROFILE

What do firms look for in prospective trainees? There is a string of obvious responses. Excellent academics, good attention to detail, confidence, ability to work in a team. Certain firms such as Linklaters and Macfarlanes emphasise the importance of intelligence above all. However some firms give more unexpected responses. They may look for candidates who have taken time off to travel or to gain general commercial experience. Baker & McKenzie, for example, encourages its prospective trainees to take time out whether just to travel or to undertake further studies.

Extra-curricular activities and non-academic achievements are important to both City and provincial firms. They look for "interesting" and "lively" personalities, with a "good sense of humour," a "resourceful nature," "ambition" and "resilience," as well as more specific skills such as IT proficiency.

Increasingly firms of all kinds appreciate students from a variety of degree backgrounds. One magic circle firm takes up to 50% non-law graduates per intake. Science and language degrees are particularly sought after and seem particularly welcomed by shipping firms. Other firms are more specific about their language requirements. Pritchard Englefield states: "Normally only high academic achievers with a second language (especially German and French) are considered." Withers looks for "a genuine international outlook and foreign languages, particularly Italian," while Wilde Sapte (soon to merge with Denton Hall) has previously specified "French, Spanish, German, Russian, Japanese or Mandarin."

Many trainees interviewed for the 'True Picture' told us that the firms welcomed people who had first careers. A significant number of trainees at Lawrence Graham have come from various backgrounds other than the usual route straight through from law school. 'Other lives' have included insurance, accountancy, armed forces, in-house legal and paralegals. Personal injury and medical negligence firms often seek people with specific experience in the medical profession, such as doctors, nurses and dentists. Equally, shipping firms tend to attract those who have had careers in the Navy or with P&I Clubs.

Personality type is just as important as past experiences. Trainees from Ince & Co think that there is no mould other than that people must have 'an air of confidence or bullishness.' In the firm's words this translates into 'hard-working competitive individuals with initiative who relish challenge and responsibility.' Above all, firms want the right 'fit.' This is more a matter of chemistry than anything else and has been variously identified by many of our trainee interviewees. Halliwell Landau trainees see themselves as people who "like a challenge," you have to be "a bit of a swashbuckler." Many trainees feel their job is not for shrinking violets. Firms of all complexions are keen to escape the idea that they take on identikit trainees. All emphasise individuality as an important quality.

Regional firms are keen that recruits have a connection with the area. Pannone & Partners look for "a connection with the north west," Donne Mileham & Haddock state "local connections are of value" and Foot & Bowden look for "a well-reasoned wish to develop a career in the south west."

Firms invest considerable sums in their trainees and, as Titmuss Sainer Dechert concludes, "We want people who will remain with us on qualifying and make their careers with us." Radcliffes "aim to recruit trainees who have a real prospect of becoming partners in due course", while Rowe & Maw say they "want trainees to become future partners." Even in these times of frequent job moves, it is clear that firms want dedication and long-term commitment from the outset.

In addition to luck, your own focus at the outset will go a long way to ensuring you get a job with the right firm for you. Read the criteria carefully and apply only to those firms where you fit the bill.

PREFERRED INSTITUTIONS

Universities

We conducted a survey amongst the largest firms in the UK offering training contracts. We asked them to identify the universities from which they preferred to recruit trainees and which institutions were their preferred providers of the CPE and LPC courses.

126 firms of all sizes and types and from all parts of England and Wales responded. Just over 63% of the respondent firms confirmed that they had no preference for a particular university. Some expressed strong sentiments that a recruitment policy which targeted certain institutions only served to reinforce old prejudices and discrimination, whilst others confirmed an unabashed attempt to recruit as many of their trainees as possible from a small number of universities.

The results of our 'preferred universities survey' show that for the first time this year, Bristol University has eclipsed Oxford and Cambridge as the institution producing the graduates most widely sought by law firms. Durham and Nottingham universities again hold top 5 positions, but this year it is Durham which takes the 4th most popular slot.

Regional bias was evident in the results, particularly so in the south west (where Bristol Exeter, Cardiff and UWE scored highly) and the north (where Durham, Newcastle, Manchester, Leeds and Sheffield performed well). The larger London firms tended to indicate preference more commonly than the regional firms and the smaller London firms.

Law Schools

Research for this publication has highlighted the trend for some firms to strongly recommend, if not mandate, the law schools which their trainees attend. Again, it was the larger City firms which tended to express stronger views as to which institutions they endorsed. Indeed the magic circle firms make no secret of the fact that they liaise closely with their preferred LPC providers to influence the way courses are taught.

Only a minority of City firms now say they have no preference. Overall nearly 40% of firms expressed a preference, but this rose to over 62% of the larger London firms (ie: over 200 solicitors).

The College of Law is still regarded as far and away the most well-respected of the CPE/LPC course providers when considering all responses. However, amongst the large City firms, three other institutions received almost equally strong endorsement; BPP Law School, the Oxford Institute of Legal Practice and Nottingham Law School at Nottingham Trent University, the latter being highly rated by firms all over the country.

The LPC unit of the Law Society conducts an annual inspection of all LPC providers nationwide. The following providers are ranked 'excellent:' Nottingham Law School, University of the West of England, Cardiff, the Oxford Institute of Legal Practice, and the University of Exeter.

The table overleaf ranks the specified universities and other institutions by the number of times each one was listed.

▶

Preferred Universities

Institution	Score
Bristol	38
Cambridge	36
Oxford	35
Durham	30
Nottingham	27
Manchester	25
Exeter	22
Birmingham	21
Sheffield	17
Warwick	15
London UCL*	13
London Kings*	11
Newcastle	11
Southampton	11
Leeds	10
London LSE*	10
London (any college)	7
Liverpool	6
Cardiff	5
Leicester	5
Edinburgh**	4
Hull	3
Leicester	3
Kent	2
Nottingham Trent	2
Reading	2
Scottish Universities	2
UWE	2
Bath	1
De Montford	1
London Imperial*	1
Liverpool John Moore's	1
Queens (Belfast)	1
Northumbria	1
St Andrews**	1
Trinity	1
York	1
No Preference	80

*Add these scores to the preferences for London (any college).
**Add these scores to the preferences for Scottish University (any college).

Preferred CPE/LPC Providers

Provider	Score
College of Law	45
Nottingham Law School	30
BPP Law School	13
Oxford Institute of Legal Practice	11
UWE	10
Cardiff	4
University of Sheffield	4
Bristol	2
Birmingham	2
De Montford	2
Exeter	2
Bath	1
Manchester Metropolitan	1
Oxford Brookes	1
Staffordshire University	1
University of Northumbria	1
UEA	1
No Preference	76

Number of respondent firms

SE		10
SW		11
NE		11
NW		9
East Anglia		3
Midlands		14
London	200+ solicitors	24
	100+ solicitors	11
	50+ solicitors	13
	25+ solicitors	5
	U25 solicitors	10
National firms		5

The Training Contract

WHICH KIND OF TRAINING CONTRACT?

A law firm training contract is not the only form of training available. There is a number of viable alternatives which are often overlooked by students, including several options in the public sector as well as in-house training.

Government Legal Services

Attracted by the 'glamour' and the high salaries of the large City practices, few law graduates ever consider the stimulating and challenging world of opportunities offered by the Government Legal Services. Positions are available for barristers and solicitors. GLS lawyers are in the unusual position of having only one client: the Government of the day. Furthermore, they are able to participate in making the law, playing an integral part in preparation of bills, the drafting of statutory instruments etc... There are currently around 1100 qualified lawyers working for approximately 30 different government organisations, not including the Crown Prosecution Service, the Foreign Office, the Office of the Parliamentary Counsel and the Scottish and Northern Ireland departments. It should be noted that, with the exception of a Welsh team in South Wales and some smaller groups scattered across the country, all government lawyers are based in London.

When it comes to training, the GLS acts as an umbrella organisation with trainees allowed a say in their choice of which government department to work in. Training can consist of three, four or five seats lasting up to a year each! These could range from criminal litigation to corporate secondments in magic circle firms. Responsibility comes early at the GLS and a trainee will quickly come into contact with senior barristers and civil service figures. While this may sound daunting, one interviewee said that while there is "an awful lot of responsibility, there is also a huge amount of support available as well." Nor are GLS trainees relegated to acting as little more than administrative support. Skills required of a trainee include a particularly good grasp of common law principles, especially as they relate to administrative and constitutional law. The ever growing importance of EU law should also be born in mind. Given the frequently complex and politically sensitive nature of the issues involved, a clear understanding of the policy implications of their advice is also key. Predictably, a "relaxed and friendly attitude," good interpersonal skills, drive, determination and an attention to detail are also held to be necessary attributes for a successful government lawyer.

Satnam Tumani started out working as a paralegal at the Serious Fraud Office, before being offered a training contract. He first spent a year working in commercial litigation at the SFO, then was sent on a three month corporate secondment to top City practice Allen & Overy. He also stayed at Allen & Overy for his third three month seat, this time in the commercial property department. He is currently working through his fourth seat (six months) at the Treasury. A typical day while he was at the SFO (and to which he will return) might have consisted of advising on new legal developments, conducting research and giving lectures on legal charges. He would probably also have been assigned a case or two to work on under the supervision of a junior lawyer, collecting witness statements, conducting interviews (voluntary or not) and drafting documents.

While at £35,000 starting salary for a newly qualified lawyer, remuneration is better than one could expect working for local government or in a high street practice, it can't compare to the higher City salaries and won't, in the words of one interviewee, "set the world on fire." On the other hand, most GLS lawyers are out of the office come six o'clock and the nightmare hours of City trainees are unknown to them. Ultimately, the GLS is likely to appeal to those whose primary motivation is not the unwavering pursuit of profit, but who are attracted by the ideal of public service and welfare. In return the GLS offers the law graduate an unrivalled range of work experience, job security (!) and such traditional public sector benefits as holiday entitlements.

Application and career info packs can be obtained via info.gls@gtnet.gov.uk.

Contact: The GLS Recruitment Team, Queen Anne's Chambers, 28 Broadway,
London SW1 9JS. Tel: (0207) 210 3304.

Contact in Scotland: The Recruitment Unit, Personnel Division, Scottish Office,
16 Waterloo Place, Edinburgh EH1 3DN. Tel: (0131) 244 3964.

Local Government

Local government offers a wide range of work for lawyers. Although the opportunities are in the main directed to those who have completed traineeships there are openings at all levels of qualification. Some Local Authorities offer training contracts.

Contact: Lawyers in Local Government, Jacqui Dixon, Head of Resources, Portsmouth City Council, Guildhall Square, Portsmouth, Hampshire PO1 2AL. Tel: (01705) 834856.

In House

Several companies, charities and other organisations are accredited to take on trainees to work within their in house legal departments. These are listed on the Law Society's website giving details of all firms, organisations and companies authorised to take trainees. However, although accredited, not all of these entities actually take on trainees on a regular basis, if at all. It is therefore advisable to telephone the legal department before sending off speculative applications. However, unlike most law firms, most of these companies guarantee a job upon qualification.

Examples of organisations providing in house opportunities are multi-national bank Nomura International Plc which takes on trainees on an ad hoc basis. Andersen Consulting, the management consultancy arm of accountants Arthur Andersen, take on one or two trainees a year, who go on secondment to City firm Field Fisher Waterhouse for their contentious seat. The Commission for Racial Equality can provide a litigation seat only for trainees to do discrimination/employment work involving employment tribunal complaints under the Race Relations Act.

Contact: www.Lawsociety.org.uk

WHICH KIND OF FIRM?

When asked how many applications they receive for how many training contracts, responses from the leading law firms show the level of competition for places. However, the results are surprising. It can appear much easier to get into one of the huge magic circle firms than a small lower-profile firm. Clifford Chance receives 2000 applications for 130 training contracts. This gives an amazingly optimistic 1 in 15 chance for each applicant. However, not all magic circle firms provide such a chance of success. The most popular is Slaughter and May, where 3000 candidates chase 75 contracts. No wonder there is a perceived sense of arrogance amongst the lucky few. More depressingly, at niche media firm Olswang 2-3000 candidates compete for only 12 places. Tiny Gray's Inn private client firm May, May & Merrimans receives 200 applications for only 1 place. The most popular top 50 firm was lower-profile Theodore Goddard, with 4000 applications for only 20 training contracts; a 1 in 200 chance.

The intention behind this book is to provide an informed choice to prospective applicants so that every application is a valuable application. It is no use drafting standard 'blurb' for every form you complete. There are very marked differences in style, culture and work type between different kinds of firms. Many students make block applications. They may apply for the top 10, or the top 20, or even the top 50. With firms as diverse as Eversheds, Linklaters, and Denton Hall in the top 20, this may be a dangerous strategy. Very careful thought should go into the type of contract you are looking for and the type of work you want.

Magic Circle

The 'Magic Circle' is a term coined for the élite top City firms: Allen & Overy, Clifford Chance, Freshfields, Linklaters, Slaughter and May.

Directors of Studies at top universities commonly direct their law students towards magic circle firms with which they have particular connections already, such as a large number of ex-alumni. This becomes an automatic path for many, with little thought going into the type of training which would suit the individual.

Our interviews with trainees have shown us that the magic circle firms provide a very particular training experience, which would certainly not suit everyone. Very careful thought should be given to whether the lifestyle will suit you. Long hours will definitely be an issue at these firms. Sometimes these will arise from firm culture rather than necessity; a need to be seen to put in the time and show the right attitude. Many of our interviewees were simply not fully prepared for the massive incursion into their lives made by work. Long hours are enforced where huge cases and transactions must comply with tight timetables and the demands of sometimes unreasonable clients. The same huge cases and transactions will be worth very big money. At the bottom of the pecking order, a trainee will often be involved only in an administrative role, such as organising documents. Big ticket work does not make for high level involvement for trainees. It may mean no client contact other than endless notetaking in meetings or pouring the coffee. It may even mean never getting to court during a litigation seat.

So much for the disadvantages. There are many obvious advantages. The name on your CV for a start. A magic circle training makes you a highly marketable commodity, both within and outside private practice. Such firms are unbeaten in terms of resources, breadth of training opportunities, quality of clients, high profile of work and salaries. Whilst many trainees will receive less responsibility than those at smaller firms, in years to come, with several years of post-qualification experience behind them, they will reap the benefits. For this reason a significant number of magic circle trainees we interviewed stated their clear intention to stay on for up to two or four years after qualification, then move on when they were at their most marketable. Many felt that by qualification stage they would still be light on certain skills.

National

National firms have offices throughout the country. Individual offices may qualify as small or medium-sized, whereas total personnel numbers may get the firm into the top 30 list. These firms often have a more diverse practice than City firms, covering private client, family and other non-commercial specialisms as well as the core litigation, property and corporate departments, providing trainees with a very interesting potential spread of seats. Many have extremely strong niche practices which are strengthened by the backing of national offices. Eversheds for example is unsurpassed for the size and strength of its employment group.

It is worth noting that some national firm contracts specify that trainees may be required to move from office to office during their training contract, sometimes to a completely different part of the country. Hammond Suddards enforces office moves for all trainees. Conversely, you may find that the practice area which interests you is not practised from your home office, in which case you must check that inter-office moves are possible. Many national firms have very different practice profiles from one office to another, and careful research is required.

Regional

Regional firms may be single-office or multi-office organisations. Many have offices which are medium-sized in terms of City firms, but will often be amongst the largest in their part of the country. Work is not likely to be as high-profile or big ticket as the top City firms, but the top regional firms market themselves as the viable alternative to the City and are capable of attracting a volume of large high-quality work from around the country and even internationally. Trainees are more likely to spend time doing rewarding work on smaller deals than doing mundane work on mega-deals. They tend to get more client contact and run more of their own cases.

'Niche'

True niche firms are too small to take on trainees to any meaningful extent. However there are many firms with niche expertise which may attract trainees interested in qualifying into that area. Our interviews have shown that such firms tend to provide a fairly broad-based training appropriate to the general work type. Only Townleys, the sports law firm, can be said to provide a niche training in that all its clients are sports clients. Work covers corporate, IP, media and many other practice areas; a classic broad based commercial training. What truly differentiates applications to these firms is an expectation that candidates will show a quantifiable and sustained interest or experience in the niche area. For example at top civil liberties firm Bindman & Partners there is heavy competition for training contracts and applicants are warned that they must be able to prove their commitment to the field.

The 'True Picture'

In preparing this section we interviewed trainees about the structure and quality of their training. We asked the 50 largest UK firms to provide us with lists of their staff trainees and newly-qualified staff. We then chose names at random from those lists, aiming to speak to five from each firm; those five representing a cross-section of experience from first seat trainees to newly qualifieds. Some firms declined to provide lists so are not included in the survey. We then interviewed trainees at selected medium-sized firms (top 50-75) as well as some much smaller 'niche-type' firms; i.e. firms with a broad practice concentrating on niche practice areas.

LEADING FIRMS: TOP 75

Leading Firms: Top 75

Ranking by size	Firm Name	Number of trainees
1	Eversheds	210
2	Clifford Chance	254
3	Linklaters	261
4	Allen & Overy	282
5	Dibb Lupton Alsop	100
6	Freshfields	138
7	Lovells	120
8	CMS Cameron McKenna	104
9	Herbert Smith	150
10	Simmons & Simmons	132
11	Slaughter and May	132
12	Beachcroft Wansbroughs	64
13	Norton Rose	103
14	Hammond Suddards	45
15	Ashurst Morris Crisp	96
16	Nabarro Nathanson	56
17	Addleshaw Booth & Co	60
18	Wragge & Co	40
19	Denton Hall	62
20	Pinsent Curtis	66
21	Berrymans Lace Mawer	38
22	Garretts	50
23	Edge Ellison	38
24	Morgan Cole	39
25	Wilde Sapte	62
26	Masons	40
27	Rowe & Maw	45
28	S J Berwin & Co	56
29	Irwin Mitchell	30
30	Berwin Leighton	38
31	Barlow Lyde & Gilbert	33
32	Osborne Clarke	31
33	Bevan Ashford	40
34	Clyde & Co	36
35	Taylor Johnson Garrett	43
36	Baker & McKenzie	44
37	Shoosmiths	29
38	Davies Arnold Cooper	34
39	Lawrence Graham	29
40	Mills & Reeve	27
41	Thompsons McClure	n/a

Leading Firms: Top 75 (cont.)

42	Stephenson Harwood	41
43	Bond Pearce	38
44	Richards Butler	59
45	Burges Salmon	28
46	Charles Russell	22
47	Theodore Goddard	30
48	Macfarlanes	39
49	Field Fisher Waterhouse	20
50	Halliwell Landau	14
51	Hill Dickinson	18
52	Blake Lapthorn	22
53	Titmuss Sainer Dechert	22
54	Weightmans	16
55	Bird & Bird	13
56	Travers Smith Braithwaite	39
57	Davies Wallis Foyster	9
58	Walker Morris	20
59	Reynolds Porter Chamberlain	16
60	Ince & Co	23
61	Paisner & Co	17
62	D J Freeman	25
63	Gouldens	26
64	Manches	20
65	Olswang	24
66	Dickinson Dees	18
67	Trowers & Hamlins	25
68	Freeth Cartwright Hunt Dickins	14
69	Russell Jones & Walker	11
70	Nicholson Graham & Jones	20
71	Withers	23
72	Holman Fenwick & Willan	17
73	Kennedys	14
74	Hempsons	10
75	Weil, Gotshal & Manges	4

Table shows largest UK firms (not including Scottish firms) in reverse order of size. Size is calculated by total number of partners and associates.

Addleshaw Booth and Co

UK ranking by size: 17
Number of trainees: 60

Addleshaw Booth & Co may appear like a trans-Pennine powerhouse with its large offices in Leeds and Manchester, fledgling but growing office in London and a top class reputation in the key commercial areas, but it does have a softer side. Seen to provide a structured yet 'flexible' training, there is opportunity to take seats in an unusually diverse range of areas, including corporate finance and family.

Addleshaws prefers its trainees to take seats in the strong corporate finance and commercial property departments, although there is some flexibility. The training in both departments was highly praised by interviewees. In corporate, for example, there are weekly lunchtime training sessions: "almost as if your LPC is continuing into your training contract." While it is unusual for trainees to split their seats, individuals can negotiate alternatives.

Increasingly trainees move between the Leeds and Manchester offices for one or more seats. This seems to be more to bring the branches together than for practical reasons and is "a trend throughout the firm, not just for trainees." The London office is still in its infancy, and at present can only offer two seats. This is likely to change as the office expands.

Inevitably, levels of responsibility and client contact vary according to seat and supervisor. Thus employment, commercial property and insurance litigation were praised for giving hands-on experience. If you make a point of asking for it, you may be able to run a small deal in corporate: "On one occasion my supervisor asked me if I fancied taking on a small deal with her support. When it got difficult she took over and we swapped roles. It was monitored very well and I got a good deal of responsibility early."

Trainees at Addleshaws have no doubts that that they have joined 'one of the big boys.' "You could literally lift the building up and plonk it down in the City and you would call it a City firm." The advantages of its size and quality of work are clear: "if I've got a question I go to some of the most experienced people in Manchester." However, trainees were keen to point out that the firm's size did not translate into an impersonal atmosphere. "Supportive," "generous" and "friendly" were common descriptions. Outside working hours, there are cross-site socials, involvement in the Leeds Law Society and Manchester TSG, football, cricket, netball and trainee social events to ensure that "a good time is had by all." Trainees also praised the office facilities: "great canteen, great food, superb gym."

Top Recommendations in Chambers Directory:
Banking, Construction & Civil Engineering, Employment Law, Family/Matrimonial, Corporate Finance, Insolvency, Intellectual Property, Litigation (Commercial), Litigation (Property), Pensions, Projects/PFI, Property (Commercial), Tax (Corporate).

Allen & Overy

UK ranking by size: 4
Number of trainees: 282 (worldwide)

Third largest in the magic circle, A&O has a heavy finance bias. Its property and litigation limbs are smaller than those of its competitors.

As the main thrust of the firm is in finance related work, it comes as little surprise that there is a requirement for trainees to do 12 months in corporate and finance-related seats. That said, A&O is one of the few firms in the City which also offers training in private client work. Although it has a strong reputation for niche, 'soft' areas such as charities, trusts and environmental work, these represent only a sliver of the firm's activities, which are corporate through and through. "If you think you are going to be interested in the financial side of the legal profession then it is a fantastic choice." If finance leaves you cold there may be better alternatives, even within the magic circle. The variety of departments is refreshing "Even though you're coming to a City firm, it is nice to do three or six months in a private client department and look at things which you won't have the opportunity to do in other firms."

Early in the first seat, trainees will be required to plan ahead and select the remainder of their seats. These choices can be modified fairly easily and we were told that the path chosen could be one that meandered between work types. The practice of seat splitting - spending only three months in a department - is not only quite common but a very popular option for those who want to spend a little more time in their preferred department or sample as many as possible. For those who have no intention of qualifying into litigation it allows for just three months of contentious training.

The atmosphere of the firm seems happy and relaxed. One trainee chose the firm because it wasn't as smug as others in the Magic Circle. "It seemed to be that the firm wasn't resting on its laurels and was not self-congratulatory." Trainees seemed by and large happy with their lot and with the allocation of seats.

The firm has its own bar which gets busy on Thursdays and Fridays and allows people from across the firm to mix freely. Hours of work are on a par with other City firms and there is not an institutional macho culture of staying late for appearance's sake. "If you walked around the building at 7.30pm to 8pm you would probably find half the lawyers still here." Hours depend on work type however.

The six-month overseas seats are extremely popular. Whilst for some offices you'd be very lucky to be selected - New York, for example - the number on offer worldwide means that if you are flexible about where you are prepared to go, the chances are you will go abroad.

Top Recommendations in Chambers Directory: Admin & Public Law, Banking, Capital Markets, Corporate Finance, Fraud - Civil, Regulation & Investigation, Insolvency, Partnership, PFI, Project Finance, Social Housing: advising lenders, Telecommunications, Trusts & Personal Tax.

Ashurst Morris Crisp

UK ranking by size: 15
Number of trainees: 96

Hovering outside the top ten firms in the City, Ashursts already has the attitude, the style, the work and the profits to compete with them. The main thrust of its work is in investment banking and finance.

There has been a marked increase in size obvious even to current trainees. This is deemed "good in some ways, bad in others." The feeling is still quite personal, with larger groups working in smaller teams to maintain that feel.

A few partners have informal days in at their homes at weekends. One trainee commented: "The last thing I went to, one of the partners had a lunch at his house in the country and invited everybody down."

Responsibility and client contact is felt to be very much dependent on how much enthusiasm and aptitude a trainee shows. "Transactions and work have a way of migrating towards those who are capable. If you are capable of doing it, it will migrate to you. If you are not capable of doing it, it won't."

There is the occasional opportunity to split a six month seat. Such an arrangement may come into play in seats such as tax or pensions. Around 14 places abroad are available at any one time. Language skills are not always essential. "In Singapore and Tokyo you're not expected to have the language. If you want to go to Frankfurt, Paris, Brussels or Milan, you've pretty much got to."

Some trainees felt that Ashursts had a historical reputation for being 'blue-blooded' and a little conservative. The growth in size seems to have changed this although the perception of trainees was that the firm still favours the traditional universities. However, "looking at the trainees coming through, it is definitely becoming a lot more international." We were told that the typical trainee is somebody who is robust, confident, capable, well-rounded and well-educated.

Top Recommendations in Chambers Directory: Corporate Finance.

Baker & McKenzie

UK ranking by size: 36
Number of trainees: 44

Until recently Baker & McKenzie held a long-standing position as the world's biggest global law firm. Its London office, however, is not amongst the largest in the UK and is therefore a very different creature from fellow global giants such as Clifford Chance.

The international work is the main attraction to trainees joining the firm. "It's an immediate reason why people apply here. They think it's a free worldwide ticket. In one sense it is and in one sense it isn't." It is possible to go abroad as part of your training contract but trainees also stress the value of being in the home office, making contacts and getting experience. For a firm which has been playing the global game for so much longer than the others, it is surprising that only in the last year have trainees been able to spend time in overseas seats. At the time of interviewing, there was one seat in Frankfurt and one in Sydney. Each was for just over three months. The numbers are so small as to make it far from guaranteed that you will be able to go abroad as a trainee. However, long term prospects for overseas experience at the firm are much brighter. The Associate Training Programme is well-established. Through this scheme two-year qualifieds can work for up to two years in an overseas office.

A Baker & McKenzie training is a hybrid experience. Those we interviewed stressed the international nature of the work on their desks and the volume of contact they had with B&M lawyers in other jurisdictions. A lot of clients are huge multi-nationals. Trainees need to communicate with the firm's offices worldwide for advice and to co-ordinate work being handled in several jurisdictions. "You have the global experience from your desktop."

They also spoke of the benefits of training with a medium sized firm. At the same time, because of the nature of some clients, those we spoke to had experienced the difficulties of very large scale corporate transactions. They know what it is like to have to devote time to more mundane document management tasks. However, partners will try to allocate smaller files to trainees. Overall there seems to be a broad spread of interesting and less interesting work for trainees to do. Litigation can be 'manic.' "We are rushed off our feet. Whenever the court clerk is on holiday a trainee will have to cover for him. We spend the whole day at court, issuing documents and running around."

The most popular seats are in the employment department, renowned as one of the biggest and best in the country. It takes four trainees each six months. Information Technology/Intellectual Property is also a popular seat. Many first seat trainees go straight into the one compulsory department - corporate. Litigation is no longer compulsory and trainees can get their contentious experience in niche departments.

Top Recommendations in Chambers Directory: Information Technology, Telecommunications.

Barlow Lyde & Gilbert

UK ranking by size: 31
Number of trainees: 33

This highly-regarded insurance litigation firm has a client base biased towards the insurance industry. Typical seats might include general insurance, reinsurance and professional negligence and a non-contentious seat such as corporate. However as one trainee said "It's not as if you're immersed in insurance the whole time" - in fact many choose the firm more for its strong litigation bent than for the insurance work. The opportunity to get to know and understand the insurance industry is a valuable one.

Trainees handle a fair amount of defendant personal injury litigation in the general insurance department. Files are small so trainees get to run their own cases, handle correspondence and have day-to-day contact with clients. This is much appreciated by trainees we spoke to. "You get to make practical decisions, which in most firms I don't think you'd be allowed near. You're still supervised but its easier to get a feel for cases and get a feel for the litigation process without being in something so big you can't really get a grasp of the issues."

In addition to straight PI, the department's work also includes clinical negligence and the 'police seat', covering civil claims against police authorities. Unusually, in the general insurance department trainees sit in an open plan bay and are not assigned to work for one particular partner or fee earner. The high point of this department is the opportunity to do a lot of advocacy. This can be "very scary" but afterwards leads to "a real sense of achievement when you've done it." Reinsurance is a different story as the cases are much bigger and the issues much more complicated.

As there are just two seats within property, not everybody goes there. There has traditionally been less of an emphasis on non-contentious corporate work than there might have been at other City firms but the corporate finance and banking departments are expanding and providing more such opportunities for trainees.

Hours were seen as anything but anti-social. "The latest I've stayed at all is 9pm and the average time is 6.30-ish." One trainee did not stay later than 6pm in the whole of her training contract.

"Quite a few" of the current trainees have worked as paralegals in the firm. Trainees have been told that the firm considered carefully whether they would fit in socially. Perhaps that's why they are perceived to recruit so heavily from the summer schemes. Once at the firm trainees will find there are frequent 'meet and greets' in the firm's Atrium area when departments mix over wine.

Trainees are always asked if they have any suggestions for functions, or how the firm should integrate with particular clients. Interaction with clients is a priority, we were told. "They want outgoing, strong, confident people. There is no point in having someone who is going to be shy and hide under the table when the chips are down."

Top Recommendations in Chambers Directory:
Insurance & Reinsurance, Personal Injury: Mainly Defendant, Professional Negligence.

Berwin Leighton

UK ranking by size: 30
Number of trainees: 38

A medium-sized City firm with a strong property and planning practice, Berwin Leighton was praised by trainees for combining City-quality work with significant responsibility, a commercial ethos and "a very small feel" with no "ivory tower syndrome."

There are four seats, of which litigation, property and corporate are compulsory. Trainees are then guaranteed their fourth choice as a 'preference' seat. Within this structure there is much flexibility, for example a straight finance seat, such as banking, can be taken as a corporate seat and it is possible to gain experience of 'sexy' niche work such as Intellectual Property/Information Technology and film finance in the commercial seat. Three-month secondments can be taken with commercial property clients and a seat is available in the Brussels office.

The PSC is taken in-house over the two years, and is supplemented by on-going legal training by way of lunchtime powerpoint presentations and seminars. One trainee noted the contrast between these classes and his degree/LPC lectures, as "this time round you can see how issues work in practice" and points are illustrated with real case histories. "In law school there is so much theory…its great to see the commercial element." Trainees were also grateful for the induction courses given at the beginning of each seat in order to give them a general introduction to that area of law. In corporate, for example, trainees are treated to an illustrated history of a company, beginning as an embryo, which "sounds naff but was really useful."

One unique element of Berwin Leighton's training is the practice in the property seat of giving each trainee the responsibility for forty files on their first day, which they will pass on to the next trainee when their six months are completed. Thus "you get an awful lot of responsibility very quickly, though you will always sit with a more senior solicitor who can help you out." While this level of responsibility is not present in all seats (in corporate, for example "you obviously wouldn't be running a merger") it does highlight the emphasis the firm places on giving trainees hands-on experience. In their litigation seat one trainee attended several conferences with counsel in chambers and even conducted an interlocutory application in open court, fully "robed up." In corporate, another trainee noted that "you are not swallowed up and are very much part of deals." "Even if we are part of the backbone helping out, people always take time out to explain where we are at, what we are doing and why we are doing things".

The atmosphere around the office is described as "friendly and supportive," with many young partners and a "close knit" trainee intake. "Fee earners and partners spend a lot of time working with you and training you into the various departments, which is definitely beneficial." The trainee social life is good, especially at the beginning "when everyone is bonding" and there are departmental events and an annual firm Christmas and Summer parties. Trainees also noted the diverse recruitment policy of the firm, with no bar to paralegals or students who have come to the law after a different career. While all trainees are focused, not wishing to be "cogs in a big wheel," the most important unifying trait is "being down to earth and getting on with life."

Top Recommendations in Chambers Directory: Planning.

S J Berwin & Co

UK ranking by size: 28
Number of trainees: 56

Established in 1982 and already in the London top 20, S J Berwin is the 'young gun' of the City. Venture capital and finance are key to the firm's corporate work. It is also strong in commercial property and developing niche reputations for specialisms such as EU, arbitration, media and sports.

Our interviewees were refreshingly clear about who and what S J Berwin thinks it is. One trainee explained why they chose the firm, saying "I didn't like the idea of going into the law and it being old and stuffy... I wanted young and dynamic." That seems to be the prevailing mood within the firm. It's not a big leap from 'dynamic' to 'sweatshop.' The idea of the firm as an aggressive environment which works its junior people into the ground is something of an urban myth amongst other City lawyers. One trainee said candidly "S J Berwin do work their trainees extremely hard. There's a lot of work and the partners here are quite strong-minded and demanding." However, they gave the impression that you are thrown into tasks with a degree of responsibility so that it's a case of giving the job your full commitment rather than being a slave to it. The trainees we spoke to were horrified at the perpetuation of the sweatshop myth.

The trainees attribute a 'new school' ethos to the fact that a lot of partners are young and a lot of clients are entrepreneurial. "Because it's less stuffy and less hierarchical, you get the opportunity of getting good hands-on experience." The impression we get is that you can make what you want of the experience: if you impress the partner you sit with and show them you are keen you will find yourself given extra responsibility. "You often find yourself working with others two or three years older than you doing the same thing on the other side. It's about how much they trust you......you have to prove yourself."

If the emphasis is on corporate and finance work, the niche seats are the icing on the cake for trainees and they are keenly fought over. Media and Intellectual Property seats are the prime examples. "It takes a bit of internal political wrangling and selling yourself to personnel and getting partners on your side. There are four or five media and Intellectual Property seats, and you need to have a good reason why they should give it to you. You'll get your corporate seat, everyone does those, litigation or whatever, but it's a bit of a battle to get into Intellectual Property and media." The Brussels and Frankfurt offices and a secondment in-house to Marks & Spencer provide an alternative to a totally office-bound training.

The words 'dynamic,''responsibility', 'hard-working' and 'youthful' tumbled frequently from the mouths of interviewees. Positive words which go hand in hand with the word 'commitment' and S J Berwin trainees must clearly be prepared to give that in return. It's hard to quantify but there also seemed to be an element of drawing the trainees into the firm and providing more than legal training. Personnel were noted for their almost pastoral approach and the firm provides everyone who wants it with a free lunch in the dining room every day.

Top Recommendations in Chambers Directory: Media & Entertainment, Travel.

Bevan Ashford

UK ranking by size: 33
Number of trainees: 40

This south west firm has long had a large healthcare presence and this has broadened considerably over the last decade. Changes in the NHS have to a large degree been responsible for the firm's success and it has acquired a strong presence in the region, particularly Bristol.

The firm is run as two profit centres. One consists of the London, Cardiff and Bristol offices. The other, 'West Country' centre consists of offices in Exeter, Plymouth, Taunton and Tiverton. Between the West Country offices there is a very large degree of interaction, especially Plymouth and Exeter. There is growing inter-office co-operation in certain areas of work, particularly PFI. Opportunities for trainees to transfer between offices are becoming more of a feature.

The size of the medical negligence department in Bristol means that every trainee will do one med neg seat and some people do two. Most trainees choose not to do the second seat but those who are put in the position of doing a year in med neg tend to be given the sweetener of getting their preferred choices for subsequent seats. This double whammy of med neg work is not a likelihood in the West Country, but it is possible in Cardiff and Bristol. That said, med neg work is generally one of the attractions of coming to the firm. Health sector strength has also allowed it to become a mainstream commercial player.

As for levels of responsibility, apparently the motto of one of the partners is that she would give trainees enough rope almost to hang themselves. "There is a safety net for you so that if you make that big mistake, someone's spotted it before it goes out and you've learnt something."

Unique to the Bristol office is the much despised post opening rota which keeps trainees occupied between one and two to three hours each day for one week in four. This is an activity that seems at odds with the rest of the contract. One interviewee thinks it is a deliberate policy decision. Why? "Maybe they worry that trainees will get too big for their boots so they give them one very menial task which will keep them in their place!"

"The thing they look for here I think is common sense" said one trainee. "There are far too many people who come in for vacation schemes who can parrot-learn anything. But when you think about how things work, particularly in litigation when you have to think pro-actively, you have to have a bit of nous. Too many people think that they can rely on their academic results and that will do."

The Cardiff trainees are likely to have a contract that specifies that they will work in both Cardiff and Bristol and Cardiff trainees have always gone to Bristol for at least one seat. Cardiff or Bristol trainees may move to the one London seat available at each rotation. The trainees saw both advantages and drawbacks to working for a firm which has seven offices in seven very different cities. Clearly it's a big advantage for people who want flexibility but not so much so for those who are a little more settled. However, in the West Country trainees do not necessarily rotate around offices. The contract is with one, although we were told of at least one case where a trainee worked in four different offices. This would appear to be on a voluntary basis.

Different specialisms are offered in different offices. Plymouth is commercial. Some of the other West Country offices specialise in private client work. Cardiff specialises in NHS and litigation. In the smaller Plymouth office, where only one trainee is taken on per year, we were told "you get to know everyone really well. They're friendly and ready to pitch in, from partner level down. Its not just the trainees - everyone opens the post in the morning."

Top Recommendations in Chambers Directory: Admin & Public Law, Clinical Negligence: Mainly Defendant, Health Care, Trusts & Personal Tax.

Bird & Bird

UK ranking by size: 55
Trainee places available: 13

A broadly-based law firm best known for its niche practice areas such as Intellectual Property, Information Technology, communications and digital media. The firm has a growing presence in other sectors such as general corporate and sports law.

The small number of trainees taken on allows for a very flexible training and, subject to the needs of each department, "you can tailor your own training contract." Thus, while seats are compulsory in company/commercial and litigation, the litigation requirement can be met within Intellectual Property and the company/commercial department is split into three groups, allowing for seats to be taken in specific areas such as Information Technology, employment or banking. However, trainees can receive work from across the department, "which is definitely useful because you get to know where you want to specialise, and where you don't." Within litigation there is also a seat in clinical negligence, which is a rare opportunity in a firm of this nature.

The general atmosphere of the firm was particularly praised by trainees. It retains a "personal touch" despite expansion. This is immediately noticeable during vacation placements, and at interview. Each department is "very much a team," with a distinct feel, and internal socialising. This is good for trainees, as it allows them to get to know most people in the firm, and makes asking questions easier; "there's no 'I'm too busy' atmosphere here."

Ongoing legal training takes the form of lunchtime legal seminars, while there is a further seminar scheme for trainees which sharpens presentational, marketing and negotiation skills. There are opportunities to go on client secondments, "which is absolutely fantastic...it gives you a lot of confidence because you are totally managing your own projects rather than getting everything overseen by a partner."

There is a "myth" that Bird & Bird is only interested in recruiting law students with a science background, according to one trainee. While a science masters or a background in pharmacology is "helpful", the majority of trainees taken on have law degrees or CPEs only. What is more important, says another trainee, is that you "have your feet on the ground." There is certainly no bar to mature students, and those who have done other things before the law; "they're not interested in everyone having the same corporate stamp on them."

Top Recommendations in Chambers Directory: Information Technology, Intellectual Property.

Bindman and Partners

UK ranking by size: 291
Number of trainees: 6 every two years

Bindmans is well known to law students who are interested in the civil liberties field, a fact attested to by the vast number of applications which drop through its letter box every year. Its ongoing involvement in the Pinochet case is just one example of the many high profile cases that the practice takes on. It is worth pointing out that the firm does a wide variety of legal aid and private client work across eight main fields of law, from crime and immigration through to employment and family. Most of the human rights/European Court work is done within the litigation department. This spread means that, unlike many civil liberties niche firms, trainees are able to gain a broad, structured training.

The level of interest in the firm means that all applicants are sent a preliminary letter, warning them that it is not enough to have done well at university and to be generally interested. The majority of the applicants who finally make the grade have some form of relevant 'quasi-legal' work experience, such as advice work, or have changed career. There is no commitment to 100% retention at the end of the contract, but trainees "are able to tap into the network of similar firms and never seem to have any problem finding places." The training has recently been reorganised to so that six trainees are taken on every two years. They will take eight month seats in three departments. You choose your combination of seats at interview stage.

In all seats, trainees are given "a good deal of independence and autonomy," and have their own rooms. The variety of cases in most departments means that trainees are able to have some of their own clients, for whom they will be the first point of contact, and to work on discrete parts of larger cases. Crime, housing and immigration are particularly good for running your own files, while clinical negligence is a department where there are fewer suitable smaller cases. Prioritisation of work is a key skill, as trainees will take work from all members of the department, and there are times "when you do feel slightly swamped." However, this full immersion approach also means that "you learn how to do things in a very rigorous way" and are "used to working on your own" by the end of the training contract. Supervision is constant, with a designated training partner in each department, and formal assessments are held every three months.

The high profile cases and fast-moving nature of much of the work does make Bindmans a "buzzy" environment. For a trainee, it is an "approachable," "relaxed" place to work. "Because its clients range from media companies to homeless people it needs to be welcoming."

Top Recommendations in Chambers Directory: Admin & Public Law, Civil Liberties, Crime, Immigration.

Bond Pearce

UK ranking by size: 43
Number of trainees: 38

Within the last two years this West Country firm has merged with Southampton firm Hepherd Winstanley & Pugh, moved into the competitive Bristol arena and very recently opened an office in Leeds. The effect has been to make it a real contender for the best quality commercial work in the south west and south east.

The trainees feel that they are very much a part of this 'watch this space' phenomenon. "There is a culture of 'we're going places.' From partner to trainee level all are taking responsibility to make sure that we do. It's the idea we've got a role to play and have to establish ourselves. That doctrine must come down to trainee level and creates a culture of involvement."

We were told of the firm's particularly strong roots in the West Country, in Plymouth and Exeter, and a sense of responsibility to the local business community. Some pro bono work comes from local chambers of commerce and certain initiatives are set up through regional development agencies. BP is very involved, in particular in the corporate and company commercial departments.

The firm actively supports the Trainee Solicitors Group in Plymouth in practical ways, understanding that it is best placed to do so as the largest firm in the city.

A number of non-commercial options, such as probate, personal injury or family, are available to trainees in the West Country offices. These have been phased out in favour of commercial seats in Southampton and do not feature at all in Bristol. "For some trainees the opportunity to do the other areas is important. BP has a nice combination – the general practice feel in Plymouth which has a wider spread of work and then the other centres which are more commercially driven." The new Bristol office is a deliberate attempt to compete for the commercial work presently in the domain of the established firms of that city. The Bristol and Southampton offices are felt to be less geared towards local clients. Trainees were proud to be working for clients with household names. There is a regular three-month secondment to B&Q on a three days a week basis.

How connected do the trainees feel with the other offices and does Bond Pearce coalesce as a single firm? "Yes it does!" said one trainee. For example at the time of interviewing the firm was planning a walk across the Sahara for Macmillan Cancer Relief, including people from all the combined offices. Senior partner Nigel Fair is thought to be an excellent figurehead and good at bringing everyone together "so you feel as though you are part of a larger network instead of just one local office." Trainees can switch between offices and indeed might ask to do so for a specific seat offered in only one location. For example, the planning and charity seats in Plymouth are often filled by trainees from elsewhere. Sometimes if one office is particularly busy, trainees from another office will be asked to help out for a few weeks or months.

In most offices trainees sit with a partner or assistant. Occasionally they may have a room by themself. In Bristol they sit in an open plan environment. In the corporate department in Southampton you can do some "stupid nights." As a contrast, in Plymouth there is a real culture for leaving at a very decent hour to pursue summer sports such as sailing. There does seem to be a strong emphasis on the social life of the firm. Staff subscribe to a social committee which organises group events. The trainees emphasised that the firm has placed a good deal of importance on social interaction within and between the offices.

Top Recommendations in Chambers Directory: Employment Law, General Corporate Finance, Personal Injury - Both defendant & plaintiff, Professional Negligence, Trusts & Personal Tax.

Burges Salmon

UK ranking by size: 45
Number of trainees: 28

One of the elite Bristol firms, by a shade the largest and certainly the longest established. Burges Salmon is known as the top agricultural practice in the country, yet this belies the fact that it is a broad church commercial firm.

The word that fell most frequently from the mouths of trainees was 'quality.' This was apparent even at vacation placement stage. "The point of the two weeks was to convince us that if you did come to pick the firm you would be exposed to a high quality of work."

The firm attracts a number of trainees who have no local connection although most are attracted by the firm's location. Many might otherwise have gone for a City firm had they not been able to find the quality they were looking for in the area. "Burges Salmon has a high enough quality of work to keep you in Bristol from a purely professional point of view." The trainees were keen to stress this. "It is first and foremost a large commercial firm. So above anything else the client base is principally commercial. It doesn't see itself as being a Bristol firm – more than half the client base comes from outside Bristol. It is a large player with some extremely big clients."

Trainees work in each of five main departments for four months. They then commonly return to the department into which they intend to qualify. Whilst the arrangement allows them to see all of the firm's traditional departments and experience a wider range of work, there is a perception that four months isn't a long time in which to prove yourself.

One trainee told us "It is a bit difficult to characterise the firm because every department gives a different impression." For example, the agricultural unit. "Apart from being a little bit mad it was a very exciting place to be. We have a national agricultural practice so you are sometimes dealing with some pretty narrow technical issues. It is actually cutting-edge law challenging the European Commission and winning, taking cases to the Court of Appeal."

The selection process for trainees seems to be particularly thorough and instils extra confidence in those who actually get through it. Trainees found the firm to have a positive attitude towards people who have had previous careers. There are several older trainees some of whom have families. From the trainees' point of view it creates a very varied atmosphere rather than "us all being 24 and straight out of law school."

The firm is growing and is seen to be changing in other ways. In the past it may have had an image as conservative and a bit stuffy. The emphasis previously was on organic growth and caution. This is seen to have changed to a more positive recruitment policy, that is "outward-looking and more aggressive." Certainly in some areas there is a perception that lawyers are "pushing things hard so you get a feeling of movement."

Top Recommendations in Chambers Directory: Agriculture & Bloodstock, General Corporate Finance, Litigation (Commercial), Litigation (Property), Pensions, Social Housing, Trusts & Personal Tax.

Clifford Chance

UK ranking by size: 2
Number of trainees: 254

Clifford Chance has long been the biggest single-office firm in the UK. Its recent merger with US and German firms make it arguably the first truly global law firm, but of more immediate relevance to prospective trainees is its London profile. This is as a corporate powerhouse with in-house facilities to match. It is often joked that Clifford Chance lawyers need never leave the building. There is a pool and a squash courts, a gym on-site, 24-hour canteen, dry-cleaners. Not quite guest-rooms for everyone but certainly beds available for partners working overnight. At first sight it is perhaps the most like most people's ideas of a US-style office culture.

One trainee, when trying to explain how the size of the firm impacts on individual trainees, drew an analogy with London itself. You are unlikely to get to know every part of it; there is no need to. You know certain districts well and have friends in others. Two adjacent districts can have a totally different feel from each other. Clifford Chance's different departments work in a similar way. As a trainee you get the opportunity to sample widely so that eventually you understand the range of options available on qualification. "The trick is to keep your choices reasonably broad. Choose wisely. It's very easy to keep all your seats narrow and then not have a good idea of what you want to do. All seats have their own character - it becomes evident eventually what works for you and what doesn't."

So wide is the choice, that seat choices are made with the help of a booklet which sets out and describes the different departments. The breadth of practice areas available was a real draw to many applicants to the firm. However, the finance orientation of the opportunities, especially on qualification, needs to be highlighted. "The firm emphasises that it wants people to do at least one finance seat. If you manage to do half your training outside of that area then that's almost unrepresentative of what the firm does. The vast majority of job opportunities will be in the finance practice. There are also far more opportunities to work abroad in finance than in other departments." The usual seat rotation for a trainee would be corporate, finance, an overseas office and then one seat fulfilling the contentious experience requirement.

The opportunity to go overseas is a major draw for trainees. Everyone who wants to go overseas goes, although not necessarily where they want to go. Many seats require a foreign language; the flip-side is that people with foreign languages are usually required in particular offices. If you have good Portuguese, you are more likely to be required in São Paulo than Hong Kong where languages are not required. Equally, if you want to go to Paris but have little French, you will not withstand the competition. All those professing to language skills are independently assessed.

Potential trainees must understand that Clifford Chance is first and foremost an international business organisation. You need an interest in high value global commerce to get the best out of it. "At the moment I'm co-ordinating a deal that involves Amsterdam, Poland, Luxembourg and the UK. I make sure documents are circulated, check facts and speak to different offices. You don't feel that you're not getting involved here. You do get involved in a deal and there's a great sense of teamwork."

Top Recommendations in Chambers Directory:
Asset Finance & Leasing, Banking, Capital Markets, Commodities, Corporate Finance, Employee Share Schemes, Financial Services (FSA, Compliance etc), Fraud, Information Technology, Intellectual Property, Investment Funds, Parliamentary: Public Affairs, Project Finance, Social Housing: Advising Lenders, Telecommunications, Travel.

Clyde & Co

UK ranking by size: 34
Number of trainees: 36

Clyde & Co is known as a shipping and insurance firm because of its key strengths in those two areas. However, there's a considerable amount more to the firm. The corporate department has been growing in line with the firm's aim to be a medium-sized multi-centre commercial firm. The larger office is in the City and a second is in Guildford. The work profile of each is similar. A third office is located in Cardiff.

The trainees we spoke to insisted that we discuss the perception of the firm as purely shipping and insurance-based. "When I applied to Clydes and they offered me a training contract I thought 'Oh yes–the shipping firm.' It is such a misconception because that is not all that we do. Some trainees do not touch shipping or insurance in their training contracts." Insurance litigation and shipping litigation, cargo and commodities work might be seen as the classical Clyde & Co training and in fact around 50% of workload is in these areas. Add to that corporate and asset finance and you find the typical two year contract. There are also seats such as employment, energy, Information Technology and other niches.

The moderate size of the firm and a relatively small number of trainees in comparison to large City firms automatically makes a difference to the atmosphere. Trainees say it means more responsibility than their counterparts at the biggest firms. For example, in corporate one trainee would find herself running the disclosure half of an acquisition or disposal. This means a lot of client contact. "Clydes is not afraid of pushing their trainees forward." Clients speak to trainees as their first point of contact, and they are introduced as an integral part of the legal team. "This helps you to grow up as a trainee because it does give you confidence. If you can deal with a difficult client, you can deal with anything - it's a skill which I learned early as a trainee." Trainees felt that this experience was in stark contrast with those of friends at other firms.

Applicants indicate which office they are interested in or whether they have no preference. Trainees can move between the Guildford and London offices, either because they want to experience a different environment for a while or because there is a specialist seat that they want to do in the other office. The mainstream seats are available in both but certain things, like Marine Casualty, are only available in Guildford.

Trainees don't share an office with their supervisors but sit on their own. There is an occasional shared office but "they bust a gut to get as many people into their own offices as possible."

Overseas seats are available in the Dubai office. The firm appears to recruit a number of trainees with relevant second languages. The seats are determined by the volume of work in the office at the time rather than a set number. One trainee found himself out there for a short while in his first seat. "I was 4-5 months into the job and they sent me abroad. I was lucky enough to be sent to visit the client and explain the deal to them. They didn't send me with another solicitor, they sent me on my own. The client was based in Kuwait, Bahrain and Oman so I went on a tour of the Middle East."

Top Recommendations in Chambers Directory:
Insurance & Reinsurance, Transport.

CMS Cameron McKenna

UK ranking by size: 8
Number of trainees: 104

The firm was born in 1997 out of a merger between two medium-sized firms, one recognised for its corporate strength, the other known as a litigation firm. The result is a firm with excellent projects and energy practices and all-round strength.

One trainee assessed the impact of the merger. "It was two firms completely reassessing what they wanted to be. It's now motivated and forward-looking." For those who had accepted training contracts just before the merger, fears about working in a big firm were not borne out. Still friendly, it just takes you longer to get to know everyone. "We are young and hungry – wanting to be successful and to prove to people that the merger was a good idea. Not wanting to sit back on our laurels." However the atmosphere is not too driven or too hierarchical. It is seen as "open and contented."

There was clear feedback that seat three was the focal point of the two years. Trainees will generally qualify into the department in which they do their third seat. "A lot of departments try to attract 3rd seaters in the hope that they will want to come back." Certain practice areas have such a strong reputation that they attract trainees to the firm. For example, healthcare and pharmaceuticals-related work is a real draw, with the firm offering companies like SmithKline Beecham as clients. The potential for those with a medical/pharmaceuticals background is clearly apparent. The breadth of work means that it might help for a trainee to be focused about what they want to achieve from their training. "I think the key for students coming in at trainee level is to find out a bit about what they might fancy doing before they end up at the firm. I think they need to have a fairly good idea about what they want to do so they can target particular seats and are then in a position to make a fully-informed decision."

Trainees stressed that the choice of CMS was made at least partly for its 'normal,' 'human,' 'non-macho,' 'down-to-earth' feel. There will be times for working late but this is not consistent and partners are more likely to tell their trainees to go home while they have the chance.

Trainees feel their voices are heard within the firm. They are encouraged to become involved and accept responsibility. The attitude is "You come and tell me if you want to do something and I will cut you a bit of slack. Tell us what you're here for. Tell us what you want to get stuck into." In our discussions with trainees at the firm it became obvious that whilst there was no overwhelming sense of competitiveness for seats, trainees need to be proactive and prepared to run some sort of campaign to get the seats they want. There's no scope for just sitting back and hoping for the best.

There are a number of opportunities for trainees to spend three or six months in overseas offices. Additionally, client secondment seats are also popular.

Top Recommendations in Chambers Directory:
Fraud - Civil, Regulation & Investigation, Health & Safety, Health Care: Pharmaceuticals, Immigration & Nationality, Insurance & Reinsurance, Product Liability, Professional Negligence.

Charles Russell

UK ranking by size: 46
Number of trainees: 22

The focus of Charles Russell has changed significantly in the last decade or so. It is no longer seen as a traditional private client specialist firm. Its commercial activities are now well-regarded, particularly in industries such as telecoms and insurance. A rarity in the City is their family practice and other niche strengths appear, for example in charities.

The appeal of a combined commercial/private client training is a very strong one for many trainees. Those at Charles Russell carry a well-founded confidence that they are getting quality in both. Trainees are encouraged to go for the mix rather than being pushed in one direction.

The practice has a low trainee to partner gearing. This may be behind the notion that trainees here get a high level of responsibility from the outset. The relatively low numbers of trainees taken each year also makes them feel like individuals.

Training contracts are available in the main London office, the new Guildford office and a long-established Cheltenham location. The latter two are much smaller operations, but at the same time large for the size of firms in those towns. The trainees at the branch offices feel the benefit of links with London in terms of back-up. The insurance litigation seat is located in the firm's satellite office in the Lloyds Building itself. Almost without exception trainees share an office with a partner for each seat but there is not, as yet, a great deal of movement between the main three offices in terms of trainee seats.

The Cheltenham and Guildford offices both reflect the breadth of work in the London office. In Guildford, for example, your seats might be litigation, matrimonial, property and company/commercial.

The growth and metamorphosis of the firm is apparent to the trainees. They recognised it was still hanging on to close interpersonal relationships that often characterise smaller firms but at the same time there was a buzz every time a new client was secured and the drive towards a new commercial profile was enhanced.

Top Recommendations in Chambers Directory: Trusts & Personal Tax.

Denton Hall

UK ranking by size: 19
Number of trainees: 62

Denton Hall is a City firm particularly known for its niche work. Its leading media, Information Technology and telecoms departments are most attractive to trainees while its energy practice has enabled the firm to establish a significant international practice. Overseas opportunities within the training contract include seats in Hong Kong, Singapore, Cairo, Tokyo, Brussels and Gibraltar. The merger with banking and finance specialist Wilde Sapte in February 2000 should broaden opportunities for trainees further. At the time of going to print information about future training at the merged firm was not yet available.

There is no doubt that media law exerts a powerful pull - glamour. "If you walk around the media floor you see pictures of the movies they've been involved in... but it looks more glamorous than it actually is. At the end of the day it's just contract law." Within the department several areas are covered, from film finance through to sports law. It is a large department but media seats are the most over-subscribed, followed by Intellectual Property. If you are very keen on doing a seat in one of these areas it is recommended that you make this clear to the recruitment department at the beginning of your training contract. Otherwise it is usually possible to get the seats you want.

Before the end of each seat trainees hand in a list of five seat choices in order of preference, and can also put down the partner with whom they wish to sit. You must take a property, a company/commercial and a litigation seat, but within that format you are able to gain experience of a wide variety of areas. For example, media, tax and pensions can each count as a commercial seat, while areas as diverse as financial services, PFI and project finance are represented within the corporate department.

On balance trainees did feel that they got enough responsibility across their training, "there's not a sense at all that they don't let you near the transaction…much the opposite, in fact." The property seat, in particular, is where they "teach you to run a file," and the variety of work is a big plus. "You do want to have some big deals, so you get to see the glamorous side and how a very large transaction works, but you also want some small deals which you are handling sizeable chunks of. At Denton Hall you get a good mixture of the two." The international element makes working on deals in the energy department particularly exciting. One trainee we spoke to had worked on wholly international projects throughout his first year.

The atmosphere at the firm was universally praised as relaxed and non-hierarchical, "it feels like a much smaller firm." The media influence does contribute to the firm's lighthearted feel, and there are many 'personalities' around the place. Recruitment seems to follow in this vein, and the firm is thought to recruit "people with a lot of strings to their bow." Those with more unconventional and interesting or relevant backgrounds seem to succeed. The pressure for places means that academic requirements are high, but trainees are "not purely brains" and often have outside sporting and music interests. If trainees have any issues they wish to bring up with partners, there are two trainee representatives, whose role is also to organise social events. The firm is keen for trainees to get involved in marketing, either by assisting in the writing of client presentations or by attending specific events. Recently trainees were encouraged to bring two 'young professional' friends to a photography exhibition sponsored by the firm.

Top Recommendations in Chambers Directory:
Energy & Utilities, Media & Entertainment, Sports Law.

Dickinson Dees

UK ranking by size: 66
Number of trainees: 18

'Dickie Dees' is Newcastle's largest firm. It has a strong corporate/commercial practice with broad expertise in several areas.

It operates a conventional seat rotation system with three compulsory seats in property, company/commercial and litigation. The fourth optional seat allows trainees to pick from a broad range of disciplines. It could include a stint in the private client department, which is another focus of specialisation.

The optional research-based Brussels seat is encouraged by the firm. Two trainees are sent every year from a small intake of seven or eight, so any expression of preference is likely to be accommodated.

Trainees were keen to play up the flexibility of the training structure and the wide range of work experience available. "You can shop around when you're in a particular department; if you're in litigation but interested in environmental law you can take work from another person who's not your supervisor." Likewise, if you're in company and you want to try banking and insolvency you're free to ask someone to send work your way. It is felt that trainees generally receive the work and the seats they want although "you have to ask or it's a bit of a lottery."

The trainees we spoke to were happy with the level of supervision they had received. They usually sit close to a partner or senior assistant and there are always others to turn to. The training partner provides a common thread throughout the two years. "He's there for anything, not just work related stuff." Another trainee underlined the existence of a good support network among his peers. "Because it is a big firm, there are a lot of young lawyers knocking about who can give you guidance."

Trainees were generally satisfied with the level of responsibility given. One second year trainee cited his start-to-finish involvement in a couple of big corporate cases as a high point of his contract. "I was sent to Jersey a month ago on my own to deal with a share acquisition. It was good, a lot of responsibility." Another hard-working trainee derived satisfaction from working through the night on a big completion.

There are certainly no typical trainees at Dickinson Dees. Many have unconventional and colourful backgrounds. As examples we were told about policemen, a teacher, a civil servant, and trainees with work experience in Australia and Africa. "The majority aren't straight from law school, they've all done something else and either changed their mind or decided to become lawyers." The firm seemingly values the breadth of experience that a diverse background and age range affords. Many, however, are from or have connections to the north east.

Interviewees pointed to the firm's friendliness. It tends to train and retain so there is little fierce competition between trainees. Social activities and nights out are organised by individual departments and there is plenty of interaction with clients on both a work and a social basis.

Client secondments are not common but the firm is not averse to alternative individual arrangements being made. One trainee recently spent time at Durham County Council and another is working more or less full time for a major Yorkshire-based client.

Top Recommendations in Chambers Directory: Agriculture & Bloodstock, Trusts & Personal Tax.

Dibb Lupton Alsop

UK ranking by size: 5
Number of trainees: 100

Dibbs is the fifth largest firm in the country and boasts offices across the north and in Birmingham, a significant London presence and offices in Brussels and Hong Kong. Though it is rare for trainees to take seats in different branches during their training contracts, many we spoke to were attracted to the firm for its national presence and "aggressive" expansionist ethos. While maintaining a broad practice across all branches, particularly in the core corporate, litigation and property areas, there are some differences of specialisation and emphasis which prospective trainees should investigate further before deciding to which office they apply. For example, if you have a particular interest in banking, aviation finance or insurance you should look to the London office. Marine insurance is mainly practised in Manchester and Liverpool.

The size of the firm and its breadth of practice means that trainees are able to take their four seats in a wide variety of fields, ranging from the traditional corporate and property through to Intellectual Property, Human Resources (employment and pensions), PFI and construction. Other opportunities include a three or six-month corporate/competition placement in the Brussels office and client secondments to ICI in Manchester and to Intellectual PropertyC Magazines in London.

Trainees must take one contentious and one non-contentious seat, but otherwise have a free rein, though most tend to choose a corporate seat. Trainees stressed the flexibility of the firm in trying to accommodate people's choices. Similarly, while trainees are recruited to each office with the intention that they qualify there, the national network of offices does allow for some movement on qualification if one job is particularly sought after.

Interviewees thought there was a good balance of responsibility and supervision. "There's always someone to ask if you're unsure and they'll give you tests and try to stretch you and maintain your interest." Across the offices litigation, insurance and employment emerged as the seats with most responsibility. In insurance, for example, you are able to do most of the work on files such as instructing counsel, instructing suitable experts, assessing levels of quantum etc. Two interviewees were particularly enthusiastic about their seats in corporate recovery, where they attended creditors meetings and were able to "really dissect the directors, asking them why and what they did and why the company went bust."

Another noticeable theme was Dibbs' willingness to recruit those who have come to law after a previous career, particularly in the commercial world and the Services. The "basic academics are a given, but Dibbs likes 'people' people too." The relatively small number of trainees at each office helps to create a "positive, cheery" atmosphere, with the Manchester office being a lot busier but "it's not a culture where you're afraid to ask." Any problems can be discussed at monthly meeting with the office Trainee Coordinator, minutes of which are e-mailed to all trainees. Departmental drinks are a monthly occurrence, while at a national level each department organises a weekend away once a year, with recent venues as diverse as Paris, Barcelona and Alton Towers.

Top Recommendations in Chambers Directory: Banking, Debt Collection, Food, Insolvency, Intellectual Property, Litigation (Commercial), Litigation (Property), Local Government,

Pensions, Projects/PFI, Property (Commercial), Shipping & Maritime Law, Transport.

Edge Ellison

UK ranking by size: 23
Number of trainees: 38

Edge Ellison is one of the Midlands' traditional big players. It has responded to its own recent internal changes by instigating the "Way Forward Plan," aimed at rejuvenating the firm's image and reputation. Training at Edges is therefore quite a distinct animal with a language all of its own. At no other law firm did trainees speak of the benefits of courses teaching you to 'recharge your batteries', 'mind-map' and 'build relationships.' "Occasionally it can get a little bit cheesy...but a lot of it is valid." The recent expansion of the London office has also affected trainees. More are taken on in London and those based in the Midlands offices are encouraged to move to London to take their corporate seat.

Most trainees take three separate seats and then return to the one in which they wish to qualify. All three offices have a similar range of work, though locations play a part. The London office leans more towards corporate work, and the Leicester office handles a lot of work for the textiles industry. Trainees often take seats in areas of strength for the firm, such as pensions, construction and planning, while the diversity of work within seats is praised as very broad. In certain niche areas where there are no official seats, such as information technology and personal injury, it is up to trainees to approach the relevant partners and create their own seats.

Trainees are given more responsibility as the contract progresses. "There is a general progression; it is never a jump from first to second year or from second year to newly-qualified." One London trainee compared the responsibility given to him in his corporate seat with that given to colleagues in larger City firms. "They just tend to throw people at deals...as a trainee here you get far more responsibility and a far greater quality of work."

As for the level of supervision, trainees were in the main positive in their comments, though one did note that partners were often very busy and have to be pursued for advice: "I think the general rule is: don't worry about asking a few stupid questions. Just don't ask them again."

"At the end of the day, you are at work for eight to ten hours a day and you've got to enjoy what you're doing. People at Edges smile a lot" was one trainee's immediate reaction to the firm's atmosphere after his vacation placement. The different atmospheres in the offices are noted: "the Leicester office is a lot smaller, people know each other from the top floor to the bottom floor, socialising is cross-office." The Birmingham office with thirteen floors is slightly less personal.

The firm is keen on trainee involvement in marketing to clients. This also leads to social events, which may even include Leicester City football ground. Trainees are sent on a marketing course in Birmingham, "the Corporate departments realise that in ten year's time, we're going to be the people making the business decisions. So, for example, with accountants and professionals, there are always big events going on at our level as well."

Top Recommendations in Chambers Directory: Pensions.

Eversheds

UK ranking by size: 1
Number of trainees: 210

Add together Eversheds' 10 offices nationwide and you get the country's largest firm. By themselves, none of the offices are monolithic in size although certain offices are largest for their region and market leaders for specific practice areas. In employment, for example, the Birmingham, Norwich, Cardiff and Ipswich offices are top of their regional piles. In the North, for environmental law both Leeds and Manchester offices hold sway whilst for construction the Leeds and Newcastle offices are unbeaten.

Part of the Eversheds ethos is that the offices should grow together and be seen as a single brand. Trainees are instilled with this ethos and seem to recognise the advantages of the 'national firm' concept. One said "all our training takes place on a national basis, so in the second week when all trainees go off to do their PSC you meet all the others there."

The national network can have advantages on a day to day basis too. Being able to call on the collective expertise of several hundred lawyers around the country with experience in diverse areas is seen as a boost. "It is that sort of thing that makes you feel part of a national firm." There is a notion that a broader range of work is handled across the entirety of the firm than at the larger City firms. This is a great source of support when a more obscure piece of advice is sought. However, whatever the rhetoric, each trainee feels very much a part of their local office. "Although there is a national identity, it is not yet a single firm – although that is the intention. There is still a bit of competition between the regions!"

The fact that the training structure differs from region to region underlines the fact that full harmonisation has not yet occurred. In Leeds and Manchester six seats of four months each are taken, whereas the traditional four-seat structure is the norm in other offices. However, many trainees feel that four months is not long enough to settle into a seat and many trainees choose to take double seats to compensate.

One obvious sign of the drive towards national harmonisation is the internal movement of trainees, with those in East Anglia and Cardiff/Bristol strongly encouraged to take seats in other branches within their region. This also allows trainees to take full advantage of local specialisms, be it PFI in Ipswich or commercial property and corporate in Norwich. Most branches are close enough that trainees do not have to move house, though help with housing and removal costs will be given if a trainee does choose to move temporarily. The growth of the Cambridge office will make this increasingly common.

The breadth of the training and of client contact was universally praised: "they cover such a wide span of work ...fom a one-man limited company right up to Plcs, and I preferred the idea of that range." Similarly, the diversity of practice areas allows trainees to take seats in areas from public law and planning through to personal injury that may not be available in many firms. Eversheds' stellar national reputation in employment attracts many trainees. In some branches this causes problems where seat demand outstrips supply. For many it can be "a frustration" that they cannot get experience in that particular seat. This is a lesser problem in Leeds and Manchester where everyone gets six bites at the cherry.

The firm has a national sports weekend rotating around the country each year as well as inter-office football matches. There is also the feeling that there's a future for qualifiers in the firm. It would be possible for a trainee or new qualifier or even someone more senior to relocate within the country and still maintain a career with the firm. Overseas seats are beginning to become a reality for trainees outside of the London office, with a Leeds trainee going to Paris on secondment this year and other possibilities available in Brussels and Moscow. Competition is fierce for these positions, so "get you requests in early."

Trainees at the firm have the impression that despite an emphasis on the development of core standards and the standardisation of systems across the offices, there is a high degree of heterogeneity amongst trainees recruited by the firm. "Some offices are good at recruiting people from different backgrounds not just "your standard 23-straight-out-of-law-school-types... it isn't single faceted." One noticeable trend is that the national offices tend to take on a large proportion of people with local links.

Top Recommendations in Chambers Directory: Admin & Public Law, Banking, Clinical Negligence: Mainly Defendant, Construction & Civil Engineering, Debt Collection, Education, Employment Law, Environmental Law, Food, Franchising, General Corporate Finance, Insolvency, Litigation (Commercial), Litigation (Property), Local Government, Projects/PFI, Property (Commercial), Social Housing, Trusts & Personal Tax.

Field Fisher Waterhouse

UK ranking by size: 49
Number of trainees: 20

Field Fisher Waterhouse is a medium-sized City firm. It is particularly distinguishable for combining traditional corporate work with top level Information Technology, Intellectual Property, media and telecoms niche work and a strong medical negligence and personal injury practice, which is, unusually, claimant based. Seats can be taken in most niche areas, and as there are five seats, trainees are able to sample a wide variety of work during their contract. The first seat is allocated and the fifth usually entails returning to the seat in which you want to qualify. Subject to Law Society requirements, the trainees work out the remaining three among themselves at a group meeting a month before the end of each seat. Field Fisher is notable for the quality of client secondments it offers, allowing trainees an insight into "life on the other side." Currently trainees are at the BBC and the Mitsubishi Bank.

Levels of responsibility and client contact were generally praised, and while bundle preparation and photocopying are not unknown, one trainee described the high point of his training as "knowing that you're getting trained and feeling yourself getting better and more confident at things." Property and litigation seem to be the seats where trainees get most opportunities to run their own files, while in corporate, due to the size of the deals, "you are likely to have a smaller part of a big pie." In corporate City work can mean City hours, but the opportunity to work on high profile deals makes this easier to bear. In the highly regarded PI/med neg department, the high value nature and technical complexity of most claims mean that trainees cannot be given their own files, but the cutting edge work and expertise of the relevant partners meant preparing for and attending trials can be "absolutely fascinating."

The atmosphere of the firm makes a strong impression. "For a law firm it is remarkably nice, relaxed and friendly." It is a frm where the suggestions even of a lowly trainee are taken seriously. "You might be sent away with a flea in your ear, but you could still suggest it and people would listen." Interviewees highlighted the influence of the expanding Information Technology and media departments in making the firm a "buzzing," dynamic place to work. A trainee social committee organises regular evenings out, sports and one-off events, such as go-karting, bowling and the infamous Jack the Ripper walk around the East End of London, while the monthly "Happy Evening" event brings together members of the firm from partner to trainee on the last Thursday of each month. "I think the trainees go along and at first they are wary of senior-looking people in case they are very important, but they soon get the idea that you can have a laugh with them."

Top Recommendations in Chambers Directory:
Franchising, Licensing & Leisure, Travel.

Freshfields

UK ranking by size:6
Number of trainees: 138

Magic Circle member, fourth biggest in the City with a head-spinningly good reputation for all things corporate, financial, commercial and litigious. Clients are blue chip and deals are big-ticket. The firm has overseas seats for around a third of its trainees.

One thing that trainees raved about was the degree of flexibility in terms of how long they can spend in any one seat. It is easy to switch to a different department after just three months if you feel that a particular seat is not what you want. The choice of seats available then depends on the location of the other trainees swapping mid-seat.

The emphasis of training is on corporate work and at least nine months will be spent in the corporate or finance departments. Litigation must also be covered and niche seats to choose from include Intellectual Property and employment, the most popular. New York, Singapore and Hong Kong are the favoured overseas destinations along with Paris and Madrid.

A healthy number of secondments to UK clients are popular alternatives to an overseas stint. One former secondee "loved it …I did interesting research as well as really practical stuff. Because it's so much smaller, queries come in and you have to answer lots of self-contained, yes/no questions yourself on the back of research. And the hours are great." As for hours back at the office, they are the cause of some of the key urban myths surrounding Freshfields. Trainees had an idea before starting of what would be required but had not really anticipated the extent to which it would impact on their personal lives. "You go in blind. You know the hours are going to be awful but it does not really strike home ."

However, not everyone agreed that a Freshfields training means excessive hours. Some felt that in certain cases they were a result of trainees having developed a 'stay-late-whatever' culture. Trainees stressed the value of the experience gained from working weekends and nights on major pieces of work. Some felt late evenings were balanced by the relatively late start (9.30am).

A number of our interviewees alluded to the sporty and confident nature of trainees. "I would definitely say that shrinking violets wouldn't really get on that well. You have to make an impression in your departments as you move through." Most guessed the Oxbridge intake to be higher than the reality (which is 56%) although they were keen to deny the 'blues and blondes' stereotype.

Uniquely, every fee-earner is provided with a lap-top so they can work anywhere. This benefit is to be extended to recruits still at law school.

Top Recommendations in Chambers Directory:
Asset Finance & Leasing, Capital Markets, Corporate Finance, Employee Share Schemes, Environmental Law, European Union/Competition, International Arbitration, Pensions, Tax (Corporate), Transport.

Garretts

UK ranking by size:22
Number of trainees: 50

In Leeds, Manchester, Reading and London Garretts lawyers are attempting something new in the legal profession. Having become de facto a part of the Arthur Andersen accountancy empire, the UK legal arm of Andersens, Garretts, is operating from within the larger organisation on the same transactions and with the same clients as its big brother.

The firm is relatively new and has only taken trainees for three years. As such it still feels like a new venture for all parties and there seems to be a bit of a pioneering feel within the firm. This is reflected in the relative youth of the partnership and the open-plan layout of departments. Trainees tend to sit near rather than with a supervisor. Each trainee has a 'mentor' who is usually only two or thee years qualified and entirely independent.

Strong links have appeared between the northern and two southern offices. Whilst all four got together for initial training on the PSC, the more routine and regular contact operates either side of the north-south divide. All are linked to a higher entity. "We get lots of training and talks about the bigger picture." This is perhaps wherein the real difference in a Garretts training lies. As part of a larger organisation, trainees find themselves sitting in open plan areas with Andersens staff and working within cross-disciplinary groups on clients' work. This is less apparent in departments such as property but very much the case with departments like HCS (Human Capital Services - employee share schemes etc.). "Everything's pushing towards greater integration with Arthur Anderson. It is good being mixed in, you're not just a typical law firm."

There is an apparent tendency to recruit bilingual trainees. "Out of six of us, two have degrees in French and a third is of Italian origin." Many chose the firm because of the worldwide spread of Andersens offices and the opportunities for trainees to spend time in one of them. The Sydney slot is especially popular.

The Leeds office suffered partner defections in corporate finance and property in 1999 and, unusually, two trainees moved to a rival Leeds firm to join them. Such partner defections have caused question marks in the legal world as to the future of the firm but trainees remained extremely upbeat.

Top Recommendations in Chambers Directory: Banking.

Gouldens

UK ranking by size: 63
Number of trainees: 26

Gouldens is a well-respected top 50 City firm with key strengths in corporate finance, commercial litigation and property. It has a unique non-rotational seat system in which trainees are allocated their own office from the outset and receive work concurrently from several different departments throughout the duration of their contract. The system permits trainees to take on a range of work from the three main departments. Its uniqueness is considered a major selling point when compared to the conventional approach. "Unless a firm has a different training system, there's a lot of conformity out there." The system was likened to school or university where students juggle a number of parallel subjects and balance competing time demands. Trainees felt they could get stuck in to lengthy cases and avoided the 'random panic' of changeover time as the seats rotated.

Trainees form early and active client relationships and see deals through from beginning to end. The emphasis on selection and self-reliance does have its advantages. "I'm not particularly interested in property," said one "so I don't want to do more of that work than I need to. You can tailor-make the experience to your own requirements, making yourself seen and heard in the particular area into which you want to qualify." This versatility allows trainees to avoid personality clashes and foment working relationships with favoured supervisers.

The trainees we spoke to were ambitious and keen to kick-start their working lives. "The lack of rotation really appealed to me. I wanted my real job to start straight away. I didn't need to be told how to do basic stuff. They offered a way of being supervised without slowing down your progress." Initiative and confidence are necessary qualities for a Gouldens trainee.

Responsibility levels are shaped entirely by individual capabilities, not an imposed structure. "it doesn't do to take on more than you're comfortable with," commented one. The firm permits exercise of early responsibility but work is thoroughly supervised, "if someone is confident and competent, they will have the room to display that but it will be checked." However, "it's always testing and you won't get bored."

Trainees receive a two-way review every six months where nominated supervisors appraise and report on performance. An interim review every 2 or 3 months looks at issues of more immediate concern. A weekly workload sheet is completed by all trainees informing the training supervisor of the spread of current activity. Some trainees felt work volume could be high. "I think it fluctuates more than a traditional seat system, we have intense periods at times." "I've had occasions when two partners have both wanted something by the next day and it's hard to deal with." He offered some pertinent advice; "if you hide in your office and worry about it, it won't work out."

Another trainee highlighted the general lifestyle concerns of a rigorous working environment, "the extent to which working five days a week does take over your life completely." She highlighted a practical issue, "because you have your own office, nobody really knows where you are and how you come and go. It's another aspect of your responsibility to make sure the work is done."

"Very open, definitely not stuffy" said one trainee of the prevailing working atmosphere. "Once you've got used to it, you can approach everyone." The social life seems to be lively, "We all get on well and go out for lunch and drinks." One trainee pointed to the absence of any intimidating hierarchy. "There's nobody here that I wouldn't regularly go out with. If I'm standing next to the senior partner, we'll talk and have a drink. There is a feeling that everyone is in it together."

In demand are confident go-getters who "can get on with it and ask questions if they can't." Strong, personable and outgoing characters are much in evidence. "It's not the right place for a shrinking violet."

Other opportunities are available at Gouldens - "if you shout loud enough, they may be there" said one keen on a foreign placement. On-going training is encouraged. One newly qualified with an interest in Intellectual Property/litigation went on a two week development course to strengthen her knowledge. One lucky trainee was seconded to technology client, Eidos, and worked in their growing legal department for six weeks. The positive experience included a business trip to San Francisco and reinforced her commitment to Gouldens on return.

Top Recommendations in Chambers Directory: Corporate Finance.

Halliwell Landau

UK ranking by size: 50
Number of trainees: 14

A northern-based firm which is second largest in the region and billed recently in the Manchester Evening News as "Manchester's fastest growing commercial firm."

The classic Halliwell Landau trainee seems to be the type who would spot an opportunity and not let go of it. Two trainees appear to have started their contracts fairly soon after identifying the firm as one to target and get a foot in the door, without adhering to the standard application process.

Such stories seem characteristic of the firm. In a period of growth new opportunities arise. Trainee numbers have almost doubled recently and new seats are emerging, such as tax, Intellectual Property and employment, the latter two being the most fought over in the firm. There are no compulsory seats but there are some busy departments. The chances are you'll do a stint in commercial litigation, PI and corporate. At the same time, we were told that if you particularly wanted experience in a department which couldn't budget for a whole trainee, a cross-department trainee seat could be established.

One of the things about a medium-sized firm, and especially one that is quite modern in its outlook, is the lack of rules. "It's always open to you to suggest a better way of doing things." Flexibility over seat issues does not mean lack of organisation. There are monthly meetings of trainees and training partners at which everyone sits down and thrashes out those issues that have been identified as important. These meetings double up as a forum for trainees to develop presentation skills, with each having to give a talk from time to time.

Unusually, the issue of trainees' financial targets came up in interviews. There seems to be a clear link between profitability and location on qualification. "You can almost make a niche for yourself if you make yourself indispensable. On the accounting side you are made aware of your billing from very early on. Some people can find it a strain - you know what the department earns, you know what the budget is and you know how much you're earning for the department from very early on. Qualification is a simple commercial decision."

At any one time, two trainees are seconded to clients. There is also a small degree of movement between the offices in London and Sheffield. A couple of trainees were working in both Manchester and Sheffield at the time of interviewing. They were apparently happy to split their time between both.

"The sort of person who will fit in" we were told "is someone who likes a challenge. The firm is a bit maverick. You've got to be a bit of a swashbuckler."

Top Recommendations in Chambers Directory: Banking, Intellectual Property, Planning, Property (Commercial), Trusts & Personal Tax.

Hammond Suddards

UK ranking by size: 14
Number of trainees: 45

Interviewing Hammond's trainees is a breath of fresh air. Without exception they seem open, clear-thinking and well-balanced in their comments on the training experience. There's a fear nothing, say what you mean and mean what you say feel to these people.

Every trainee will spend at least four months in each of the firm's London, Manchester and Leeds offices. Six seats will be done in total. There's a mixed reaction to this aspect of the training. It is accepted as being of great benefit whilst being loathed with a passion at the same time. "We do have a lot of contact between the offices - you know who to approach and how to get things done, so it does have its benefits." Trainees see the necessity for full integration of a truly national office, but for those who have established their personal lives in one city it is a hardship to have to spend eight months living in the other two. We were told that even if you had children you would be required to move.

Hammond's current second year trainees and newly qualifieds were recruited before a perceived change in policy. It seems that a number of them came from the ranks of paralegals and mature students. Concerns were expressed by a majority of our interviewees that the present recruitment policy was honing in on fresh-faced graduates from a more limited Oxbridge/Redbrick background who would have fewer commitments and ties to any particular area and thus complain a little less about the requirement to move between different offices.

The honesty we noted amongst the trainees at Hammonds should not be assumed to come from a greater dissatisfaction with their lot. Without exception, those interviewed were very enthusiastic about their training and the firm in general. They also attributed their own frankness in interviews to the fearless, open environment. "There's not so much fear of reprisal. Everything that I say to you I would repeat to any partner if asked."

The person who would thrive at the firm is "someone who wants to go to a firm which doesn't sit back and wait for work to come in. It would attract people who like a challenge." There's a vague attitude in the City that Hammonds is a 'northern upstart.' It is unanimously regarded as fielding some of the most aggressive lawyers in the UK profession. Perhaps this is why it is amongst the most profitable law firms in the country. The Leeds office in particular was seen by the trainees to have a "punchy go-get" approach to winning new business. The trainees gave us the impression that they understood the aims and strategy of their firm and that they had a longer term future with it.

Top Recommendations in Chambers Directory:
Employment Law, General Corporate Finance, Litigation (Commercial).

Herbert Smith

UK ranking by size:9
Number of trainees: 150

Sometimes seen as the barracuda of the City, Herbert Smith has the top-ranked litigation practice in the country. There's no doubt that for high profile commercial litigation you can't get any bigger, badder or better. If you're set on going for the top of the pile in commercial litigation then maybe you'll look no further. But if you're looking for a corporate career in a City firm then Herbert Smith is as viable an option as any of the others. More than half of the new positions for qualifiers are in the corporate/commercial field.

It was not a big surprise that most interviewees cited the firm's reputation in litigation as their reason for training with Herbert Smith. However, a growing number liked the fact that they could train with the firm and gain a fairly equal balance of contentious and non-contentious experience. This is not always the case with similarly sized firms, some of which might only offer three or six months of contentious work.

For some, a downside might be that an overseas seat is by no means guaranteed here. "If you wanted to go abroad, I'd say, join Clifford Chance, A&O or Freshfields - don't join Herbert Smith. We are expanding our foreign offices but don't have many trainees out there yet."

As with many City firms, the amount of responsibility you will be given depends on three things - you, your supervisor and timing. "If you are capable of being trusted, you'll get decent work and more responsibility." At the same time, "you can shine like a supernova and not get noticed" if the partner you're sitting with is overly preoccupied. That third element - timing - can be the difference between loads of good work or months of mundane tasks. Herbert Smith gets involved in very big ticket work. Some trainees felt that being involved in a smaller team on a smaller deal in corporate is likely to give you more hands-on experience than being a part of a larger team on a mega-deal. Similarly, if you get involved in a huge long-running piece of litigation, depending on the stage it is at when you arrive in that department, you might well spend months on discovery. It's often luck of the draw.

What sort of person is Herbert Smith aiming for? Said one trainee "they are all fairly academically proven and that doesn't mean Oxbridge - although it used to. The firm is going out of its way to foster an image of being made up of varied types. To a certain extent, that's probably true. Characterwise, they're confident, not cocky, personable, and not lacking in social skills."

Top Recommendations in Chambers Directory: Admin & Public Law, Energy & Utilities, Fraud - Civil, Regulation & Investigation, Investment Funds, Litigation (Commercial), Partnership, Professional Negligence.

Ince And Co

UK ranking by size: 60
Number of trainees: 23

Ince and Co is a top-50 London commercial firm best known for its shipping and insurance practice. There is a radically different 'partner-group' approach to training within a fluid departmental structure. Although trainees rotate seats, they carry work with them between different partner groups across department lines.

The business groups structure is formed around loose associations of partners with certain specialisations. The three groups have no titles but are roughly divided into dry shipping, collision work and insurance. Trainees can also take on work from the growing corporate department to broaden their experience. They rotate around the office, sitting with four different partners. Trainees do not officially join a business group until they are two years qualified.

The training is "completely different," explained one trainee. "In a way, we're independent contractors. We have to go and tout for work among people we're interested in working for." Trainees can arrange their workload to receive the broadest or narrowest experience they require. Regulation of workload is important. "It can work very well if you organise your work properly. It can break down because you're accepting too much." The autonomy and lack of structure suits some very well.

Responsibility arrives early to those who can handle it. Trainees work on large ongoing cases rather than small aspects of big transactions. "The day to day work is yours." This can be daunting for new recruits. "I think the workload is high here," admitted one. "There's no spending all morning on the internet like in other places." He went on to say that the sink or swim approach can be quite frightening, but equally it can lead to a high level of job satisfaction when it works.

Our interviewees had mixed responses about supervision levels - the consensus seems to be that the system is there if needed. A training principal and mentor figure oversees progress in the form of organised six-monthly reviews. "S/he is also amenable to confidential informal chats."

The amount of client exposure varies between cases. Some are paper-heavy and involve foreign clients in other time zones. Some are face to face and involve quick settlement. Trainees may be required to sit in client meetings and make a contribution, not just take notes, from an early stage. "The client contact is very genuine - you do actually get to talk to them."

Ince's trainees can feel overloaded at times. It can be difficult to strike the balance between taking enough work on to get yourself recognised and doing too much. A word of warning; "taking too much on and doing it badly is just as bad as not doing enough."

There are numerous highs to counterbalance the working stress. One trainee went straight into court and made an applications within a couple of months of joining. Another was given a free hand. "I drafted an opinion that went out almost word for word. You get more of a sense of worth of what you're doing."

All those interviewed were quick to dismiss the notion of a typical trainee. "Not here, there is no mould." Some identified a common thread - an air of confidence or bullishness. "I think they look for people who can take knocks and stand their ground." Even at interview stage, "it's not an identikit hiring process, no limitations are placed on candidates. There's a really diverse crew."

Several Ince trainees bring a non-law or industry background with them to the firm. One had spent time with an oil company before joining, which put a lot of his current work in the offshore energy/insurance sector into context.

Opportunities for overseas travel are a big drawcard at Inces. Permanent secondments or placements are rare in such specialised fields until after qualification, but case by case travel has thrown up some interesting destinations for trainees, such as Yemen and Newfoundland. Individual responsibility is high on the agenda as a trainee will have to travel alone, take witness statements, meet experts and handle details themselves.

Top Recommendations in Chambers Directory:
Insurance & Reinsurance, Shipping & Maritime Law.

Irwin Mitchell

UK ranking by size: 29
Number of trainees: 30

Irwin Mitchell has a presence in Sheffield, Leeds, Birmingham, and to a less established extent, in London. Each office has a spread of work but is known for different strengths. In Sheffield, for example, the personal injury and medical negligence departments are key whilst in Leeds the firm has its core of Intellectual Property litigators.

Trainees were attracted to the firm because it is seen to do so well in a range of different work types from company/commercial through employment and personal injury to family, criminal or wills in the private client department. Then there is the popular Business Crime Unit.

Personal injury used to be the pull but now the commercial work seems to be the main attraction. "Now because we have quite a good sized commercial department, people apply for that reason. They begrudge being put into PI at first, but once they have been in it for a month or so they change their minds." Flexibility was the strongest message given.

Trainees don't belong to any one office. "If you express a preference to stay in a particular area they will generally try to accommodate you." Usually people are happy to move offices, particularly between Leeds and Sheffield because it is a different experience, even though they are in reasonably close proximity. It can sometimes prove a bit unsettling though when trainees have just begun to put down roots.

What's good about the training at Irwin Mitchell? Looking back, one newly qualified told us that it was "feeling 'well, just a minute, what's the difference now that I'm qualified?' and realising that there isn't really very much difference because I was dealing with clients on this level before." in litigation, we were told, there's a lot of work that you can run with as a trainee; the sort of work that is "Right! Off you go." All trainees praised the levels of client contact and some indicated that this spilled over into actively marketing for new business and reinforcing client relationships socially.

Top Recommendations in Chambers Directory:
Clinical Negligence: Mainly Claimant, Personal Injury; Mainly Plaintiff, Product Liability, Social Housing

Lawrence Graham

UK ranking by size: 39
Number of trainees: 29

The firm has seen significant growth in the last three years, in part due to the acquisition a couple of years back of the property department of Forsyte Saunders Kerman. This augmented its well-recognised property strength. Training covers litigation and corporate work as well as niche seats such as shipping or telecommunications. Lawrence Graham is sometimes seen as one of the City's quieter firms in terms of self promotion.

Trainees interviewed cited the size and generalist nature of the practice as the things that had appealed to them. "You do quite a breadth of work. The property and litigation departments are as big as the company department." Depending on the department, during each of the four six-month seats trainees are in a room with a partner or an assistant or sitting close by in an open plan environment.

There are relatively few trainees compared to the numbers of partners and assistants. In total there are only about 30 at any time. This was felt to have the effect of ensuring that trainees get more responsibility than they might get if 'one of a herd.' Of his company seat, one trainee said "The involvement at the front line was more than I expected. I got to go to a lot of meetings with clients – three or four times a week at least. And I got to do a lot of drafting agreements on smaller deals."

Trainees perceived that the 'work till you drop' culture had bypassed the firm. One said "I would say that everyone gets on well with each other, in terms of being sociable, laid back and enthusiastic about the work they are doing." The easygoing approach is thought to come straight from the senior partner. "He is the first one to say he wants everyone to have another life other than work. Most people work hard and play hard as well. I think in some firms there is only an emphasis on work."

The firm has a gym on-site and the location is seen as an advantage, not far from Covent Garden and the West End. The firm displays art quite prominently; "models, sculptures, paintings, everything. Sometimes we have private openings." A second, smaller office at St Mary's Axe houses the shipping and insurance litigation departments.

As to the type of new recruit the firm is looking for, the trainees didn't think there was a type. A significant number of the trainees have come from various backgrounds other than the usual route straight through from law school. These 'other lives' have included insurance, accountancy, the armed forces, in-house legal departments and paralegal positions.

Top Recommendations in Chambers Directory:
Trusts & Personal Tax.

Leigh, Day and Co.

UK ranking by size: 285
Number of trainees: varies

A claimant-only litigation practice with a top reputation, Leigh, Day and Co. offers a very specialised training in the fields of clinical negligence and complex claims PI. Much of its work is high-profile, including multi-party actions such as recent instructions from victims of the Paddington rail crash. It takes on many complex referrals from other firms. As with other niche practices, its size means it cannot take on all trainees at the end of the contract, but its name is such that moving on presents few problems. When recruiting, the firm looks for candidates with an already proven commitment to these fields, and an "ability to stand on their own two feet." Many trainees have previous work experience in a relevant area, such as medicine and/or have an academic background such as scientific training or a masters degree in environmental law.

One year is spent in each department. This not only enables trainees to see matters through to the end, it also allows for a high level of immersion into the cases. "You get a lot more nitty-gritty, 'in the trenches' hands-on experience" said one trainee. "Every day you are dealing with clients, instructing experts, instructing counsel, doing court hearings or shadowing someone else who is doing them." Certainly, the complexity of the cases does not seem to hinder trainees' involvement, whether it is it legal and scientific research, drafting witness statements or representing clients at Legal Aid hearings.

Trainees do most of their work on their supervising partner's cases, but can also "get stuck in" to other work within the department. This provides them with more variety. Client contact is greater in the complex claims department. This involves handling smaller cases, acting for those injured as a result of industrial disease or product liability. There is also some probate work during both seats, (which satisfies the Law Society's requirement for non-contentious work) and the possibility of some top level public law experience.

The litigious nature of the firm means that most work is done in teams, engendering a close-knit environment "where people really do talk to each other." It also means that hours are not nine to five, and a high level of commitment is required, but the vocational ethos of the firm means that "people are here because it is what they want to do." Every Friday evening the whole firm "chews the cud" over a few drinks and nibbles.

Top Recommendations in Chambers Directory:
Clinical Negligence: Mainly Claimant, Personal Injury.

Linklaters

UK ranking by size: 3
Number of trainees: 261

It's hard to find a commercial practice area at which Linklaters doesn't excel. Second in size in the City's magic circle, the firm is a powerhouse for finance and related work and leading for commercial property. It runs an unusual six seat training structure and has a completely different approach to its trainees, known as "the fresh approach."

Future trainees are focused on their training contract from the time they are recruited. Not only will they attend one of the chosen service providers for the LPC, but they maintain contact with the human resources department and begin making their seat choices before the contract commences. One of their first tasks is to decide where they want to qualify. The different departments beauty parade to the new intake before the beginning of the contract and in discussion with the graduate recruitment team each trainee will select their six seats. Trainees are 'encouraged' to spend two of those seats in one particular department. This is the 'home' department into which the trainee has decided s/he will probably ultimately qualify.

It's no small task to make decisions so early on but there is scope for change if it becomes apparent that someone has made a flawed decision. Some interviewees expressed concern that a trainee would have to be brave to try to change their seating plan. On the other hand, this element of certainty might cut out other problems, such as the need to market yourself to departments prior to each seat rotation or having to deal with a big rush on a limited number of departments on qualification. So far the trainee jury is out.

As most specialist departments feed off the mainstream corporate work, there is an unwritten rule that trainees will generally be required to do a corporate seat. Many people will only choose to do a fleeting spell in litigation yet others might opt for it as their core department. All this decision-making has the effect of making trainees appreciate that their career is in their own hands. "We're masters of our own destiny."

If you want a career with an international aspect then look closely at Linkaters. Whilst you can't guarantee where you go, you can pretty much guarantee that you will go overseas if you request it. Some slots are phenomenally popular, for example the seven busy New York seats are the most difficult to secure, but those who go out there rave about the environment, getting an amazing apartment each and getting really stuck into a lot of work.

There is a very hard-working environment at Linklaters and the trainees and newly qualified solicitors stressed that when we spoke to them. Whilst the prestige is there in the high calibre of the clients and work, trainees are under no illusions that they will have a pivotal role in really high profile work.

The Linklaters personality is chatty, outgoing, confident and ambitious. One trainee told us that on her first day it seemed that everyone she met was attractive, incredibility bright and had an Oxbridge background. She knew that this was a sweeping generalisation but felt that there was a kernal of truth in the statement. It was noteworthy that interviewees constantly referred to how bright everyone is. It is clearly of great significance to them to be a part of the intellectual elite of the legal fraternity.

Top Recommendations in Chambers Directory: Capital Markets, Corporate Finance, Employee Share Schemes, European Union/Competition, Financial Services (FSA, Compliance etc), Fraud - Civil, Regulation & Investigation, Investment Funds, Litigation (Commercial), Litigation (Property), Pensions, Pensions Litigation, PFI, Project Finance, Property (Commercial), Tax (Corporate).

Lovells

UK ranking by size: 7
Number of trainees: 120

As the fifth biggest firm in the City, Lovells has a reputation for not having put all its eggs in one basket. Corporate finance and banking vie with commercial property and litigation for the accolade of best-known practice area.

Lovells has had a reputation as a 'nice' firm for a few years now and it wasn't so long ago that people referred to it as "Lovely White and Clean." The image is a mixed blessing for the firm which is trying to represent itself as a thrusting corporate practice. The firm recently changed its name after a high-profile merger with German firm Boesebeck Droste.

"There's scope for all sorts of experiences" was a consistent description of the training environment. One trainee summarised it as follows; "It has a broad practice base in that it is quite prominent in litigation, so there is a variety of seats. I get the impression that at some other firms you can be expected to do two corporate seats whereas at Lovells you would just need to do something slightly corporate-based in one of them."

Something that did come through was that, hand in hand with the chance to carve their own training experience, trainees need to make their own destiny. "They're always trying to look out to give you good experience but at the same time it's a two way street - you've got to appear interested. You've got to push yourself. No-one is going to shout for you."

A City training takes a considerable amount of commitment and there's no denying that sometimes your personal life will suffer as a result. Is your life taken over by the job? One trainee said "I have worked a few all-nighters. Sometimes you do wonder if the hard work does really pay off, but here I feel a sense of achievement. They do acknowledge that you do work hard and do work long hours. If there's not a lot on they would much rather you go home and have a bit of a life. When times are busy they expect the full whack."

Lovells has a wild card up its sleeve for those who want it - pro bono work. A majority of the City firms are involved with legal advice centres these days, they have become a fashionable add-on to the training experience for a number of reasons. One trainee involved in the pro bono scheme said "We've won a pro-bono award for two years on the trot now. We have our own pro bono officer. I'm working on a lobbying exercise for a charity. I've also got small claims cases, social security tribunals, Criminal Injuries Compensation Board cases. If you want to get involved you can. You'll get the papers given to you and boom - you're away!" Pro bono work is done on the firm's time as well as your own time. "Every pro bono matter has a client matter number, as would any fee paying client. There's good support and recognition amongst the partners and the fee earners that we're allowed to do this."

There are around 20 overseas seats in the US, Asia and Europe and enough secondments to clients that if you want to spend your third seat out of the London office then it is quite likely that you can.

One trainee was keen to point out that the firm's managing partner is a woman.

Top Recommendations in Chambers Directory: Corporate Finance, European Union/Competition, Fraud - Civil, Regulation & Investigation, Insurance & Reinsurance, Parliamentary: Public Affairs, Pensions Litigation.

Macfarlanes

UK ranking by size: 48
Number of trainees: 39

The medium-sized City firm that smacks of quality. Macfarlanes was chosen by one of our interviews because "It seemed like a very solid, well-managed firm that really emphasised the idea of training." Indeed they do; we had no complaints from trainees on that score. "They don't have enormous amounts of trainees here so you don't tend to get put in nightmare seats with people who aren't interested ... and they wouldn't put you in a very specialised seat unless you really requested it."

Trainees are encouraged to 'walk' unaided quite early on. This means having a go at tasks such as drafting, before seeking help. "What you're not thanked for is putting your hand up and pleading ignorance before you've even given it a shot. If you've got something down on paper, it might be a dog's dinner but it's a start. If you go and see the partner concerned and say 'Look here's a start, but I'm really not quite sure' then you're going to get a lot further."

The firm has a reputation as fairly conventional. "It is conservative - with a small 'c'... but I think we feel a little less taken for granted than at the very big firms" One interviewee told us of an occasion when a trainee was in the throes of a very late night in the corporate department. The head of department insisted on helping and took some of the trainee's photocopying off to do himself.

Macfarlanes retains the hallmarks of the old style City firm, providing a full service to private clients as well as corporate clients. Some trainees find this a real draw to the firm, whilst for others it plays no part in their choice. In addition to its main corporate profile, Macfarlanes does some other relatively uncommon things exceptionally well. In advertising and marketing work it is a sector leader. "The clients are fun but they can be difficult. They might send through a hand-written fax asking "Is it OK?" on an advert they're putting on air that day. They operate to very close deadlines and expect a tremendous amount from you." Trusts and personal tax, probate, family, agriculture and equity are all areas in which trainees can experience working for the high net worth individual rather than the corporate client. Often this allows a type of lawyer-client relationship which is much more difficult to achieve with corporate work.

Interviewees felt the approach of the firm was to try and recruit people who are as bright as possible. "They sort of pride themselves on having bright people working for them." One trainee said "One of the senior partners told me he wants the partner who goes along to the meeting to be the most impressive person there. If the partner can't make it, the assistant has got to know what he's talking about back to front. If the assistant is delayed the trainee must be able to deal with the meeting. I've been in that situation where the partner I've been working with hasn't been available and I've run the meeting for an hour and a half before he's shown up. On other occasions I've been sent to do half-day meetings on my own."

There isn't an atmosphere of heavy competition at the firm. "You don't feel you're being ground into the floor all the time and pushed, pushed, pushed..." Another trainee agreed. "You're expected to deliver but you're not fighting amongst your colleagues for supremacy. Its not Lord of the Flies. No-one is going round chucking spears at each other!"

Top Recommendations in Chambers Directory: Advertising & Marketing, Agriculture & Bloodstock, Trusts & Personal Tax.

Masons

UK ranking by size: 26
Number of trainees: 40

A large national firm which is essentially a specialist construction practice supported by broader specialist groups. Leeds, Manchester and Glasgow offices work in conjunction with the main London office. This manifests itself in a training contract that has a heavy leaning towards construction work with eight months being spent in that department.

The definition of construction work at the firm is wider than it is at most. Both contentious and non-contentious are covered and specific groups have been set up for Oil & Gas, Power & Water and so on. The firm has a volume of PFI work and this too cuts through into the construction department. Another focus area is in Information Technology.

The training contract breaks down into six seats of four months in London. In Leeds however it is four seats of six months. It is possible to move between offices for some seats and some trainees interviewed had asked to do this. An overseas placement to the Brussels office is on offer at each rotation. In addition to the construction/Information Technology/PFI core areas are niche seats such as environmental law, health and safety and the very popular tax and financial planning seat - the Masons name for private client work.

Many of the projects and cases the firm handles are of a scale that precludes 'front line' activity by trainees but it appears that the firm has taken steps to ensure that trainees are not exposed only to this scale of work. There is an initiative to bring in smaller construction cases which are not the size that Masons usually deals with, but which are brought in on the basis that they will be done by the trainees. "The money in dispute is usually relatively small, but you still have to go through the same process....they are there in construction and they are certainly there in places like Information Technology as well because the firm is getting involved in a lot of small start-up Information Technology companies – so there is that level of work."

In both Manchester and Glasgow a revolutionary hot-desking system is being trialed. In Glasgow for example there are 17 fee-earners working with just three support staff. Each fee-earner has a mobile phone, a laptop and a trolley for their files. Whoever gets there first in the morning gets to choose the best desk. This system appears to challenge established notions about how an office works and is certainly enthusiastically welcomed by trainees.

In the other offices, trainees we spoke to indicated that they felt the firm was free from hierarchy. "It is not too big for you to recognise almost everyone by sight and you get to know partners from other departments." People obviously are aware of the hierarchy, but "you don't have it rammed down your throat all the time."

Top Recommendations in Chambers Directory: Construction & Civil Engineering, Environmental Law, Information Technology.

Mills & Reeve

UK ranking by size: 40
Number of trainees: 27

East Anglia's largest law firm, Mills & Reeve offers traditional corporate and commercial training along with the possibility of seats in a large number of niche fields and regional specialisations. Notable amongst these are the firm's employment, Intellectual Property, education, agriculture and particularly health practices. Trainees are encouraged to take seats in more than one of the firm's Cambridge, Norwich and Birmingham offices "in order to further the integration process." Birmingham is particularly popular in this regard, with trainees eager to sample its reputable medical negligence and health departments and top notch client base of NHS trusts and Health Authorities.

Five seats are the norm which, combined with the diversity of practice, allows for a high degree of flexibility as to which seats are taken and their structure. That said, certain areas such as Intellectual Property, employment, agriculture and medical negligence are particularly popular and not all can necessarily be accommodated. Split seats and short term client secondments are possible and current trainees noted the high incidence of qualification into chosen practice areas.

Trainees are entrusted with an increasing level of responsibility during their training contracts. "you are given enough rope, but not enough to hang yourself." All trainees spoken to felt they were given enough client contact, though its nature varied across departments. Employment was particularly praised. One corporate trainee commented "as a regional firm, there is more possibility to get trainees fully involved in deals than would be the case in multi-million pound City deals." Advocacy is also taken seriously and litigation trainees are regularly sent out to conduct agency work and even tribunal hearings.

All trainees spoke of the firm's friendliness. All noted the influence of the branch locations in creating an informal, yet professional ethos. Involvement in local Trainee Solicitor Groups and in firm and marketing events seems to keep trainees busy on the social side. While each office differs in the actual events laid on, there are firm-wide Christmas parties which bring the trainees from different branches together and all offices get trainees involved in marketing the firm to fellow young professionals.

Top Recommendations in Chambers Directory:
Agriculture & Bloodstock, Construction & Civil Engineering, Education (mainly institutions), Employment Law, General Corporate Finance, Health Care, Insolvency, Litigation (Commercial), Litigation (Property), Personal Injury: Mainly Defendant, Professional Negligence, Trusts & Personal Tax.

Nabarro Nathanson

UK ranking by size: 16
Number of trainees: 56

A large medium-sized full-service commercial firm, which has recently moved to new premises in Holborn, from its long held West End location near London's Green Park. Also has offices in Reading and Sheffield. Has a particularly strong reputation in areas such as property and planning.

Our interviewees felt that the firm's property slant needs to be emphasised. "All the trainees are desperate to stay on here. We are all hoping for jobs in the areas we're interested in, which if you're not interested in commercial property is not the easiest thing. There are loads of vacancies for newly qualifieds in commercial property and they prefer to take people they've had from an early stage" said one second year trainee. "It does become a stressful time as people are jockeying into position. Because its such a nice place to be and because we enjoy each other's company so much - it becomes an unpleasant factor. We wish we could all stay on." Only one seat needs to be done in commercial property, but the contentious seat could be in property litigation.

There's a notion that the style of the firm is not quite as formal as at those in the City. "It's not a workhouse, not 'City' - much as the senior partner would hang me if he heard me say that!"

The summer student scheme is seen to be the best route to a training contract. The firm is an "interesting mixed bag of people," including a number of antipodeans and South Africans, Americans, Asians, those with previous careers and all types of personalities. Trainees interviewed were convinced that the firm was recruiting widely as a deliberate policy to avoid 'types.' A 'buddy' scheme operates, whereby experienced trainees take new recruits under their wing.

Trainees sit with assistants but a partner keeps an overall watch over their activities. The trainers themselves get regular training in how to supervise. Some felt that it was very much in the hands of the trainee how much responsibility they got. "I have been given good work but at other times I've felt like a donkey."

Contact NN is a unique marketing scheme run at this firm whereby the trainees have a budget to organise events for young professionals. The aim is to foster long-term relationships with trainee accountants, surveyors, bankers etc. As well as being useful for the firm it is very popular amongst trainees.

Overseas opportunities include Paris and Brussels. There's a popular UK secondment to a sports management company. There's also a limited amount of movement between the offices. Whilst Reading recruits its own trainees, the very popular main Intellectual Property dept is in Reading and for that reason a London trainee might ask to do six months there. One of the other Reading opportunities is in Private Client; a work type not always on offer at the largest firms. Trainees saw Reading as having a more intimate atmosphere, less pressurised than London. Sheffield also recruits separately and presently has six trainees. It has all but lost its old Coal Board image, although the Coal Board is still a major client.

Top Recommendations in Chambers Directory: Environmental Law, Information Technology, Litigation (Property), Local Government, Pensions Litigation.

Norton Rose

UK ranking by size: 13
Number of trainees: 103

Unusually, Norton Rose splits training into six seats of four months. This is seen as a real advantage, allowing trainees to network widely throughout the firm. For those with no fixed ideas as to where they want to qualify, it provides experience in a larger number of practice areas. For those who stumble upon a seat that they really enjoy, it is possible to go back and spend a further four or even eight months there. On qualification, some will have spent a year in the departments they finally choose. "You're way ahead" said one newly qualified.

Although its not unusual to hear this from a trainee at a large City firm, we were told that in the litigation department some of the deals are so massive that trainees don't feel that they necessarily get exciting work. One said that they thought that "those who go to litigation think its going to be glamorous and exciting and the expectation is really high, but when you get there you have to be reasonably senior before you get to the interesting stuff." If you're in a team where you have paralegal support, then it's OK they went on to say. "On the other hand, if you don't have paralegal support you can go through some bad weeks."

In sharp contrast, there will be times when you get plenty of responsibility. One trainee spoke about being asked to run a whole due diligence report by herself when she was in the corporate department. She had to co-ordinate the input of all the other departments and liaise with the client. "When we were in the meetings I had an assistant with me who was completely supportive all the way through. I was the one running it - and that was a medium-sized deal. If you are going to give that type of responsibility, you have to provide the support. They did." Trainees consistently praised their level of involvement in the corporate and banking departments.

However, some felt that client contact, for example attending meetings, is "something you have to push for. It's something you need to make clear that you're interested in." Another stressed that attendance at meetings was deal dependant "I would have liked to have gone to more meetings than I have done, but that's because I think that it's the way you learn the most."

The choice of overseas seats presently includes five in Paris, four in Singapore, two in Greece and one or two in Moscow.

Some trainees mentioned an increasing tendency to recruit from more established universities but at the same time the firm is not only after fresh young graduates with no wider experience. In one particular intake only half had come straight from UK universities and then law school. Others had studied in different countries and some had come from different careers.

Top Recommendations in Chambers Directory: Asset Finance & Leasing, Aviation, Fraud - Civil, Regulation & Investigation, Investment Funds, Shipping & Maritime Law.

Olswang

UK ranking by size: 65
Number of trainees: 12

Olswang is a leading media firm which has expanded considerably since its formation in 1981, largely on the back of the media and communications revolution. Its particular strengths are in film finance, defamation, broadcasting, Information Technology and telecommunications. It is also consistently increasing its corporate finance capacity. There is a distinct unstuffy, entrepreneurial edge to the atmosphere, and to the training. On arrival in reception you become immediately aware that you are in a very different kind of firm "instead of going in and sitting on a big leather Chesterfield with a copy of Country Life and The Lady on the table, there are cool seats and Sky TV on the wall."

Training at the firm follows this entrepreneurial vein. Trainees are given "as much responsibility as they can or want to take on" subject to supervision. Particularly in the entertainment, corporate and litigation seats "if you are displaying an ability to get on with it, then you can get on with it." The standard pattern is for trainees to take an entertainment seat, a litigation seat, a property seat and a corporate seat, as the firm is keen that you get "as broad a spectrum as possible." Thus, in litigation, which is divided into five separate departments, the seat can be split after three months to allow the trainee to see another area.

Every seat provides a guarantee of interesting clients and work. The corporate department in particular is taking on a growing amount of other work, but media clients, be they production companies, record labels or newspapers, are still significant in all departments. One trainee cited several high-profile defamation trials, and his name credited as "trainee solicitor" on a recent British film as the highlights of his training. The work is often cutting edge, particularly in fields such as internet litigation, where the law is still young.

Competition for places at Olswang is fierce, but prior experience in the media or advertising is not a prerequisite. More important seems to be an enterprising attitude and a "sparkling" personality. You also have to fit into the firm's culture. "Its not a 'big men strutting round boasting about their chargeable hours' type of place." For those who make it, there is more good news – the last few years have seen a 100% retention rate.

Top Recommendations in Chambers Directory: Defamation, Information Technology, Media & Entertainment.

Osborne Clarke

UK ranking by size: 32
Number of trainees: 31

Osborne Clarke is an established high profile corporate and commercial giant in Bristol, with offices in Reading and London and a new alliance with firms in Belgium, Denmark, Germany, Holland and Spain. The firm has a top reputation in finance, litigation and pensions, but is moving into new fields, particularly Information Technology and telecoms, with gusto. Several trainees were drawn to the firm for its perceived dynamism: "This firm is progressive, it's going somewhere. I wasn't keen on the larger firms because they were already there."

Trainees are encouraged to move around the offices during their training contracts, and many take up this opportunity, if just to take a seat that was full in their own branch. The London office leans towards corporate and Information Technology. Reading has more opportunities in commercial and employment. There is only one official placement overseas, in Frankfurt, but trainees have been able to go to associated firms in Paris and Barcelona, "it's up to the trainee to get their foot in the door." This year one trainee has arranged a seat in Paris. "The main thing to remember there is that it is not a 'jolly.' You have to have the language ability." The Frankfurt office practises mainly UK law, but with only four staff members and no library, is "not very autonomous," having to rely on materials being faxed through from the UK. This makes the seat a challenging one: "more responsibility…less support. Legally-wise it is not more difficult than a UK seat, but 'scary-wise' it is."

Trainees we spoke to generally appreciated the levels of responsibility and work given to them. "I had a supervisor who was able to gauge what type of work I could be given. Through the six months I just seemed to be on an ideal learning curve." One trainee's seat in litigation was marked by court work. "I did about ten or twelve hearings in chambers. In my first one I was up against a barrister and I felt I had been thrown in at the deep end. Afterwards I felt it was a high point of the seat because you have to quickly pick yourself up and make sure you are on top of the game." More unusually a London trainee cited his time in the corporate seat as very hands on: "there was one large takeover involving lawyers in 18 other jurisdictions. I was the contact point for the foreign lawyers, which involved sending them instructions and coordinating their advice as it came in."

The firm's recruitment does not seem geared towards a typical trainee, with some trainees coming from the paralegal and Legal Executive route and others coming to the law after several years in the armed forces, business, teaching and the Arts. This diversity is appreciated by trainees: "it seems to work quite well because it means that everyone has something to add to their work and to the culture." "There are no stuffed shirts at OC." This is well-illustrated by the firm's extremely media-friendly managing partner who was an actor before training as a lawyer.

Top Recommendations in Chambers Directory: Banking, General Corporate Finance, Health & Safety, Insolvency, Intellectual Property, Litigation (Commercial), Pensions, Trusts & Personal Tax.

Pinsent Curtis

UK ranking by size: 20
Number of trainees: 66

Pinsent Curtis is a high-quality established national firm with offices in Birmingham, London and Leeds. On top of its general corporate/commercial practice the firm handles a significant amount of professional negligence work and has regional strengths such as property litigation and employment in Leeds and projects/PFI work in Birmingham. Although to the outside world lawyers at the firm have developed a reputation as technical perfectionists, this seems to belie the trainee experience of its personnel. Several trainees we spoke to were drawn to it for its national approach coupled with the relaxed atmosphere encountered there. This was confirmed after joining: "the working atmosphere is great…you are allowed to have a personality."

There are several opportunities for trainees to move between the offices during the training contract, though this is more common to and from London than between Birmingham and Leeds. Trainees might come to Birmingham, for example, to sample PFI work, while London trainees must go to Leeds or Birmingham for a property or tax seat. Client secondments are possible, as is a placement at the Brussels office. One respondent was very enthusiastic about his three months in Brussels, "it was fantastic to see how Brussels worked and to demystify it. It wasn't just Europe being petty after all, it actually is a system that does work quite well." While splitting seats is not usual in Birmingham and London, the Leeds office seems more flexible, especially in the second year when qualification is nearing. "If, for example, you're in a contentious seat, and you decide that its not for you, if you approach the right people you can get moved".

While litigation is the only compulsory seat, trainees will usually also take corporate, property, and one other seat. Of these others, employment is particularly popular as is the commercial seat, along with PFI and Information Technology/Intellectual Property. A seat praised for hands-on training was professional negligence, with trainees able to undertake a lot of court work and advocacy for clients such as the Solicitors Indemnity Fund.

In litigation you may get routine tasks on occasions, "it depends on what work the department has at the time," but there are also many opportunities to get more involved in cases. Similarly in corporate the "work is more as part of a team and you are given as much responsibility as you can demonstrate you can handle," with some degree of document management, research and proof-reading agreements. As in most firms long hours are likely in the run up to completions, but trainees accept this as par for the course. The London corporate seat is "pretty full on"… "a baptism of fire," but hours are no worse than Leeds and Birmingham.

The firm was described by one trainee as "very employee-oriented"…"approachability is number one…everyone stops, listens and helps." All trainees are appointed a mentor, usually an assistant solicitor, to smooth their path. The social side is similarly well catered for, either with local TSGs or in-house. In Birmingham the corporate department organises a rounders match between corridors and the property department sets up a treasure hunt around the city. Departmental drinks are a regular event in London, while organised sports run across the branches and there is an annual Pinsents dinner every year.

Top Recommendations in Chambers Directory: Admin & Public Law, Employee Share Schemes, Employment Law, Franchising, Litigation (Commercial), Litigation (Property), Local Government, Professional Negligence, Projects/PFI, Tax (Corporate).

Richards Butler

UK ranking by size: 44
Number of trainees: 59

Top 30 in London by size this medium-sized practice has quality niches in media and shipping/commodities.

Richards Butler offers four five-month seats and a final four-month seat. Trainees think this a winning formula as they get to cover an additional area of law. There's a clear focus on secondments to client companies. One trainee told us that was what swung her decision to come to the firm. "You'll only get one seat on secondment but in my intake five of us went…practically all of us. Seats with media clients are particularly popular." Overseas seats in Paris, Hong Kong and Abu Dhabi are keenly fought over. A significant number of successful applicants to Richards Butler appear to have had at least a few years doing other things after university. A number are in or approaching their 30's.

Most trainees will spend some time in a shipping-related seat although not all of them click with this type of work. One felt that their confidence suffered during their time there as the work was very technical and the people in the department were "super-intellectual." "Unless you have a strong interest or contacts in that area you're not likely to qualify into it." Another, however, chose to come to the firm because of its strength in shipping and was in his element in that seat. Trainees felt that the chances of getting their preferred seats seemed quite high. Media seats are extremely popular. Unfortunately, trainees reported that a reasonable number of qualifying trainees had not previously been offered jobs with the firm. "Its a shame because I've enjoyed the atmosphere here so much… but there could be some culling." It is advisable to check the current situation on interview and to be aware that things can change considerably within a firm over the course of a two year contract.

The trainees we interviewed thought the firm was very friendly. One cited the enthusiasm of a trainee who showed her around the office as a key deciding factor at interview, another stressed "it's not an environment of 'one firm, one voice.' Diversity in personality is encouraged. At Richards Butler I felt that there was an ethos of not being condescending towards the trainees because of their position."

Trainees often cite the size of a firm as a primary reason for their choice. The feedback we got was that its medium size was a great advantage. In most practice areas it's a 'hands on' training. "Even if you're in a first seat, you'll get small files and your own responsibility and you can be stretched. You're trained rather than treated as a little bundler!" one said. Another commented that "the training is very much a case of letting you find your own level and they will keep feeding you responsibility until you peak."

Top Recommendations in Chambers Directory: Commodities, Licensing (gaming, betting & liquor) & Leisure, Media & Entertainment.

Rowe & Maw

UK ranking by size: 27
Number of trainees: 45

A respected mid-sized firm which has experienced a recent shift in size. With the increase in size has come a shift in emphasis. It is now powering up its corporate work and this has fed through to the training experience. The compulsory seats are litigation and corporate.

Most of the trainees and newly qualifieds we spoke to had applied to the firm at a time when it had produced a novel little recruitment brochure, full of cartoons and printed on recycled paper. A couple of our interviewees said that they viewed it as a declaration of difference on the part of the firm and possibly an indication that the firm didn't take itself too seriously. It was cited as a significant factor in the decision to train with the firm. "…other firms I went to seemed to be very determined to project an incredibly glossy, quite intimidating image. Here I felt that it was a bit more relaxed and not quite so 'in your face'."

Trainers are sent on a course to learn how to manage their trainees and how to manage their stress. Levels of responsibility vary from seat to seat, of course, and from department to department but trainees felt that there was a good emphasis on responsibility. One told us "When I was in litigation I was there a week and I was told to go to the High Court and do an application. So I was thrown in." The 'hands on' nature of work was emphasised in our interviews. "When I was in the general litigation seat I had three small claims court appearances during my seat. The nature of the clients and the firm means that you can sometimes get the smaller work that a trainee can do hands on to keep the costs down." As with any other City firm though, trainees did find that in corporate they were working longer hours and were less up at the front line on the larger deals. However, they wanted to point out that the more administrative tasks were interspersed with significant work, such as drafting parts of the documentation.

Trainees believe that their relative scarcity within the firm means that they are utilised at a higher level than they might be in a firm where the trainee population is higher. There is a perception that recruitment is concentrated on a relatively small number of Redbrick and Oxbridge universities.

Our interviewees were keen to let us know how well trainees, assistants and partners mix and how it was relatively easy to get to know a fair proportion of the firm. "I'm in my third seat now and I know the bulk of the partners and all the trainees and I know quite a lot of other people by sight."

Including the firm's Brussels office, there are five or six seats outside of the London office at any one time. These are popular and include secondments to clients such as ICI, Unilever and General Electric. Again, a relatively small number of trainees ensures that if you want to take one of these opportunities you almost certainly can.

Top Recommendations in Chambers Directory: Partnership, Pensions, Pensions Litigation, Professional Negligence, Travel.

Russell Jones & Walker

UK ranking by size: 69
Number of trainees: 11

Russell Jones & Walker is a well-respected national claimant litigation firm with a top reputation for personal injury and clinical negligence. It also has a high profile criminal division which owes much to its niche involvement in white collar fraud and police federation work. The head office in London supports a nationwide network of over 350 lawyers and offices in all the major provincial centres.

Interviewees at the firm gave the impression that trainees taken on are universally open, warm and friendly - mature and well-rounded individuals. Many spoke negatively of 'hardball', antagonistic interviews at large City firms and had been motivated to find a firm more in tune with their own personalities. Trainees at Russell's are bright and open-minded. "We've all been taken on for personality reasons, not specific academic background - it doesn't matter which university you went to."

The firm maps out a conventional four seat, six month programme for trainees shortly after arrival so they can plot and chart their development. These will usually comprise of some of the following - personal injury, criminal, commercial litigation, employment, family and conveyancing. The list reflects the relative descending order of size of the practice areas, thus nearly all trainees will do a stint in PI. The firm is primarily litigious but trainees have to spend six months in one of the two small non-contentious departments, either family/probate or conveyancing to satisfy Law Society requirements. Russell's trainees believe they have been adequately exposed to their clients, although naturally there is inter-seat variance. "There was a lot of speaking to individual clients in the property department, mainly over the phone. I haven't had a great deal of face-to-face client exposure, but this is something I will look to build on in the future." Another described her own mix of experience. "In PI there wasn't much, you talked to a client when you went on a conference or when you went to a meeting but in employment - you actually had your own clients and dealt with them a lot more."

The firm has a visible media profile and many of our interviewees picked up on this theme. "Medical negligence involves a lot of high profile cases at the High Court which attract a lot of media attention. That was interesting to get involved in, reading about your cases in the paper the next day." Another drew some satisfaction from single-handedly holding the fort in the private client/family department while the partners were on holiday. "I was given a lot of responsibility. I covered the department on my own for two weeks which was very scary." One trainee spoke of a Court of Appeal hearing in which she had managed to achieve the desired outcome. 'It's a high point when what you've actually been trained to do works."

One trainee found it a struggle to adapt to the demanding nature and irregular hours of the criminal seat. "You had to hit the ground running. I was sent out to cover a trial for a week and found it quite difficult. It can be quite emotional if you're easily affected by things like that."

Socially, there's a lot happening, people get on easily throughout all levels "from partner to postroom or photocopying department." Three pounds a month buys trainees admission to the social club that organises events. Already, summer cricket, a boat party and a Christmas pantomime have gone down well. Marketing events such as client entertainment evenings also provide a forum for work and social activities to mix. Trade Union links have provided trainees opportunities to attend union open days and seminars in the past. They can get involved in advice centre work for in-house union clients and at the Royal Courts of Justice. Opportunities for language training also exist.

Top Recommendations in Chambers Directory:
Clinical Negligence: Mainly Claimant, Personal Injury; Mainly Claimant.

Shoosmiths

UK ranking by size: 37
Number of trainees: 29

Shoosmiths is based in Northampton and has seven other offices dotted around the Midlands and the south east. In these areas it has a strong market position in commercial litigation, corporate finance and property, and is also notable for its PI and food practices.

Unlike some other national firms, it is rare for Shoosmiths' trainees to move around the offices, with firm cohesion emphasised instead through national and departmental training days and an integrated Information Technology system. For this reason, it is important that intending Shoosmiths trainees research further into the separate branches as there are important differences in size and areas of law practised. For example, while the Northampton office offers a full range service, the Nottingham office is limited to the three core departments. Southampton is known for its specialisation in marine law, while Reading undertakes some Information Technology work and has a strong PI department. The offices also take on different numbers of trainees, with Nottingham, for example, taking only one or two a year. This means that socialising and integrating fully with the whole office begins early on, "there's never any question that you're just 'the trainee'…you're another pair of hands in the team."

There is a flexibility across the board which means that if trainees in smaller offices want to take a seat in another area of law, they can apply to take it in another branch. Similarly, at Northampton it is possible to split your seats, and seats can be 'created' if there is a niche area practised with no formal seats and a trainee expresses a particular interest. Client secondments are possible, and while there are no overseas placements, the firm does support any individual iniatives in that direction. This year one trainee is going to Brussels on secondment with the Law Society.

The most noticeable theme that emerged from Shoosmiths' trainees was the levels of responsibility and client contact they were given: "it's very hands on…I've had my own files in all my seats." "In corporate partners give trainees one aspect of a client problem to deal with, perhaps just a small thing, but this is discussed directly with the client."

The firm's broad litigation practice also ensures that trainees are given ample opportunity to hone their advocacy skills and case preparation work: "you're not expected to sit and take notes, you're expected to contribute." One trainee's high point was attending a two week trial at the Technology and Commercial Court, "I did most of the preparation for that and my boss let me run the case…we managed to win that one." The PI seat is also notable in this respect as it is situated within the technical team who deal with more complex claims and the trainee works as part of a team of fee-earners. To ensure that trainees are never out of their depth, supervision is thorough: "every day my supervisor would spend an hour going through my work with me explaining where the red pen was going, and why."

The different sizes and locations of all the offices mean that their atmospheres do differ slightly, with socialising at the smaller offices being office-wide. At Northampton, where many of the trainees come from elsewhere, "the trainees tend to come out all together… it's an extension of student life really." Each trainee is assigned a 2nd year mentor on their first day to help them adjust to their new role. Any problems can be taken to the mentor, the Trainee Partner or Trainee Co-ordinator in Personnel. Trainees at all the offices are involved in local TSG events, such as the annual Northampton TSG ball and are also encouraged to take a direct role in marketing the firm to new clients, regularly organising events with local young professionals. This marketing role is much encouraged by the firm; "they can't get enough of you marketing!"

Top Recommendations in Chambers Directory:
Debt Collection, Food.

Simmons & Simmons

UK ranking by size: 10
Number of trainees: 132

This top ten City firm has a broad practice and is top-ranked for some interesting niche work such as employment, environmental, Intellectual Property and patents, telecoms and transport. Its biggest practice areas are corporate and finance-related however. These departments have lately been the target of agressive recruitment drives by US firms moving into London.

Simmons' trainees were attracted to the firm by its broad church approach. None of them had been drawn to firms that were overly specialised but at the same time there was an appreciation that the niche departments were the most keenly fought over. Employment is a prime example. The Intellectual Property and commercial departments are also popular.

Overseas seats can also be very competitive. For the New York opening trainees might find themselves up against stiff competition from half a dozen others. Generally, they are satisfied with the extent to which seat choices are met and with levels of responsibility given. For example, one corporate-related department set up a 'grab a trainee' system to ensure sufficient interaction with clients. If anyone is going for a meeting and thinks it at all appropriate they will 'grab a trainee' from that department and take them along , explaining things on the way. This system was created after consultation with trainees and junior assistants who expressed a desire to give feedback on the type of experience they were getting in the department.

Simmons trainees told us how they could give feedback to their immediate supervisor or indeed a supervising partner and in fact could talk more generally about how the training was working out with their overall principal - someone to whom they could turn over the two year contract. One trainee was quite clear about how honest he could be in his seat appraisals "Everything I have wanted to say I have said. The supervisors are open to criticism."

Work type aside, why Simmons & Simmons? One trainee said that he thought it was a more open-minded firm than many of the others in the top ten. He had done a specialist degree at a rare department in a university that was not usually considered top ranking. He felt that his academic credentials had been dismissed without consideration by many of the firms he applied to but not by Simmons & Simmons. The firm is overwhelmingly viewed as friendly and relaxed in atmosphere.

Top Recommendations in Chambers Directory:
Employment: Mainly Respondent, Environmental Law, Food, Intellectual Property, Telecommunications, Transport.

Stephenson Harwood

UK ranking by size:42
Number of trainees: 41

Given that it is not one of the giants, this is a firm with a surprisingly large number of overseas offices. This is explained by its well-respected shipping practice.

In the second or third of the four seats, trainees have the option of spending time in Hong Kong, Singapore, Madrid or Greece. More often than not, the overseas seats are linked to the shipping practice. One trainee painted a vibrant picture of his time in Singapore. "It is just such a great experience. It gives you a very different perspective of the firm, seeing how it operates in a completely separate jurisdiction. Singapore was great – because it is a small office you get great exposure to clients. Going to meetings you feel actually very much a part of things."

The three compulsory seats are litigation, property and corporate. Whilst it concentrates on corporate work, the firm offers training in areas that many of the larger firms do not, such as family or private client. Shipping does play a part in the two years of training for most people. "I think it took me a bit of time to get into it. It is a lot of terminology, it is like a whole new world in itself. It is a very exciting area because on any sort of project, whether it is finance or litigation, you are automatically dealing with three or four jurisdictions at any one time."

Litigation is "quite an active seat" a second year trainee told us. "I had about two big cases with a partner and a few small cases. One of them was a County Court case which I did by myself. Then you have lots of other work that you do here and there for different people. Lots of research and going to court filing documents and things like that."

What of the really long hours? "We don't do it! We just don't do it!"

Taylor Joynson Garrett

UK ranking by size: 35
Number of trainees: 43

Top 25 in London by size, TJG is a commercial firm with a cluster of niche operations backing up its corporate and banking practice. It is known for top quality Intellectual Property work and a real involvement with technology and life sciences clients.

In the main, it was the general qualities of the firm which attracted the trainees we spoke to. It was of the right size and the trainees thought that there was a chance to be seen as an individual rather than one of a herd. "Its a firm full of individuals rather than a law factory" one trainee told us. Trainees seem to come from reasonably wide-ranging backgrounds and there is a fair smattering of those who have already had other careers or taken at least a year off after degree or LPC. "There's a good mix of personalities and people have a wide range of ideas about why they're here, what they want to do, where they're going and what they want to qualify into" said one trainee.

The amount of responsibility given to trainees varies between seats and tends to increase when the trainer in question is satisfied that the trainee can handle it. "If you get some work, do it well and impress, you'll get more responsibility. In both my previous seats, litigation and commercial property, I had a dozen files which were pretty much run by me with supervision. I had a lot of contact with clients and went to court etc."

There's a couple of overseas seats available to second year trainees, one in Brussels and one in Hong Kong. There is competition for these; four or five people apply for the two seats. Within the London office, some seats are more popular than others and it's not a case of getting the seat you want each time. However trainees we spoke to thought that overall people got two or three of the seats that they wanted.

And the work ethic? "It has a corporate atmosphere, but people are generally pretty approachable." "You're certainly not discouraged from having your own life." On staying late; "It might be crazy at times and you might be staying late for a while" but generally it is not onerous.

Top Recommendations in Chambers Directory:
Intellectual Property.

Townleys

UK ranking by size: 403
Training places available : 1/2

Townleys is the only firm in the country handling exclusively sports work. It acts for many high profile clients across a broad spectrum of work types. The recent growth of sports as a commercial industry has made the practice of law in this area fast-moving and fascinating, particularly in fields such as EC/Competition law.

The firm's one or two training contracts per year are very hot property. To stand any chance of an interview candidates will need an excellent academic record and to show a demonstrable interest in sport, usually including work experience in that sector. It also helps to have "something you can bring to the firm," be it advanced language skills or expertise in an area such as Information Technology or Intellectual Property. It is not enough "just to read the newspaper and be interested in sport."

The firm is very small, and the training very flexible. Strictly speaking there are four seats within the five 'departments' but seats can be split, lengthened and shortened according to interest and the firm's requirements. The departments are: commercial and governance, litigation/ADR, broadcasting and media, Information Technology/rights management and company/commercial. There is also the opportunity to do a short stint in commercial property.

Trainees are given a lot of responsibility from an early stage. On her first day, one trainee went to a conference with counsel. "You can't be slack, you can't expect to have any time being eased into the job. You have to be brave about it because it can be intense." However, as trainees work as part of a team all sitting in the same room, "there is great communication within the firm. Within our group we are very aware of what everyone is doing... you are never left to go on a frolic of your own." This means that trainees are able to run their own files with full supervision, and "are always involved; your opinion does matter and you are always taken into account."

Similarly, Townleys is not loath to give its trainees client contact, "here you are expected to develop relationships with clients right from day one." Clearly, as clients are "few, large and very significant", this will usually be in a supporting role, but trainees are regularly sent to help represent the firm at sport conferences and events. One trainee took part in the free legal advice clinic given by Townleys at the Football Expo conference in Cannes. "It was quite frightening, but you learn very fast. And you have other solicitors from the firm sitting next to you if you can't answer any questions".

The firm is based in Islington, "away from the hustle and bustle of the City," which adds to its relaxed feel. Everyone goes to the pub together on a Friday night, and there is a "real family atmosphere." This means "that when you're working with people, because they know you as a person they can't ever treat you badly professionally." Pro bono work is a significant feature of the training contract, with free legal advice to Kick Racism out of Sport, and preparing and running an immigration appeal tribunal hearing work being two recent examples. And of course, there is the sports work itself: "it is a big thrill if you see something you've been working on in a big national newspaper, on the TV or in the specialist press." Certainly it can be a "nightmare" watching a football match with a Townleys trainee. "Any time I watch TV I'm thinking, that's an interesting sponsorship...I see why they've done that."

Top Recommendations in Chambers Directory: Sports.

Trowers and Hamlins

UK ranking by size: 67
Number of trainees: 25

Trowers and Hamlins is a top-50 London firm with a leading reputation in social housing. The firm also has strong corporate/commercial and litigation departments. London heads a spread of offices including Exeter and Manchester in the UK as well as several Middle East Gulf states.

Trowers' trainees sit in four seats of six months, drawn from a list of company/commercial, property, public sector, litigation and private client. They are unlikely to have any choice over the first seat but the firm is accommodating over further selections and most trainees are satisfied. Two property seats are usually completed, one of which will be housing.

The high profile housing theme touches most of the seats and generates related work such as private finance and commercial work for housing organisations and trusts. Despite this specialisation, trainees can steer their focus toward other areas such as commercial litigation. "I don't think an interest in housing is a prerequisite for joining. There is a pretty good variety."

Trowers are keen to throw trainees into the cut and thrust of housing work and get their hands dirty. As with all property-related seats it is busy. "You are thrown in at the deep end, given your own files and have 10 phone calls a day from clients." There is less direct responsibility and client contact in litigation. Ultimately trainees are content with the support system in place. "You're never abandoned and can always ask questions if you're worried. I've never been pushed to breaking point. It's been nicely busy."

A mentoring system exists in which trainees are allocated a junior partner in the first year. They can be approached for confidential career advice and personal guidance. New first year intakes are also allocated a second year chaperone. "We have to drag them around when we go out so we get to know each other!"

Our interviews indicate that the Trowers' type is as likely to have been to Oxbridge as not, is as likely to be from the north as the south-east. "I think it's a good mix. Some of us are very loud and some are quiet but the balance does work." Another trainee felt the firm was looking for individuals who weren't overly opinionated - "someone who's outgoing and does extra-curricular activities, personable people with something to say but not too arrogant."

The major external drawcard at Trowers are the highly popular but oversubscribed Gulf seats, several of which become available annually. Abu Dhabi and Oman provide regular opportunities and there is talk of Bahrain and Cairo on the horizon. The work available there is high value commercial and corporate involving oil and gas blue-chips and the governments.

Domestically, someone is sent to Exeter every rotation. This does raise a few groans from some quarters, but those who get sent have a positive experience, gain lots of individual responsibility and get a good deal into the bargain. "You get a flat and expenses. This is quite good money-wise if you can rent your London flat out!"

Future trainees are well-looked after. At a recent law fair in Nottingham, current trainees were sent to meet the intake for next year and it was a warm gesture on the firm's behalf to invite them down for the Christmas dinner, avoiding the usual loss of contact between acceptance of the training contract and starting proper. Trainees also attend a series of seminars, many for housing and charities clients, at which they help to organise and run the events. Another trainee was encouraged by his supervisor to do some environmental marketing and contribute to publications.

Top Recommendations in Chambers Directory: Social Housing.

Walker Morris

UK ranking by size: 58
Number of trainees: 20

Part of the 'Yorkshire Big 6', Walker Morris is a single office Leeds commercial firm with strengths in several key fields including property, litigation, insolvency and banking.

Many Walker's trainees are drawn to the firm due to local preference or disillusionment at the London City pressure-pot. The 'realistic scenario-based' interview process and 'human approach' are frequently cited.

Trainees take part in a six-seat four-month rotation, typically seeing all the main departments - commercial property, corporate and commercial litigation. Rarely can trainees influence the first seat but can express a preference over the next two. First pickings are always handed to second years, many of whom will opt to repeat key favourites or potential qualification departments. The firm encourage trainees to thrash it out among themselves.

The six-seat system is a double edged sword. "On the one hand you've got variety, but you may miss out on greater depth." Second year seat repetition is the antidote to scratching the surface, "most people are able to repeat seats in the ones that they enjoyed - I did two in banking." The fast turnaround can be a lifesaver for those stuck in unpopular or 'personality clash' seats. "If you're not enjoying it, you're not stuck for too long, but if it's a seat you're enjoying you could have eight months there - so there is flexibility."

Walkers trainees feel they are given plenty of responsibility. "I never felt I was looking into a canyon about to jump into it, but I was given a high level of responsibility." Another had good things to say about corporate, "I would work with just the partner on the deal. Once I was given the discharge of an administration order to do on my own and had absolutely no idea what to do, but it was good to see it through." Levels of supervision received some criticism, and it was thought that the appraisal system could be more efficiently administered. One trainee was keen to avoid the 'work hard, play hard' cliché but felt that Walkers was regarded as one of the more lively firms competing in the busy Leeds young lawyer environment. "Some firms are so stiff, I do think we have a good fun firm reputation!" Another trainee thought the firm was the "most laid back in Leeds," comparing the intensity of the working culture and highlighting the absence of high-pressure cost targets. "Sometimes it's good fun to do long shifts to finish off a transaction. But too many crazy hours are enough! We work long hours but nowhere near some London firms. I wanted a life!"

Walkers look for "confident communicators." Several interviewees felt women had been particularly well-represented and successful at trainee level. One brought a previous career as a quantity surveyor with him to the firm, although another felt the slightly older and varied career trainees of previous years were giving way to a younger, brasher 'City-type' intake. Maybe the sign of change to come.

There is scope at Walkers for client secondments, particularly in year two and post-qualification. One trainee went to investment bank Hambros last year and another to accountancy firm Baker Tilly. An arrangement with a French firm provides a fourth seat in Paris most years, although fluency is a pre-requisite. One trainee had a great time and enjoyed the office atmosphere despite working a 24 hour shift on his birthday! "I was actually required to work, there's nothing more boring than going somewhere and feeling like a spare wheel…professionally, I grew a lot in confidence when I was there."

Top Recommendations in Chambers Directory: Insolvency.

Weightmans

UK ranking by size: 54
Number of trainees: 16

Weightmans is a large Liverpool based insurance litigation practice with a domestic network of smaller offices spanning Manchester, Birmingham and Leicester.

As a defendant-based litigation firm, contentious seats are the norm although a non-contentious seat is chosen from property, company/commercial, licensing or employment. Even this may have a litigation bias. One trainee for example spent his time in employment doing 80% work on industrial tribunal cases, "about as litigious as it gets." The Liverpool office is the largest. Trainees from the other offices may have to spend a seat elsewhere to gain the requisite balance.

All trainees do general insurance litigation, which usually encompasses a mixture of personal injury and road traffic accidents. There are also some interesting specialist seats available in the professional indemnity division, one acting for police forces in civil claims and one dealing primarily with a major client, The Motor Insurers Bureau, involving claims against uninsured drivers.

Trainees normally get the seats they want. "There is always the odd exception but most people are reasonably contented." Awareness of the firm's specialisations is advisable. "Make sure it's personal injury or civil litigation you want. The mainstream corporate/commercial departments are relatively small; maybe 75% of firm is insurance litigation."

A unique computerised court clerk rota system allows each trainee to spend about two days a month honing their advocacy skills. Any applications that can't be covered are put on standby. "We don't just sit behind counsel and cover trials but actually do our own applications. It gives you that extra exposure." Several trainees made the point that as a defendant firm, client contact was likely to be more limited than claimant firms, usually confined to the phone. Once trainees receive the initial instructions, the authority is usually there for them to deal with it throughout so there is less scope for further contact. In the commercial seats, you will get more client exposure. One trainee had "meetings with witnesses, going to insurance premises etc. - I've been allowed to do a fair bit." Another trainee was philosophical, "I would have liked more but I can understand why they don't sometimes. They're paying the bills and want the best advice. I think in future more client exposure will be made available."

Client entertainment events occur regularly and trainees are actively included, particularly at police events. "We're introduced to them at conferences, trials and development meetings. We're not excluded in any way because we're not qualified." Weightmans' reputation is based on a strong regional presence and many of the trainees are drawn from the north-west constituency, including Merseyside, Cheshire, Greater Manchester and North Wales. One felt it wasn't a deliberate ploy, "its just that if you're local, you're more likely to have heard of the firm." Another made the point that, "it may well be the case that most of the applications come from the north west and they may have a preference for people from the area." The firm is trying to expand its national presence but it remains for the time very much a north west stalwart.

Beyond geographical affiliation, there are few other similarities between trainees, bar "we're all confident, focused and friendly." There is a mixture of Oxbridge, Redbrick and former-poly students, those from both law and non-law backgrounds. Some have stepped up from paralegals although there is a perception that this may not happen as much in the future. One mature trainee in her thirties had young children and came from the civil service. Another trainee brought a background in amateur dramatics with him.

Top Recommendations in Chambers Directory:
Personal Injury: Mainly Defendant, Professional Negligence.

Withers

UK ranking by size: 71
Number of trainees: 23

Withers' traditional strengths lie in its prestigious family and private client departments. In recent years, however, it has increased its corporate and commercial capability. It also has quality niche practices within its mainstream departments, notably charities and agriculture. Trainees with a strong interest in family law, or any other of its niche practices, are thus able to gain a good training in that area whilst "keeping their options open."

All trainees are expected to take a seat in the private client department ("don't worry, it's not all tax- there's probate and charity stuff too"), and have a choice as to the other three within the four remaining departments. These are corporate, property, litigation and family. It is not possible to split seats to gain experience of all five, but it may be possible to split a seat within a department. For example within litigation you can do three months in employment and three months in trusts litigation. There are some interesting differences between departments, with family, private client and property being seen as traditional and 'old school,' with more regular hours. The litigation and corporate departments are "younger, dynamic and more laid back," but prone to longer hours.

The firm has a significant European element to its work, with many Italian clients within the UK, offices in Milan and Paris and an associated office in Madrid. This means trainees with language skills get a chance to use them, though there are no overseas placements at the moment. Trainees spoken to were all enthusiastic about the diversity of the training experience: "there's something for everyone in this firm."

The nature of many of Withers' clients ("famous and/or rich") means that trainees will rarely front cases themselves, but also that they are training with top lawyers in the field. "The calibre of the people you are working with is amazing. They have a huge amount of experience behind them." The nature of the work is varied, often complex and always interesting; for example in the family department it ranges from ancillary relief and private children work through to domestic violence and some child abduction. Another bonus is the international element to much of the work.

The size and diversity of the firm make for a friendly atmosphere, "you don't get lost" and there is very much a culture of "everyone pulling together." Trainees go out with the head of training for a pizza evening every six months, while informal socialising is regular, from partners down to trainees, "more just popping their heads round the door and asking if you want to go out."

Top Recommendations in Chambers Directory:
Agriculture, Family, Trusts and Personal Tax.

Wragge & Co.

UK ranking by size: 18
Number of trainees: 40

The giant of commercial law in Birmingham, Wragge & Co has been expanding significantly in recent years.

If we were to award a "Happiest Trainees in the UK" prize it would go to Wragges. Interviewees were unanimously more than happy with their lot.

They spoke positively about the relationship between the partnership and its staff. One corporate client is reported to have said that if they could bottle the atmosphere at the firm they would make millions. So what's behind it all? One trainee attributed it to the openness of the partnership. "You know all about the business, what's going on and what the firm wants from you. You know where the firm is going - its strategy. It's very, very open and it makes you want to invest in it. The fact that they ask you how things could be made better makes you committed to the firm."

The same culture of involvement seems to be evident in the way trainees work. One told us how he had been kept up to speed on all developments in a large corporate transaction whenever other tasks had kept him away from meetings. He had always felt that he knew how the deal was progressing and that the strategy and decision-making by the key partners had been discussed with him. He had come to the firm in order to get a hands on training and he had no complaints.

Being known by the partners was important to the trainees. One told us how the senior partner always teases her about reading the sports pages in the newspaper when she was supposed to be researching in the library. Another remarked how partners seemed to take an interest in trainees as individuals, asking how they were getting on in other departments.

There are three compulsory seats during training; corporate, property and litigation. Six months is spent in an optional seat. The degree of flexibility over this optional seat was encouraging. Not only could it be split in some circumstances, eg. three months each in pensions and employment but, we were told, if a trainee specifically requested a department a new seat might be created. There is an increasing breadth of options on qualification. The firm has expanded so much of late that last year 15 qualifying trainees were able to choose between 24 jobs. That meant no real competition for any particular job. Qualifiers could essentially pick and choose where they ended up practising.

Top Recommendations in Chambers Directory: Construction & Civil Engineering, Employment Law, Environmental Law, General Corporate Finance, Information Technology, Intellectual Property, Litigation (Commercial), Litigation (Property), Pensions, Property (Commercial), Tax (Corporate).

US FIRMS IN LONDON – THE TRUE PICTURE

The US firms are still 'the great unknown' for students. Little seen at law fairs (although certainly beginning to make their presence known) they have traditionally taken on very few trainees, often on an ad hoc basis from paralegals or speculative applications. However, the US firms in London are increasing in size and quality. For the first time Sullivan & Cromwell appear with City firms at the top of UK corporate finance tables. Widely publicised adverts attract lawyers to earn over £1million per year. Magic Circle firms report that trainees are headhunted for jobs at US firms on qualification. There are even apocryphal stories of headhunters gatecrashing City firm client events, sidling up to trainees and asking them if they are interested in working for a different kind of firm. The marketing and recruitment offensives are on.

Most US firm London offices are young and small compared to City firms. They were staffed initially by US attorneys practising the law of the NewYork Bar or as appropriate, principally in capital markets and project finance. Initially their expansion was fuelled by the recruitment of experienced UK qualified staff from top firms. Paralegals were heavily used to handle less important work. However, as the number of UK lawyers increases, they are becoming keener to "grow their own" ie train lawyers from the earliest stages. The Law Society requires one UK qualified partner for every two trainees so many offices have awaited expansion before recruiting seriously. It also requires training across at least three different practice areas, and experience in contentious work. The increased breadth of practice in many London offices means that they are now able to take on trainees for the first time.

Many firms already receive up to 2000 speculative applications for one or two places. The aim of this article is to provide an informed choice for applicants. It is important not to be blinded by the higher salaries or the prospect of international travel. It should be noted that these offices are UK outposts of US firms. They are set up to service a particular work-type and client base, usually corporate and finance-based. They are rarely full service and may have a very limited scope in terms of practice area specialisation, although many are rapidly gaining breadth. Applicants should be sure that the work type genuinely interests them.

Certain clear themes came out of our research. Interviewees continally compared their experience with their perceptions of trainee experience at City firms, and found their environment to be less formal, less structured, often in an evolutionary stage. Trainees think that they receive a high level of responsibility and autonomy. For this reason there seems to be a culture of recruiting a high proportion of mature trainees; those who have had previous careers or alternative experiences.

One of the main advantages of the London office of a US firm is that it offers a friendly, informal small office culture with opportunities to be noticed, combined with the backup and opportunities of a huge international network of offices. The perception of the US firm culture as demanding 'blood, sweat and tears' was not borne out by our interviews. However, reading between the lines, long hours can still be expected.

Cleary, Gottlieb, Steen & Hamilton

Number of Trainees: 4

One of the leading US firms in Europe. With ten offices world-wide, the firm's London office has been established for almost 30 years. The firm has leading corporate finance, banking and competition practices. The London office works very closely with New York. It is staffed by US and local lawyers in roughly equal proportions.

Currently summer schemes are only available to US and European candidates. The firm looks for relevant US experience and a second career which demonstrates a greater level of maturity. Following a two stage interview process, prospective candidates spend an afternoon in the firm's offices meeting current trainees and associates who subsequently give feedback to the partners.

The training contract is divided nominally into four six-month seats. However, trainees usually spend their first year in London doing a mixture of M&A, capital markets, tax and regulatory work as the office is not departmentalised. An example given of a typical stint is 3 months in capital markets, 4 months in corporate and M&A, 2-3 months in project finance, with small routine matters undertaken on a single-handed basis integrated throughout. This is followed by a compulsory 6 month seat in Brussels primarily to gain experience in EU competition law (comprising 80-90% of the workload). The final seat is usually back in London. The main alternatives are a litigation seat in the US or a tax option.

Undertaking the NY bar is compulsory for trainees who do not already hold the qualification. Ongoing legal training is provided via office and Europe wide seminars covering all areas of UK and US law using know- how staff and external course providers. Language training is also available.

A partner supervises trainees in all work undertaken. The level of supervision varies depending on the supervisor and the office at which the seat is being undertaken - Brussels tends to have a more rigid supervision regime. Client exposure varies greatly from being extensive in smaller transactions to limited, for example, where cost considerations prevail. Generally, however trainees are treated as equivalent to full first year associates in other European offices, with considerable independence and autonomy. Trainees are given the same yearly formal assessment as other employees. Ongoing discussions to assess appropriate placements in future are encouraged, if not formalised.

The London office is described as an "extremely friendly, fun and amazing place" in which to work. The "good learning environment" is attributed to a combination of its "interesting, diverse and international" people, the sophisticated nature of the work and the firm culture ("the London office is small but you get the feeling that it is very much part of a huge firm"). The downside of the smaller office with the heavy workload may be insufficient feedback at times. Hours can be extreme because of the nature of work although possibly no more than in any City corporate department and apparently not to the degree commonly understood as the "typical US firm image" of working long hours continually.

The firm pays very well; £33,000 on commencement of training contract with the highest qualification salary in a London firm. This is apparently in recognition of the extra pre-qualification training undertaken by UK trainees.

Coudert Brothers

Number of Trainees: 8

A New York firm with 27 offices worldwide. Very well-established in the UK, with a broader practice than many US offices currently aspire to. Training is split into four 6 month seats with a guaranteed seat abroad, usually in Brussels. Three of the four seats are undertaken in core practice areas, namely corporate and commercial, banking and finance, EC competition and regulatory law (in Brussels), litigation (compulsory) and real property. Additional areas to choose from are energy and utilities, funds and telecommunications, Information Technology and multimedia. Placements in Paris and Hong Kong and secondments to major commercial and institutional clients are arranged on a case by case basis and will be extended with increasing capability. An in house training programme with workshops, seminars, videos, related discussions and external conferences is available to trainees.

Trainees agree that training is not formalised or structured - "there is less spoon-feeding. You need to be proactive and organise your own training to some extent. "Quality of work can be "hit or miss" depending on what's going on but trainees "are not as far down the food chain as you might think." Quality of work and responsibility afforded to trainees was described as "amazing" and "unique."

There is a strong perception that the office is "New York controlled everything has to be cleared by them".

Trainees describe the working environment as "competitive, commercial and professional" but "everyone gets along with each other" and there is "lots of dialogue between people." Typical trainees tend to be more 'complete' as individuals as opposed to being straight out of an educational establishment. Those who are most suited to the prevailing culture tend to have language skills and are older than their counterparts in City firms often by reason of previous work or life experience.

LeBoeuf, Lamb Greene & McRae

Number of Trainees: 9

Less high profile than the other US firms in London, it nevertheless possesses one of the most well-rounded practices with both corporate and finance transactional work as well as insurance, commercial litigation and commercial property. Best known for its international energy work and international projects work.

Trainees spend up to 12 months doing contentious work, with the remaining twelve in non-contentious. Both periods are split roughly into two 6 month seats. Choice of practice areas in which trainees gain experience is by an ongoing process of informal discussion and formal assessment on an individual basis. As one trainee commented, "nothing is set in stone - you can make a difference for yourself." The practice is not heavily departmentalised and rather than simply "dropping work" when rotating into the next seat, trainees tend to carry over matters and see them to completion.

With a "nice cultural blend of US/ UK" staff, the atmosphere is described as "studious, not frenetic." Fee earners are keen to help and "you really get the sense that everyone is involved". There is no pecking order ("the partners are very laid back"). Working hours tend to be regular unless the workload dictates otherwise, most notably, in the corporate department sphere. Trainees observe that the pay is better than many City firms but without the expected US "billing target" culture. Having said that, "when there is work that has got to be done, late nights do happen, but they don't work you to death" and the prevailing attitude is; "you have to have a social life and you are not expected to be there at all times."

There is a "varied intake" of trainees who tend to be older with a broad experience of life. They "can combine academic vigour with all-round personal and professional attributes.

Opportunities to get involved in pro-bono work stem from the firm's participation in the Lloyds Community Programme as legal advisors to the East London Small Businesses Centre and its clients. Trainees get the chance to work in teams providing advice on all aspects running a small business from raising start-up capital to know-how matters. Trainee secondments to some of the firm's clients are generally arranged on an opportunistic basis. Opportunities for placements in the firm's overseas offices are currently restricted by Law Society requirements as there less scope to practice English law there.

"This is not a place for shrinking violets" or

those who are inclined to "wait for something to happen". They do not have preconceived ideas about academics (although they generally expect applicants with good academic backgrounds) or age of applicant. Desirable characteristics are a fairly robust attitude with the ability to demonstrate a flexible or adaptable character and a level of good commercial acumen. Trainees are expected to be proactive in dealing with their work and ensuring what they get out of their training contracts.

Mayer Brown & Platt

Number of Trainees: 2

A top Chicago firm with a strong New York office with a City presence going back 20 years. Although it has only recently developed an English law capability, the practice is growing fast with particularly strong banking and international securitisation practices. At the moment the firm has no trainees, the last having recently qualified. It will be taking on two trainees in September 2000 and a further two in 2001 with a view to taking on an increasing number in subsequent years.

The training contract will be formally organised into "seats" in the future, although the work content is likely to be more mixed in nature. Core practice areas are corporate, banking and finance and specialist work in CIS/ Russian matters. There are opportunities for in-house placements with some of the firm's clients, such as a major investment bank. A 3 month litigation seat is undertaken by placement with UK City firm, Stephenson Harwood. There may be future opportunities for litigation placements in one of the firm's US offices.

There is "lots of variety" in the work and tasks such as proof-reading are "rare." Trainees are given a high level of responsibility. As soon as they can be trusted to know what they're doing, they are given all the responsibility they want and client contact is encouraged. Ideal candidates appear to be those with strong personalities who seek responsibility and are quite confident. They may well be older or have had previous work experience.

With a current complement of 30 lawyers, the offices are comparatively small. People have "grown up with and know each other" and the atmosphere is "less formal and much friendlier" than one would normally expect in a City firm, yet there is also "quite a buzz." The atmosphere is thought not to be restrictive, with few barriers in terms of hierarchy or responsibility given. Although working hours are consistently high on average, they are not excessive.

McDermott Will & Emery

Number of Trainees: 1

Not a typical "Wall Street" firm, this Chicago based firm with branches throughout the US has a diverse range of clients with US and European interests and main strengths in cross-border banking, capital markets and projects. With a clear objective to compete directly with its UK City counterparts the firm has attempted to establish a full service English law firm from scratch over the last year.

With currently only one trainee, anticipated training contract arrangements are yet to be finalised. Applications for between 5-10 training contracts in the year 2002 will be accepted in summer 2000.

Rather than a rigid seating structure, there is greater choice of seats and cross-over of work between departments. Within Law Society rules, trainees can choose practice areas they cover over four 6 month seats, namely, corporate and corporate finance, litigation, tax, banking and finance, Information Technology and Intellectual Property, telecoms and employment. Scope for secondments to clients and pro bono work as part of the training contract are thought likely although as yet not planned. The opportunity to do a foreign seat is currently under review, as is an initial induction at the firm's head office in Chicago. Pay is in the higher regions of rates offered by city firms and working hours are generally comparable.

Trainees can expect to be constructively involved in deals right from the beginning, undertaking a variety of interesting tasks. "You are given a lot more responsibility and expected to know your stuff and apply what you've learned". They are expected to work hard to complete tasks as necessary but without the "macho experience" of "staying on every night for the sake of it."

In this environment, a certain amount of confidence is absolutely essential, as is a willingness to learn and the ability to accept when you're wrong or don't understand something. It will suit those who are fairly strong-willed and can hold their own opinions, however the perceived necessity in typical US firms to "develop a hide like a rhino" is not the case as the atmosphere is more friendly. Other desirable attributes are a very good background knowledge which basically boils down to a good understanding of commerce and business and the ability to "muck in". Considered an integral part of "the face of the firm", trainees will be encouraged to have maximum interface with clients in all contexts ranging from beauty parades to social events.

All members of the firm (excluding the Chairman) are expected to meet a chargeable hourly target of 2,000 hours per annum. There is a bonus scheme based on criteria including number of hours worked beyond target number.

The London office is unusual in that there are very few US attorneys based there. It is more like a high profile City firm with big US back-up. Being a newly established office, the atmosphere is very "young and exciting." There is a sense of everyone experiencing the office's development together. During strategy meetings, points of view across the board are all considered and there is no fear in expressing opinions as all are taken seriously.

Sidley & Austin

Number of Trainees: 11

Dual US/English law firm recommended for securitisation, derivatives and telecommunications.

Training is organised on a flexible basis into five training seats split into three 6 month seats and two 3 month seats covering corporate, international finance and banking, property, tax and the information industry (Intellectual Property, Information Technology and telecoms). The Law Society requirements for experience in contentious work are currently met by carrying out theoretical case work in London culminating in a mock trial at the firm's Chicago office. This is currently under review with potential scope for placement with a barristers' chambers.

Trainees are generally happy with the level of responsibility given and report on a responsive attitude to their feedback if this is not the case. The degree of client exposure varies enormously depending on the work and individual supervisor. Trainees participate in recruitment initiatives such as law fairs, firm brochures and annual client events.

Trainees are impressed by the "excellent" quality of educational resources provided in the form of lectures given by external consultants or senior partners in-house. Experience is "pretty hands on", with one trainee commenting that "you don't necessarily realise at the time, but it's staggering just how much you learn over time".

Fewer trainees means a more sociable environment with an absence of cliques. Trainees come from a broad age group (between 23 to 30 years) and diversity of backgrounds (approximately 50% law to non law graduates). A relaxed attitude prevails, with "dress down" Fridays.

The "newness" of the atmosphere, as opposed to "entrenched" attitudes perceived in City firms, and the prevailing US ethos which discourages hierarchy ("you can talk to the partners") are considered a bonus in the context of an evolving training programme. Trainees regard themselves as being "treated with respect" with a high level of autonomy regarding working hours - "people are not always looking over your shoulder."

Weil, Gotschal & Manges

Number of Trainees: 6

One of the largest offices of a US firm in London, with a predominance of UK qualified lawyers. Leading securitisations and derivatives teams. As is the case with other firms of its kind, the atmosphere is very young ("there are no old or unapproachable people") and casual - they dress down every day. The atmosphere is supportive and industrious - "everyone is here to work", yet "small enough for people to socialise." Having observed its size almost doubling over the past 1½ years, one trainee commented that this must be one of the fastest growing offices of its kind - "full of opportunities."

Practice areas covered in London include corporate, litigation, capital markets, banking, Intellectual Property, property. A seat in New York is available, where securitisation, tax and property are likely areas of practice. In London, the corporate group runs a dedicated training programme comprising a series of seminars and lectures by members who tend to be selected for their "young and approachable" qualities. Trainees are given a variety of work and levels of responsibility according to previous experience. The banking and capital markets seat is split into two separate seats, and training programmes are also run in conjunction with each. No such training programmes are run during the litigation seat. Training tends to be less rigid here than elsewhere, and experience is more "hands on." There is opportunity to do pro bono work in this context at the High Court's Citizens' Advice Bureau. Secondments to clients tend to occur post qualification and language training is provided when needed.

Trainees are seen as "all very different in personality", and the general feeling is that aside from academic prerequisites, candidates are assessed as to whether they would fit in. They are all quite ambitious - one noted that there "doesn't appear to be a glass ceiling for women" with the male to female ratio estimated as approaching 50:50.

This is a place where "you have the chance to shine" but by the same token "you can't hide either." The "work hard, play hard" culture is seen as "more merit-based" than at typical City firms. This is exemplified by the 'spiky' bonuses available from trainee level upwards to those who do something "a bit extra" for the firm, such as introduce a new client or performed particularly well on a job.

White & Case

Number of Trainees: 13

Training is divided into four 6 month seats usually including a foreign seat in Paris, Brussels, Singapore or Hong Kong. There is a certain degree of choice in practice areas which include corporate, banking, litigation, competition, project finance and Intellectual Property.

Trainees can expect to be involved in high profile matters at levels which are appropriate to their experience. They are given a high level of responsibility ("they will let you run with things and take charge") and generally "feel an integral part" of the team. There is consistent comment that none have "felt out of depth" in handling those cases which have been allocated to them single-handedly. Dealing with "very high quality work" which is varied in nature and working for lots of different people, several testify to "a gradual building up of competence" and a "steady accumulation of knowledge and confidence."

An "exciting" atmosphere comprises roughly 50:50 US to UK/ European staff working in different languages, integrating UK work with that from the firm's other overseas offices. There is a prevalence of those with language skills and Oxbridge graduates are thought to have "an edge." With emphasis on individuality among trainees, there is a variety of "personalities" who have "done something a bit unusual" before joining.

Notwithstanding the high quality of work, the atmosphere is intimate and personal as the office is so small. Trainees sense they are "better known as an individual and regarded as a valuable asset" rather than just another commodity. "They expect higher standards and reward appropriately." Although trainee salaries are little higher than he market rate, they rise on qualification to almost double the market rates. There is some financial recognition for hours worked when financial reports are done, although this is nominal only.

Training contracts available per year: London Firms

Firm Name	Contracts pa	Firm Name	Contracts pa
Clifford Chance	130	Olswang	12
Linklaters	125	Titmuss Sainer Dechert	10-15
Allen & Overy	120	Charles Russell	10-12
Eversheds*	100-110	Watson, Farley & Williams	10-12
Freshfields	90	Field Fisher Waterhouse	10
Herbert Smith	90	Ince & Co	10
CMS Cameron McKenna	80	Kennedys	10
Lovells	80	Nicholson Graham & Jones	10
Slaughter and May	c.75	Paisner & Co	10
Norton Rose	60-70	Penningtons	10
Dibb Lupton Alsop*	60	White & Case LLP	10
Simmons & Simmons	50-60	Withers	10
Ashurst Morris Crisp	45-50	Bristows	8
Landwell	45	Mishcon de Reya	8
Garretts*	40	Russell Jones & Walker	8
Beachcroft Wansbroughs*	37	Sinclair Roche & Temperley	8
S J Berwin & Co	35	Weil, Gotshal & Manges	8
Denton Hall	c.30	Holman Fenwick & Willan	7
Nabarro Nathanson*	30	Reynolds Porter Chamberlain	7
Wilde Sapte	30	Capsticks	6-8
Rowe & Maw	25	Sidley & Austin	6-8
Baker & McKenzie	22-25	Biddle	6
Taylor Joynson Garrett	22	Cadwalader, Wickersham & Taft	6
Berwin Leighton	20	Farrer & Co	6
Gouldens	20	Hempsons	6
Macfarlanes	20	Lewis Silkin	6
Richards Butler	20	Harbottle & Lewis	5
Stephenson Harwood	20	Speechly Bircham	5
Theodore Goddard	20	Orchard	4-6
Travers Smith Braithwaite	20	Boodle Hatfield	4-5
Barlow Lyde & Gilbert	16	Anthony Gold, Lerman & Muirhead	4
Clyde & Co*	16	Bircham & Co.	4
Masons*	15-17	Coudert Brothers	4
Lawrence Graham	15	Davenport Lyons	4
D J Freeman	12-15	Jeffrey Green Russell	4
Trowers & Hamlins	12-15	Le Brasseur J Tickle	4
Bird & Bird	12	Pritchard Englefield	4

Training contracts available per year: London Firms (cont.)

Firm Name	Contracts pa	Firm Name	Contracts pa
Radcliffes	4	Teacher Stern Selby	3
Sharpe Pritchard	4	Dawson & Co	2-3
Warner Cranston	4	Holmes Hardingham	2
Wedlake Bell	4	Laytons	2
Finers Stephens Innocent	3-6	Lee Bolton & Lee	2
Russell-Cooke, Potter & Chapman	3-4	Mayer, Brown & Platt	2
Salans Hertzfeld & Heilbronn HRK	3-4	Payne Hicks Beach	2
Beale and Company	3	Cumberland Ellis Peirs	1-2
Cleary, Gottlieb, Steen & Hamilton	3	Townleys	1-2
Fenners	3	May, May & Merrimans	1
Goodman Derrick	3	Bindman & Partners	6 every 2 years
Sheridans	3	Leigh, Day & Co	varies
Tarlo Lyons	3	Davies Arnold Cooper	varies

Training contracts available per year: Regional firms

Firm Name	Contracts pa	Firm Name	Contracts pa
Addleshaw Booth & Co	c.40	Weightmans	8
Pinsent Curtis	25-30	Cobbetts	7
Edge Ellison	25+	Davies Wallis Foyster	at least 6
Hammond Suddards	25	Harvey Ingram Owston	6
Wragge & Co	25	Howes Percival	6
Morgan Cole	20	Shadbolt & Co	6
Bevan Ashford	19	Steele & Co	6
Burges Salmon	18	Blake Lapthorn	5
Shoosmiths	16	Cartwrights	5
Bond Pearce	15-20	Lester Aldridge	5
Mills & Reeve	15-20	Donne Mileham & Haddock	4-5
Hewitson Becke + Shaw	15	McCormicks	4
Irwin Mitchell	15	Palser Grossman	4
Osborne Clarke	14-16	Taylor Vinters	4
Mace & Jones	12	Knight & Sons	3-4
Martineau Johnson	10-12	Boyes Turner & Burrows	2-3
Walker Morris	10	Wiggin & Co	2-3
Dickinson Dees	8-10	Berg & Co	2
Cripps Harries Hall	8	Taylor Walton	2
Halliwell Landau	8	Whitehead Monckton	2
Lawrence Tucketts	8	Withy King	2
Pannone & Partners	8		

The table represents the top 50 firms by size plus firms with an A-Z entry. For those firms marked with an asterisk the number may include contracts available in regional branches. See A-Z section for further details.

TRAINEES ABROAD

If we had a pound for every trainee who told us that the chance of spending time in an overseas office was a key reason for their choice of firm, then we would probably have had enough to buy a one-way ticket to most of those international locations. Top favourites are New York, Hong Kong, Singapore and Paris but in these days of globalisation, the list of potential locations grows ever longer. In the Middle East, Dubai is a trainee hot spot. Seats in Eastern Europe are now more common and trainees from UK firms are now working as far afield as China, Brazil, Venezuela and Russia. Closer to home, secondments to Brussels offices are plentiful.

The main thing to remember is that although the time abroad is primarily to give you experience of working in another jurisdiction, you are, with some exceptions, unlikely to deal in foreign law – these are offices practising UK law. Of course some offices will be staffed by lawyers who are dual qualified.

Repeatedly, those trainees who spoke to us about their overseas experience told us that it was hard work. Offices abroad are much smaller than main offices in London and this can have the effect of requiring a trainee to shoulder more responsibility. Almost without exception, trainees seem to welcome this added responsibility. Some spoke anecdotally of tasks which they had never dreamed they would be able to perform whilst others told us that being the only trainee or one of very few had meant that their jobs had become much more diverse and challenging for the period of their overseas stay. All had enjoyed the time and for most it was the highlight of their training. We spoke to Nabeel Ikram At Lovell White Durrant about his six months in a litigation seat in Hong Kong. He worked on a number of smaller and medium sized cases and found that he had a considerable amount of responsibility.

Work aside, the social life in many overseas locations can be pretty special. New York is a hard-working, hard-playing and high-living six months. At Linklaters, for example, each of the seven trainees gets their own apartment in the city. No wonder each successful applicant for the post will have beaten up to half a dozen others for the chance. Nabeel Ikram told us that while he was in Hong Kong there were around 40 trainees from various London firms plus the local trainees. Having spent the first couple of weeks getting to know everyone via an age-old network, passed down through the 'generations' of Hong Kong trainees, the vibrancy of the city comes into full effect. "Typically, clubs stay open till six or seven in the morning and you might go to five or six places in one night." Nabeel said. "Lovells have their own Junk and speedboat which trainees can book and take out." Add to this free gym membership, a salary uplift, a cleaner twice a week who will do your ironing and a rent free apartment shared between two. "For me socially" said Nabeel "the main thing was being able to spend two weeks on Bali or one of the Philippine islands or the Thai islands."

By contrast, a trainee at another firm who spent six months in the Prague office felt that although the city was beautiful and she had enjoyed her time working overseas, she didn't feel like raving about the experience in the same way as some of those who had been to the 'sexier' locations. "I was there in Winter" she told us "and after six months it's quite boring compared to living in London."

How do you ensure that you get a preferred seat abroad? Generally, trainees felt that the decision was in most cases based on merit and suitability for a job. Language ability is an essential for some seats like Paris, São Paulo or Milan, for example, but it is unnecessary for most of the Eastern seats or the US. Amusingly, at one firm we were told of a tendency amongst some trainees to dumb down their language ability in order to avoid being sent to an overseas seat which is not of their choice. Ironically, the very skills that they professed to have upon application to the firm had become a liability to them in terms of securing a popular spot overeseas. At firms with a heavy emphasis on work overseas, the trick to securing certain of the most popular seats is apparently still, to a degree, a case of waging an effective campaign of self promotion. With the firms that only have one or two overseas offices, it is often the case that at least half of the trainees will have decided against time abroad as a result of commitments in the UK, or simply a desire to spend all of their seats in the home office. Sometimes trainees have told us that they feared six months away from the action in London might mean that they were out of sight and out of mind, but invariably, the award of an overseas seat will be an endorsement of recognised ability.

Almost always, it is second year trainees who go abroad. By that time they are seen to have grasped the basics and be of more use. A majority of seats will be in the company/commercial field, many with an international finance bias. Additionally, litigation seats may be on offer in some offices such as Hong Kong, where the local law differs little from English law. Shipping seats crop up in Piraeus, Singapore, Caracas and Hong Kong, amongst other locations.

A Brussels seat will almost certainly entail EU/Competition and trade law. Trainees will never be short of company as so many firms have representation in the city. However, this type of work doesn't suit everyone and some trainees feel that the work lacks the drive of more transactional based areas.

Seats in Muslim countries might involve a necessary cultural adjustment. More modest female dress codes and modification of behaviour between men and women so as to fit in with cultural norms are typical of the Middle Eastern seats for example. But as many a seasoned traveller would point out to you, if you're unhappy about having to adjust to local custom, maybe you shouldn't be there in the first place.

The overwhelming feedback from those we spoke to is that working as a trainee abroad is an unmissable experience in terms of both work and social life. If you do get the chance you will probably love it!

Places abroad

Firm Name	Places Abroad pa	Firm Name	Places Abroad pa
Linklaters	100	Theodore Goddard	4
Clifford Chance	98	Masons	3
Freshfields	c.40	Osborne Clarke	3
Slaughter and May	c30	Titmuss Sainer Dechert	3
Allen & Overy	25	Dickinson Dees	2
Lovells	20	Rowe & Maw	2
Simmons & Simmons	18	S J Berwin & Co	2
Ashurst Morris Crisp	14	Shadbolt & Co	1/2
CMS Cameron McKenna	12	Cobbetts	1
Eversheds	Up to 12	Holmes Hardingham	1
Norton Rose	12	Pinsent Curtis	1
Richards Butler	10	Walker Morris	1
Herbert Smith	8	Baker & McKenzie	varies
Stephenson Harwood	8	Barlow Lyde & Gilbert	varies
Watson, Farley & Williams	8	Clyde & Co	varies
Wilde Sapte	8	Coudert Brothers	possibily available
Hammond Suddards	6	Mishcon de Reya	possibly available
Trowers & Hamlins	4-6	Sinclair Roche & Temperley	varies
Berwin Leighton	4	White & Case LLP	varies
Taylor Joynson Garrett	4		

Overseas Offices

Firm name	Overseas Offices
Baker & McKenzie	Almaty, Amsterdam, Bahrain, Baku, Bangkok, Barcelona, Beijing, Berlin, Bogota, Brasilia, Brussels, Budapest, Buenos Aires, Cairo, Caracas, Chicago, Dallas, Frankfurt, Geneva, Hanoi, Ho Chi Minh City, Hong Kong, Houston, Hsinchu, Juarez, Kiev, Madrid, Manila, Melbourne, Mexico City, Miami, Milan, Monterrey, Moscow, Munich, New York, Palo Alto, Paris, Prague, Rio de Janeiro, Riyadh, Rome, St Petersburg, San Diego, San Francisco, Santiago, Sao Paulo, Singapore, Stockholm, Sydney, Taipei, Tijuana, Tokyo, Toronto, Valencia, Warsaw, Washington DC, Zurich
Linklaters	Alicante, Amsterdam, Antwerp, Bangkok, Berlin, Brussels, Cologne, Frankfurt, Gothenburg, The Hague, Hong Kong, Hungary, Leipzig, London, Luxembourg, Madrid, Malmo, Milan, Moscow, Munich, New York, Paris, Prague, Romania, Rome, Rotterdam, Sao Paulo, Shanghai, Singapore, Slovakia, Stockholm, St Petersburg, Tokyo, Washington DC
CMS Cameron McKenna	Aberdeen, Almaty, Amsterdam, Arnhem, Beijing, Berlin, Bristol, Brussels, Bucharest, Budapest, Chemnitz, Dresden, Dusseldorf, Frankfurt, Hamburg, Hilversum, Hong Kong, Leipzig, Moscow, Munich, Prague, Singapore, Stockholm, Stuttgart, Tashkent, Toronto, Utrecht, Vienna, Warsaw, Washington DC
White & Case LLP	Almaty, Ankara, Bangkok, Bratislava, Bombay, Brussels, Budapest, Hanoi, Helsinki, Ho Chi Minh City, Hong Kong, Istanbul, Jeddah, Johannesburg, London, Los Angeles, Mexico City, Miami, Moscow, New York, Palo Alto, Paris, Prague, Riyadh, Sao Paulo, Singapore, Stockholm, Tokyo, Warsaw, Washington DC
Clifford Chance	Amsterdam, Bangkok, Barcelona, Beijing, Berlin, Brussels, Budapest, Dubai, Dusseldorf, Frankfurt, Hong Kong, Leipzig, Madrid, Milan, Moscow, Munich, New York, Padua, Paris, Prague, Rome, Sao Paulo, Shanghai, Singapore, Tokyo, Warsaw, Washington DC
Coudert Brothers	Almaty, Antwerp, Bangkok, Beijing, Berlin, Brussels, Denver, Frankfurt, Ghent, Hanoi, Hong Kong, Jakarta, Los Angeles, Montreal, Moscow, New York, Palo Alto, Paris, San Francisco, San Jose, Singapore, St Petersburg, Sydney, Tokyo, Washington DC
Allen & Overy	Amsterdam, Beijing, Brussels, Bratislava, Budapest, Dubai, Frankfurt, Hong Kong, Luxembourg, Madrid, Milan, Moscow, New York, Rome, Paris, Prague, Singapore, Tirana, Tokyo, Turin, Warsaw
Freshfields	Amsterdam, Bangkok, Barcelona, Beijing, Berlin, Brussels, Cologne, Frankfurt, Hanoi, Ho Chi Minh City, Hong Kong, Madrid, Milan, Moscow, New York, Paris, Rome, Singapore, Tokyo, Washington DC
Lovells	Beijing, Brussels, Chicago, Ho Chi Minh City, Hong Kong, Moscow, New York, Paris, Prague, Singapore, Tokyo, Washington DC
Denton Hall	Almaty, Beijing, Brussels, Cairo, Dubai, Gibraltar, Hong Kong, Istanbul, Moscow, Singapore, Tokyo and associated offices at Barcelona, Berlin, Chemnitz, Cologne, Copenhagen, Dresden, Dusseldorf, Frankfurt, Gothenburg, Hamburg, Madrid, Malmo, Munich, Oslo, Paris, Stockholm, Vienna

Overseas Offices (cont.)

Firm name	Overseas Offices
McDermott, Will & Emery	Boston, Chicago, Los Angeles, Menlo Park (Silicon Valley), Miami, Moscow, New York, Orange County, St. Petersburg, Vilnius, Washington DC
Richards Butler	Abu Dhabi, Beijing, Brussels, Doha, Hong Kong, Islamabad, Muscat, Paris, Piraeus, Sao Paulo, Warsaw
Osborne Clarke	Barcelona, Brussels, Copenhagen, Cologne, Frankfurt, Hamburg, Lyon, Milan, Paris, Rotterdam
Weil, Gotshal & Manges	Brussels, Budapest, Dallas, Houston, Menlo Park (Silicon Valley), Miami, New York, Prague, Warsaw, Washington DC
Cleary, Gottlieb, Steen & Hamilton	Brussels, Frankfurt, Hong Kong, Moscow, New York, Paris, Rome, Tokyo, Washington DC
Sidley & Austin	Chicago, Dallas, Hong Kong, Los Angeles, New York, Shanghai, Singapore, Tokyo, Washington DC
Simmons & Simmons	Abu Dhabi, Brussels, Hong Kong, Lisbon, Milan, New York, Paris, Rome, Shanghai
Titmuss Sainer Dechert	Through its union with Dechert Price and Rhoads the firm has other offices in Brussels, New York, Paris, Washington, Philadelphia, Boston, Hartford, Harrisburg and Princeton
Mayer, Brown & Platt	Chicago, Berlin, Charlotte, Houston, Cologne, Los Angeles, New York, Washington
Salans Hertzfeld & Heilbronn HRK	Almaty, Baku, Kiev, Moscow, New York, Paris, St Petersburg, Warsaw
Herbert Smith	Bangkok, Beijing, Brussels, Hong Kong, Moscow, Paris, Singapore.
Holman Fenwick & Willan	Paris, Rouen, Nantes, Piraeus, Hong Kong, Singapore, Shanghai
Ashurst Morris Crisp	Brussels, Delhi, Frankfurt, Paris, Singapore, Tokyo; associated offices in Milan, Rome and Verona
Clyde & Co	Hong Kong, Singapore, Dubai, Caracas, Paris, Piraeus (Associate Office: St Petersburg)
Stephenson Harwood	Brussels, Guangzhou, Hong Kong, Madrid, Piraeus, Singapore
Watson, Farley & Williams	Copenhagen, Moscow, New York, Paris, Piraeus, Singapore
Masons	Brussels, Dublin, Guangzhou (PRC), Hong Kong, Singapore
Slaughter and May	Brussels, Hong Kong, New York, Paris, Singapore
Trowers & Hamlins	Abu Dhabi, Dubai, Oman, Bahrain, Cairo
Eversheds	Brussels, Monaco, Moscow, Paris
Norton Rose	Brussels, Moscow, Paris, Singapore
Wilde Sapte	Brussels, Hong Kong, Paris, Tokyo
Bird & Bird	Brussels, Hong Kong, Paris
Cadwalader, Wickersham & Taft	New York, Washington, Charlotte
Ince & Co	Hong Kong, Singapore, Piraeus (consultancy)
S J Berwin & Co	Brussels, Frankfurt, Madrid
Sinclair Roche & Temperley	Bucharest, Hong Kong, Shanghai
Dibb Lupton Alsop	Brussels, Hong Kong
Hammond Suddards	Brussels (plus secondment opportunities to Hong Kong)

Overseas Offices (cont.)

Firm name	Overseas Offices
Pritchard Englefield	Frankfurt, Hong Kong
Shadbolt & Co	Hong Kong, Paris
Taylor Joynson Garrett	Brussels, Bucharest
Theodore Goddard	Brussels, Paris (plus associated offices worldwide)
Barlow Lyde & Gilbert	Hong Kong
Beachcroft Wansbroughs	Brussels
Berwin Leighton	Brussels
Cobbetts	Brussels
Davies Arnold Cooper	Madrid
Dickinson Dees	Brussels
Field Fisher Waterhouse	Brussels
Kennedys	Hong Kong (associated offices in Beirut, Belfast, Dublin, Karachi, New Delhi, New York, Paris, San Francisco)
Macfarlanes	Brussels
Nabarro Nathanson	Brussels
Nicholson Graham & Jones	Brussels
Olswang	Brussels
Penningtons	Paris
Pinsent Curtis	Brussels
Wedlake Bell	Guernsey
Wiggin & Co	Los Angeles
Withers	Paris

TRAINEE SALARIES

Trainee salaries: London firms

Firm Name	1st year trainee salary	2nd year trainee salary	Qualification salary
Cleary, Gottlieb, Steen & Hamilton	£33,000	£39,000	£59,500
Gouldens	£25,000	£27,000	£40,000
Mayer, Brown & Platt	£25,000	£26,000	£42,500
McDermott, Will & Emery	£24,000		£50,000
Weil, Gotshal & Manges	£24,000	£26,000	£35,500
Coudert Brothers	£23,500-£24,000	£24,500-£25,000	£35,000
White & Case LLP	£23,000	£25,000	£45,000
Sidley & Austin	£22,750	£24,750	£33,000
Biddle	£22,500	£26,000	£33,000
Paisner & Co	£22,500	£24,000	£34,000
Watson, Farley & Williams	£22,000-£23,000	£24,000-£26,000	£35,000
Theodore Goddard	£22,000	£25,000	£33,500
S J Berwin & Co	£22,000	£24,500	£35,000
Berwin Leighton	£22,000	£24,000	£34,000
Rowe & Maw	£22,000	£24,000	£34,000
Titmuss Sainer Dechert	£22,000	£24,000	£34,000
Holman Fenwick & Willan	£21,750	£22,750	£33,000
Field Fisher Waterhouse	£21,600	£23,600	£31,500
CMS Cameron McKenna	£21,500	£24,000	£34,500
Dibb Lupton Alsop	£21,500	£24,000	£34,000
Stephenson Harwood	£21,500	£24,000	£34,000
Wilde Sapte	£21,500	£24,000	£34,000
Macfarlanes	£21,500	£24,000	£33,000
Richards Butler	£21,500	£24,000	£33,000
Ashurst Morris Crisp	£21,500	£23,500	£35,000
Trowers & Hamlins	£21,500	£23,500	£35,000
Charles Russell	£21,500	£23,500	£34,000
Warner Cranston	£21,500	£23,000	£34,000
Clyde & Co	£21,500	£23,000	£33,000
Denton Hall	£21,000-£22,000	£23,000-£24,000	£34,000
Speechly Bircham	£21,000-£22,000	£23,000-£24,000	£34,000
Slaughter and May	£21,000	£24,000	£38,800
Barlow Lyde & Gilbert	£21,000	£24,000	£35,000
Landwell	£21,000	£24,000	£35,000
Lawrence Graham	£21,000	£24,000	£34,000
Clifford Chance	£21,000	£24,000	£33,500
Norton Rose	£21,000	£24,000	£33,500
Allen & Overy	£21,000	£24,000	£33,000
Freshfields	£21,000	£24,000	£33,000
Herbert Smith	£21,000	£24,000	£33,000
Linklaters	£21,000	£24,000	£33,000
Nabarro Nathanson	£21,000	£24,000	£33,000
Simmons & Simmons	£21,000	£24,000	£33,000
Travers Smith Braithwaite	£21,000	£24,000	£33,000
Baker & McKenzie	£21,000	£23,500	£35,000-£36,000

Trainee salaries: London firms (cont.)

Firm Name	1st year trainee salary	2nd year trainee salary	Qualification salary
Taylor Joynson Garrett	£21,000	£23,500	£33,500
Cadwalader, Wickersham & Taft	£21,000	£23,000	£40,000
Olswang	£21,000	£23,000	£35,000
Nicholson Graham & Jones	£21,000	£23,000	£34,000
Farrer & Co	£21,000	£23,000	£33,500
Boodle Hatfield	£21,000	£23,000	£33,000
Masons	£21,000	£23,000	£33,000
Reynolds Porter Chamberlain	£21,000	£23,000	£33,000
Bristows	£21,000	£23,000	£32,500
Ince & Co	£21,000	£23,000	£32,000
Holmes Hardingham	£21,000	£23,000	£31,000
Capsticks	£21,000	£23,000	£28,000
Bird & Bird	£21,000	£22,500	£34,000
Beachcroft Wansbroughs	£21,000	£22,500	£30,000
Sinclair Roche & Temperley	£21,000	£22,000	£33,000
Lewis Silkin	£21,000	£22,000	£32,000
Garretts	£21,000	£21,000	£34,000
Lovells	£21,000		£33,000
D J Freeman	£20,500	£23,000	£34,000
Withers	£20,500	£22,600	£32,000
Davenport Lyons	£20,500	£21,500	£30,000
Teacher Stern Selby	£20,000	£22,250	£31,000
Tarlo Lyons	£20,000	£22,000	£30,000
Dawson & Co	£20,000	£22,000	£28,000
Salans Hertzfeld & Heilbronn HRK	£20,000	£21,500	
Harbottle & Lewis	£20,000	£21,000	£31,500
Penningtons	£20,000	£21,000	£31,000
Sharpe Pritchard	£20,000	£21,000	
Payne Hicks Beach	£19,500	£21,000	£31,000
Mishcon de Reya	£19,500	£21,000	
Radcliffes	£19,000	£21,000	£29,500
Russell Jones & Walker	£19,000	£21,000	£27,000
Finers Stephens Innocent	£19,000	£20,000	£31,500
Bircham & Co.	£19,000	£20,000	
Bindman & Partners	£19,000	£19,000	
Sheridans	£18,800	£20,000	£27,000
Goodman Derrick	£18,500	£19,500	£30,500
Beale and Company	£18,500		£32,000
Le Brasseur J Tickle	£18,000	£20,000	£30,000
Lee Bolton & Lee	£18,000	£19,000	£29,000
Pritchard Englefield	£18,000	£18,250	£30,000
Russell-Cooke, Potter & Chapman	£17,500	£18,500	
Leigh, Day & Co	£17,000	£18,000	
Anthony Gold, Lerman & Muirhead	£16,500	£18,000	£24,050
Eversheds	£15,000-£21,000	£16,000-£23,000	

Trainee salaries: Regional firms

Firm Name	1st year trainee salary	2nd year trainee salary	Qualification salary
Wiggin & Co	£21,600	£25,200	£31,600
Pinsent Curtis	£21,500	£24,000	£27,000
Shadbolt & Co	£19,000	£21,000	£28,000
Hammond Suddards	£17,000	£19,000	£25,500
Walker Morris	£16,798	£18,000	£26,000
Addleshaw Booth & Co	£16,000-£16,500	£17,000-£17,500	£26,000
Boyes Turner & Burrows	£16,000	£17,000	£23,500
Burges Salmon	£16,000	£17,000	£27,000
Halliwell Landau	£15,750	£16,750	£26,000
Weightmans	£15,700	£17,500	£24,500
Edge Ellison	£15,500	£17,000	£26,500
Howes Percival	£15,500	£16,750	
Irwin Mitchell	£15,500	£17,500	
Martineau Johnson	£15,500	£17,000	£26,500
Pannone & Partners	£15,500	£17,500	£24,500
Shoosmiths	£15,500	£16,750	£24,500
Wragge & Co	£15,500	£17,500	£27,000
Dickinson Dees	£15,250	£16,250	£23,250
Osborne Clarke	£15,000-£15,500	£16,000-£16,500	£27,000
Cobbetts	£15,000	£16,500	£15,000+
Mills & Reeve	£15,000	£16,000	£25,500
Cartwrights	£14,750 - £15,350	£15,950 - £16,550	£23,500
Taylor Vinters	£14,535	£16,050	£25,000
Hewitson Becke + Shaw	£14,500	£15,500	
Bond Pearce	£14,250	£13,500	£21,000
Davies Wallis Foyster	£14,000	£15,000	
Lester Aldridge	£14,000	£15,000	£23,500
Palser Grossman	£14,000	£15,000	£20,000
Cripps Harries Hall	£13,500	£15,500	£22,250
Blake Lapthorn	£13,000	£14,500	£22,000
Donne Mileham & Haddock	£13,000	£15,500	£21,000
Withy King	£12,200	£14,000	
Mace & Jones	£11,000	£11,500	
Whitehead Monckton	£11,000	£12,000	

The table represents firms in decreasing order of first year salary. The table only includes firms which have supplied figures for at least two headings. ***Salaries listed for London firms represent salaries paid in London office only****. All figures represent the most up-to-date available at time of going to press.* *See A-Z section for further details.*

Perks: Nationwide

Firm Name	Sponsorship and Awards	Benefits	Sports Facilities
Addleshaw Booth & Co	CPE and LPC fees paid, together with a maintenance award of £3,500.	Profit related pay, season ticket loan.	Corporate membership of gyms.
Allen & Overy	CPE and LPC fees and £4,500 maintenance p.a. (£4,000 outside London and Guilford).	Private medical insurance, season ticket loans, subsidised restaurant.	Gym membership.
Anthony Gold, Lerman & Muirhead	£1,000 paid for LPC fees and interest free loan.	A season ticket loan, PRP, private medical care, permanent health insurance.	Subsidised gym.
Ashurst Morris Crisp	CPE and LPC funding and maintenance allowance.	Season ticket loan, medical cover, life cover, subsidised annual health check.	Membership of a gym/squash club.
Baker & McKenzie	CPE Funding: Fees paid + £4,500 maintenance. LPC Funding: Fees paid + £4,500 maintenance.	Permanent health insurance, life insurance, private medical insurance, group personal pension plan, luncheon vouchers, interest-free season ticket loan.	Gym membership.
Barlow Lyde & Gilbert	Financial assistance is available for both the CPE and LPC.		
Beachcroft Wansbroughs	LPC Funding: Fees paid + £3,000 maintenance - London. £2,500 paid towards fees - Out of London.	Pension, luncheon vouchers, private health scheme.	
Beale and Company		Season ticket loan (after 6 months), private health insurance (after 2 years), discretionary entertainment and social events.	
S J Berwin & Co	CPE and LPC Fees paid and £3,750 maintenance p.a.	PRP, free lunch, health insurance.	Corporate sports membership.
Berwin Leighton	CPE funding: Fees paid + £4,000 maintenance. LPC funding: Fees paid + £4,000 maintenance.	Private health insurance, season ticket loan, life assurance.	Subsidised gym membership.
Bevan Ashford	Available for LPC only.		

Perks: Nationwide (cont.)

Firm Name	Sponsorship and Awards	Benefits	Sports Facilities
Biddle	CPE and LPC fees paid and maintenance grant offered.	BUPA, life assurance, season ticket loan.	
Bird & Bird	LPC and CPE fees paid. Maintenance grant of £3,500.	Season ticket loan, life insurance, medical insurance, PHI.	
Blake Lapthorn	LPC: loan of £4,000 repayable from salary.	Trainee accommodation (first year).	
Bond Pearce	LPC financial assistance.		
Boodle Hatfield	CPE Funding: Fees paid + discretionary maintenance. LPC Funding: Fees paid + discretionary maintenance.	Season ticket loan, discretionary Christmas bonus.	
Boyes Turner & Burrows	CPE and LPC loan of £3,000 and only one loan per applicant. Interest free and re-paid over training contract.	Free medical insurance.	
Bristows	CPE and LPC funding, £4,000 p.a. plus fees.	Excellent career prospects, a competitive City package, firm pension scheme, life assurance and health insurance.	
Burges Salmon	In addition to CPE and LPC tuition fees, maintenance grants of £3,500 to LPC students and £4,000 to students studying for both CPE and LPC (£2,000 p.a.) are paid.	Rates of pay are substantially in excess of the Law Society recommendations and reviewed on 1 November each year.	
Cadwalader, Wickersham & Taft	CPE Funding: Fees paid + £4000 maintenance. LPC Funding: Fees paid + £4000 maintenance.	On joining: permanent health insurance, season ticket loan and BUPA.	
Capsticks	Scholarship contributions to CPE and LPC courses.	Bonus scheme, PHI, death in service cover.	
Cartwrights	Up to £5,000 paid towards LPC fees and £2,400 interest free loan.		

Perks: Nationwide (cont.)

Firm Name	Sponsorship and Awards	Benefits	Sports Facilities
Charles Russell	CPE and LPC fees paid and annual maintenance (currently under review but no less than £3500).	BUPA immediately, PHI and Life Assurance after 1 year's service, 23 days holiday (under review).	
Cleary, Gottlieb, Steen & Hamilton	LPC funding; Fees paid plus £4,500 maintenance award.	Pension, health insurance, long-term disability insurance, employee assistance programme.	Health club.
Clifford Chance	CPE and LPC fees paid and £4,500 maintenance p.a. (£4,100 outside London and Guilford).	Prize for first class degrees and distinction in LPC, interest free loan, private health insurance, subsidised restaurant, fitness centre, life assurance, occupational health service, and permanent health assurance.	
Clyde & Co	CPE and LPC Fees paid if no local authority funding.	Interest free ticket loan, staff restaurant and weekly free bar (London); monthly staff lunch and monthly free bar (Guildford).	Subsidised sports club.
CMS Cameron McKenna	CPE and LPC Funding: Fees paid and a maintenance grant of £4,250 (London and Guildford), £4,000 (elsewhere).	Private medical insurance, Season ticket loan, Personal Health Insurance, Life assurance, 22 days holiday, Travel bursaries for future trainees.	Corporate gym membership.
Cobbetts	CPE and LPC grant available.	Social Club and Y Club.	
Coudert Brothers	CPE Funding: Fees paid + £3,750 p.a. maintenance. LPC Funding: Fees paid + £3,750 p.a. maintenance.	Pension, health insurance, season ticket loan.	Subsidised gym membership.
Cripps Harries Hall	Discretionary LPC Funding: Fees - 50% interest free loan, 50% bursary.	PPP, DIS, PHI.	
Cumberland Ellis Peirs	It is not the firm's policy to offer vacation placements or sponsorship.	Season ticket loan, luncheon vouchers.	
Davenport Lyons	The firm does not generally offer financial assistance other than in exceptional circumstances.	Season ticket loans. Client introduction bonuses.	Contributions to gym membership.

Perks: Nationwide (cont.)

Firm Name	Sponsorship and Awards	Benefits	Sports Facilities
Davies Arnold Cooper	CPE and LPC: grants covering course and examination fees. Discretionary interest-free loans for maintenance up to £4,000.		
Davies Wallis Foyster	LPC funding.		
Dawson & Co	Discretionary. On application.	Season ticket loan.	
Denton Hall	CPE and LPC funding: fees and a maintenance grant of £3,750 for an outer London institution, and £4,000 for a London or Guildford institution.	Holiday entitlement rises by 1 day after each full year served, luncheon vouchers, private health cover, season ticket loan.	Gym membership.
Dibb Lupton Alsop	CPE and LPC fees paid and a maintenance grant for both years.	Pension, health insurance, life assurance, 23 days holiday.	
Dickinson Dees	LPC fees paid and £2,000 interest free loan.		
D J Freeman	CPE or LPC Funding.	Subsidised meals in staff restaurant; BUPA after three months; a variety of social and sporting events.	
Edge Ellison	CPE Funding: Fees paid LPC Funding: Fees paid & £3,500 maintenance.	Private health cover, pension (post qualification/25 years of age).	
Eversheds	CPE/LPC fees and maintenance grants.	Regional variations.	
Farrer & Co	CPE Funding: Fees paid + £4,000 maintenance; LPC Funding: Fees paid + £4,000 maintenance.	Health and life insurance, season ticket loan.	Subsidised gym membership.
Fenners	CPE and LPC funding to be discussed with candidates.	Health insurance, season ticket loan.	
Field Fisher Waterhouse	Tuition fees and maintenance grant paid for CPE and LPC.	25 days annual holiday, season ticket loans, health insurance, private medical healthcare.	
Finers Stephens Innocent	Contribution of £1,000 towards LPC course fees.	20 days holiday, private medical insurance, death in service insurance, long term disability insurance, season ticket loan.	Subsidised gym membership.

Perks: Nationwide (cont.)

Firm Name	Sponsorship and Awards	Benefits	Sports Facilities
Freshfields	CPE and LPC fees paid and £4,500 maintenance p.a. (£4,000 outside London and Guildford).	Life assurance; permanent health ins; group personal pension; interest-free loan for a season travel ticket, after six mths free m'ship to the firm's private medical ins scheme; loan scheme; subsidised staff restaurant.	Subsidised gym membership.
Garretts	CPE + LPC fees paid and £3,750-£4,000 grant p.a.	BUPA; S.T.L.	Subsidised gym membership.
Goodman Derrick	LPC fees plus maintenance grant.	Medical Health Insurance, season ticket loan.	
Gouldens	CPE and LPC fees paid and £4,500 maintenance p.a.	BUPA, season ticket loan, subsidised sports club membership, group life cover.	
Halliwell Landau	A contribution will be made to either CPE or LPC fees.		A subsidised gym membership is available.
Hammond Suddards	CPE and LPC fees paid and maintenance grant of £4,100 p.a.	Subsidised accommodation in all locations. Flexible benefits scheme which allows trainees to choose their own benefits from a range of options.	
Harbottle & Lewis	LPC fees paid and interest free loans towards maintenance.	Lunch provided, season ticket loans.	
Harvey Ingram Owston	Assistance with LPC funding is considered on application.		
Hempsons		Non-contributory pension. Season ticket loan for London based trainees. Holiday entitlement: 20 Days. Life cover.	
Herbert Smith	CPE and LPC fees paid and £4,500 maintenance p.a. (£4,000 outside London).	PRP, private health insurance, season ticket loan, life assurance.	Gym.
Hewitson Becke + Shaw	Funding for the CPE and/or LPC is not provided.	The PSC is provided by the College of Law during the first year of the Training Contract. This is coupled with an extensive programme of Trainee Solicitor Seminars provided by specialist in-house lawyers.	

Perks: Nationwide (cont.)

Firm Name	Sponsorship and Awards	Benefits	Sports Facilities
Holman Fenwick & Willan	CPE Funding: Fees paid + £4,000 maintenance. LPC Funding: Fees paid + £4,000 maintenance.	Private medical insurance, permanent health and accident insurance, season ticket loan.	Subsidised gym membership.
Holmes Hardingham	Discretionary funding for LPC.	Private health and insurance, interest free season ticket loan.	
Howes Percival		Payment of PSC course fees.	
Ince & Co	LPC fees. £4,000 grant for study in London. £3,500 grant for study elswhere.	STL, corporate health cover, PHI, discretionary bonus.	
Irwin Mitchell	CPE and LPC fees paid and £3,000 maintenance grant.		
Kennedys	£9,000 towards fees and assistance for LPC only		
Knight & Sons	Interest free loans may be available but are strictly subject to individual negotiation.		Subsidised gym membership.
Landwell	CPE and LPC: fees and £4,500 maintenance.	Interest-free season ticket loan, permanent health insurance, life assurance, private medical cover, subsidised restaurant.	Subsidised fitness centre.
Lawrence Graham	CPE Funding: Course Fees and £3,750 maintenance grant. LPC Funding: Course Fees and £3,750 maintenance grant.	Season ticket loan.	On-site gym.
Lawrence Tucketts	Interest paid on for LPC up to £6,000.	Subsidised health insurance.	Subsidised sports and health club facility.
Laytons	CPE Funding: yes; LPC Funding: yes.		
Lee Bolton & Lee	A contribution towards LPC funding but dependent upon being offered a training contract.	Season ticket loan, non-guaranteed bonus.	
Lester Aldridge	Discretionary.	Life assurance scheme.	

Perks: Nationwide (cont.)

Firm Name	Sponsorship and Awards	Benefits	Sports Facilities
Lewis Silkin	Full fees paid for LPC.	Life assurance, critical illness cover, health insurance, season ticket loan, subsidised conveyancing costs.	
Linklaters	CPE and LPC fees paid in full. A maintenance grant is also provided of £4,500 for London and £4,000 for outside of London. Language bursaries are also offered, upon completion of the LPC.	PPP medical insurance, life assurance, pension, season ticket loan, in-house dentist, doctor and physiotherapist, 24 hour subsidised staff restaurant.	In-house gym as well as corporate membership to Holmes Place.
Lovells	CPE and LPC course fees are paid, as well as a maintenance grant (in 1999/00) of £4,500 for London and Guilford and £4,000 elsewhere.	PPP, PHI, season ticket loan, staff restaurant, life assurance.	Gym membership.
Mace & Jones		Health Insurance.	
Macfarlanes	CPE and LPC full fees. £4,500 maintenance for courses in London and Guilford. £4,000 for courses elsewhere. Prizes for those gaining distinction and commendation.	Profit related pay; interest free season ticket loans; permanent health insurance*; private medical insurance*; subsidised conveyancing; subsidised firm restaurant. *After 12 months service.	Subsidised health club/gym.
Martineau Johnson	CPE and LPC funding; £3,500 maintenance for LPC.	Pension, Life Assurance, Private Medical Insurance, PHI & Travel Loans.	
Masons	CPE and LPC funding and a living allowance for each.	PRP, pension, life assurance, private health care, subsidised restaurant and season ticket loan (London).	
May, May & Merrimans	Discretionary loans for LPC.		
Mayer, Brown & Platt	50% funding for CPE and LPC plus maintenance grant.	Private medical insurance, season ticket loan, life assurance (4x basic salary).	
McDermott, Will & Emery	CPE and LPC funding; Tuition for relevant courses.	Private Medical and Dental Insurance, Life Assurance, Permanent Health Insurance, Non-Contributory Pension, Interest-Free Season Ticket Loan.	Gym Membership.

Perks: Nationwide (cont.)

Firm Name	Sponsorship and Awards	Benefits	Sports Facilities
Mills & Reeve	The firm pays the full costs of the LPC fees and offers a maintenance grant for the LPC year. Funding for the CPE is discretionary.	Life assurance at two times pensionable salary and a contributory pension scheme.	
Mishcon de Reya	LPC funding and bursary.	Health cover, season ticket loan, permanent health insurance, life assurance.	Subsidised gym membership.
Morgan Cole	Full funding of fees for attendance on the LPC for those trainess who will commence training with the firm.		
Nabarro Nathanson	CPE and LPC sponsorship and a maintenance grant. London and Guilford: £4,500. Elsewhere: £4,000.	Trainees are given private medical health insurance, 25 days' holiday entitlement per annum, a season ticket loan and access to a subsidised restaurant. Trainee salaries are reviewed annually.	
Nicholson Graham & Jones	LPC Fees and expenses paid. CPE fees.		
Norton Rose	£1,000 travel scholarship, £500 loan on arrival, 4-6 weeks unpaid leave on qualification.	Life assurance (25+), private health insurance (optional), season ticket loan.	Subsidised gym membership.
Olswang	Pay LPC RCPE fees and grants of £2,500.	Upon qualification: pensions, medical cover, life cover, dental scheme.	Gym membership.
Osborne Clarke	LPC fees paid.	None until qualified.	
Paisner & Co	LPC funding: Yes; CPE Funding: No.		
Payne Hicks Beach	Fees for the CPE and LPC are paid.	Season travel ticket loan, life assurance 4 x salary, permanent health insurance.	
Penningtons	LPC funding is available. Awards are given for commendation or distinction in LPC.	Season ticket loan, life assurance.	Subsidised sports and social club.
Pinsent Curtis	CPE/ LPC funding. In addition generous maintenance grants are offered for both CPE and LPC.		

Perks: Nationwide (cont.)

Firm Name	Sponsorship and Awards	Benefits	Sports Facilities
Pritchard Englefield	£2,000.	Some subsidised training, luncheon vouchers.	
Radcliffes		Health insurance, season ticket loan, life assurance, PHI.	
Reynolds Porter Chamberlain	CPE Funding: Fees paid + £4,000 maintenance. LPC Funding: Fees paid + £4,000 maintenance.	Four weeks' holiday, two bonus schemes, private medical insurance, season ticket loan, four office parties per year.	Subsidised gym membership.
Richards Butler	CPE and LPC fees and maintenance paid.	Life insurance, Private Patients' Plan, Interest free season ticket loan, subsidised staff restaurant.	
Rowe & Maw	CPE and LPC fees paid and £4,000 maintenance p.a.	Interest free season ticket loan, private health scheme.	Subsidised membership of sport clubs.
Russell Jones & Walker	CPE/LPC Funding: interest free loan to assist with fees available (£1000).	Season ticket loan, pension, private healthcare, permanent health.	
Shadbolt & Co	LPC fees partly payable when trainee commences work.	Permanent health insurance.	
Sharpe Pritchard		Season ticket loan.	
Sheridans	LPC funding is variable for those who have accepted training contracts.	Life assurance.	
Shoosmiths	Funding up to £6,500 maximum plus £1,500 maintenance grant.	Life assurance, contributory pension after 3 months.	
Sidley & Austin	CPE and LPC fees paid and maintenance p.a.	Healthcare, disability cover, life assurance, interest free season ticket loan.	Contribution to gym membership.
Simmons & Simmons	In the absence of Local Authority funding we will pay LPC and, where necessary, CPE fees and offer a maintenance allowance of £4,000 for London or Guildford and £3,600 elsewhere.	Season ticket loan, fitness loan, PRP, group travel insurance, group accident insurance, group health insurance.	

Perks: Nationwide (cont.)

Firm Name	Sponsorship and Awards	Benefits	Sports Facilities
Sinclair Roche & Temperley	CPE and LPC fees paid and £4,000 maintenance p.a.	Private health cover, discretionary bonus, PHI, accident insurance.	Subsidised sports club membership.
Slaughter and May	CPE and LPC fees and maintenance grants are paid; some grants are available for postgraduate work.	BUPA, STL, pension scheme, 24 hour accident cover.	Membership of various sports clubs.
Speechly Bircham	CPE and LPC funding: Fees paid + £3,000 maintenance.	Season ticket loan, private medical insurance, life assurance.	
Steele & Co		Permanent health insurance, accident insurance, legal services.	
Stephenson Harwood	£6,700 fees paid for CPE and LPC and £4,500 maintenance p.a.	LVs, subsidised membership of health club, season ticket loan and 22 days paid holiday per year.	
Tarlo Lyons		Contribution to private health insurance and season ticket loan.	
Taylor Joynson Garrett	CPE and LPC fees paid and £4,000 maintenance p.a.	Private medical care, permanent health insurance, STL, subsidised staff restaurant, non-contributory pension scheme on qualification.	
Taylor Vinters		Benefits are currently under review but are likely to include private medical insurance, life insurance and a choice of other benefits. Full details will be available on application.	
Teacher Stern Selby	CPE Funding: none; LPC Funding: unlikely.		
Theodore Goddard	CPE and LPC fees paid in full. £4,200 maintenance paid for London and South East, £3,750 elsewhere.	Permanent employment offered from the outset. Contributory pension, permanent health insurance, private medical insurance, death in service benefit and staff restaurant.	Subsidised sports club membership.

Perks: Nationwide (cont.)

Firm Name	Sponsorship and Awards	Benefits	Sports Facilities
Titmuss Sainer Dechert	LPC fees paid and £4,000 maintenance p.a. for those living in London and £3,750 for those outside (where local authority grants unavailable).	Free permanent health and life assurance and interest-free season ticket loans.	Subsidised membership of a local gym.
Travers Smith Braithwaite	LPC and CPE fees paid and £4,000 maintenance p.a.	Private health insurance, season ticket loans, luncheon vouchers.	Subsidised sports club membership.
Trowers & Hamlins	CPE and LPC fees paid and £4,000-£4,250 maintenance p.a.	Season ticket loan, private health care after one year's service, Employee Assistance Programme & discretionary bonus.	
Walker Morris	CPE Funding: Fees + £1,000; LPC Funding: Fees + £1,000.		
Warner Cranston	CPE/LPC fees and maintenance grant plus interest-free loan.	BUPA, IFSTL, life assurance, permanent health insurance, pension contributions (after qualifying period).	
Watson, Farley & Williams	CPE and LPC Fees paid and £4,000 maintenance p.a. (£3,600 outside London).	Life assurance, PHI, BUPA, STL, pension.	Subsidised gym membership.
Wedlake Bell		On qualification: life assurance, medical insurance, PHI and travel loan.	Subsidised gym membership.
Weightmans	50% grant and 50% interest free loan for CPE and CPC course fees.		
Weil, Gotshal & Manges	The firm will pay tuition fees and a maintenance allowance for CPE/LPC.	Pension, Permanent Health Insurance, Private Health Cover, Life Assurance, season ticket loan.	Subsidised gym membership.
White & Case LLP	CPE and LPC fees paid and £4,000 maintenance p.a. Prizes for commendation and distinction in the LPC.	BUPA, life insurance, pension scheme, permanent health scheme, season ticket loan.	Gym membership contribution.
Wiggin & Co	CPE and LPC Fees and £3,000 maintenance p.a. Brochure available on request.	Life assurance, private health cover, pension scheme, permanent health insurance.	

Perks: Nationwide (cont.)

Firm Name	Sponsorship and Awards	Benefits	Sports Facilities
Wilde Sapte	CPE and LPC fees paid and £4,000 maintenance p.a.	Interest free season ticket loan, death in service benefit, PPP, PRP, contributory pension at age 28 after qualification, staff restaurant.	
Withers	LPC and CPE fees paid and £4,000 maintenance p.a. and cash prize for distinction or commendation in CPE and LPC.	Interest free season ticket loan, private medical insurance, life assurance, social events, cafe facilities.	
Wragge & Co	CPE and LPC fees paid, £3,500 maintenance grant for LPC students, and £3,000 per year for CPE students.	Life ass., perm. health scheme, pension, int. free travel loans.	

The table represents the top 50 firms by size plus firms with an A-Z entry. Some information has been summarised. Gaps and omissions show that full information has not been supplied.
See A-Z section for further details.

After Training

PROSPECTS FOR NEWLY QUALIFIED

With the upturn in the economy and the spectre of recession a fading memory, prospects bode well for newly qualifieds both in the area of private practice and industry.

Private Practice

The majority of practices which experienced restructuring or re-organisation during the previous recession have now stabilised their operations and have been in the business of active expansion for some time. It has for some time been the trend for strategic advisors or trouble-shooters to recommend focus onto core strengths so the tendency among many medium-sized firms has been to hive off peripheral practice areas. This has led to more movement of lawyers than ever before, in a profession which was traditionally static and inward-looking.

Obviously some practice areas are more attractive than others in a 'boom' economy. Insolvency lawyers, for example, have had to tighten their belts and rebrand themselves as 'Corporate Recovery' lawyers and there is little call for insolvency litigators at the moment. Not surprisingly, lawyers have been tracking the unprecedented growth in the new media industry. In response to rising demands for legal services occasioned by rapid industry development, firms have expanded or re-branded related practice areas such as IP, Information Technology and telecoms or set up new specialist units. Opportunities both in private practice and the industry sector appear limitless for newly qualifieds who have been fortunate to receive relevant specialist training during their seats or have industry related backgrounds.

Industry and Banking

It is not difficult to see the allure of the in-house culture. Among the advantages are more predictable working hours, more opportunity to become commercially involved and incentivised pay structures which translate into potential for large bonus payments or share options. Negative points are lack of infrastructure and less hands on supervision.

There are always a number of positions for newly qualifieds within the industry, particularly those with experience in banking and/or capital markets work. However these tend to come up throughout the year rather than in March and September when training contracts in private practice end. Secondments to industry during training or afterwards are very useful for making contacts and may give additional insight into recruitment opportunities. However candidates are at their most marketable from the industry perspective when they have gained two to four years' experience in private practice.

In most cases, the best experience candidates can gain is general company and commercial work. This may have a specialist slant, for example, corporate M&A, IP/ Information Technology or employment. Opportunities for property lawyers are increasing. Those for litigators are more limited.

Having said this, much of a candidate's success has to do with attitude. Because teams are small, employers are very keen to find the right "fit" and this factor will often take precedence over experience. Commercial awareness is clearly an important attribute which can be cultivated by keeping abreast of developments in industry-related publications such as the Financial Times, the Wall Street Journal, Commercial Lawyer and International Financial Law Review. In addition to this, candidates must be able to demonstrate an interest and understanding of the in-house environment. They must be able to communicate effectively with business people to help effect transactions and have enough gravitas to be able to say "no" to over-eager businessmen and manage risk effectively. The ability to handle a variety of issues and feel comfortable working on new or unfamiliar matters is an asset.

Salaries for newly qualifieds

Chambers recruitment consultancy has conducted a survey of salaries in private practice, industry and banking. The results are set out in the following tables.

LARGE CITY FIRMS (60+ partners)

Date of Qualification	Average Salary
September 1999	£33,000 - £35,000
September 1998	£36,000 - £38,000
September 1997	£42,000 - £44,000
September 1996	£48,000 - £51,000
September 1995	£53,000 - £56,000
September 1994	£58,000 - £60,000
September 1993	£62,000 - £72,000
September 1992	£65,000 - £84,000

There has been publicity generated by the continued growth of US firms paying salaries far in excess of City market rates. The reality, however, is that the large firms clearly have not felt under pressure to respond. The numbers being recruited by the US firms are still small.

However, one large firm introduced a discretionary bonus scheme enabling their staff to earn a bonus of up to 30% of salary. This has generated considerable debate in the market. Several firms are said to be considering a similar move. It is unclear, however, whether this will become a trend.

MEDIUM CITY FIRMS (20 to 60 partners)

Date of Qualification	Average Salary
September 1999	£31,000 - £33,000
September 1998	£35,000 - £37,000
September 1997	£38,000 - £40,000
September 1996	£43,000 - £48,000
September 1995	£46,000 - £52,000
September 1994	£51,000 - £55,000
September 1993	£56,000 - £65,000

The figures in this table do not apply to those leading medium-sized firms which pay salaries in line with the large firms (see Table 1 above). Indeed, a trend this year has been the increasing willingness on the part of some medium-sized firms to pay their best 3-5 year qualified corporate or banking assistants slightly more than the highest salaries in the large City firm table. A small number of medium-sized firms have abandoned salary bands altogether in order to give them the flexibility to retain their own high flyers and attract those from other firms.

SMALL CITY FIRMS (20 partners or fewer)

Date of Qualification	Average Salary
September 1999	£30,000 - £32,000
September 1998	£31,000 - £35,000
September 1997	£35,000 - £37,000
September 1996	£38,000 - £42,000
September 1995	£40,000 - £50,000
September 1994	£47,000 - £55,000
September 1993	£55,000 - £65,000

The ranges in these tables generally reflect the type of work the firm undertakes and the state of the market. Firms with a litigation bias will tend to be at the lower end of each band whilst those with strong corporate and/or property practices will pay salaries at the higher end.

SALARIES IN THE WEST END, HOLBORN & WESTMINSTER

The majority of firms in these locations undertake their annual salary reviews in Autumn rather than Spring/Summer. We have, therefore, only calculated the figures based on those firms that undertook reviews in Spring/Summer. These figures show a 3-5% increase, which is in line with the City firm reviews. It is likely that those firms carrying out salary reviews in Autumn will also follow this trend.

Larger West End & Holborn firms (20 partners or more)

Date of Qualification	Average Salary
September 1999	£30,000 - £33,000
September 1998	£31,000 - £35,000
September 1997	£33,000 - £40,000
September 1996	£40,000 - £45,000
September 1995	£45,000 - £50,000
September 1994	£50,000 - £55,000
September 1993	£60,000 - £63,000
Salaried Partner	£60,000 - £100,000

Smaller West End & Holborn firms (20 partners or fewer)

Date of Qualification	Average Salary
September 1999	£23,000 - £30,000
September 1998	£25,000 - £31,000
September 1997	£32,000 - £34,000
September 1996	£35,000 - £38,000
September 1995	£36,000 - £41,000
Salaried Partner	£45,000 - £70,000

Westminster firms

Date of Qualification	Average Salary
September 1999	£29,000 - £31,000
September 1998	£31,000 - £33,000
September 1997	£34,000 - £36,000
September 1996	£37,000 - £40,000
September 1995	£40,000 - £44,000
September 1994	£44,000 - £50,000
September 1993	£50,000 - £56,000
Salaried Partner	£50,000 - £75,000

At the time of writing there is a commercial property boom. Those commercial property solicitors who qualified in September 1997 or before will therefore attract the higher salaries in each band.

Senior solicitors will only earn salaries at the high end of the scale if they have developed or are starting to develop their own client following.

[Tables reproduced from 'Private Practice in London: Salary Survey' by kind permission of Chambers and Partners Recruitment Consultants.]

US FIRMS IN LONDON

Firms Paying 'Mid-Atlantic' Salaries

Date of Qualification	Average Salary
September 1998	£40,000 - £50,000
September 1997	£45,000 - £56,000
September 1996	£52,000 - £60,000
September 1995	£55,000 - £67,000

These are the US firms that pay salaries mid-way between City and New York salaries, i.e. a premium of 20-30% on City salaries.

Due to increasing competition from those US firms paying New York salaries (see table 8 below) some are considering increasing their salaries further.

Benefits packages (including pension contribution) tend to match those of the large City firms and holiday is usually 25 days.

Firms Paying New York Salaries

Date of Qualification	Average Salary
September 1998	£60,000 - £70,000
September 1997	£70,000 - £75,000
September 1996	£80,000 - £85,000
September 1995	£85,000 - £90,000
September 1994	£97,000
September 1993	£99,000
September 1992	£100,000

These firms pay the highest salaries in London, which at a junior level can mean a premium of up to 100% on City salaries.

At the time of writing there are about ten such US firms recruiting English qualified solicitors. Whilst they are recruiting steadily, they are not yet the most active recruiters of English solicitors.

Most do not make pension contributions. Holidays are usually 20 days as opposed to 23-27 days offered by most City firms. Several have told us, however, that they are reviewing their holiday entitlement. There has been greater dissatisfaction than they had anticipated in the London market at the prospect of shorter holidays.

QUALIFYING IN OTHER JURISDICTIONS

In an increasingly competitive international legal and business world, many lawyers view dual or foreign qualification as a desirable addition to their professional skill-set, enabling them to offer a broader and more comprehensive service.

Becoming an English Solicitor

Lawyers from Europe, Africa, the Caribbean and Australasia are among the main groups of overseas professionals who annually seek to add their name to the Roll of Solicitors of England and Wales.

The QLTT (The Qualified Lawyers Transfer Test) is a Law Society accredited conversion test that permits lawyers qualified in selected countries outside the UK, as well as UK barristers to retrain and requalify as solicitors. The test covers four heads: Property, Litigation, Principles of Common Law and finally Professional Conduct and Accounts.

The Law Society determines which heads candidates must pass, dependent on their primary professional qualification. Candidates need to apply for a certificate of eligibility from the Law Society before applying to sit the test. Foreign qualified lawyers will usually have to pass sections of the test in conjunction with a two year experience requirement, although this may be reduced if they have already completed an 'articles-style' training scheme overseas.

A full list of jurisdictions that fall under the umbrella of the Qualified Lawyers Transfer Regulations (QLTR) and the appropriate subjects and experience requirements can be obtained from The Law Society or via their website.

Contact: The Law Society, 113 Chancery Lane, London WC2A 1PL, Tel: (020) 7242 1222 www.lawsoc.org.uk

The Law Society confirms the following types of previous experience which may be taken into account during the application process. Evidence of dates, written confirmation from employers or head of chambers etc. need to be submitted with any application:

- Up to 12 months pupillage certified as satisfactory by the pupil master.
- Any period spent in practice at the Bar (i.e. – tenancy or squatting).
- Any period spent in legal employment in the office of a solicitor or lawyer in private practice.
- Any period spent in legal employment with the Crown Prosecution Service or with the Magistrates/Court Service.
- Any period spent in legal employment in the Civil Service, Local Government, a public authority, commerce or industry, provided that the employment is in a legal department which is headed by a solicitor, barrister or lawyer of at least 5 years standing.

For barristers, the experience must have been gained in England, Wales or Northern Ireland. Experience gained overseas may count if it occurred in a common law jurisdiction and, in all cases, should be within the last 5 years.

Any unusual requests which do not fit into the above category requirements are usually considered by the Transfer Casework Committee.

Test and Study Providers

There are two official test 'providers' – recognised educational establishments offering the examination service and preparatory training and tuition courses. The Law Society refer potential participants to both.

The College Of Law administers and runs the

test. It also offers a range of preliminary tuition options to prepare candidates for examination. These fall under three different categories: Distance Learning Courses, Evening Lectures/ Weekend Courses and Revision Sessions.

Contact: The QLTT Department, The College Of Law, Braboeuf Manor, St Catherine's, Guildford GU3 1HA. Tel: (01483) 460 225

BPP Law School runs the test twice yearly after focused study courses and sessions on key areas. Face to face methods or distance learning are available.

Contact: Ruth Cohen, QLTT Manager, BPP, 67-69 Lincoln's Inn Fields, London WC2A 3JB. Tel: (020) 7430 2304

Qualifying as a Scottish lawyer

Qualified solicitors from England and Wales seeking to practice in Scotland firstly need to be fully admitted to the Roll in England and Wales. A certificate of good standing is required from the Law Society to The Law Society of Scotland.

There are no structured preparatory lectures or organised tuition programmes for the inter-UK transfer test held in Edinburgh, an examination consisting of three two-hour papers. The Law Society of Scotland and Strathclyde University administer and oversee a home study programme, providing learning texts and communication support.

On successful completion of the transfer test, solicitors will be eligible to be admitted to the Roll of Scottish solicitors, and can thereby practice freely. A £250 administration fee is required, payable to The Law Society of Scotland. Additionally, examination fees are charged at £50 each.

Contact: The Law Society Of Scotland, 26 Drumsheugh Gardens, Edinburgh EH3 7YR. Tel: (0131) 226 7411, Fax: (0131) 225 2934

The US Bar

Qualification at one of the US Bars permits solicitors to practice in the US as attorneys or to represent US clients in the UK. Some feel this makes them more marketable to the growing number of US firms based in London and beyond. City Of London law firms based in New York may also look favourably upon this additional qualification.

There are only a small number of course providers authorised in the UK to prepare for and administer the examination. Central Law Training is a Birmingham-based legal education and training organisation. The New York Bar lecture programme and examinations are conducted from their London facilities. To be eligible for the NY Bar exam you must hold a 3 year full-time or 4 year part-time LLB degree qualification. There is the option of a five-month lecture programme or home study course. The former is the more popular option as it allows close contact and communication with the lecturer and other course students.

A California Bar programme is also offered, although less interest has been shown in this, as it additionally requires 12 months experience in practice as a solicitor and is only available via the home study method.

NY Bar exams are conducted twice yearly. The lecture programme commencing in February prepares for a bar exam in July and a September lecture programme leads to final examination the following February. Lectures take place on Friday evenings and Saturdays (drinkers and socialites beware!) at the Cafe Royal on Regent Street.

Pass rates on the lecture programme run at around 70-80%. Bar-Bri legal texts are used, the preparatory papers used by most US students. Central Law are also considering a placement scheme where all participants spend 4 weeks with a US law firm, although this remains embryonic at this stage.

Contact: Central Law College, Wrens Court, 52-54 Victoria Road, Sutton Coldfield, B72

1SX. Tel: (0121) 362 7703

Costs : Lecture Programme – £2300 + VAT. Home Study Course – £2600 + VAT

The University of Holborn also offers two courses in preparation for the New York Bar Exam. Students must have completed the equivalent of a three year degree course, based on English common law, at a recognised law school or university. Students can opt for the eight week review course or part-time fifteen week course, both of which take place at the college in London on Friday evenings and at weekends, preparing them for the twice-yearly examinations in New York.

The review course covers an eight week period starting in October for the February examinations or in March for the July examinations. The courses are held on weekends. Students are taught by qualified American attorneys, many of whom were initially UK barristers and several of whom practise in New York.

Contact: University Of Holborn, 200 Greyhound Road, London W14 9RY. Tel: (020) 7385 3377. Fax: (020) 7381 3377
www.holborncollege.ac.uk

Any eligibility queries can be addressed to the New York State Board of Examiners, 7 Executive Centre Drive, Albany, New York 12203, USA.

Qualifying as an Australian Solicitor

Increasingly, the sun-drenched climate and laid-back charm of Australia offers an attractive alternative to over-stressed northern hemisphere professionals seeking a lifestyle-driven career change. Australia's federal system supports several states with different legal jurisdictions and varying rules governing admission requirements to the professional bodies of solicitors and barristers.

Below, we provide brief information for one popular choice – the state of New South Wales incorporating the principal city of Sydney. Contact details for solicitors professional associations in Victoria and Queensland are also listed.

In New South Wales, a person is admitted as a Legal Practitioner to the Supreme Court of New South Wales and, once they have obtained a practising certificate from the state's Law Society, they are free to practice as a solicitor or barrister.

The Legal Practitioners Admission Board is the appropriate admitting authority in New South Wales and is responsible for administering the application process. English solicitors are required to apply for admission under Rule 100 of the Legal Practitioners Transitional Admission Rules 1994, which advises as to the requirements for transfer.

These requirements may necessitate further academic and practical legal training, although certain academic exemption clauses and practical exemptions exist dependent upon prior qualifications and relevant work experience. These courses can be studied at either the Legal Practitioners Admission Board itself or various educational establishments in New South Wales. A series of fees for registration, processing, admission etc. are payable to the Board for its services.

Contact: The Legal Practitioners Admission Board, Level 4 ADC Elizabeth Building, Corner King and Elizabeth Streets, Sydney, NSW 2000, Australia. Tel: +61 2 9392 0300. Fax: +61 2 9392 0315

Contact: The Law Society of New South Wales, 170 Philip Street, Sydney, NSW 2000, Australia. Tel: + 61 2 9926 0333 Fax: + 61 2 9231 5809. www.lawsocnsw.asn.au. Email: lawsociety@lawsocnsw.asn.au

Contact: Law Institute Of Victoria, 470 Bourke St, Melbourne, Victoria 3000, Australia. Tel: + 61 3 9607 9311. Fax: + 61 3 9602 5270. www.liv.asn.au

Contact: Queensland Law Society Inc. Law Society House, 179 Ann St, Brisbane, Queensland 4000, Australia. Tel: + 61 7 3842 5888. Fax: + 61 7 3842 5999. www.qls.com.au

ALTERNATIVE CAREERS FOR LAW STUDENTS AND QUALIFIED LAWYERS

Even in a 'bull' market where there are plenty of jobs available, supply of law graduates and lawschool graduates will always outstrip demand. Not all are able to obtain training contracts or pupillages and not all want to. However, the skills acquired from a legal training provide a head start in a wide range of graduate jobs. Many employers favour law students even for positions with no legal dimension. They value a proven intellectual ability, an eye for detail, and the ability to identify salient points within complex issues.

Below we outline a selection of the possible alternative careers available to someone with a legal training.

Corporate Finance

Corporate finance is an attractive industry option for law graduates seeking a high-powered corporate career. A highly commercial outlook is essential to counter any preconceptions by employers about the pedantic nature of lawyers.

There are two stages at which a career change is most easily instigated. The first is immediately after graduation. Most large investment and merchant banks run structured graduate recruitment programmes. Completion of the CPE and/or LPC is not necessarily limiting, although some organisations express a concern that the commencement of legal training may raise questions over commitment to a corporate career.

Elizabeth Fisher, training and recruitment consultant at Dutch merchant bank ABN-Amro received 900 applications for 24 graduate jobs this year. She welcomes applicants from any discipline. Numeracy is a prerequisite. 'Law students are desirable, especially those with corporate finance skills and commercial documentation skills.'

The other option is to qualify as a lawyer and obtain a couple of years PQE. Recruitment to banks and financial institutions at this stage occurs on an ad-hoc basis. Related commercial experience in a City firm is highly sought after.

Corporate financiers require high levels of numeracy and law students will be competing with graduates from conventional maths and science backgrounds, a point underlined by the recruitment manager at top investment bank, Schroders. 'We receive many applications from graduates with straight law degrees. They tend to have very strong analytical skills, good communication skills and a thorough knowledge of legal documentation in a 'deal-driven' environment.'

Banking

Transaction Management

Most large international banks employ teams of legal workers, usually in capital markets and derivatives. They will typically work alongside lawyers as part of documentation teams, assisting and supporting the completion of the deals. This is a competitive but potentially very lucrative career option. There are few structured entry routes into this specialisation. Law school LPC training and/or an LLM in international finance might be a relevant starting point, although recruitment would always be based on individual-led non specific criteria.

Compliance

Most major banks and financial institutions contain legal departments that have a compliance section. The head of legal services may also be head of compliance, for example. Such in-house legal departments offer a structured career path for those with a keen interest and superior abilities in banking. A career could start as an assistant monitoring internal banking rules and checking that external regulations are complied with. This may be fairly routine initially, but experience and career development provides greater scope for involvement in strategic issues. Senior managers at compliance departments in major international banks are highly paid.

General - Graduate
Numerous other opportunities are available to law graduates in the training programmes run by the majority of domestic and international banks. NatWest bank run two annual graduate schemes, regular management and Information Technology/analyst. Both receive large numbers of applicants from both law graduates, and indeed some qualified solicitors. The head of Information Technology graduate recruitment at NatWest recently took on a 1/2 year qualified solicitor as an analyst. Amongst other skills she had 'superb attention to detail'. No specific Information Technology degree is required.

Accountancy / Tax / Management Consultancy

The large accountancy and consulting firms offer many similar advantages to the big City law firms and represent an increasingly popular option. All offer structured graduate training in a wide choice of disciplines (including auditing, tax, actuarial, corporate finance, Information Technology and management consultancy). In addition they offer the chance of overseas placements, respectable remuneration and plenty of opportunities for career development. They also offer varied high-quality work with blue chip clients, and often have a strong legal dimension, with a growing international trend towards affiliation with law firms. The 'Big Five' firms offer many more places than even the largest law firms, and have many regional offices.

Laurence Youngman graduated from UCL with a degree in law. Having realised that the law was not for him, and that he'd "reached the limit for full time study," he still wanted to work in a career where he could utilise his nascent legal skills. On the recommendation of a friend he investigated the option of doing tax consultancy at an accountancy firm and liked what he saw. He is now working in tax investigation at Arthur Andersen, where he enjoys the intellectual and adversarial challenges of the work, and has many opportunities to utilise his academic training. "Everything in tax derives from statute and case law, so there is a lot of legal interpretation."

Trainees study for exams leading to professional qualifications in one of the main disciplines (usually in tax or auditing). This opportunity to combine work and study straight after graduation was another factor in Laurence Youngman's decision to switch from law. "I just wanted to be out there, training on the job." Accountancy qualifications (ACA or ATII) are highly recognised in the business world, giving trainees a wide variety of options on qualification.

Contacts:
Arthur Andersen - Corinne Dubedat, Graduate Recruitment, 1 Surrey Street, London WC2R 2PS. **Tel** - 0500 592800. **Web** - www.arthurandersen.co.uk/careers

Deloitte & Touche - Deborah Black, Deloitte & Touche, Hill House, 1 Little New Street, London EC4A 3TR. **Tel** - 0800 323333. **Web** - www.graduate.deloitte.co.uk

Ernst & Young - Vanessa van den Bergh, Ernst & Young, Becket House, 1 Lambeth Palace Road, London SE1 7EU. **Tel** - 0800 289208. **Web** - www.eyuk.com

KPMG - Mrs Jane Brundle, Graduate Recruitment KPMG, 1 Puddle Dock, Blackfriars, London EC4B 0BL. **Tel** - 0171 3112789. **Web** - www.kpmgcareers.co.uk

PricewaterhouseCoopers - (contact central number to find out branch details) **Tel** - 0808 1001500. **Web** - www.pwcglobal.com/uk/graduate_careers/

Stock Exchange / LIFFE

Despite the transfer of regulatory authority from the Stock Exchange and LIFFE to the Financial Services Authority (FSA), both institutions have in the past recruited graduates and lawyers to certain key positions within the organisations, and may continue to do so in the future.

There are key roles available for lawyers to assist

with the listing of stocks on the exchange, check that yellow book requirements are satisfied and communicate with top City firms. There are constant ongoing regulatory issues to advise on but also individual investigations such as insider trading and irregularities on the trading floor. Teams of lawyers in the exchanges will monitor and check these activities and react to complaints from public members. Although junior clerical roles may be occasionally available to unqualified law graduates, Kathryn Bull, personnel manager at the Stock Exchange, generally recruits 'qualified lawyers with 2-3 yrs PQE. We would take them on for positions in the market regulation, investigation and compliance sections, on an ad-hoc basis.'

The Stock Exchange also has a general, unstructured graduate recruitment intake recruited on a demand basis. They look for good academics and usually at least one year's industrial/corporate experience, gained either at university or after. Second jobbers, perhaps those with some legal experience, are also welcome to apply.

IT/Contracts Management

Many large software and hardware companies, such as Compaq, Dell and IBM negotiate huge commercial contracts for sales and distribution deals. These organisations usually contain dedicated contracts departments and/or in-house legal teams. They may take on law graduates, LPC- trained but not necessarily qualified, to work in tandem with the sales force drawing up contracts within certain parameters. The work can be 'glamorous' and international involving travel to high-tech areas of the globe such as the United States and the Asia Pacific region. Contracts professionals are highly sought after and well-paid. The positions may have the potential to lead into a formal offer of sponsorship through a training contract or an in-house position. It goes without saying that commercial acumen and an interest and understanding of Information Technology are essential.

Legal Marketing

Opportunities to enter legal marketing have expanded significantly as increasing numbers of firms develop their marketing capabilities to compete with the already established departments in larger City firms. Claire Forbes, public relations manager at the Chartered Institute of Marketing receives a large number of enquiries from law and business graduates seeking to enter the field. 'We have a dedicated careers service handling these enquiries and specialists in legal marketing who can give advice.'

There are three main strands to the work of legal marketing departments;

• strategic business development

• communication (PR, internal communications, events, publications, web-site development, press enquiries)

• research/analysis

All are viable career options for law students and professionals although the communications dimension is likely to appeal to those with a business/marketing/ sales background. Lawyers may also find there are opportunities to work in marketing in a research/analytical capacity.

The CIM administers the most widely recognised professional qualification for graduates, the PostGraduate Diploma in marketing. This is a one year full time course that provides a solid theoretical underpinning. This can be done by students themselves, although increasingly, law firms such as Herbert Smith are taking high calibre graduates and sponsoring them through the course on a two year part time basis.

John Hilsdon, a legal marketing consultant at the CIM believes most of the opportunities for graduates are away from the big commercial departments. 'The trend is increasingly for small and medium practices to grow their marketing departments.' Marketing and business skills are nearly always preferred over legal abilities. 'Its a question of stepping away from legality,' says John Hilsdon. 'At an earlier age, they're less likely to have been moulded into a legal mindset.' This does not preclude law students from becoming marketers although entering at post - law school/training contract stage may raise questions over commitment and ability to be effective.

Legal Teaching / Academic

Opportunities are available for those with legal qualifications to teach at the major legal educational establishments - universities and former polytechnics, The College of Law and other private course providers. Qualifying and experience criteria differ substantially, however, so be aware of academic and practical requirements.

The College of Law usually recruits only qualified solicitors or barristers as course tutors. Stella Smith, head of marketing for the Guildford branch says 'many of our lecturers and tutors start in their late twenties and bring with them a couple of years commercial experience after qualification before entering the teaching profession.' The College offers a basic foundation skills teaching course for lawyers to adapt their knowledge to the educational environment. There are a limited number of research and admin. assistants, maybe 5/6 in each school, assisting the qualified lecturers. Qualification is not a prerequisite for these positions, many are acquiring academic experience post-university before moving onto training contracts.

Academic institutions such as traditional universities and former polytechnics are far less likely to take on qualified solicitors for lecturing positions. A conventional academic route is most frequently followed which will usually involve postgraduate research at least to LLM level. Early planning at university undergraduate level is essential.

Political Researcher

Opportunities exist in The House Of Commons and Whitehall for research and assistant positions with MPs, peers and other government departments. The aptitudes and skills of law students are particularly in demand. Salaries paid from MPs' staff allocations are often quite low, but the lure and glamour of Westminster's political machinery is a big drawcard. Entry routes are typically informal and unstructured, work experience and contacts usually provide the best leads. Writing to local MPs is a well-tried strategy. The internal magazine for Westminster staff, The House Magazine (available through the Parliamentary Information Unit) frequently carries vacancy classifieds.

Government and Public Affairs

Government and public affair consultancies, otherwise known as political lobbying organisations, are a very specialised branch of public relations dealing with clients seeking to expand their political profile and influence government legislation. The nature of the work - very close monitoring of legislation and official documentation lends itself to the skill-set of legal minds. Jeremy Galbraith, senior manger at Burson-Marsteller government and public affairs, one of London's largest agencies, believes lawyers are well-placed to succeed, 'I studied law myself; obviously many of the skills are similar as it involves scrutiny of parliament.' He added 'it's unlikely we would take on a law graduate straight from university unless they had related experience, such as working for an MP as a researcher.'

There are about thirty public affairs agencies located in London close to the corridors of political power. Many have Brussels offices. Fewer opportunities exist in Edinburgh and Cardiff. The work is very specialised and the firms are small so few run organised graduate programmes, but openings are there for ambitious individuals with related experience.

Information Management

Most law firms contain information and library departments where personnel are employed as information managers / officers, database managers and librarians. It is a growing professional area as information and communication technology continues to expand its role in business.

Michael Martin, careers advisor at the Library Association's information section describes an increasingly common career option, 'someone with a first law degree could do a one year postgraduate degree or diploma in information management and then has the opportunity to be employed by a law firm as an information officer.'

Several educational and academic institutions run full time (1 year) or part-time (2 year) courses in librarianship/information management. Specialist recruitment agencies will recruit professionals at various stages of experience into private practice or commercial in-house legal departments as information officers / managers. INFOmatch, linked to the Library Association's commercial section are one prominent agency.

Contact :
The Library Association / INFOmatch
7 Ridgmount St
London
WC1E 7AE
Tel - 0207 525 0500

Legal Recruitment

FRES (the Federation of Recruitment Employment Services), one of the recruitment industry's professional bodies and regulators estimate that the industry as a whole is worth $16bn annually to the UK economy and is growing at almost 12% a year. High-end professional recruitment is increasingly seen as a career of choice for ambitious commercially minded graduates. The experience, contacts and industry knowledge that lawyers can bring to niche agencies marks legal recruitment out as an obvious choice for career changers.

London is home to approximately 20 good legal recruitment agencies while the major legal centres of the north, Manchester and Leeds, also offer expanding possibilities. Salaries in sales-driven environments can sometimes be high.

Company Secretary

The Institute of Chartered Secretaries and Administrators (ICSA) qualification provides a good alternative to training as a solicitor or barrister. A career as a Company Secretary is ideally suited to those with a background in legal studies and can lead to a broad and fulfilling commercial role in industry, private practice, charities or the public sector.

Company Secretaries occupy a key role in commercial businesses at a time when public and political concern about corporate governance, ethics, accountability and good practice is at an all-time high. To succeed in this role it is essential to be able to keep abreast of current legislation, regulation and best practice. A good company secretary will be authoritative, able to identify potential problems, understand the issues and have the expertise to provide the right solutions, he or she will help to keep their organisation on track, in order for it to prosper and develop.

The Companies Act requires every UK registered company to appoint a Company Secretary, the post holder for a public company having to be suitably qualified, usually as an ICSA qualified chartered secretary, or as a lawyer or accountant. The Board of Directors will appoint the company secretary and will look to that person for advice and guidance, and will rely upon that persons expertise to ensure various statutory duties and obligations are fulfilled.

The role of the Company Secretary will vary according to the size and nature of the employer but it generally includes - providing advice to directors and employees on company law matters and corporate governance, compliance issues, company administration (e.g. - the AGM), reports and accounts, legal - negotiating, drafting and records maintenance.

The ICSA offers a professional qualification that is practical and vocational. Unlike the LPC and BVC courses, it is usual to find a role as a trainee company secretary first and commence working (and therefore earning!) in your chosen field before qualifying. Employers will usually fund the ICSA course / exam fees and provide study leave. Full qualification is usually achieved in two years. Salaries are moderate to high, increasing with seniority and plc's will generally pay more than limited companies.

Trade Mark Attorneys

Full or partially trained barristers and solicitors are very attractive propositions for firms of

Trade Mark Attorneys. The work involves instructions from a client typically with a new product, the name or emblem of which is likely to need protection worldwide. The vocational training takes at least two years and as with the related work of EPAs, it requires great attention to detail and an ability to deal with large amounts of information quickly and efficiently. Contact the Institute of Trade Mark Attorneys Tel (0208) 686 2052.

European Patent Attorneys

EPAs act for clients in an international arena, obtaining, protecting and dealing with patents for their clients' inventions. Advocacy opportunities include tribunals of the European Patent Office and, domestically, the UK Patents Office and Patents County Courts. Richard Williams of Hepworth Lawrence Bryer & Bizley confirmed that firms like his do recruit legally trained individuals as trainee EPAs. "Candidates need a good 2.1 degree in a science or engineering subject and the ability to understand a broad range of technical matters. It's not for the faint hearted as it takes on average, up to five years to become fully qualified. The rewards are likely to more than compensate though." For further information contact the Chartered Institute of Patent Attorneys Tel (0207) 405 9450 www.cipa.org.uk

Alternative Routes To Obtaining Training Contracts

There are several junior alternatives to becoming a solicitor, which depending on your ultimate objective, can act as a stepping stone or 'back-door route' to obtaining a training contract or as fulfilling and rewarding career options in their own right.

Paralegal Work

Paralegal posts in private practice and local authorities are often filled by law students who have done their LPC but failed to secure training contracts. The work is usually administrative, often helping with discovery in large litigation matters, but paralegals sometime undertake the same work as trainees. It can be a useful insight into different firms. Increasingly, companies with in-house legal departments are taking on paralegals - this occasionally has the potential to develop into a structured training contract.

Legal Executive

An obvious alternative to becoming as solicitor is to become a legal executive for a law firm or for an in-house legal department. Responsibility levels are lower which may suit some people, and occasional progression to articled trainee status may be possible - although it must be said this is rare. Positions arise mainly in litigation, conveyancing or probate. Senior legal executives can expect a good level of remuneration but cannot become a partner in a private practice firm. Legal secretarial work may be an option for those with good office and organisational skills. Pay is relatively high compared to other secretarial and clerical positions.

Licensed Conveyancer

This is less frequently undertaken option for law graduates, but another available option nonetheless. Opportunities exist for freelance work, or with a local authority, an in-house department or a private practice firm.

Outdoor Clerk

This vital and important role is a key way of acquiring hands-on legal experience. Tasks usually include delivering documents to court and barristers chambers, lodging and sealing documents with the appropriate court office, attending hearings before masters on administrative issues and taking notes during proceedings. Although the smooth, sharp-suited wide-boy image lingers, outdoor clerks are well respected by firms lawyers and it represents a very practical means of gaining insights into the working of the courts and the machinery of the legal system. If it is your intention to progress on to a training contract, some background research into the policy and attitude of the firm would be advisable.

PRO BONO

Pro bono work is the provision of legal services for free. It can range from community legal work (to meet some of the need not covered by legal aid) to business start-up work to human rights work such as Caribbean 'death row' cases. Says Yasmin Waljee, pro bono coordinator at Lovells, "at the end of the day, we all become lawyers – even if we work on major transactions – to help people, to try and give something back to the community."

Many students who are attracted to the high status, well-paid and demanding life of a City commercial lawyer also have a social conscience and are keen to use their legal skills for the common good. Pro bono work provides trainees or pupils with this opportunity.

Law Firms

While solicitors often argue that pro bono has always been an integral part of their work, the larger firms are becoming involved on a more organised level. In addition to internal pressure from lawyers keen to get involved, there are now external pressure from clients who may only instruct firms who undertake pro bono work. Firms are increasingly realising that there are side benefits to be gained from this work. Apart from intangible advantages such as creating a more balanced lifestyle and increasing morale, pro bono work also gives commercial lawyers, and in particular trainees, experience in areas of law and situations they would often otherwise never see. Linklaters, for example, has recently started taking out cases from the Free Representation Unit to give advocacy experience to lawyers from partner down to trainee level. City trainees who work in legal advice centres are often grateful for the direct client contact and responsibility this work provides.

City pro bono initiatives

Eight of the top twenty City firms have now appointed specific pro bono co-ordinators. These are Lovells, Linklaters, Clifford Chance, Freshfields, Allen & Overy, Herbert Smith, Simmons & Simmons and Slaughter and May. According to Yasmin Waljee at a larger firm "you have a much better opportunity of getting involved if the firm does have a coordinator" because centralised organisation leads to more effective use of resources and targeting of work. In many of these firms, lawyers in different departments can use specialist skills. At Lovells, for example, the banking department assists with setting up and running community credit unions, while the environmental department is assisting with a millennium funded project to establish Britain's first solar-powered pub.

At City firms, pro bono work comes from a wide variety of sources, ranging from law centres and charities through to partners' and clients' own initiatives. At A&O, the pro bono coordinator believes that the most effective system is to "partner up with grass roots charities, who have the expertise. We can use them; they can use us." One example of such direct targeting is their Business on Board scheme, which places business lawyers on the boards of small to medium sized charities.

Co-ordination also ensures that pro bono work is given priority. As Richard Dyton at Simmons & Simmons puts it, "if a trainee is down to go to Battersea legal advice centre on a Monday night, and a senior assistant wants 300 pages copied, that's not on." With the exception of evening advice work, most pro bono work is done on the firm's time. As Yasmin Waljee points out "how can a firm take credit for something that someone does in their own private time. If someone shows a sense of community spirit outside office hours it has nothing to do with the firm."

As a trainee at a firm with a strong pro bono commitment, you can get involved in a wide variety of work. Many run legal advice centres, and set up seminars for interested trainees to enable them to give advice on housing, employment and assorted everyday legal queries. You can also get involved in larger pro bono cases that your department may have taken on. The litigation department at Allen & Overy, for example, does a lot of work for Liberty. As a litigation trainee you may find yourself working on a major human rights test case.

Another common role for trainees is to handle small claims matters for charities, consumer groups and law centres. Apart from the advocacy experience and the sense of fulfilment gained, such work can often be unusual, to say the least. One Lovells trainee was amazed to find himself in court defending a client in a breach of contract claim against an irate organiser of a mail order bride service "complete with mullet, big sheepskin coat and Dirty Harry shades." After trying to intimidate the judge in court, it later emerged that the plaintiff had threatened his client that if he contested the case he would command aliens to beam him up.

Death Row Work

One area of particular interest to aspiring trainees is Privy Council death row work. With some exceptions, such as the Soho crime and media practice Simons Muirhead & Burton, it is mainly City firms who undertake these cases as they are very expensive, and often time consuming. All the firms involved are organised onto panels, with A&O coordinating the Jamaica panel, Lovells in charge of Trinidad and Tobago, and Simons Muirhead & Burton coordinating Belize cases.

Human rights lawyers have long been involved in this area, stemming both from their opposition to the death penalty and from their concerns about the quality of justice in the areas concerned. As the Privy Council remains the final appeal court for these jurisdictions, it is open to lawyers in this country to apply to it for stays of execution and for leave to appeal against sentences. A system has thus built up whereby prisoners on death row in these jurisdictictions write requesting assistance and the relevant panel coordinator will hand out their case to one of the firms on their panel.

The role of the solicitor who takes on the case is to coordinate with criminal counsel and to prepare the petition. This involves reading through the original trial transcripts to find any procedural errors or problems with the evidence, and preparing a case. As this necessitates a grounding in criminal law, it is mainly assistant solicitors and partners who undertake this work, in coordination with counsel. Trainees will assist with research and administration.

If there is evidence of a procedural error or of wrongful conviction, the case will be presented before the Privy Council, sitting in Downing Street. If leave to appeal is granted, the firm will run the full appeal. This is a challenging task, involving coordination with lawyers in the relevant jurisdiction and the panel's own employed clerks to get new affidavits from the prisoners and to collate new evidence. As at the leave stage, the appeal will be heard at Downing Street, with counsel providing advocacy.

Death row work can be hard and often emotionally draining. Much of it, such as applying for stays of execution, is last minute, involving late nights and plenty of urgent phone calls to the Caribbean. However it is also incredibly stimulating. Apart from the obvious satisfaction gained when you manage to succesfully overturn a death sentence, you also get the chance to work with top counsel in the human rights field, who also give their time for free. Occasionally, the work can also be groundbreaking, with a recent Trinidad case leading to a change in the way international law can impact on domestic law.

The Bar

At the bar, coordinated pro bono work is more established, and intending barristers have long been involved with the Free Representation Unit. FRU provides representation for people who cannot afford it at employment tribunals, social security tribunals and disability appeal tribunals. All intending representatives must attend a training day and undertake a period of 'seconding'. CPE and third year law students can take out cases in the latter two tribunals, while employment tribunal representation is open to

BVC/LPC students. It is important to note that most FRU work is London-based, and all representatives need to be able to visit the London office two or three times a week.

FRU reps pick up case papers from solicitors or advice agencies with the hearing date already set, and will have sole conduct of the case from that moment on. They may have to prepare the bundles for an employment tribunal or get further evidence in a disability appeal tribunal. As Danny Shapiro, pupil at 2 Crown Office Row and current chairman of the FRU explains, both representative and represented benefit from the arrangement. "It is a massive help to people who otherwise face a daunting tribunal, requiring detailed knowledge of the law which they do not possess. And its a great experience for the representative in dealing with all stages of the case, in particular advocacy before a tribunal."

Once barristers are qualified, they are also able to join the panel of the Bar Pro Bono Unit. This charity provides free legal advice and representation across all areas of the law, from planning to personal injury. All barristers who join must do at least three days a year of work provided by the Unit, and the level of its effectiveness was seen at the recent Liberty Human Rights Awards, where barrister Amanda Barrington-Smythe was recognised for her work on a Death Row case, assigned to her by the Unit.

Student pro bono

If you want to get involved in pro bono work before you start your training, you can ask your local law centre or relevant campaign group if they need volunteers. Another opportunity is the FRU (see above). One encouraging development in this area is the College of Law's recent opening of a legal advice centre at its London branch. This scheme, which the College hopes to extend to all its branches from September 2000, gives BVC and LPC students the opportunity to interview clients and provide written legal advice on a variety of legal problems.

Specialist Practice Areas

BANKING
(including Capital Markets & Derivatives)

Area of law

Banking law is essentially concerned with the formation of commercial agreements and contracts between borrowers and lenders. In practice it covers the world of finance from regulatory work to derivatives and securities. A mainstream banking lawyer is concerned with the documentation of lending money. This centres around a loan agreement and the preparation, negotiation and drafting of that document. The work usually involves taking security in favour of the lending bank.

Banking lawyers, while not primarily responsible for the structuring of corporate finance transactions, are actively involved in the form that the documentation relating to the raising of money should take. On a new transaction, the banking lawyer acts as commercial 'dealmaker.' S/he advises and assists on structuring issues, working on the completion of a deal and the eventual drafting and signing of a loan agreement and the security. The deals vary in size and complexity both within firms and between firms but many of the underlying principles are constant.

The area of regulation, largely concerned with financial services generally, continues to increase in scope and importance and provides different opportunities for lawyers who favour an advisory role instead of commercial transactions. It is primarily focused in London.

Type of work

Top level banking work is highly polarised and concentrated in the world financial centres. "You get to work in a handful of glamorous cities like New York, Hong Kong and Paris!" said one senior banking lawyer. Within the UK, there is a chasm between work done by the inner core of top City specialists and other firms. The complexity and value of the transactions are greater at the larger City firms, whose clients tend to be international merchant and investment banks. There are also prominent and reputable national firms based in the northern financial centres such as Addleshaw Booth & Co and Dibb Lupton Alsop.

At the leading City firms with strong banking practices – such as Allen & Overy and Clifford Chance – deals are cutting edge and clients are prestigious. Reflecting the global nature of the practices themselves, top City banking deals can span continents and cover the front pages of the Financial Times. Stephen Lucas at Clifford Chance believes that this creates a "culture of high level support and a great degree of sophistication." Modern technology and the use of precedents frequently means a time-critical deal can be pulled off quickly instead of having to reinvent the wheel every time.

Regional firms with well-developed banking practices see a very different type of work. Their client base may consist of smaller retail banks or building societies. As Richard Papworth from Addleshaw Booth & Co in Leeds explains, "the reality is that you won't see a huge number of multi-billion pound international financings. However the quality of the work can be high and young lawyers have a lot of opportunities to get actively involved."

Banking involves less 'pure law' than other practice areas – "there is more emphasis on the preparation of contracts and the financial side of things than on legality – the satisfaction tends to come from the delivery and completion of projects, seeing something through from start to finish." The work is dominated by transactions but there is a fast turnaround. This can be an attractive feature to those with short attention spans; "you don't get bogged down in things which go on for years. You see things through relatively quickly."

Although perceived as a niche area, banking overlaps with many other disciplines. Invariably lawyers will be involved in financing a range of things – property, corporate acquisitions or a power project for example. Stephen Lucas from Clifford Chance described this spread – "you are very often managing a transaction involving a number of different specialisms. You become the focus for that because you represent the deliverer or the recipient of the finance so you have to manage a large team." Banking is not a support department. It occupies a frontal position facing the clients – the providers of the money.

Among the more complex structured banking transactions, you will touch on a cross-section of almost all basic legal knowledge and will need to know how these areas work. Stephen Lucas describes how it involves a peripheral knowledge of many other areas – "If a company wants to buy another publicly listed company but doesn't have the money to do so, it borrows from banks, it will secure that borrowing on its assets and on the assets of the target company – its shares, its intellectual property and real estate. When the financing and the loan agreement are underway, you need to understand the corporate regime that will allow company A to buy company B because that is what you're funding. Although you're not documenting that corporate sale purchase agreement you need to understand the way it works, because it has to tie in with the financing.'

On a day to day level, banking lawyers operate in small transaction management teams spanning the range of seniority. It is a meeting intensive environment involving a lot of documentation, managing several supporting aspects of the transaction such as the availability of funding. There is a high premium placed on technical ability and judgement. At Addleshaw Booth, juniors would be permitted to handle the documentation for a straight forward bank or building society loan from very early on. More complex transactions require additional experience and supervision but this is an area of law where early responsibility is common. "I love doing what I do," said one young lawyer enthusiastically, "sealing big transactions and negotiating contracts. Banking law is the pivot which allows you do that."

Newly qualified banking lawyers will usually see a good deal of the work – mainly because they will be given a lot of drafting and asked to attend a lot of meetings. This has its rewards: "the interaction with the business world is excellent – banking law gives such a good understanding of financial markets." On a new deal, banking lawyers will assist on structuring issues, give advice and work on the completion of a deal, culminating in the drafting and signing of a loan agreement. One young lawyer summed up the appeal: "I really enjoy the big deals" and contact with "very on the ball clients!"

The lifestyle implications for banking lawyers can be tough and days rarely predictable. One lawyer humorously confirmed its commonly held reputation for long and strenuous hours – "banking could certainly be recognised as being at the stickier end of quality of life," but the pay-off can be huge. "There is so much adrenalin in deal completion." The demands are intensive because of the cyclical nature of transactional management – peaks and troughs rather than core repeat business is the norm. Trevor Borthwick from Allen & Overy estimates 60% of his workload might involve documentation and drafting and 40% client management and meetings, although this can and does change frequently. A normal 50 hour week can easily rise to 75 or 100 hours as a deal nears completion. Working into the early hours is not uncommon, even in the early stages of a career. However, banking lawyers universally speak of the buzz of completing a deal – a major motivational force.

Dedication is a fundamental requirement as transactions vary from the very simple to very complicated ones. Some keep you in the office from 9-6 pm, some keep you there from 9-6 am and you can gravitate towards the type of complexity and deal that suits you – often dependent on the firm or its specialist area. On a public bid financing with a deadline dictated by the share price there will be a huge amount of pressure to get the deal done. As a complex transaction it will require a lot of very hard work over a short, concentrated period of time. Other banking transactions, such as a syndicated loan to a blue-chip corporate, may see the time-table relaxed. In the specialised structured and acquisition finance end of banking law the commitments are greater.

Banking law is definitely placed at the glamorous end of the profession. Certainly, prestigious high finance deals and international travel are common. "The banking lawyer is always more glamorous than his tax counterpart!" said one categorically. Another lawyer enjoyed the travel and exposure to other cultures, "I've been able to travel to Moscow and other exotic cities taking advantage of several working opportunities!" However it is also hard work and you should enter banking law for the right reasons. One lawyer loved his area but was understated and philosophical. "Some people will say there is nothing glamorous about international travel, hotels or getting on the front page of the FT. Sometimes you're exhausted."

There are certain macho stereotypes associated with banking lawyers. The practitioners interviewed were keen to stress that these are unfair caricatures of a small minority. Like the banking profession itself, lawyers are frequently outgoing and dynamic and sometimes exhibit a certain bravado. Trevor Borthwick believes most lawyers are "sober and hardworking." Salary rewards are high, however, and the 'work hard, play hard' maxim is never far from the norm.

Skills needed

Banking is a complex and technical area in which strong practical intelligence and analytical skills are required. A keen interest and understanding of business and international finance is essential. Trevor Borthwick was drawn to the "commercial and intellectual challenges" and "absolutely loves it!" Given the fluctuating nature of the work, other beneficial qualities include the ability to dedicate to the task, to see it through to completion. "Don't enter banking law if your career is fourth on the priority list – you need commitment," stressed a recently qualified City lawyer. "A sense of humour is desirable as well!"

The importance of diligence, accuracy and care cannot be overstated. "If you're careful, you'll make a good banking lawyer," suggests Stephen Lucas. You need to possess the capacity to do routine work in the early stages of a career. Despite high academic pedigree, one City lawyer thought those that could absorb all aspects of the work eventually developed very effective drafting technique. For international finance work, languages can definitely help in overcoming cultural barriers.

Banking regulation lawyers are removed from the cut and thrust of the deal but provide vital advisory services to their clients. These roles draw on different skills and Richard Papworth believes that the regulatory field of banking suits those with more academic inclinations – the provision of advice in this field draws heavily on inter-personal abilities and powers of persuasiveness over the wide range of people at the regulatory authorities.

Career options

Many young lawyers at City firms view banking law as an ideal platform for the financial markets with the potential to open up future doors. There is frequently an overlap and fluidity with the banking world itself. It is relatively common for lawyers with a couple of years PQE to move to an investment banking or corporate finance role. With slightly more legal experience, movement to an in-house legal position within a bank is another common option. However, Stephen Lucas from Clifford Chance warns against making the wrong career move - "If you want to become a banker, become a banker not a lawyer. It's really that simple. Don't spend time at university studying law, CPE, LPC, articles etc. – you'd be a four year qualified banker by the same stage. If you want to be a banking lawyer, but decide it's not for you, there is ample opportunity soon after qualification to move into banking." This is a big-money world. Salary levels in all related areas are similarly placed, if not even higher. Even at very junior levels, secondments to international banks are made available by most firms and can provide a taster of things to come.

The firms

There is no such thing as a 'banking' firm per se. Two City firms, Allen & Overy and Clifford Chance, stand out ahead of the other firms in the sophistication and size of their banking practices. For these firms banking work is the engine driving their international expansion. Clifford Chance is a global law firm with offices all over the world. A banking lawyer here would have the opportunity to be involved in multi-national deals anywhere on the compass. Allen & Overy does not have as many offices worldwide, but lawyers here work on cutting edge deals involving all the latest financing techniques.

There are other City firms which also have highly developed banking practices. Freshfields, for example, has a long history acting for the Bank of England. Its work is therefore often skewed to the regulatory or litigious aspects of the business, although it does also work on large deals. Other notable City firms include Linklaters who have a strong reputation acting for banks and companies, and Lovells who do a lot of work for Barclays.

A recent development in the City has been the advent of the American firms, which are rapidly developing their banking practices. Shearman & Sterling are strong through their US law capability and have a sizeable team handling high finance cross-border European and transatlantic deals.

As expected, the cutting edge banking work is handled by the City firms. However, most of the large commercial regional firms also have banking practices. Much of their work is centred around acting for the major clearing banks. In the main commercial centres such as Leeds, firms also handle high premium transactions although the value of the individual deals is generally smaller.

Key firms include Osborne Clarke in Bristol which handles work for Nat West. Its team is smaller compared to the large City firms – one partner and three assistants – but all are pure transactional lawyers and work full time on deals. In the north, Dibb Lupton Alsop and Addleshaw Booth & Co are among the key regional banking firms with a strong presence in Manchester and Leeds; both have a good reputation for acquisition finance work. In Scotland, Dundas & Wilson CS dominates the scene. It is involved with most of the major transactions in the Scottish market, such as the syndicate lending to Stagecoach Holdings plc to acquire Hong Kong's Citibus group and the Royal Bank of Scotland.

Leading Firms

London	Banking	Capital Markets & Derivatives
Allen & Overy	******	******
Ashurst Morris Crisp	***	*
Baker & McKenzie	*	****
Berwin Leighton	*	
Clifford Chance	******	******
CMS Cameron McKenna	***	
Denton Hall	**	
Dibb Lupton Alsop	*	
Freshfields	*****	******
Gouldens	**	
Hammond Suddards		**
Herbert Smith	***	*
Linklaters	*****	******
Lovells	*****	*****
Macfarlanes	**	
Nabarro Nathanson	*	
Norton Rose	*****	***
Shearman & Sterling	**	
Sidley & Austin		****
Simmons & Simmons	**	****
Slaughter and May	****	***
Stephenson Harwood	**	
Taylor Joynson Garrett	**	
Theodore Goddard	**	
Travers Smith Braithwaite	**	
Watson, Farley & Williams	*	
Weil, Gotshal & Manges	**	****
Wilde Sapte†	****	

† Denton Hall and Wilde Sapte will merge on 1 February 2000

Leading Firms

East Anglia	Banking
Eversheds, Cambridge, Ipswich, Norwich	*****

Midlands	Banking
Dibb Lupton Alsop, Birmingham	**
Edge Ellison, Birmingham	***
Eversheds, Birmingham	****
Gateley Wareing, Birmingham	***
Martineau Johnson, Birmingham	***
Pinsent Curtis, Birmingham	*****
Wragge & Co, Birmingham	*****

North East	Banking
Addleshaw Booth & Co, Leeds	******
Dibb Lupton Alsop, Leeds	****
Dickinson Dees, Newcastle	****
Eversheds, Leeds	*****
Eversheds, Newcastle	**
Garretts, Leeds	***
Hammond Suddards, Leeds	*****
Pinsent Curtis, Leeds	*****
Robert Muckle, Newcastle	**
Walker Morris, Leeds	****
Ward Hadaway, Newcastle	**

South	Banking
Bevan Ashford, Exeter	**
Blake Lapthorn, Fareham	*
Bond Pearce, Bristol, Plymouth,	*****
Bond Pearce, Southhampton	*****
Burges Salmon, Bristol	*****
CMS Cameron McKenna, Bristol	**
Lyons Davidson, Bristol	*
Osborne Clarke, Bristol	******

North West	Banking
Addleshaw Booth & Co, Manc	******
Chaffe Street, Manchester	****
Cobbetts, Manchester	*
Davies Wallis Foyster, Manc	*
Dibb Lupton Alsop, L'pool, Manc	******
Eversheds, Manchester	******
Garretts, Manchester	******
Halliwell Landau, Manchester	******
Hammond Suddards, Manchester	***

Wales	Banking
Eversheds, Cardiff	*****
Morgan Cole, Cardiff	****

Firms and their star ratings are based on Chambers' Directory 1999–2000. Six stars represent a top-ranked firm, five stars a second-ranked firm, etc.

CORPORATE LAW

Area of law

All commercial law firms are keen to be involved in corporate work. Transactions in this area command large fees and receive coverage in the national and regional press. Experienced corporate lawyers are much in demand and are among the highest paid in the profession, earning six figure salaries in some instances.

The core of corporate work relates to mergers and acquisitions (M&A) and corporate restructurings. Requiring large amounts of capital, this type of work is often interdependent with finance (banking and capital markets work) and thus often comes under the umbrella name of corporate finance. Companies fund their acquisitions by a variety of means. They may restructure, disposing of certain assets not considered essential to their core business in order to raise capital. If they are privately held, they may decide to raise finance by 'going public.' This involves an offering of their shares to the public (an equity offering), including institutional investors like pension funds, on any of the public stock exchanges such as the London or New York Stock Exchanges. If they are already public companies, they may make a rights issue (offer of new shares). They may also raise money via debt. This may take the form of loans from the 'market' (bonds) or from banks or other specific financial institutions (see banking). Finance is often raised by a combination of these methods for a complex high value deal.

Other areas of corporate practice are joint ventures and buy-outs. Buy-outs can be simply the present management raising capital to take control of their company (an MBO). Buy-Out companies like 3i often fund this type of deal. Often the buy-out company will itself pinpoint the deal and take a controlling interest in the target. These sorts of deals can involve the buy-out company borrowing a large amount of capital proportionate to its underlying value, hence the term 'leveraged buy-outs.' Companies can bring in other buy-out companies to spread the risk and the values of the buy-outs can be as large as any public take-over. Ashurst Morris Crisp for example, advised Cinven and Citicorp Venture Capital on the £825m acquisition of William Hill. Joint ventures can be structured in the form of a partnership through the formation of a new company or under a contractual arrangement. These can be as huge as the £800m HMV Media Group joint venture (advised by Rowe & Maw) which includes the HMV, Dillons and Waterstones music and book retail outlets.

Type of work

Corporate work depends on the size and location of the firm. Large City firms act for listed companies on the stock exchange, and deal with household names such as BT, BP and Tesco. Smaller City and regional firms tend to advise leading regional private companies and a handful of FTSE 250 companies.

The distinction between stock exchange and private company work is more than just the size of the company. Private companies' M&A work is amicable because the deal can only proceed if all parties agree to it, whereas stock market companies can be subject to hostile take-overs.

Lawyers advising on private company acquisitions will help draft the sale and purchase agreements, arrange the financing for the deal and carry out a process known as 'due diligence.' The sale, purchase and financing negotiations are usually carried out between company board members and lawyers. Trainees are not expected to take a lead role in negotiating the agreement, although they may be asked to attend the meetings. A private company sale takes about a month to complete. Whereas a trainee can expect to be involved in one or two deals at a time, newly qualifieds can expect to be working on several at once under the supervision of different partners.

Trainees and students on work experience tend

to carry out due diligence work - a time consuming but necessary task to ensure honesty between a purchaser (known as a bidder) and a company being purchased (known as a target). If a target claims to be the largest widget manufacturer in the country, then it could be the trainee's job to check this is true. Trainees will also be expected to check that the target is not involved in outstanding litigation and does not have damaging 'change of control' clauses, which could harm profitability after a takeover.

Stock exchange deals are different. Private companies have few shareholders (owners). Stock exchange-registered companies can have millions. This makes them vulnerable to hostile takeover bids from rival companies who can buy shares and thereby obtain a controlling stake.

To help public companies combat this threat, the stock exchange has developed a detailed takeover code to govern both friendly and hostile M&A activity. The code sets a strict timetable for companies to make and respond to potential bidders and sets out detailed guidelines for the treatment of shareholders. Lawyers advising these companies know this code inside out, and will explain what company directors should be doing at every stage of a potential acquisition. If a merger or acquisition is agreed, corporate lawyers will advise on the formation of the new or modified company and any required financing.

Typical lawyer

Corporate work is not for the faint hearted. Clients are willing to pay premium rates to have transactions completed quickly. Lawyers involved in M&A or hostile takeovers can find themselves attending news conferences and being quoted in daily newspapers. This high-profile work does come at a price. Evening, weekend and even overnight work is common, and corporate lawyers routinely work from eight in the morning to eight at night. By way of compensation, three year qualified corporate lawyers in City firms can earn £50,000 per year. The regions are not far behind, with Leeds and Birmingham lawyers able to earn up to £40,000 per year. US law firms tend to either pay their London lawyers a premium on top of the highest City salaries (a three year qualified can earn up to £60,000 per year), or the equivalent of New York salaries meaning a similar qualified lawyer can take home £80,000 per year. In return the lawyer has to work longer hours. Whereas partnership generally comes earlier outside London, the earning potential of an equity partner generally follows the maxim of bigger partership, bigger income. Large regional equity partners can earn between £100,000 and £300,000, whereas the equity partners in the larger City firms can take home anything between £200,000 and £500,000.

The hours a trainee is expected to work depends on the type of deal and the individual managers. A partner in a medium-sized London firm said trainees could expect to work an average of five-and-a-half days a week. Working three twenty-hour days in a row may be unusual, but should not be dismissed out of hand. In public company takeover work strict timetables under the yellow and blue books must be adhered to. This often results in 'all-nighters' to ensure that all the due diligence exercise is water-tight and that all the necessary final agreements and documentation are prepared according to the timetables. Private company work can be equally time pressured with the client pushing for the best deal in the shortest time. However, trainees and newly qualifieds who excel in company work seem to thrive in pressure situations where the need to have an eye for detail is paramount.

Outside London, there is less public company work but the demands put upon corporate lawyers are no less exacting. Clive Watts of leading South of England firm, Osborne Clarke, describes the work ethic in his firm: "Commercial clients wherever they are based demand priorities which can on occasions involve long hours. However, there is no regime which encourages late hours." The reward for working in a large commercial department of a smaller firm (both in the regions and in London) is often involvement in a client's affairs at an earlier stage. "Both newly qualifieds and trainees can be involved (with appropriate supervision) in the drafting of the base commercial agreements from share purchase agreements to funding agreements," Watts states. These larger regional firms also provide the opportunity, like their City counterparts, for qualified lawyers to be seconded to major clients. Osborne Clarke has had a corporate lawyer at South Western Electricity plc for example.

Because corporate work is often a whole new world for trainees, they can find it takes time to adjust. But Mark Rawlinson, corporate partner with Freshfields, would urge trainees not to be put off in their first few months. "I hated my first six months in the corporate department and found it difficult," says Rawlinson." But a senior property lawyer who had been a captain in the marines said to me that I'd make a good corporate lawyer, so I went back and tried it again. After the first 18 months, it began to get more interesting. The trouble is as a trainee everything moves at 100mph and there's such a lot to take in."

Many corporate lawyers find they get a 'buzz' out of their work. Nigel Boardman, who heads the corporate department at top City law firm Slaughter and May comments, "If you enjoy seeing the deals you do in the newspapers and meeting high quality, high profile people on deals where there's a lot of money at stake - then you'll enjoy corporate law. You spend much of your time in meetings, so you need good presentation skills. You must be able to think on your feet, make a decision and justify it. This could include telling a government minister or company director that they don't have the power to do what they want to do. You need to have confidence, tact and clear communication skills to explain why." Above all, however, there can be no substitute for what fellow Slaughter and May partner, George Goulding, describes as "a good eye for detail." He explains, "Even the biggest deals can get unstuck on the smallest point. You need to have the patience and understanding to get it right." Inter-personal skills often distinguish between the good and the excellent corporate lawyer, but attention to minutiae is a prerequisite from trainees upwards.

Career options

A sound grounding in corporate finance makes an excellent springboard for working in industry. Many lawyers move in-house to major companies at an early stage of their careers, tempted by salaries comparable with private practice, but more predictable hours.

Moves in-house do occur at partner level, but they are less common.

Another popular move among young corporate finance lawyers is to join the banking world, either as an in-house lawyer or as a corporate finance executive or analyst. This is a chance to move from 'lawyer' to 'client.' Those who have made the transition seem to enjoy the dynamic pace of life and are glad to have shed the advisory role. Such moves generally occur early on, but high profile moves of senior partners to investment banks is not uncommon.

Becoming a company secretary and advising board members on their internal legal compliance procedures is an alternative route. This position is suitable for senior lawyers with a general range of company and commercial skills and salaries can be in excess of £100,000.

Although an in-house career is increasingly common for corporate lawyers, the majority of lawyers are happy working in private practice. Nigel Boardman originally trained at Slaughters in 1973 and has remained in the corporate department - apart from a two year break working for a major bank - ever since. If you enjoy corporate work, it seems you are reluctant to leave the lifestyle behind.

The Firms

As you might expect corporate finance work is dominated by City firms such as Freshfields, Linklaters and Slaughter and May. These three firms act for most of the major corporates and have the largest departments in the country - Freshfields has 47 partners and 158 assistants and Linklaters numbers 43 partners and 199 assistants. Sixty per cent of Slaughter and May's whole practice is corporate and it acts as primary counsel for more FTSE100 companies than any other UK firm. However Linklaters has its Alliance with five large Continental European firms which has raised its profile in European M&A. Freshfields has merged with highly rated German firm, Deringer. Clifford Chance has become the leading firm across Western Europe and has recently merged with leading German firm, Pünder and the large New York practice of Rogers & Wells.

Medium sized City firms such as Macfarlanes, Travers Smith Braithwaite and Gouldens are transactionally focused, regularly acting on £100m deals. Macfarlanes acted for Dr Solomon on its $700m take-over by NASDAQ quoted Network Associates. Macfarlanes' corporate department numbers 14 partners and 20 assistants, Travers has 17 partners and 33 assistants and Gouldens has 15 partners and 28 assistants. Although significantly smaller than the larger firms, this does not affect their ability to provide a quality service on a range of transactions from £10m to over £1bn in value. Gouldens in particular is noted for its excellent profitability and for paying its newly qualified corporate lawyers some of the highest salaries in the City.

Most City firms, regardless of size, do corporate work of some form. Smaller firms such as Harbottle & Lewis (known for its media work with clients like Richard Branson) and Warner Cranston also handle corporate transactions such as Thermo Electron's £40m acquisition of Graseby Group from Smith Industries. Even a small West End firm such as Manches (known for its family work) gets involved in corporate work with deals ranging from £2m to £100m. Firms at this end of the market may also handle more AIM (Alternative Investment Market) or OFEX flotations. Many of the media firms have expanded their corporate departments. Firms like Olswang now act on large deals such as advising the BBC on its £400m twin joint venture structure with Flextech and its joint venture with Discovery to launch overseas channels.

One recent trend has been the emergence of the London offices of the largest US firms. Invariably transactionally focused, many newly qualifieds are attracted to what Richard Cole (partner with leading international firm, Mayer, Brown & Platt) describes as "taking a slice of high quality, corporate finance work normally only found at the biggest magic circle firms." For example the firm advised Deutsche Telekom on its $2bn acquisition of the Central European and Russian mobile telephone assets of MediaOne. The large London offices of US firms like Weil Gotshal & Manges, Sidley & Austin, and Mayer, Brown & Platt now have many English qualified lawyers. Richard Cole also comments that "the young English lawyers gain from being able to observe the styles of both English and US lawyers." Mayer Brown & Platt takes on two trainees a year and has begun to second its UK qualifieds to its New York and Chicago offices. However, lawyers at the biggest City practices also benefit from time at leading New York firms. Slaughter and May for example has solicitors with Cravath, Swaine & Moore, Davis Polk and Wardwell and Simpson Thacher & Bartlett.

The major commercial centres such as Brimingham, Leeds and Manchester have a concentration of sophisticated firms involved in large corporate deals – Wragge & Co in Birmingham, for example, and Addleshaw Booth & Co in the North West. Both have sizeable corporate departments - Wragges has 13 partners and 24 assistants and Addleshaw Booth has 15 corporate partners and 37 assistants in Manchester alone. Their client lists are also impressive, including such companies as Powergen and British Airways (Wragge & Co) and Airtours (Addleshaw Booth & Co). Bristol may lag behind Leeds and Birmingham in terms of corporate activity as a whole but Osborne Clarke and Burges Salmon have corporate departments and a flow of work as large as any other regional practice. Both firms have 11 corporate partners and over 20 assistants. Burges Salmon is known for its roster of rail and road transport clients such as Great Western Trains. Osborne Clarke is known for its work for 3i and Bristol issuing house, Rowan Dartington.

Most commercial firms around the country will have some corporate capability, from small East Anglian firms such as Greenwoods in

Peterborough with clients like Emap, to large South Wales firms like Edwards Geldard with clients ranging from Pendragon plc to the Welsh Development Agency. Corporate work in the regional firms tends to cover a range of work from commercial agreements to company acquisitions and disposals. The largest deals on a regular basis tend to be private company disposals and acquisitions, management buy-outs and the occasional company listing. Work for household name companies is a regular occurrence at the leading firms. Southampton firm Paris Smith & Randall's recent deals include Hawker Pacific Aerospace's acquisition of the repair and landing gear business from BA, followed by a refinancing of debt for $60 million. In Leeds, now the UK's second legal centre, high-premium work is not uncommon even at the smaller firms. Walker Morris, for example, acted for Yorkshire Water plc and its subsidiary Yorkshire Environmental Solutions Ltd in the £120 million acquisition of 3C Waste Ltd.

Leading Firms

London	Number of solicitors in corporate team		
	40+	20-40	1-20
Allen & Overy	*****		
Ashurst Morris Crisp	*****		
Baker & McKenzie		*****	
Barnett Alexander Chart			*
Beachcroft Wansbroughs			**
S J Berwin & Co	*		
Berwin Leighton	*		
Biddle			****
Bird & Bird			****
Charles Russell			***
Clifford Chance	*****		
CMS Cameron McKenna	**		
Coudert Brothers			**
D J Freeman			*****
Denton Hall	**		
Dibb Lupton Alsop		****	
Eversheds		****	
Field Fisher Waterhouse		**	
Fox Williams			****
Freshfields	******		
Gouldens		******	
Hammond Suddards		***	
Harbottle & Lewis			****
Herbert Smith	*****		
Hobson Audley Hopkins & Wood			****
Howard Kennedy			***
Lawrence Graham		**	
Laytons			**
Lewis Silkin			***
Linklaters	******		
Lovells	****		

Leading Firms

London	Number of solicitors in corporate team 40+	20-40	1-20
Macfarlanes	***		
Manches			**
Marriott Harrison			***
Memery Crystal			****
Middleton Potts			*
Nabarro Nathanson	*		
Nicholson Graham & Jones		**	
Norton Rose	*****		
Olswang		****	
Osborne Clarke		***	
Paisner & Co			******
Pinsent Curtis		****	
Radcliffes			*
Rakisons			**
Richards Butler		****	
Rowe & Maw	*		
Simmons & Simmons	**		
Sinclair Roche & Temperley			****
Slaughter and May	******		
Stephenson Harwood		****	
Taylor Joynson Garrett		****	
Theodore Goddard		*****	
Titmuss Sainer Dechert		****	
Travers Smith Braithwaite	***		
Warner Cranston			*****
Watson, Farley & Williams		**	
Wedlake Bell			**
Wilde Sapte		*****	

South East	Corporate
Argles Stoneham Burstows, Crawley	***
B.P. Collins & Co, Gerrards Cross	**
Blake Lapthorn, Fareham, Portsmouth, Southampton	******
Bond Pearce, Southampton	******
Brachers, Maidstone	**
Clarks, Reading	******
Cripps Harries Hall, Tunbridge Wells	***
Donne Mileham & Haddock, Brighton, Crawley	*****
Garretts, Reading	****
Kimbell & Co, Milton Keynes	***
Manches, Oxford	****
Morgan Cole, Oxford, Reading	******

South East	Corporate
Mundays, Esher	****
Nabarro Nathanson, Reading	**
Osborne Clarke, Reading	*****
Paris Smith & Randall, Southampton	*****
Pitmans, Reading	****
Rawlison & Butler, Crawley	****
Shadbolt & Co, Reigate	**
Shoosmiths, Solent	**
Stevens & Bolton, Guildford	****
Thomas Eggar Church Adams, Chichester, Horsham, Reigate, Worthing	****
Thomson Snell & Passmore, Tunbridge Wells	****

Leading Firms

South West	Corporate
Anstey Sargent & Probert, Exeter	**
Bevan Ashford, Bristol	*
Bevan Ashford, Exeter	***
Bond Pearce, Exeter, Plymouth	****
Bretherton Price Elgoods, Cheltenham	*
Burges Salmon, Bristol	******
Cartwrights, Bristol	*
Charles Russell, Cheltenham	***
Clark Holt, Swindon	**
Clarke Willmott & Clarke, Bristol, Taunton	*
CMS Cameron McKenna, Bristol	*
Foot & Bowden, Exeter, Plymouth	*
Lawrence Tucketts, Bristol	***
Laytons, Bristol	**
Lester Aldridge, Bournemouth	*
Lyons Davidson, Bristol	***
Michelmores, Exeter	**
Osborne Clarke, Bristol	******
Stephens & Scown, Exeter, St Austell, Truro	**
Trumps, Bristol	*
Veale Wasbrough, Bristol	*
Withy King, Bath	*

Wales	Corporate
Berry Smith, Cardiff	***
Bevan Ashford, Cardiff	**
Edwards Geldard, Cardiff	*****
Eversheds, Cardiff	****
Hugh James Ford Simey, Cardiff	**
Morgan Cole, Cardiff	******

Midlands	Corporate
Browne Jacobson, N'ham	***
Dibb Lupton Alsop, B'ham	****
Edge Ellison, B'ham, Leicester	****
Eking Manning, N'ham	**
Eversheds, B'ham	*****
Eversheds, Derby, Nottingham	***
Freeth Cartwright Hunt Dickins, N'ham	*
Garretts, Birmingham	**
Gateley Wareing, B'ham	***
George Green & Co, Warley	**
Harvey Ingram Owston, Leicester	*
Hewitson Becke + Shaw, N'hampton	**
Higgs & Sons, Brierley Hill	*
Howes Percival, N'hampton	**
Kent Jones and Done, Stoke-on-Trent	**
Knight & Sons, N'castle-under-Lyme	**
Lee Crowder, B'ham	**
Martineau Johnson, B'ham	***
Pinsent Curtis, B'ham	*****
Shakespeares, B'ham	*
Shoosmiths, N'hampton, N'ham, Rugby	**
Wragge & Co, B'ham	******

East Anglia	Corporate
Ashton Graham, Bury St Edmunds	**
Birketts, Ipswich	***
Eversheds, Ipswich, Norwich	******
Garretts, Cambridge	***
Gotelee & Goldsmith, Ipswich	**
Greene & Greene, Bury St. Edmunds	**
Greenwoods, Peterborough	***
Hewitson Becke + Shaw, Cambridge, Peterborough	******
Mills & Reeve, Cambridge, Norwich	******
Prettys, Ipswich	***
Taylor Vinters, Cambridge	*****

Leading Firms

North West	Corporate
Aaron & Partners, Chester	*
Addleshaw Booth & Co, Manc	******
Berrymans Lace Mawer, Liverpool	*
Brabner Holden Banks Wilson, Liverpool	***
Cartmell Shepherd, Carlisle	*
Chaffe Street, Manchester	***
Cobbetts, Manchester	***
Davies Wallis Foyster, Liverpool, Manchester	**
Dibb Lupton Alsop, L'pool, Manchester	*****
Eversheds, Manchester	*****
Garretts, Manchester	***
Halliwell Landau, Manchester	****
Hammond Suddards, Manchester	*****
Kuit Steinart Levy, Manchester	**
Pannone & Partners, Manchester	*
Wacks Caller, Manchester	**

North East	Corporate
Addleshaw Booth & Co, Leeds	******
Andrew M. Jackson & Co, Hull	**
Dibb Lupton Alsop, Leeds, Sheffield	*****
Dickinson Dees, Newcastle	*****
Eversheds, Leeds	******
Eversheds, M'brough, Newcastle	***
Garretts, Leeds	**
Gordons Wright & Wright, Bradford	*
Gosschalks, Hull	*
Hammond Suddards, Leeds	******
Irwin Mitchell, Leeds	**
Irwin Mitchell, Sheffield	***
Keeble Hawson Moorhouse, Sheff	*
Lupton Fawcett, Leeds	*
Pinsent Curtis, Leeds	*****
Robert Muckle, Newcastle	**
Rollit Farrell & Bladon, Hull	**
Walker Morris, Leeds	****
Ward Hadaway, Newcastle	**
Watson Burton, Newcastle	*

Firms and their star ratings are based on Chambers' Directory 1999–2000. Six stars represent a top-ranked firm, five stars a second-ranked firm, etc.

CRIME
(including Fraud)

Area of law

General criminal lawyers act for defendants in magistrates' courts, Crown Courts and courts martial. Whatever the seriousness of the charge, the basic process they will follow is the same. The difference is in the detail. Less serious offences are dealt with in the magistrates' courts, with the accused usually represented by the solicitor. More serious cases are tried in the Crown Courts. Though solicitors can now take exams to enable them to work as advocates in the Crown Courts, most still prefer to use a barrister.

In addition to expertise in criminal law and procedure, lawyers need to be familiar with mental health, immigration and extradition issues. Fraud work requires a knowledge of insolvency law, financial services regulations and commercial litigation (particularly freezing injunctions and search and seizure orders). This chapter deals mainly with general criminal law.

Type of work

Criminal lawyers lead a hectic life, particularly in small practices, where the administrative pressures are greater. In a typical day, you might get into the office at 8.30 am, having already spent some of the night at the police station as duty solicitor. At 9.30, it's off to the magistrates' court for procedural and remand hearings, or perhaps a plea in mitigation. Lunch may be on the hoof, and the afternoon is spent interviewing clients and conferring with counsel. After that, there may still be some paperwork to deal with and you could be back in the police station that night. When at last you get home, you'll have to spend some of your 'free' time preparing for the next day's court hearing.

It can be fun though. Unlike in many legal careers, you are not office-bound, and there are plenty of opportunities for advocacy. Dealing with criminal clients can often be challenging, but is not as hard you might think. "Major criminals can be very, very interesting people" says Gerry McManus of Manchester firm Burton Copeland. "A lot of them have a number of problems, drug problems, drink problems, health problems, psychiatric problems" says Mark Studdert, partner in Camden practice Hodge, Jones and Allen "but in the general well of things they are easy people to deal with, because they are unwilling participants in the system and want the case to go away as soon as possible."

The immediacy of the work is another plus, and criminal lawyers are often able to see the fruits of their advice and work within a relatively short time. This is particularly true for lawyers who are accredited to work as duty solicitors at magistrates' courts. Their role is to provide advocacy for those who cannot afford representation. Their clients often have no idea of how the process works, and are very grateful for their intervention, which can often lead to immediate results. Because the work is date driven, cases have a quick turnover, and even murder cases are dealt with in under a year. "There is a lovely rhythm to criminal work" says Girish Thanki, partner with niche firm Thanki Novy Taube. "You finish it, you bill it, you get the money within a couple of months. Whether you're upbeat because you got the desired result or annoyed because you failed to, it's all over quickly and things are moving on."

Criminal law is an area in flux, with the Access to Justice reforms, Government Legal Aid reforms and the Human Rights Act likely to impact strongly on the present system. One major change will be the advent of block contracting of criminal legal services. This will result in legally aided criminal defence work only being carried out by a limited number of franchised firms that can demonstrate their ability to handle the work. This may have the effect of ending high street criminal practice and concentrating criminal work in the hands of larger, specialist practices. The precise effects of the

Human Rights Act are uncertain as yet, but all courts will have to take its provisions into account in all cases. With specific articles dealing with, amongst others, the right to privacy, the right to a fair trial and freedom of expression, this will mean extra tools in the hands of the defence lawyer at every stage of the criminal process.

All this change makes it a very interesting time to become a criminal lawyer. As Mark Studdert, points out: "there have been major pieces of legislation every year that I've been in practice. Not only changing specific laws, but also the whole procedural approach. You are very much at the cutting edge of legislative changes, and of how society is dealing with its problems."

As a criminal trainee you will probably be thrown in at the deep end, with your own caseload and appearances in the magistrates' courts from day one. One of the most important elements of your training will be attending police station interviews or just listening to tapes of them. However, you will also get to assist senior lawyers and barristers in more serious assault, rape and murder cases, and may get to sit through major trials. This breadth of opportunity and responsibility is one of the main attractions of the training.

Some practitioners handle general crime together with fraud. However fraud work (particularly the regulation and investigation side) is a very different kettle of fish from general criminal work. Leaders in this field tend to specialise in corporate investigations. Work is generally initiated by the SFO, SFA, DTI and Customs & Excise investigations. Ian Burton, for example, advises professionals facing disciplinary proceedings and represented the defendants in the Maxwell, BCCI and Barlow Clowes affairs. Stephen Pollard of Kingsley Napley represents Nick Leeson, the ex-Barings trader. There are overlaps with civil liberties, and Rod Fletcher of Russell Jones & Walker handles miscarriages of justice cases and represented police officers prosecuted following the Birmingham Six and Guildford Four investigations.

Skills needed

A good criminal lawyer has a variety of skills. An eye for fine detail is essential, such as the ability to grasp the most complex forensic evidence or to spot an inconsistency in police testimony. Contrary to popular law student opinion, however, criminal practice is not simply a question of factual disputes, and a strong understanding of the law is also necessary. "There will nearly always be some legal issues in a case," says Mark Studdert, "and the longer you do the job, the more you will realise this."

When acting as an advocate, you must be sharp and resolute on your feet, with finely honed social skills. Gerry McManus is clear on this point: "You will need to read people, read magistrates. If you sit and watch magistrates for ten minutes you can completely change the way you will present your client's case." Advocacy skills take time to develop, but they are important."There is an appalling lack of flair in young advocates these days. A bit of imagination is needed to put the most mundane point in a way that makes it sound attractive. Advocacy can swing it."

You must also be able to deal effectively with clients. "Those with prior experience in psychology or counselling usually make excellent criminal lawyers" says Greg Powell of Powell Spencer. "You need to be able to listen really well to people's stories and stay calm in situations that provoke anxiety." It is also vital that you are able to understand the clients and to build up a relationship with them. "You may not have a lot of sympathy but you have to have a lot of empathy," says Gerry McManus. "You need to know how to deal with drug addicts and people who have fallen into the gutter and give them some kind of way out, even if they can't imagine it themselves."

The volume of work in criminal law also means that you need good organisational, administrative and IT skills. You may have to run up to one hundred cases at one time, which makes careful collation of information and a foolproof diary system essential to avoid administrative chaos.

Above all, if you want to be a criminal lawyer, you'll need to love your work and be 100% committed to it. You'll probably be paid a lot less than your contemporaries and you'll be working just as hard, if not harder.

Fraud specialists often have a background in corporate/commercial work or litigation. They need a head for figures, good project management skills, an ability to cope with mountains of paperwork and an ability to assimilate complex financial evidence.

Career options

At the moment most high street practices handle criminal work, though, as explained above, this may change with increasing specialisation. For those seeking a good general criminal practice, Greg Powell of Powell Spencer & Partners has a tip. "Ask a senior probation officer, social worker or the Citizens Advice Bureau which firms they have a good relationship with."

Specialist criminal firms offer high profile criminal and civil rights work. However, training contracts in these firms are scarce as some are unable to offer experience in all areas of law required by the Law Society. Advancement for assistants is often slow in these firms as they usually have a small number of partners.

Aspiring criminal lawyers often have a preference for Legal Aid work. Many firms which specialise in family and child care also have criminal departments, enabling trainees to handle the full range of Legal Aid work during training. In terms of quality, such firms are often regarded as highly as specialist criminal practices.

In the past, criminal practitioners seeking higher financial rewards sometimes transferred to the Bar. This is less common today as solicitors keen to act as advocates can now appear in the higher courts.

Those seeking more of a nine-to-five existence can opt to work for the Crown Prosecution Service, but salaries are likely to be lower.

Fraud work is carried out in two types of firm: niche practices which often act for individual defendants; and larger City practices which represent financial institutions, banks and companies. It is unlikely that you will experience this area of work during training, but the best route in is via a commercial litigation department. After a few years' forensic investigation experience in private practice, lawyers could work for or set up their own litigation support companies.

The Firms

Crime

In London, the leading criminal firms are found in the West End or high street. Bindman & Partners specialises in cases with civil liberties implications. Notable actions include representing environmental protesters in connection with Twyford Down and the Newbury Bypass. Fisher Meredith and Hodge Jones & Allen have very strong legal aid practices and handle a wide range of work from violent offences and drugs charges to some white collar crime. Powell Spencer & Partners in north west London have built up a community-based practice and have a Youth Court specialist.

In the regions, the majority of firms regularly handle the full range of criminal work. In High Wycombe, Dukes Arnold du Feu is a specialist criminal firm and undertakes all defence work and complaints against the police. Bobbetts Mackan in Bristol are well known for their representation at courts martial. The leading firm in the North West is Burton Copeland in Manchester, fielding the largest criminal defence team in the country. They lead the way in the use of DNA testing in criminal trials, and often defend well known sporting celebrities.

Fraud

In London, the firms can be divided into those undertaking criminal fraud work and those undertaking regulatory work.

In criminal fraud the specialists are mostly small niche firms. Kingsley Napley recently represented different parties in the Deutsche Morgan Grenfell affair. Peters & Peters acted for Kevin Maxwell, and for Stephen Hinchcliffe who was investigated by the SFO when his retail chain of shops collapsed.

Generally, it is the City firms who dominate in regulatory work. Norton Rose represented Barings Bank during the Bank Supervision Investigation. Stephenson Harwood acted for Sir Jack Lyons in the Guinness affair. Allen & Overy, Clifford Chance, CMS Cameron McKenna and Herbert Smith all field well respected teams. Some of the smaller niche criminal fraud practices, such as Kingsley Napley and Peters & Peters, are trying to move into this lucrative area.

Outside London, the best firms handle both types of work. Burton Copeland dominates the North, and is considered the best fraud practice outside London. It handles high quality work, including prosecution and defence and stock exchange fraud. Irwin Mitchell, based in Sheffield, is another strong practice in the region. In the Midlands, commercial firms Freeth Cartwright Hunt Dickens, Nelsons and Edge Ellison have the largest teams. Blake Lapthorn has the strongest reputation in the South East, particularly for tax, mortgage and tachograph fraud.

Leading Firms

London	Crime
Alistair Meldrum & Co, Enfield	****
Andrew Keenan & Co	*****
Bindman & Partners	******
Birnberg Peirce & Partners	******
Christian Fisher	*****
Claude Hornby & Cox	****
Darlington & Parkinson	****
Dowse & Co	****
Dundons	****
Duthie Hart & Duthie	*****
Edward Fail Bradshaw & Waterson	******
Fisher Meredith	******
Hallinan, Blackburn, Gittings & Nott	*****
Henry Milner & Co	*****
Hickman & Rose	*****
Hodge Jones & Allen	******
J.B. Wheatley & Co	****
J.R. Jones, Ealing	*****
Joy Merriam & Co	****

London Firms	Crime
Kingsley Napley	*****
Magrath & Co	*****
Mattila Solicitors	****
McCormacks	****
Offenbach & Co	******
Powell Spencer & Partners	******
Reynolds Dawson	*****
Russell-Cooke, Potter & Chapman	*****
Saunders & Co	******
Simons Muirhead & Burton	*****
T.V. Edwards	******
Taylor Nichol	******
Thanki Novy Taube	******
Tuckers	****
Venters & Co	****
Victor Lissack & Roscoe	*****
Whitelock & Storr	******
Winstanley-Burgess	****

South East	Crime
Bernard Chill & Axtell, Southampton	*****
Bradleys, Dover	*****
David Charnley & Co, Romford	*****
Dukes Arnold Du Feu, High Wyc	******
Eric Robinson & Co, Southampton	*****
Gepp & Sons, Chelm, Colchester	******
Marsh, Ferriman & Cheale, Worthing	*****
Max Barford & Co, Tunbridge Wells	*****
Park Woodfine, Bedford	*****
Pictons, Hemel Hempstead	******
Pictons, Luton, St. Albans, Stevenage, Watford	******
Stephen Rimmer & Co, Eastbourne	*****
Twitchen Musters & Kelly, Southend-on-Sea	******
White & Bowker, Winchester	*****
Woodfine Batcheldor, Bedford	******

South West	Crime
Bobbetts Mackan, Bristol	******
Crosse & Crosse, Exeter	*****
Douglas & Partners, Bristol	******
Foot & Bowden, Plymouth	*****
John Boyle and Co, Redruth	******
Stephens & Scown, Exeter	*****
Wolferstans, Plymouth	*****
Woollcombe Beer Watts, N. Abbot	****

Midland	Crime
Banners, Chesterfield	******
Barrie Ward & Julian Griffiths, Nottingham	******
Berryman & Co, Nottingham	******
Brethertons, Rugby	******
Eddowes Waldron, Derby	*****
Elliot Mather, Chesterfield	*****
Fletchers, Nottingham	******
Freeth Cartwright Hunt Dickins, Nottingham	*****
George, Jonas & Co, Birmingham	******
Glaisyers, Birmingham	******
Hawley & Rodgers, Loughborough	*****
Kieran & Co, Worcester	******
Marrons, Leicester	*****
Nelsons, Nottingham	******
Parker & Grego, Birmingham	*****
Rees Page, Wolverhampton	*****
Silks, Warley	*****
The Johnson Partnership, N'ham	******
The Smith Partnership, Derby	******
Tyndallwoods, Birmingham	*****
Woodford-Robinson, Northampton	******

Wales	Crime
Gamlins, Rhyl	******
Graham Evans & Partners, Swansea	******
Huttons, Cardiff	******
Leo Abse & Cohen, Cardiff	****
Martyn Prowel Solicitors, Cardiff	******
Robertsons, Cardiff	******
Spicketts, Pontypridd	*****
Spiro Grech & Co, Cardiff	*****

East Anglia	Crime
Belmores, Norwich	*****
Cole & Co, Norwich	*****
Copleys, Huntingdon	******
Fosters, Norwich	*****
Gotelee & Goldsmith, Ipswich	*****
Hatch Brenner, Norwich	******
Hegarty & Co, Peterborough	*****
Hunt & Coombs, Peterborough	******
Lucas & Wyllys, Great Yarmouth	*****
Overbury Steward Eaton & Woolsey, Norwich	******
Thomson Webb Corfield & Masters, Cambridge	*****
Wilkinson & Butler, St Neots	*****

North West	Crime
Betesh Fox & Co, Manchester	****
Brian Koffman & Co, Manchester	****
Bridgewood Hopkinson & Wozny, Manchester	****
Burton Copeland, Manchester	******
Cunninghams, Manchester	****
Farleys, Blackburn	***
Forbes & Partners, Blackburn	****
Garstangs, Bolton	*****
Jackson & Canter, Liverpool	***

North West	Crime
Jones Maidment Wilson, Manc	*****
Linskills Solicitors, Liverpool	***
Maidments, Manchester	*****
Middleweeks, Manchester	***
Miller Gardner, Manchester	*****
R.M. Broudie & Co, Liverpool	****
Russell & Russell, Bolton	*****
The Berkson Globe Partnership, Liverpool	*****
Tuckers, Manchester	*****

North East	Crime
David Gray & Company, N'castle	*****
Gosschalks, Hull	****
Grahame Stowe, Bateson, Leeds	*****
Henry Hyams & Co, Leeds	****
Howells, Sheffield	*****
Irwin Mitchell, Sheffield	*****

North East	Crime
Levi & Co, Leeds	*****
Lumb & Macgill, Bradford	******
Max Gold & Co, Hull	*****
Myer Wolff & Manley, Hull	****
Sugaré & Co, Leeds	******

Firms and their star ratings are based on Chambers' Directory 1999–2000. Six stars represent a top-ranked firm, five stars a second-ranked firm, etc.

EMPLOYMENT LAW
(including Pensions and Employee Benefits)

Area of Law

If you are fascinated by human nature, curious about the internal workings of corporate Britain and want to be involved in the cases provoking legislative and social changes affecting everyone who has ever had a job, then perhaps you should think about employment law.

The work of an employment lawyer is a rich and varied mix of advisory, pre-emptive, contractual and litigious work. Contentious work may be in an employment tribunal, county courts or the High Court. Many employment cases which start in the employment tribunal become test cases which are appealed to the higher courts so they may end up in the Court of Appeal, House of Lords or even the European Court of Justice. In tribunals employees ('applicants') may claim for redundancy pay, unfair and wrongful dismissal, sex, race and disability discrimination against their employers ('respondents'). Claims for breach of contract may also be made in the High Court or county courts depending on the value of the claim.

Specialist employment teams are divided along partisan lines. The 'fat cat' firms (City firms with a corporate client base and high charge-out rates) work for employers and highly-paid senior executives. The 'right on' firms act mainly for Trade Union clients and other individuals. They often have allied practices in defendant personal injury.

Almost every high street practice, Citizens Advice Bureau and law centre purports to give employment advice to individuals. In fact the practice area is now so law-intensive that even specialists have a hard time keeping up with almost weekly changes from the European and domestic courts.

Type of Work

"Employment law guru" Janet Gaymer is head of the leading London employment team at Simmons & Simmons. The firm acts primarily for employers although it does handle cases for senior executives and individuals with particularly complex cases. Janet spends much of her time building relationships with clients and developing an understanding of their businesses. "Long-term client relationships are hugely important," she states, "because so much of employment law is a question of industrial relations, communications and strategy planning." Advice may be one part of a highly politicised industrial relations problem. "I have to maintain an apolitical detachment to a certain degree. You may be acting for a right-wing newspaper and a Labour-controlled local authority at the same time. Of course you're conscious that the instructions you're receiving may be coloured, but this does not affect the advice you give."

Lawyers acting for trade unions tend to be more ideologically motivated. Michael Short, head of employment at Rowley Ashworth, obviously relishes his battles on behalf of union members. He represented several hundred thousand employees from various manufacturing unions in their campaign to reduce the engineering industry's working week. "I suggested they set up a fund and all contribute a small amount. Then selected 'stormtroopers' in certain key areas went on strike, backed by resources from the fund. Eventually we got a challenge from British Aerospace and were served with affidavits. The last of these arrived at about midnight, with a hearing set for ten the next morning. We stayed up all night to draft our responses, but it was worth it – the working week was reduced from 39 to 37 hours." For Michael Short, this was far more satisfying than a 'big money' case.

Corporate cases can prove equally satisfying, particularly when acting for the individual. Chris Booth, a partner in the employment department at Pinsent Curtis in Leeds, represented the former finance director of Magnet Ltd in his claim for wrongful dismissal. "Very few cases actually go to trial," he says, "but this one lasted six weeks. In the end, we won a £500,000 settlement." Chris Booth adds, "it felt good helping the small fish win and sometimes you go beyond mere professional relationships. The FD is quite a good pal of mine now, because he thinks I did a good job."

Employment, or labour law, is by its nature highly politicised, regulating as it does the power struggle between workers and employers. Naomi Feinstein, employment partner at City firm Lovells says, "with the Labour Government in power and more and more European law in this area things are likely to be very lively in employment law for some time to come."

Assistant solicitor Matthew Smith is five years qualified. His typical day may be as follows:

"8.30am: arrive in office nursing hangover and facing pile of urgent paperwork. First draft Notice of Appearance in Employment Tribunal proceedings, setting out employer's side of story in 'drunken sacking' unfair dismissal case. Make and inhale large cup of strong coffee. Consider recent instructions to draft contract of employment for senior executive.

Next turn (slightly depressed) to considering implications of Transfer of Undertakings Regs on business sale being handled by corporate colleagues. Corporate partner in charge thinks himself rather an expert on TUPE and has written detailed note on his understanding of position; i.e. TUPE does not apply. Tactfully but firmly (in view of your junior position and partner's greater ego) break it to him that TUPE does apply. All seller's employees will transfer automatically to purchaser of company. Draft letter of advice to client about potential redundancies. Client will panic. Include advice on how best to break news and consult with employees while avoiding major public relations disaster.

Receive any number of phone calls from clients' personnel managers throughout day. What do fiendish Working Time Regulations say about paid holiday? Appropriateness or otherwise of taking disciplinary action against employee in love triangle with two colleagues. Love triangle not problem. Threatening colleagues outside work is.

8.30pm: Leave office having stayed late to prepare submissions for Employment Tribunal. No need to instruct counsel so will do own advocacy, not just sit behind barrister and fall asleep. If witnesses perform well, satisfaction of seeing evidence hit home, expertly followed up by (own) strong submissions on law. If not, rise manfully to challenge of pulling things round in closing speech or, (last resort) settling with applicant."

As a trainee there is plenty of opportunity for hands-on involvement in an employment seat, and much of that is quality work with a high element of law to it.

Pensions and Employee Benefits

Strong employment practices often go hand in hand with pensions and employee benefits practices in the employer firms. Corporate clients often offer sophisticated benefits to their employees, particularly senior executives, and there is detailed law governing these benefits.

Skills Needed

Cliché or no cliché, an employment specialist must be a 'people person.' "It sounds trite," says Janet Gaymer, "but you have to like and be interested in people and want to know what makes them tick." If someone has been dismissed without notice or an employer has lost a key member of staff, he or she will often come to you in an emotional state. You need sensitivity to handle such a situation. At the same time, a sense of humour is essential and can sometimes get you through difficult client meetings.

The work is all about people, agrees Sue Nickson, head of employment at Hammond Suddards, and it concerns live issues. "At parties if you let slip that you're an employment lawyer someone always asks for advice about a problem – it's far safer to say you're a dentist." Having said that, Sue would not do anything else, "apart perhaps from opening a wine bar in Sydney!"

Lawyers working for union firms obviously need to be sympathetic to their clients' interests and, according to Stephen Cavalier, head of Employment Rights at Thompsons, they need to realise that a legal solution may not always be the best approach. "Many cases are not simply about compensation," he comments, "but perhaps a wider industrial issue that needs resolving."

Versatility and flexibility are also high on the list of essential qualities required by successful employment lawyers. "One day you can be advising a theatrical company, the next workers on an oil rig," says Janet Gaymer, "it certainly keeps you on your toes." European influence on employment law also demands quick changes in strategy and advice.

Above all, says Naomi Feinstein, this is a technical area and you have to have a detailed knowledge of relevant statutes and to keep up-to-date with case-law.

Career Options

Janet Gaymer read law at Oxford in the late 1960s and then did a part-time masters degree (LLM) at LSE while working at Simmons & Simmons, where she was admitted in 1973. She started specialising in employment law "purely accidentally – I just got handed an unfair dismissal case," and hasn't looked back since. She has been a partner since 1977.

Michael Short qualified at Lovell White & King (now Lovells) and was enjoying work as a civil litigator in the City firm. Then, "someone who knew my political interests and background (my family has strong connections with the Labour party) told me about a job at Rowley Ashworth involving employment law and working with trade unions." Short made the move and now advises those considering a career in employment law to look beyond the City for their training. "At Rowley Ashworth we often find that applicants from the City have worked on a lot of very similar cases. Other firms may offer more variety."

There are options to go in-house, but as Sue Nickson comments, "few companies have a large enough legal team to include a full-time employment lawyer." It is more likely that a move in-house would combine employment law with perhaps general commercial litigation. If the idea of working for a company rather than a law firm appeals, an alternative step is to work more generally in a human resources department. There are openings in the academic world for employment experts, and lawyers considering this path should gain as much lecturing experience as possible. Towards the top end of the professional scale, lawyers may apply to chair employment tribunals; many partners in leading employment practices combine their practice with part-time tribunal chairs.

Remaining in private practice seems to be the popular choice among the lawyers we interviewed and they expressed confidence in the choice of employment law as a career. "Employment law's stability in economically turbulent times has obvious irony, but it provides comforting reassurance for those in the field," says Michael Short. "Like most litigation, the volume of our work increases in times of recession."

The Firms

Employment Law

Simmons & Simmons leads the field among the employer firms in London. It has recently acted for the London Borough of Camden on a high profile sex discrimination claim brought by the Deputy Chief Executive and Borough Solicitor. International practice Baker & McKenzie has traditionally commanded a lot of respect. With 57 offices worldwide the firm has been at the forefront in advising large UK plcs and foreign multi-national companies on European Works Councils. However the recent departure by one of its leading stars, Fraser Younson, to set up a new employment group with US firm McDermott Will & Emery, may herald additional opportunities at the latter practice. Eversheds has a leading practice in London and around the country, particularly in Wales and the Midlands. Recently advising PolyGram on the employment aspects of its merger with Seagram/Universal, it counts PricewaterhouseCoopers and the Financial Services Authority among its most active clients in the past year. Lovells has a respected practice as do Rowe & Maw, Fox Williams and a number of others.

The leading employee practice in London, which also has offices throughout the country, is Pattinson & Brewer, a firm whose trade union credentials date back to the turn of the century. One of the partners recently acted in 'Palmer v ABP,' a House of Lords case on inducements by employers to abandon trade union representatives. Other leading national firms are Rowley Ashworth, Russell Jones & Walker and Thompsons, all of which have major trade union practices.

Morgan Cole, whose team leader Sue Ashtiany is the current Chair of the Employment and Discrimination Law Group, dominates in the south east of the country. The firm's major clients include the Equal Opportunities Commission and Oxford University. In the west country, Osborne Clarke and Burges Salmon, Bristol's largest firms, hold sway. The former was recently involved in 67 Protective Award Employment Tribunal applications in connection with a major plc and the latter in the management buyout of Spillers Pet Food business to form Dalgety Agriculture Ltd. Bond Pearce in Plymouth are also strong and have been involved in test cases concerning the Disability Discrimination Act and health and safety law in the last year.

Manchester's large commercial firms – Addleshaw Booth & Co, Dibb Lupton Alsop and Hammond Suddards are key players. Addleshaws' "blue chip" range of FTSE 100 company clients affords them high calibre work such as advising American Airlines on various matters in connection with the proposed merger with British Airways. Hammonds are the sole provider of employment law advice to Motorola Ltd. Dibbs have recently advised on various matters in connection with the MBO of Camelot Theme Park by Granada. In contrast, the five-partner niche firm Short Richardson & Forth is considered the outstanding employment law practice in Newcastle. The firm does a lot of tribunal work and has a nationwide practice with an equal amount of contentious and non-contentious work. In Leeds, leading firm Pinsent Curtis has particular strength in discrimination law, advising household names such as Zeneca on setting up voluntary European Works Councils.

Pensions and Employee Benefits

The large City firms are all active in pensions and employee benefits, especially Linklaters, Clifford Chance and Freshfields who have good reputations for both types of work, although Linklaters leads the field in employee benefits. They are involved in high profile work which recently included design and implementation of the ProShare Award-winning British Airways global share plans. Niche firm Sacker & Partners is very well-known for pensions work, acting for major organisations which include the Trustee of Electricity Supply Pension Scheme and Express Newspapers.

In the regions, it is the large commercial firms with corporate clients who specialise in these areas, with Pinsent Curtis being the key player in employee benefits outside London. Addleshaw Booth & Co have a strong presence in Leeds and Manchester with clients such as Asda and the Bradford & Bingley Pension Schemes. Also strong on the pensions side is Dibb Lupton Alsop who act for trustees of substantial pension schemes including the Alliance & Leicester and the Universities' Superannuation Scheme.

Leading Firms

London	Employment	Employee Benefits	Pensions
Allen & Overy	**	****	*****
Ashurst Morris Crisp		****	
Baker & McKenzie	*****	**	****
Beachcroft Wansbroughs	**		
Biddle			******
Bindman & Partners	***		
Boodle Hatfield	*		
Charles Russell	**		
Clifford Chance	**	******	*****
CMS Cameron McKenna	***		****
Denton Hall	*		
Dibb Lupton Alsop			*****
Eversheds	****		*****
Field Fisher Waterhouse		*	
Fox Williams	****		
Freshfields	*	******	******
Hammond Suddards			***
Herbert Smith	***	*****	**
Hodge Jones & Allen	***		
Langley & Co	*		
Lawford & Co	**		
Lewis Silkin	***		
Linklaters	*	******	******
Lovells	****	****	******
Macfarlanes	*		
Nabarro Nathanson			******
Nicholson Graham & Jones		**	
Norton Rose	*	***	
Osborne Clarke	*		
Paisner & Co	**		
Pattinson & Brewer	******		
Pinsent Curtis	*		
Richards Butler	**		*
Rowe & Maw	****		******
Rowley Ashworth	*****		
Russell Jones & Walker	****		
Sacker & Partners			******
Salans Hertzfeld & Heilbronn HRK	**		
Simmons & Simmons	******		**
Slaughter and May	***	*****	*****
Speechly Bircham	*		

Firms and their star ratings are based on Chambers' Directory 1999–2000. Six stars represent a top-ranked firm, five stars a second-ranked firm, etc.

London	Employment	Employee Benefits	Pensions
Stephenson Harwood	**		
Taylor Joynson Garrett			****
Theodore Goddard	**		
Thompsons McClure	****		
Titmuss Sainer Dechert	*		
Travers Smith Braithwaite		***	***

East Anglia	Employment	Pensions
Eversheds, Ipswich	******	
Eversheds, Norwich	******	***
Greenwoods, Peterborough	***	
Hewitson Becke + Shaw, Camb	******	
Leathes Prior, Norwich	**	
Mills & Reeve, Cambridge	******	
Mills & Reeve, Norwich	******	
Prettys, Ipswich	**	
Steele & Co, Norwich	*****	
Taylor Vinters, Cambridge	****	

Midlands	Employment	Employee Benefits	Pensions
Browne Jacobson, Nottingham	***		
Dibb Lupton Alsop, Birmingham	*****		
Edge Ellison, Birmingham	*****		******
Eversheds, Birmingham	******	**	*****
Eversheds, Derby			*****
Garretts, Birmingham			***
Hewitson Becke + Shaw, N'hampton	******		****
Higgs & Sons, Brierley Hill	****		
Martineau Johnson, Birmingham	***		
Mills & Reeve, Birmingham	***		
Pinsent Curtis, Birmingham	*****	******	****
Shakespeares, Birmingham	**		
Tyndallwoods, Birmingham	*		
Wragge & Co, Birmingham	******	**	******

Firms and their star ratings are based on Chambers' Directory 1999–2000. Six stars represent a top-ranked firm, five stars a second-ranked firm, etc.

North East	Employment	Employee Benefits	Pensions
Addleshaw Booth & Co, Leeds	*****	*****	******
Beachcroft Wansbroughs, Sheffield	***		
Bridge McFarland Solicitors, Grimsby	**		
Dibb Lupton Alsop, Leeds	*****		******
Dibb Lupton Alsop, Sheffield	*****		******
Dickinson Dees, Newcastle	****		***
Eversheds, Leeds	***		******
Eversheds, Newcastle upon Tyne	*****		
Ford & Warren, Leeds	***		
Garretts, Leeds		**	
Gordons Wright & Wright, Bradford	**		
Hammond Suddards, Leeds	*****	*	*****
Hay & Kilner, Newcastle upon Tyne	*		
Irwin Mitchell, Sheffield	**		
Jacksons, Stockton-on-Tees	***		
Malcolm Lynch, Leeds		*	
Nabarro Nathanson, Sheffield	***		***
Pinsent Curtis, Leeds	******	******	**
Read Hind Stewart, Leeds	***		
Rollit Farrell & Bladon, Hull	****		
Short Richardson & Forth, Newcastle	****		
Thompsons McClure, Newcastle		****	
Walker Morris, Leeds	***		***
Ward Hadaway, Newcastle	**		
Wrigleys, Leeds			**

North West	Employment	Employee Benefits	Pensions
Addleshaw Booth & Co, Manchester	******	*****	******
Beachcroft Wansbroughs, Manchester	*		
Cobbetts, Manchester	**		
Davies Wallis Foyster, Liverpool	**		*
Davies Wallis Foyster, Manchester			*
Dibb Lupton Alsop, Liverpool, Manc	*****		******
Eversheds, Manchester	****		*****
Garretts, Manchester		**	
Halliwell Landau, Manchester	**		***
Hammond Suddards, Manchester	******	*	***
Mace & Jones, Liverpool, Manchester	*****		
Masons, Manchester			***
Pannone & Partners, Manchester	**		
Thompsons McClure, Liverpool, Manc	***		
Whittles, Manchester	****		

Firms and their star ratings are based on Chambers' Directory 1999–2000. Six stars represent a top-ranked firm, five stars a second-ranked firm, etc.

South East	Employment	Pensions
Brachers, Maidstone	*	
Clarks, Reading	*	****
Clarkson Wright & Jakes, Orpington	*	
Cripps Harries Hall, Tunbridge Wells	*	
Donne Mileham & Haddock, Brighton	***	
Henmans, Oxford	***	
Morgan Cole, Oxford,Reading	******	
Pattinson & Brewer, Chatham	*	
Pickworths, Watford	*	
Stevens & Bolton, Guildford	*	
Underwoods, St. Albans	**	

South West	Employment	Employee Benefits	Pensions
Bevan Ashford, Bristol	*****		
Bond Pearce, Plymouth	******		
Burges Salmon, Bristol	*****	*	******
Cartwrights, Bristol	**		
Eversheds, Bristol	***		
Lester Aldridge, Bournemouth	**		
Michelmores, Exeter	*		
Osborne Clarke, Bristol	*****	*	******
Pattinson & Brewer, Bristol	***		
Stephens & Scown, Exeter	**		
Stone King, Bath	**		
Thompsons McClure, Bristol	***		
Thrings & Long, Bath	**		
Veale Wasbrough, Bristol	***		

Wales	Employment	Pensions
Edwards Geldard, Cardiff	***	
Eversheds, Cardiff	******	*****
Morgan Cole, Cardiff	*****	
Thompsons McClure, Cardiff	***	

Firms and their star ratings are based on Chambers' Directory 1999–2000. Six stars represent a top-ranked firm, five stars a second-ranked firm, etc.

ENVIRONMENTAL LAW

Area of Law

Don't assume that to be an environmental lawyer you must be a fully paid up member of Greenpeace and passionate about saving the planet. There certainly are careers for the passionate and crusading, but these are unlikely to be in private practice as a solicitor. Most environmental lawyers are instructed by corporate clients. Their role is primarily damage limitation - pre-emptive advice to prevent mistakes and the avoidance of damaging negative publicity and defence from prosecution when mistakes are made. It also includes a considerable involvement in transactional work, ensuring that environmental liability arising out of corporate acquisitions and disposals is fully apportioned and understood. A small minority of lawyers act for the Environment Agency, environmental pressure groups and private individuals.

Type of work

The caseload of an environmental lawyer will be split between contentious and non-contentious matters. Unusually for work often carried out in commercial firms contentious work may involve criminal law such as defending clients from criminal prosecution for breach of regulations. On the civil side it may involve tortious claims from those who suffer loss as a result of environmental impact as well as disputes as to liability following a mishap. On transactional work the environmental lawyers have a vital input where there is a sale or purchase of a business or land, drafting contractual provisions for the allocation of risk. There is also 'standalone' work; advice to clients, perhaps on the likely extent of their obligations following a change in the law or the introduction of new EC Regulations. This may cover issues such as waste, pollution control, water abstraction and nature conservation.

Most environmental litigators have wider practices. A number are commercial litigators with experience of environmental defence work, others do a mix of contentious and non-contentious work. Chris Papanicolaou, partner at Gouldens says that there is plenty of scope for getting involved in defending clients against prosecution by the regulatory authorities. He has seen an upturn in the numbers of prosecutions over the last 18 months since the authorities really began to flex their muscles. "In the magistrates court I might find myself running an argument on abuse of process. Or I might argue that the regulator has interpreted the law incorrectly." He points out that if there are still arguments being run over the 1954 Landlord and Tenant Act then it's going to take years before the environmental legislation of 1990/91 and onwards is interpreted properly. This means a lot of argument in court.

This is a key point. The fact that the area of law is relatively new means a substantial amount of research and interpretation to be carried out. A trainee can really come into his or her own in their environment seat given that they might become- almost by accident - the most expert person in the team on a new piece of legislation or EC Directive. Chris Papanicolaou told us that this was how his career in environmental law took off. "In 1989 the Environmental Protection Bill came out. I was the one who read it and did the report for the senior partner." Ross Fairley, senior associate at Allen & Overy, agrees. "There's far more of a role to play for a trainee in advising on the law because the area is so new. I think the appeal is that someone can come in and if a piece of legislation is in development their views can be as valid as people who have been in the area for five or six years."

Many specialists approach non-contentious work from a property or planning base. Others at the largest firms may be kept more than busy in a support role to the corporate lawyers. Environmental insurance is another niche, and there are firms who have cornered the market for claimants in multi-party environmental tort litigation.

Skills needed

"You have got to be a jack of all trades - a versatile lawyer" says Stephen Tromans, ex-head of Simmons & Simmons' environmental department, now at the Bar. Your range of work will span civil and criminal litigation, contract and tort, drafting and general regulatory advice. You certainly need a sound knowledge of how business and corporate structures work. It is therefore important to take a corporate seat during your training contract.

Of course you need an interest in environmental matters, property and planning issues perhaps, and maybe an appreciation of the countryside that you can use to fuel your interest in environmental law. It's by no means necessary but it doesn't hurt to have a very basic knowledge of the sciences as you'll need to read and understand technical reports. It's not your job to interpret them but you ought to be able to make sense of them so that you can appreciate how the law will apply to your client's business.

Your research, interpretation and presentation skills will be tested daily by clients treating your office as a 24-hour advice line. Ross Fairley confirms this. "I can get asked detailed and obscure questions over the phone. That's when you ask your trainee to do research into new areas of law." Chris Papanicolaou agrees "You sometimes have an information officer's role." Any development in the law must be communicated to those of your clients who might be affected by it.

In addition to the chance to shine on your own quite early on, you will need to be able to work as part of a team. "A trainee will also play their part on corporate deals, and that will mean helping out whoever they're sitting with drafting and doing the dreaded but important due diligence work" says Ross Fairley. "There's a lot of corporate support, an awful lot." Almost never is a corporate transaction led by environmental issues and so at times you'll have to expect to be regarded as a necessary evil by those who are pushing the deal forwards.

Career options

A decade ago solicitors suddenly saw environmental law as a new emerging practice area and got pretty excited about it. Commercial reality has tempered that excitement and lawyers now understand that it is not the growth area that everyone perceived it to be. Only the large London firms and a few large regional firms can offer specialism in environmental law. However, if you are lucky enough to become a specialist you will gain experience fast and be much in demand.

The Local Authority route is an alternative to starting out in private practice. A training contract with a LA may put you into contact with regulatory work, environment-related planning issues, waste management and air pollution cases and a role in advising the LA of its own liability in relation to property and business activities.

In-house positions are few and far between. Whilst it might be more common in the US for a company to have a lawyer responsible for environmental/Health and Safety issues, over here an in-house lawyer is more likely to have a general corporate counsel role. Paul Kelly at Northumbria Water, for example, deals with environmental law matters, commercial contracts, civil and criminal litigation as well as water and drainage law. Certain environmental pressure groups such as Greenpeace have their own lawyers.

The Department of the Environment, Transport and the Regions employs over 80 lawyers, generally recruited from within the Government Legal Service but with a small number coming from private practice. There are opportunities for trainees on GLS funded schemes in the Department (see GLS section). Chris Muttukumaru, the department's director of legal services, points out that the variety of work available for lawyers in the department allows for a flexible career. Work covers litigation, the drafting of subordinate legislation, preparation of bills, straight advisory work and contract drafting. He stresses that someone with a real interest in the way government operates would be best suited for such a role.

Another career option is with the Environment Agency for England and Wales. The Agency has responsibility for protecting and enhancing the environment through the regulation of the most potentially polluting corporate activities. It also protects water resources, flood defence and fisheries. The legal workload is diverse and includes the prosecution of environmental crime, civil litigation, the maintenance of the Thames Barrier and regulating the disposal of radioactive waste. Peter Kellett of the Agency's Head Office legal staff observes "The work is stimulating, highly politicised and vital. Our goal is firm but fair regulation to safeguard the environment for current and future generations." The Agency employs 56 solicitors and two trainees, seven barristers and five legal executives who work from eight regional offices and a head office in Bristol. Opportunities exist for further progression into management. Vacancies are generally advertised in the legal press. Anyone interested should contact the Regional Solicitor in the relevant office.

The Firms

In London, the strongest environmental practices are those of City firms Freshfields and Simmons & Simmons. Freshfields has an international practice based largely around energy work such as the environmental aspects of the Azerbaijan-Georgia international pipeline. Simmons has a niche in contaminated land issues and has advised the MoD on contaminated land issues and nuclear licensing. The teams fielded by these firms are among the largest in the country and handle a significant amount of non-contentious transactional work in addition to the defence of their clients on criminal and tortious matters. Leading claimant practice Leigh, Day & Co is a figurehead firm for multi-party and negligence work.

Niche firm Andrew Bryce & Co is the south east's leader, although the practice is tiny in comparison to those of the three top firms in the south west. Bond Pearce, Burges Salmon and Osborne Clark are each amongst the strongest commercial players in the region.

In Wales, the Cardiff offices of Eversheds and Morgan Cole boast the strongest environmental teams, whilst the Midlands leaders include Birmingham firms Wragge & Co, Edge Ellison, Pinsent Curtis. Sole practitioner Richard Buxton in Cambridge is the East Anglian leader, acting for the Environment Agency amongst others.

Eversheds top the tables in both the north west with Masons and the north east with Nabarro Nathanson. In Scotland Brodies WS and The Morton Fraser Partnership lead whilst in Northern Ireland the main name is Belfast's Cleaver Fulton Rankin.

Leading Firms

London	Environment	London	Environment
Allen & Overy	*****	Lawrence Graham	***
Ashurst Morris Crisp	**	Leigh, Day & Co	****
Barlow Lyde & Gilbert	**	Linklaters	**
Berwin Leighton	***	Lovells	**
S J Berwin & Co	**	Nabarro Nathanson	**
Bristows	**	Nicholson Graham & Jones	**
Clifford Chance	***	Norton Rose	**
CMS Cameron McKenna	*****	Rowe & Maw	*
Denton Hall	***	Simmons & Simmons	******
Freshfields	******	Slaughter and May	**
Gouldens	*	Stephenson Harwood	*
Herbert Smith	**	Trowers & Hamlins	*

South East	Environment
Andrew Bryce & Co, Coggeshall	******
Blake Lapthorn, Portsmouth	***
Bond Pearce, Southampton	**
Brachers, Maidstone	***

South East	Environment
Donne Mileham & Haddock, Brighton	**
Griffith Smith, Brighton	**
Stevens & Bolton, Guildford	*
White & Bowker, Winchester	**

South West	Environment
Bevan Ashford, Bristol	***
Bond Pearce, Plymouth	*****
Burges Salmon, Bristol	*****
Clarke Willmott & Clarke, Taunton	****
Fynn & Partners, Bournemouth	**
Lawrence Tucketts, Bristol	**

South West	Environment
Lester Aldridge, Bournemouth	**
Lyons Davidson, Bristol	****
Osborne Clarke, Bristol	*****
Stephens & Scown, Exeter	**
Veale Wasbrough, Bristol	***

Wales	Environment
Edwards Geldard, Cardiff	*
Eversheds, Cardiff	***

Wales	Environment
Morgan Cole, Cardiff	***

Midlands	Environment
Browne Jacobson, Nottingham	**
Edge Ellison, Birmingham	*****
Eversheds, Birmingham	****
Kent Jones and Done, Stoke-on-Trent	***

Midlands	Environment
Knight & Sons, Newcastle-under-Lyme	**
Pinsent Curtis, Birmingham	*****
Tyndallwoods, Birmingham	***
Wragge & Co, Birmingham	******

East Anglia	Environment
Eversheds, Norwich	*****
Hewitson Becke + Shaw, Camb	*****

East Anglia	Environment
Mills & Reeve, Norwich	*****
Richard Buxton, Cambridge	******

North East	Environment
Addleshaw Booth & Co, Leeds	****
Dibb Lupton Alsop, Sheffield	***
Dickinson Dees, Newcastle upon Tyne	***
Eversheds, Leeds	******

North East	Environment
Hammond Suddards, Leeds	***
Nabarro Nathanson, Sheffield	******
Pinsent Curtis, Leeds	***
Rollit Farrell & Bladon, Hull	**
Wilbraham & Co, Leeds	***

Firms and their star ratings are based on Chambers' Directory 1999–2000. Six stars represent a top-ranked firm, five stars a second-ranked firm, etc.

EUROPEAN UNION / COMPETITION

Area of law

This is a specialist practice area and covers both domestic and EU competition law and non-competition EU law. Many firms handle work spanning all these departments although most have particular strengths. Practice in these areas primarily concerns the implications of EU Articles 81 and 82 – the prohibitions on anti-competitive agreements and the abuse of a dominant market position. The forthcoming UK Competition Act aims to enforce these principles more strictly in domestic law, further fusing the competition sphere, and will have major implications for the legal profession.

Merger control and clearance is a major area of activity within the competition sphere – the regulation of both UK and European mergers which may have a bearing on competition in member state countries. Domestic competition law brings practitioners into close contact with regulatory bodies such as the Office of Fair Trading and the Department of Trade and Industry. Non-competition EU law covers the general principles of EU law and specialist areas such as the anti-discrimination provisions of the EU treaty. It is therefore of relevance to those seeking to specialise in employment or human rights law.

The volume of work generated by the EU is huge. It is now so pervasive that almost any practice area has to consider the impact of European law. Its legal directives have a huge bearing on a variety and a range of issues – affecting product liability, pensions, the environment and employment. In some of the big City firms the competition departments are outgrowing their role as niche areas and account for increasing levels of the firm's workload. There are several smaller City and regional firms with strong competition practices.

Type of work

All areas within competition are growing fast – it is a fairly specialised field in its own right and few junior lawyers would expect to sub-specialise initially. A senior lawyer from a reputable regional firm outlined the broad flavour of the work. "Many of the regional and smaller City firms try and deal with most things. Our main areas are merger control, UK competition law (Competition Act), EU Articles 81 and 82, state aids, sectorial regimes such as gas and telecoms and also public procurement."

Ralph Cohen from City firm SJ Berwin described the spread at his practice. "It could involve dealing with merger clearances, acting as general counsel and reviewing all forms of agreement with respect to competition laws, assisting companies in getting deals approved by regulators and explaining to clients why they are required to be competitive."

The large City firm Slaughter and May have a heavily mergers and acquisitions-related practice. Much of their work concerns obtaining approval in the relevant jurisdiction for the merger to take place. There is also significant stand-alone monopoly work – investigation of those companies that are alleged to have abused their market power. Michael Rowe, one of the firm's young competition lawyers, believes the proportion of work in these areas tends to reflect the client base of the firm. "Many of our clients are number one or two in their market, so monopoly and merger work frequently surfaces."

There are areas of competition where smaller niche firms tend to predominate. These include anti-competitive agreements, anti-trust measures and compliance agreements, review of industrial agreements and licence and supply agreements.

There is an increasingly significant regulatory aspect to competition work which exhibits different characteristics and involves a sizeable level of contact with officialdom in the EU cities. "You have to be prepared to talk to officials!" says Ros Kellaway from Eversheds. The amount of regulatory involvement will depend on the firm – some large City firms such as Denton Hall have made a specialisation out of it. One regional lawyer describes its growth – "Ten years ago no-one knew anything about regulation, now there are people in top City firms who do nothing but telecoms regulation."

Competition work can fall under both contentious and non-contentious umbrellas and it depends entirely on the practice where the focus will be. The emphasis is usually on providing strategic and preventative advice to avoid recourse to litigation. One lawyer stressed the importance of these services. "Although litigation is increasing, contentious work is a small part, probably under 10% of our business. In a sense, if you get to court you've been defeated."

The proportion of contentious work is likely to increase dramatically as the full impact of the Competition Act comes into force. Ros Kellaway believes the practice area as a whole may be moving in this direction. "Many member states are moving to more adversarial competition regimes – this may appeal to litigation people who want to specialise in this form of competition."

EU/competition law demands a greater knowledge of how markets operate than other corporate practice areas. Michael Rowe thinks there is less legality. "I actually spend a lesser proportion of my time researching black letter law or doing things that are strictly legal. I focus more time on reading into markets, developing an understanding of how markets operate, of how competition operates within those markets." Ralph Cohen makes a similar point. "It's unlike usual commercial practice in that the objective being sought is very different. There is no deal-making, it's all about commercial transactions complying with the regulators."

One senior partner believes it is technically more exacting. "As a corporate lawyer you need a lot of skills but you don't need to be quite as intellectually rigorous as you do in an area like competition. It is quite complex." Ros Kellaway stresses that it is "qualitatively different" to other practice areas because it is fundamentally about how markets work and the economics of these arrangements. "It is very different to a straightforward legal understanding. You have to understand a very different body of law, a different legal order – the final analysis is an economic market analysis."

There is major exposure to power and politics in the work of a competition lawyer and you will be immersed in industries that have their own sensitivities. Quite a high proportion of the work involves the exercise of advocacy skills, either in written form when putting together a brief or arguing a case – the essential aim being to tell a story that is credible and persuasive when appearing before the regulators.

Michael Rowe spent part of his training period distilling large amounts of statistical information and preparing appendices for files on behalf of senior lawyers. Greater responsibility was soon handed out and shortly after qualification he got actively involved in drafting and filing. Initially, he says, "my drafts were supervised but over time you get given a free hand."

Within competition law, client contact and meetings are frequently undertaken. Initially it may be with sales and marketing personnel and your own firm's partners, later with in-house counsel. As part of a team, a young lawyer's contact with clients may start off in an advisory role although this would progress to personal contact over time. Although it is a specialist area of law, positions of autonomy and greater responsibility are soon awarded with ability.

One regional competition lawyer described a typical day for a newly qualified junior. "Hours from 8.30 until 6.30, a meeting with and taking instructions from a client. Maybe working on a big merger case, fishing around on the internet for facts and figures, writing up merger filings, digging round for information, an hour maybe in the library, small amounts of drafting – although this is a difficult area of law, you will be given the opportunity to explain it to clients."

The amount of drafting required will depend on the size of the practice. The larger firms will have commercial departments that draft the agency and distribution agreements but competition lawyers may draft clauses to deal with specific relevant points. One partner was keen to get her juniors involved. "More and more these days clients will ring up with specific problem queries – this is the sort of thing we throw at the juniors: here's a little self-contained problem, go and sort it out."

A City practitioner outlined a similar range of duties. "The workload might include assisting with a merger filing, analysing products and businesses, advising on drafting agreements and attending an OFT meeting with a partner." Juniors are often involved when instructed on a new case and are required to research the background to the market, absorb information and become an expert very quickly – "the ability to see the wood from the trees is important," says Ralph Cohen.

Most competition firms have a Brussels office ("it would be difficult to function successfully without one,") and most firms are keen to send junior lawyers on placements there. Although some UK firms do the majority of active work on-site domestically, presence in Belgium is useful for "keeping eyes and ears open" and maintaining close contacts with the politicians and power-brokers! Some lawyers believe the new fully functioning domestic Competition Act may switch the focus more to the UK, but for the time being the ability to provide an effective pan-European service is strengthened with a Brussels presence. Anti-dumping and trade law is still one area of competition which remains very heavily Brussels-driven.

The trans-national nature of competition law brings with it a high degree of glamour, frequent travel and prestigious clients. Overseas trips and high-profile cases are common. According to one lawyer, "compared to the conveyancers, it can be glamorous! – we certainly to and fro a lot more, not just to Brussels but all over, you do pick up a fairly international clientele." The highlight for her is "working in an area of law that it is very rapidly developing. You open the paper every day and there are two or three stories that are of crucial relevance to something you're working on. Its a very immediate area – so it can be glamorous!"

Michael Rowe is pleased with his career choice and supports this view. "It's definitely a more interesting field of law to be in because there are so many options – you're more likely to travel, you're more likely to get a greater degree of responsibility at an earlier stage in your career but as with any other practice area, there will be times when you're in the office late and you're churning out something that has to be done. At those moments, it feels very unglamorous!"

Lifestyle-wise, competition is easier on the body then other areas of business law. "You don't have to sell your soul to being here 24 hours a day," said one lawyer. The hours can be cyclical in that they are governed by the number of transactions that are in the office at any one time, however they are becoming more regular as new areas of competition open up. Another competition expert believes the specialist areas give you more control over your life. "It is better in that it is far less meeting driven than corporate, you're more in control of your own destiny. There is flexibility to take time out during the day and make it up later."

Skills needed

Adaptability and a broad understanding are vital ingredients for success in competition. "You're dealing with another legal system and the application of competition rules – regulations that affect many different facets of our lives," says Ros Kellaway. "Ultimately, there's a need to recognise that it is a different body of law with different sets of constructions." An interest in business and markets is crucial in this field. A fundamental understanding of how they operate and how competition functions is essential – a mix of law and economics.

Competition is a complex area of law so technical skills like drafting are high on the agenda, supported by a clear analytical mind and top-level academic credentials. Attention to detail, thoroughness and good mediation and lobbying skills are also hugely desirable. You have to be a good facilitator as personal and influencing skills are very highly rated when dealing with the regulators. Michael Rowe says "You need to be an effective communicator, both in written and oral forms. Decisiveness is a must – clients are very frustrated by those who waver and sit on the fence. There are so many judgment calls involved that you have to be prepared to exercise your judgment and make a decision."

Linguistic ability is certainly an advantage and a seat in Brussels provides everyone with ample opportunities to practise French and German. "I've had so much opportunity to improve my French," said one keenly. It is particularly useful for communicating with commission officials. Non-linguists should not be put off however, "I wouldn't rate myself as a linguist but I've certainly not encountered any barriers or hurdles because of my absence of fluency."

This is a competitive field and highly qualified Europeans with a string of academics are always vying to enter the field. However, one partner feels there is a great demand for fundamental legal abilities. "Yes, it's good to have someone with a wide perspective, but the key questions are really – Are they clever? Can they communicate? Can they draft? Thousands of CVs cross my desk of people who think it would be an exciting area to be in. To be successful, enthusiasm and ability are essential!"

Political and economic understanding can augment core legal skills, and in terms of background knowledge "it does help to know the way the wind is blowing in Brussels" said one top regional lawyer. She recently took on a very junior assistant who hadn't any Brussels experience but was sufficiently good that it didn't make any difference to the firm's desire to recruit her. "We've recently sent her off for a six week spell out there." It is worth noting that this is a practice area where a high proportion of women have successfully made their mark in senior positions.

Career options

At the bottom end, EU/competition can be competitive and difficult to break into – more so perhaps than other areas of law, but there are still opportunities to be had. Ros Kellaway says the irony is, "that although there are enormous volumes of work generated by the EU, there are still relatively few practices with large departments and only a small number of niche practices." She receives a large number of unsolicited CVs from students keen to break into this area of practice but only some have the right mix of ability and practical experience. Don't be put off. The number of active firms and size of competition departments are set to carry on growing – this is very much an upwardly moving area of law. High academic credentials, technical and communication skills top the requirement list. Failing to qualify into an EU department, Ros Kellaway offers some alternative entry routes. "The best method is to enter a mainstream corporate department and work towards specialisation or go for employment which is hugely dominated by an EU dimension."

Competition is a specialist area but there are a reasonable number of options available as more companies take on in-house competition lawyers. The skills you develop in industry analysis and understanding of markets could well be employed in a broader business context. There is not a huge transference or movement out of private practice to in-house or mainstream business at the moment although success in this practice area certainly provides great potential for it.

The firms

The leading firms are those which handle a high volume of M&A (mergers & acquisitions) work. These include Freshfields, Linklaters, Lovells and Slaughter and May. Freshfields have acted for a major German consortium over the privatisation of Berlin Airports and have acted for Manchester United. Their recent merger with German competition practice, Deringer Tessin Herrmann and Sedemund has underlined their commitment to Europe. The same is true of Linklaters who have linked up with a number of European firms. They were advisors in 1999 in the gaining of EC approval of UK financial support for the Channel Tunnel Rail Link. British Airways and Microsoft are other prestigious active clients.

Lovells are widely regarded as having one of the best stand-alone EU/competition practices (not dependent purely on the firm's corporate work). They also have a strong Brussels office. Slaughter and May have an excellent reputation in merger control work.

More commercially-based London firms with less of a corporate practice are involved in competition work, often through their IT and IP practices. For example: Bristows handle competition work for IT, consumer electronics and pharmaceutical clients; Denton Hall are a leading energy and utilities practice and Theodore Goddard have some good technology and media clients.

There are only a few EU/competition practices outside London. In the south, Burges Salmon in Bristol dominate with a good reputation for their work with transport clients. Pinsent Curtis and Wragge & Co lead the field in Birmingham, while Addleshaw Booth & Co are among the top northern firms.

Leading Firms

London	EU
Allen & Overy	*****
Ashurst Morris Crisp	*****
Baker & McKenzie	**
Bristows	*
Clifford Chance	***
CMS Cameron McKenna	*
Denton Hall	****
Eversheds	**
Freshfields	******
Herbert Smith	*****

London	EU
Linklaters	******
Lovells	******
Norton Rose	****
Richards Butler	**
Rowe & Maw	*
S J Berwin & Co	****
Simmons & Simmons	***
Slaughter and May	******
Theodore Goddard	**

South & Wales	EU
Burges Salmon, Bristol	***
Edwards Geldard, Cardiff	**

East Anglia	EU
Eversheds, Cardiff	**
Maitland Walker, Minehead	**

Midlands & East Anglia	EU
Eversheds, Birmingham	**
Martineau Johnson, Birmingham	**

Midlands & East Anglia	EU
Pinsent Curtis, Birmingham	***
Wragge & Co, Birmingham	***

North	EU
Addleshaw Booth & Co, Leeds, Manc	***
Eversheds, Leeds	***
Eversheds, Manc, Middlesbrough	***

North	EU
Eversheds, Newcastle upon Tyne	***
Pinsent Curtis, Leeds	***

Firms and their star ratings are based on Chambers' Directory 1999–2000. Six stars represent a top-ranked firm, five stars a second-ranked firm, etc.

FAMILY LAW

Area of law

Family law covers divorce and any resulting financial settlements, domestic violence and issues relating to children. The former includes the growing area of the breakdown of unmarried relationships ('co-habitation'), while the latter includes private issues relating to children (such as residence, contact, surrogacy and adoption) and public law work (where children are taken into care by local authorities). While many lawyers practice in all these areas, the increasing specialisation of the profession means that there is a growing division between those who do largely financial/matrimonial and some private child work, and those who specialise in children and public law work. The division is often dependent on where the firm is situated, with high street and specialist legal aid firms doing the majority of public law work.

Of course all family lawyers require an up to date knowledge of family law, but there is more to the practice than that. Those working on the financial side also require an understanding of property, tax and pensions. Those on the public law side may need a grounding in criminal law, welfare law, education law and mental health issues.

Type of work

It is the job of the divorce lawyer to guide people through one of the most stressful periods of their lives. Their clients are often emotional, bitter and oblivious to logical argument, and the lawyer must be able delicately to circumvent the emotion. They must assist them to articulate their true concerns, and to ensure that they can see the bigger picture. Clients range from 'high net worth' individuals with substantial property and assets to people with very little money, but a painful contact battle to fight. The well-known London firms acting for wealthy and often high-profile clients must also learn how to deal with the media interest in their cases. Mishcon de Reya, for example, represent the Duchess of York and Jerry Hall.

High income matrimonial work often involves complex commercial, financial and tax problems, often with an international aspect. "An element of my work is looking at balance sheets, trust documents, pension funds and property transfers," says Richard Sax of Manches. A typical day may include meeting a new client who wishes to divorce her wealthy Italian husband and is worried about gaining custody of her children and calling the Cayman Islands to sort out another client's tax problem. For Mark Harper, partner at Withers, the most interesting cases are those involving competing jurisdictions in several different countries, which may make the finances harder to sort out on divorce, or that a divorce cannot be obtained in another jurisdiction.

Family work in a small or high street practice often involves both divorce and childcare work. A typical day will be very different from a day spent at Withers, Manches or Mishcon de Reya. Your first client of the morning may walk in off the street with her children, having fled from her violent husband. She needs an emergency loan, temporary accommodation and an injunction to prevent her husband from attacking her and her children. Your second client has a first appointment to discuss his potential divorce. The first interview in divorce cases is often a challenge. "The impact of the emotional consequence of a marriage is huge," comments Peter Jones, of Leeds firm Jones Myers Gordon, "I've had clients in front of me who have been in physical shock when their spouse has walked out. You need a lot of patience, you need a lot of understanding, but you still need to move them foward."

Public childcare work can be the most disturbing of all types of family law. It comes into play when a local authority has concerns about the welfare of a child and applies to the court to have the child taken into care. Childcare lawyers will thus represent either the parents, the local authority or the guardian appointed by the court to look after the child's interests. Parents in these cases often have a history of violence, alcoholism or mental illness while the children themselves could have the same problems and could also be victims of mental, physical or sexual abuse. Philip Kidd of Exeter firm Tozers, recently had to interview two children with armed police standing by because the father was looking for them with a gun. Acting for children, he says, requires particular skill. "You have to remember you're acting for a vulnerable human being," says Kidd, "My youngest child client was just seven days old, and the rest range from toddlers to teenagers. I see older children more often to check whether they continue to give the same instructions as their guardians. You can get into close relationships - but not too close, obviously, because you walk away at the end of the case."

As a trainee in a West End family department, your job will involve taking notes in client interviews, drafting documents, researching points of law and court work. The court work can vary from preparing bundles, to running to court to lodge documents in time, to attending court with counsel. In addition you will usually have a structured training programme, plenty of supervision and support and earn a reasonable salary.

In a high street practice you are more likely to be thrown in at the deep end and given more responsibility early on. You might arrive at work with nothing scheduled and within an hour have to make emergency applications to court on behalf of a woman who was assaulted by her partner the previous evening. The afternoon may involve assisting counsel on your own.

Skills needed

Family Law is as much about human behaviour as it is about the law. Mark Harper stresses that "you need to understand human weakness and to be able to be non-judgmental because you do hear the most extraordinary stories about emotional messes that people make of their lives." In order to gain the trust of your client and to enable their case to be properly represented, you must maintain a balance between detachment and empathy. "It is important to be objective and still to be sympathetic even if part of you wants to laugh or cry."

One important part of this objectivity is ensuring that the client understands the importance of compromise. As Peter Jones comments: "When the lawyers walk away, particularly if there are children involved, the parties still have to maintain a relationship." Thus it is vital that a family lawyer has what Jones calls "non-confrontational skills...the ability to negotiate from strength but without making it litigious." While many relationship breakdowns do end up in court, "the more you litigate, the more you cost your clients, and most of it is money down the drain." As the alternative forum of mediation becomes more popular, fewer people will seek recourse to the courts, and lawyers will have to become skilled in this very specific environment, which can be highly charged, but may lead to a resolution more suited to the parties' immediate needs.

It is vital to establish a clear line of communication with your client. This involves listening properly to their instructions, so that you can successfully gauge their main concerns, and making sure that they understand your advice fully. Mark Harper is clear on this point. "You can take very few steps in any family law case without meeting your client or writing to tell them what's going on and seeking their instructions."

Childcare work requires particular skills, such as the ability to deal with very distressing situations and distressed clients. Says Libby Wright, from niche child law firm Goodman Ray, "While it is **not** your job to be a counsellor for your client, representing your client effectively involves talking to them about the whole context of what's going on, how they feel about it and how others may see things differently." This can be difficult. One of her recent clients was a young woman of sixteen whose baby had been taken into care following an alleged non-accidental injury. Over a period of one and a half years, almost every time that she rang, the young woman was in tears.

Representing parents can be particularly challenging. "A case may concern serious allegations of abuse or neglect by a parent," says Libby Wright, "but you need to be able to separate any emotional response you might have to the case from your job as their solicitor." Most newly-qualified solicitors who specialise in childcare will start by representing parents, as at the moment you need to be at least three years' qualified (and have experience doing childcare work) before you can apply to get on the Law Society's Children Panel, from which most representatives for children are selected.

If you are representing children, there may be further requirements. "You need to be able to get on your hands and knees and play around with a five year old child for an hour to find out what they want,"says Philip Kidd.

Many childcare cases also involve medical experts such as family paediatricians, consultant child psychiatrists and radiographers. "If you need to ask a consultant neurosurgeon whether a child's bilateral subdural haematoma was likely to be an accidental injury, you need a fair amount of medical knowledge," adds Philip Kidd. You will also need to be fully conversant with the legal aid system as parents automatically get legal aid if their child is taken into care.

For the financial side of matrimonial work, you'll need a reasonable commercial acumen and a head for figures. You must also be "dogged and determined" says Mark Harper, "and not be deterred by mountains of documents that may be produced to mislead you as to where the assets are."

Above all, whatever type of family law you are doing, you must be comfortable spending your time with troubled, emotional and, often, angry people. It can be tough, but this humanitarian aspect is what can make family law so rewarding for the right kind of lawyer.

Career options

In the prestigious London firms, and in some large regional outfits, trainees may be able to do a family seat as part of their training. The work will generally be for wealthy private clients and will focus on divorce and financial disputes. In the high street, work will be a mixture of private and legal aid cases. Some high street family departments are mixed with conveyancing or criminal departments, so you will receive a grounding in several areas. There will be the opportunity to handle childcare work from day one.

There is no typical career path into family law, and some lawyers come to it after working for several years in City firms. However, because it is such an emotional and demanding field, most family lawyers have been committed to it from very early on in their careers. According to Mark Harper, it certainly helps to have gained some prior experience in counselling or dealing with people. "If you've only studied law through books, it can be quite overwhelming dealing with all this raw emotion."

Many family lawyers derive their vocation from the cutting edge element of much of the work and the pace of legislative change. As Peter Jones puts it, "Its developments attempt to reflect, perhaps faster than most areas of law, the change of views of society." At present the main issues under the microscope are no-fault divorce, pension sharing and the rights of cohabitees and gay and lesbian couples. "The next five years are not going to be complacent," says Jones, "and it stops you from being bored."

The alternatives to private practice are limited, but qualified lawyers can work in-house for local authorities and charities such as the NSPCC. In rare cases, those with good advocacy skills might go to the bar, but this is preferably done at an early stage in their career. Family lawyers occasionally move into mediation or social work, but the remuneration in these fields is poor and the pressure can be just as great as private practice.

The firms

Withers and Manches have the largest and most well known family departments in London. They are retained by a large number of wealthy and high profile clients and have particular expertise in complex financial settlements and children's issues, pre-nuptial agreements and work with an international dimension. Bates, Wells & Braithwaite is another prestigious firm, with expertise in jurisdiction disputes and international child abduction. Charles Russell and Farrer & Co are other examples of leading firms in this market. Bindman & Partners and Hodge Jones & Allen are two reputed legal aid practices who recruit trainees.

The leading firms in the south east are Blandy & Blandy in Reading and Morgan Cole in Oxford. Both regularly handle financial settlements over the £1m mark and have significant public law practices. Lester Aldridge, based in Bournemouth leads the field in the south west, with high value divorce settlements and an unusual niche in Japanese divorce referrals. In Wales, Hugh James Ford Simey has offices around the region, and is able to provide a full range service from care and adoption through to ancillary relief. Birmingham's Barbara Carter is the Midlands' top children work lawyer, while larger firms such as Freeth Cartwright Hunt Dickens in Nottingham and Nelsons in Derby offer both matrimonial and children teams. Buckle Mellows, Eversheds and Fosters are the best known firms in East Anglia, while Farleys, Pannone and Partners and Jones Maidment Wilson are leaders in the north west. In Leeds the large commercial firms Addleshaw, Booth & Co. and Dickinson Dees handle very large financial disputes, while Irwin Mitchell and Jones Myers Gordon have a broad practice.

Leading Firms

London	Family
Anthony Gold, Lerman & Muirhead	**
Barnett Sampson	***
Bates, Wells & Braithwaite	*****
Bindman & Partners	***
Charles Russell	*****
Clintons	***
Collyer-Bristow	****
David du Pré & Co	*
David Truex and Company	**
Dawson & Co	**
Dawson Cornwell	****
The Family Law Consortium	***
Farrer & Co	*****
Fisher Meredith	***
Forsters	*
Goodman Ray	***
Gordon Dadds	*****

London Firms	Family
Hodge Jones & Allen	**
Kingsley Napley	****
Levison Meltzer Pigott	*****
Manches	******
Margaret Bennett	*
Miles Preston & Co	*****
Mishcon de Reya	****
Osbornes	*
Payne Hicks Beach	***
Reynolds Porter Chamberlain	***
Russell Jones & Walker	**
Russell-Cooke, Potter & Chapman	**
Sears Tooth	*****
Stephenson Harwood	**
The Simkins Partnership	*
Withers	******
Wright Son & Pepper	*

South East	Family
Blandy & Blandy, Reading	******
Brachers, Maidstone	****
Buss Murton, Tunbridge Wells	****
Charles Russell Baldocks, Guildford	****
Coffin Mew & Clover, Portsmouth	****
Cripps Harries Hall, Tunbridge Wells	****
Darbys Mallam Lewis, Oxford	*****
Donne Mileham & Haddock, Brighton	****
Henmans, Oxford	****
Iliffes Booth Bennett, Uxbridge	****
Leonard Gray, Chelmsford	*****

South East	Family
Linnells, Oxford	*****
Manches, Oxford	*****
Matthew Arnold & Baldwin, Watford	****
Max Barford & Co, Tunbridge Wells	****
Morgan Cole, Oxford	******
Paris Smith & Randall, Southampton	****
Pictons, St. Albans	****
Rowberry Morris & Co., Reading	*****
Thomson Snell & Passmore, T. Wells	*****
Whitehead Monckton, Maidstone	****

South West	Family
Battens (with Poole & Co), Yeovil	****
Bond Pearce, Plymouth	*****
Burges Salmon, Bristol	*****
Clarke Willmott & Clarke, Taunton	*****
Coodes, St. Austell	****
E. David Brain & Co, St. Austell	****
Faulkners, Frome	****
Foot & Bowden, Plymouth	*****
Gill Akaster, Plymouth	*****
Hartnell & Co, Exeter	*****
Hooper & Wollen, Torquay	*****
Ian Downing, Plymouth	*****
Lawrence Tucketts, Bristol	****

South West	Family
Lester Aldridge, Bournemouth	******
Nalder & Son, Truro	****
Nash & Co, Plymouth	****
Stephens & Scown, Exeter	*****
Stone King, Bath	****
Stones, Exeter	***
The Stokes Partnership, Crewkerne	****
Tozers, Exeter, Plymouth, Torquay	*****
Trumps, Bristol	*****
Veale Wasbrough, Bristol	*****
Withy King, Bath	****
Wolferstans, Plymouth	*****
Woollcombe Beer Watts, Newton Abbot	*****

Wales	Family
Granville-West, Newbridge	**
Harding Evans, Newport	**
Hugh James Ford Simey, Cardiff	***
Larby Williams, Cardiff	***
Leo Abse & Cohen, Cardiff	**

Wales	Family
Martyn Prowel Solicitors, Cardiff	***
Nicol, Denvir & Purnell, Cardiff	***
Spicketts, Pontypridd	**
Wendy Hopkins & Co, Cardiff	***

Midlands	Family
Barbara Carter, Birmingham	***
Blair Allison & Co, Birmingham	***
Blakesley Rice MacDonald, Ch'field	**
Blythe Liggins, Leamington Spa	*
Challinors Lyon Clark, West Bromwich	**
Elliot Mather, Chesterfield	**
Freeth Cartwright Hunt Dickins, Nott'm	***
Goodger Auden, Burton-on-Trent	**
Hadens, Walsall	**
Lanyon Bowdler, Shrewsbury	**

Midlands	Family
Morton Fisher, Kidderminster	**
Nelsons, Derby, Grantham	***
Rupert Bear Murray Davies, Nott'm	***
Tyndallwoods, Birmingham	***
Varley Hibbs & Co, Coventry	*
Wace Morgan, Shrewsbury	***
Warren & Allen, Nottingham	*
Woodford-Robinson, Northampton	*
Young & Lee, Birmingham	***

East Anglia	Family
Buckle Mellows, Peterborough	***
Cozens-Hardy & Jewson, Norwich	**
Eversheds, Norwich	***
Fosters, Norwich	***
Graeme Carmichael, Ipswich	**
Greenwoods, Peterborough	***
Hatch Brenner, Norwich	**
Hunt & Coombs, Peterborough	***
Miller Sands, Cambridge	***
Mills & Reeve, Cambridge, Norwich	**
Rudlings & Wakelam, Thetford	**
Silver Savory Smith, Cambridge	***
Ward Gethin, King's Lynn	***

North West	Family
Addleshaw Booth & Co, Manchester	**
Burnetts, Carlisle	**
Cuff Roberts, Liverpool	**
Farleys, Blackburn	***
Forbes & Partners, Blackburn	**
Green & Co, Manchester	***
Jackson & Canter, Liverpool	**
Jones Maidment Wilson, Manchester	***
Morecroft Urquhart, Liverpool	**
Nightingales, Manchester	**
Pannone & Partners, Manchester	***
Rowlands, Manchester	**
Stephensons, Salford	**

North East	Family
Addleshaw Booth & Co, Leeds	******
Andrew M. Jackson & Co, Hull	***
Archers, Stockton-on-Tees	*
Askews, Redcar	*
Blacks, Leeds	**
Cranswick Watson, Leeds	***
Crombie Wilkinson, York	*
Dickinson Dees, Newcastle upon Tyne	*****
Gordons Wright & Wright, Bradford	***
Gosschalks, Hull	**
Graham & Rosen, Hull	**
Grahame Stowe, Bateson, Leeds	**
Hay & Kilner, Newcastle-upon-Tyne	***
Henry Hyams & Co, Leeds	**
Irwin Mitchell, Sheffield	*****
Jacksons, Stockton-on-Tees	**
Jones Myers Gordon, Leeds	*****
Philip Hamer & Co, Hull	**
Punch Robson, Middlesbrough	**
Samuel Phillips & Co, Nwecastle	***
Sinton & Co, Newcastle upon Tyne	**
Zermansky & Partners, Leeds	*****

Firms and their star ratings are based on Chambers' Directory 1999–2000. Six stars represent a top-ranked firm, five stars a second-ranked firm, etc.

INTELLECTUAL PROPERTY

Area of law

Intellectual property lawyers divide the field into two broad areas: patent work (hard IP) ie. the protection of inventions; and non-patent work (soft IP) ie. trade marks, design rights, copyright, passing off, anti-counterfeiting and confidential information. 'Hard IP' has links with product liability work. Both types of IP overlap with IT (information technology), telecommunications, broadcasting and digital media.

Type of work

IP clients include manufacturers and suppliers of hi-tech and engineering products, leading brand owners, teaching hospitals, universities, scientific institutions and media clients (including broadcasters, newspapers, publishers and artists). IP work can be contentious and non-contentious. Disputes usually revolve around an allegation of infringement of one or more intangible property rights existing in an invention, a literary/artistic work, a trade mark or a product.

"You'll be instrumental in defending a leading brand and fighting off competitors in the market place," says Vanessa Marsland, an IP partner at Clifford Chance. "One of my clients is Kimberley Clark which owns the Andrex brand of toilet paper. Last year their competitor, Fort Sterling, started packaging its rival Nouvelle eco-toilet paper with the message that softness was guaranteed. If customers disagreed, they could exchange the product for a packet of Andrex. Kimberley Clark felt the offer was confusing, and that people might believe that Nouvelle was endorsed by Andrex." Clifford Chance carried out a number of street surveys to see if people really were confused. "I've got an interesting job," Marsland jokes, "I show people packets of toilet paper." But she won the case.

Richard Kempner, a partner in the Leeds office of Addleshaw Booth & Co, handled the first supermarket 'look-alike' case, defending Asda, makers of Puffin biscuits, against United Biscuits,' makers of Penguin chocolate biscuits. United claimed that Asda was passing off the Puffin as the Penguin, and that the Puffin name and picture breached its Penguin trade marks. The case ended in a draw. Asda won on trade mark infringement, but United Biscuits won on passing off, forcing Asda to alter its packaging.

Asima Khan, a newly qualified solicitor with Addleshaw Booth, worked on the Puffin-Penguin case as a trainee. "IP lets you see the corporate side of work but in a more interesting way," she says. "I was surprised there was such high-profile work outside London. Before starting my IP seat, I helped produce market research questionnaires which were part of Asda's defence. At the beginning of my IP seat, I attended the closing speeches of the case at the Royal Courts of Justice. It was so exciting playing a part in a case like that."

Internet IP law is a fledgling area of work, constantly throwing up new issues. Clifford Chance's Vanessa Marsland is involved in a variety of cases concerning trade mark infringement on the Internet. Many cases, she says, involve complex international issues. "If you're trading globally on the Internet and infringe someone else's rights, are you guilty of infringement all over the world or just in the country where you're physically located?"

An IP lawyer's day might begin with an early morning hearing in the Patents Court. Your client, a French company, has brought an action for patent infringement. The other side's applying to strike it out on a technical ground. They fail. By mid-morning, you're on the phone to the client to tell them the good news and discuss possible options for a settlement. When you get back to the office, there's a message waiting for you from an American bio-tech company. They're forming a joint venture with a multinational pharmaceutical company, and want you to draft various licensing agreements. They have to be finished within 48 hours. You've been working at it for an hour when the phone rings. It's one of your most important clients. They have evidence that their goods are being counterfeited, and want to know what steps they can take to protect their trade marks. You advise them to commence proceedings immediately, and apply the next day for an order preventing the other side from destroying evidence. You get on the phone to counsel's clerk and say you'll need one of his top barristers the next morning. Then you spend the rest of the evening taking evidence from your client and preparing the affidavit in support of the next day's application. You get home late, slump into bed and wake up in the middle of the night worrying about those licensing agreements. There's another long day ahead of you tomorrow . . .

Typical lawyer

Patent law requires a basic understanding of science, and you'll need at least science A-levels. Non-scientists need not be discouraged, however. For most other kinds of IP work, a science background is usually irrelevant. "Non-scientists would certainly be able to handle most trade mark and copyright disputes", says Nicholas Macfarlane, an IP partner at Lovells. "I think a good IP department should have a mix of scientists and non-scientists. Curiosity in things artistic and technological is a good ingredient, and you should be interested by what your clients do."

The varied subject matter in IP law tends to attract 'characters,' says Michael Hart, co-ordinating partner of the IP/IT group at Baker & McKenzie. "IP lawyers are more quirky and eccentric than most. I suppose it takes a certain sort of person to deal effectively with a complicated biotech dispute one day and Barbie dolls the next." IP lawyers also need to be all-rounders, doing a mixture of contentious and non-contentious work. "If you only litigate, there's a danger of ending up as a dogged old war-horse," says Michael Hart. "Conversely, if you do nothing but non-contentious commercial work, you are less exposed to how the courts can construe your contracts. Handling both areas makes each one easier. IP law is really good fun and I have never wanted to do any other type of law".

Few students know much about IP when they begin their training contracts, which is why most large firms with an IP specialism send trainees on a course in Bristol run by the Intellectual Property Lawyers' Association. The residential course counts as half an MA and is taught by partners from major IP firms.

Career options

Many IP lawyers began their careers as litigators or general commercial lawyers and only started to specialise as they saw niche areas opening up. Constantly developing technology keeps this field moving and there are ever-increasing opportunities to specialise in IP from early on in your career. If you choose the right firm, you'll probably be able to do at least one IP seat during training.

IP knowledge is equally valuable outside private practice. Manufacturing, pharmaceutical and research companies employ patent specialists and there are in-house legal teams at Proctor & Gamble, Reckitt & Colman and Unilever. Non-patent lawyers find their way into the media world: all major publishers and television companies have in-house IP lawyers.

Alternatives to strictly legal practice include more general business/management posts within the organisations mentioned above. Many broadcasting companies now employ lawyers in positions such as Head of Business and Legal Affairs. Additionally firms of trademark agents and patent attorneys are often keen to recruit these with a legal training.

The Firms

In London, firms specialise to such an extent that they are considered separately for patent and non-patent work. Bird & Bird and Simmons & Simmons are considered outstanding in both fields. Simmons & Simmons have a particular reputation for bio-tech patent work and trade marks, recently acting in the 'SmithKline Beecham v Merck' case. Bird & Bird offer a full IP service and acted in a third of all patent actions which went to full hearing in the High Court in 1998. Recent activities include anti-counterfeiting work for the FIFA World Cup. Other London firms with strong practices in both hard and soft IP work include Clifford Chance, Lovells, Bristows, Eversheds and Taylor Joynson Garrett. Clifford Chance acted in the 'Coflexip v Stolt Comex' patent case and advised Mars Electronic in relation to the reverse engineering of electronic products. Lovells are respected for a wide range of IP work and boast an impressive list of clients, including Volvo and The Guardian. Bristows have long been known as leaders in patent work and also have a substantial non-patent practice which includes a trade mark filing service. Eversheds has seen its IP practice grow significantly since the merger with Frere Cholmeley Bischoff and recently conducted a series of multi-national patent cases re medical devices ('Boston Scientific Corp v EGP') before the European Court of Justice. Taylor Joynson Garrett continues to enhance its profile and has been acting in leading patent cases 'Hoechst Celanese Corporation v BP Chemicals Ltd' and the Eli Lilly case. Smaller London firms noted for their IP work include Willoughby & Partners (trade marks and anti-counterfeiting in particular) and Needham & Grant (highly respected for both patent and non-patent work).

The leading firms in the south east are The Law Offices of Marcus O'Leary in Bracknell, and Willoughby & Partners in Oxford, who have taken over parts of the now-defunct Dallas Brett. Osborne Clarke in Bristol have the best dedicated IP practice in the south west and an excellent reputation for soft IP work in particular, while Wragge & Co, who have a strong patent litigation practice, are considered the top IP firm in the Midlands. Hewitson Becke + Shaw are pre-eminent in East Anglia with Mills & Reeve, who are known for their expertise in non-contentious bio-tech work and experience in the general science and electronics field, not far behind. Addleshaw Booth & Co have the largest practice in the north, with 17 lawyers spread between Leeds and Manchester. Their principal rivals are Dibb Lupton Alsop in the north east and Halliwell Landau in the north west. The leading firms in Scotland are Maclay Murray & Spens and McGrigor Donald, with the latter firm having acted for 3i plc in the establishment of Roslin Biomed Ltd, a company set up to exploit the 'Dolly the Sheep' technology in the field of xenotransplantation.

Leading Firms

London	IP Patent	IP Non-Patent
Allen & Overy	**	***
Ashurst Morris Crisp		**
Baker & McKenzie	***	****
Bird & Bird	******	******
Briffa		**
Bristows	******	*****
Charles Russell		*
Clifford Chance	*****	******
CMS Cameron McKenna		**
Denton Hall		**
Dibb Lupton Alsop		**
Eversheds	**	*****
Field Fisher Waterhouse		**
Freshfields		**
Gouldens		*
Hammond Suddards	**	***

London	IP Patent	IP Non-Patent
Henry Hepworth		*
Herbert Smith	*****	****
Linklaters	*****	****
Llewelyn Zietman		***
Lovells	*****	*****
Macfarlanes		**
Nabarro Nathanson		**
Needham & Grant	*****	***
Norton Rose		**
Olswang		***
Roiter Zucker		**
Rowe & Maw		**
Simmons & Simmons	******	******
Slaughter and May		***
Stephenson Harwood		***
Taylor Joynson Garrett	******	******
Titmuss Sainer Dechert		**
Wilde Sapte		*
Willoughby & Partners		****
Withers		*

East Anglia	IP
Eversheds, Cambridge, Norwich	*****
Greenwoods, Peterborough	****
Hewitson Becke + Shaw, Camb.	******
Mills & Reeve, Cambridge, Norwich	*****
Taylor Vinters, Cambridge	**

Midlands	IP
Browne Jacobson, Nottingham	**
Dibb Lupton Alsop, Birmingham	**
Edge Ellison, Birmingham	****
Eversheds, Birmingham	***
Eversheds, Nottingham	***
Freeth Cartwright Hunt Dickins, Nottingham	***
Hewitson Becke + Shaw, N'thampton	***
Martineau Johnson, Birmingham	*****
Pinsent Curtis, Birmingham	*****
Shoosmiths, Northampton	***
Wragge & Co, Birmingham	******

North East	IP
Addleshaw Booth & Co, Leeds	******
Dibb Lupton Alsop, Leeds, Sheffield	******
Dickinson Dees, Newcastle upon Tyne	**
Eversheds, Leeds	*****
Hammond Suddards, Leeds	*****
Irwin Mitchell, Leeds	*
Lupton Fawcett, Leeds	****
Pinsent Curtis, Leeds	*****
Walker Morris, Leeds	****

North West	IP
Addleshaw Booth & Co, Manch.	******
Davies Wallis Foyster, Liverpool	*
Dibb Lupton Alsop, Manchester	***
Eversheds, Manchester	**
Halliwell Landau, Manchester	******
Hammond Suddards, Manchester	***
Hill Dickinson, Stockport	*****
Kuit Steinart Levy, Manchester	**
Lawson Coppock & Hart, Manchester	**
Philip Conn & Co, Manchester	*
Taylors, Blackburn	**
Wacks Caller, Manchester	*

South East	IP
Donne Mileham & Haddock, Brighton	*****
Garretts, Reading	***
Lochners Technology Solicitors, Godalming	****
Nabarro Nathanson, Reading	****
Pitmans, Reading	***
The Law Offices of Marcus J. O'Leary, Bracknell	******
Willoughby & Partners, Oxford	******

South West	IP
Beachcroft Wansbroughs, Bristol	***
Bevan Ashford, Bristol	*****
Burges Salmon, Bristol	*****
Clarke Willmott & Clarke, Bristol	***
Humphreys & Co, Bristol	****
Laytons, Bristol	****
Lester Aldridge, Bournemouth	****
Osborne Clarke, Bristol	******

Wales	IP
Edwards Geldard, Cardiff	***
Eversheds, Cardiff	***
Morgan Cole, Cardiff	***

IT & TELECOMS

Area of law

The boundaries between IT, telecoms, IP, broadcasting, e-commerce and digital media are growing ever more blurred as internet 'convergence' issues tighten their grip over the broader communications industry. With IP enjoying a section in its own right and broadcasting and digital media covered under media, this section will focus on IT, e-commerce and telecommunications law. IT work (including e-commerce) consists principally of outsourcing (where outside IT specialists are brought in to set up and run a company's computer systems), systems development, IT contract drafting and on-line/internet advice. Telecoms largely revolves around proffering advice on the regulatory statutes which govern telecommunications companies and are designed to protect the interests of consumers. Competition law is also of ever growing importance in the telecoms field, as mega-mergers bring monopoly issues to the forefront. The transactional side of telecoms, highlighted this year by several major mergers within the industry, differs little from standard M&A work, though a certain knowledge of regulatory matters is of course necessary.

Type of work

A typical day for an IT lawyer might include advising on a new software development contract, reading through a system integration contract, advising on an internet issue and popping down to court for a hearing on a major system. Osborne Clarke's Paul Gardner, an expert in computer games, is currently advising a games publisher on what copyright allows you to depict in terms of club strips in football games and several games console manufacturers on how close to the Sony games console they can design their products without infringing copyright.

For internet and communications lawyer David Naylor of US firm Weil Gotshal & Manges there is no such thing as a 'typical day.' A week's work might consist of advising internet and communications startups on all aspects of internet law from content liability to on-line contracting through to advising more mature internet companies on building business networks across Europe and acting for telecoms companies on UK and EU commercial and regulatory matters. He would be in frequent contact with the firm's US and Brussels offices in relation to cross-border work for US and EU clients and collaborating with the corporate department on funding issues and acquisitions in commercial internet deals. Foreign travel is not as frequent as you might think, as London is a major hub for the telecoms industry anyhow and "our office is so phenomenally busy. It is glamorous though, and I have always wanted to be part of the internet revolution."

Skills needed

According to Paul Gardner, IT law spans the regulatory/transactional divide (though the latter predominates) requiring the IT lawyer to be both a "deal-maker" and have an excellent understanding of "hard" regulatory matters, especially in connection with the internet. The world of IT/digital media is far from an "ivory tower," and the successful practitioner will need both a good grasp of the commercial world and the ability to "keep up to speed with industry practices." A sensitivity to the needs of artists in related areas, such as music, is also of the first importance, as is a willingness to "roll up your sleeves" and get involved at the coalface. David Naylor agrees, "you need real mental dexterity and a gut feel for the issues, as you need to stay on top of a dynamic industry that is growing exponentially in several different directions. But perhaps more than anything else, you must be the sort of person who feels challenged and thrilled by change."

For straight telecoms work, a general grounding in corporate together with some industry knowledge and maybe a background in economics are particularly useful attributes. You should not be afraid of technical language or jargon and being innovative certainly helps. A knowledge of competition law is also an absolute must.

The Firms

IT

The leading IT firms in London include the outstanding Bird & Bird, corporate leviathan Clifford Chance and Baker & McKenzie. Bird & Bird are particularly well known for their public sector procurement work, especially when it comes to telecoms related project finance and for their superb technical expertise. Baker & McKenzie, best known for their litigation strength, acted for Symbian in relation to the licensing of the EPOC operating system for small computers and mobile telephone handsets, which could revolutionise the way we use the internet. Clifford Chance is seen to be equally at home dealing with regulatory and corporate matters, though clients are principally major corporate users within the financial and trading sectors. In the related field of internet/e-commerce law, Bird & Bird scores highly once again, being hailed as a "true convergence practice" and counting well known names such as Demon Internet amongst its clients. Olswang are famed for their e-commerce expertise and their work on behalf of large internet service providers. They advised Microsoft Web TV on its UK trial service, including arrangements with broadcasters and distributors.

Nabarro Nathanson's Reading outpost is seen almost unanimously to be the leading IT practice in the south of England. Known for both contentious and non-contentious work, the practice is admired for its "unrivalled" advice when it comes to IT project work. Wragge & Co are the unrivalled IT kings of the Midlands, having handled a major £75m outsourcing contract for the Driving Standards Agency.

In the north, Masons' Leeds and Manchester offices and Rotherham's Oxley & Coward are the leading lights in the IT sphere. Masons' Leeds office includes a well known expert in data protection law, while Manchester is best known for its PFI/IT project work. Oxley & Coward acts on behalf of both public sector clients and industry-orientated corporates. Maclay Murray & Spens are clearly the leading IT practice north of the border, having acted for 3i in relation to a large scale technology investment in Scotland.

Telecoms

The telecoms sector continues to be dominated by the large London firms and a handful of ambitious American interlopers. The key players in the capital are still regulatory wizards Bird & Bird, City corporate heavyweights Clifford Chance, Allen & Overy and Simmons & Simmons and international US outfit Baker & McKenzie. Bird & Bird acts primarily on regulatory matters. They advised BT, as external UK counsel, on the establishment of its new US$20bn joint venture with AT&T. Clifford Chance are best known for their corporate and financial telecoms practice, as are Allen & Overy, who also have an excellent international profile. Simmons & Simmons, whose partners are well known to leading telecoms industry figures, acted for One2One on all aspects of its MMC (Monopolies And Mergers Commission) reference by the UK telecoms regulator. Baker & McKenzie, unsurprisingly given their global reach, acted for Iridium in 34 jurisdictions worldwide in relation to telecoms licensing, spectrum allocation and operational issues arising from the establishment of the global low earth orbit satellite. Eversheds' Leeds office and Cheltenham's Wiggin & Co, which has extensive City and international contacts, remain the only regional telecoms practices of note.

Leading Firms

London	Computer/IT	Telecoms
Allen & Overy	****	******
Ashurst Morris Crisp	**	***
Baker & McKenzie	******	******
Berwin Leighton	**	
Bird & Bird	******	******
Bristows	***	
Charles Russell		***
Clifford Chance	******	******
CMS Cameron McKenna	**	
Coudert Brothers		**
Denton Hall	*****	*****
Dibb Lupton Alsop	**	
Field Fisher Waterhouse	****	***
Freshfields	**	*****
Hammond Suddards	***	
Harbottle & Lewis	***	
Henry Hepworth		
Herbert Smith	***	
Kemp & Co	***	
Linklaters	***	*****
Lovells	*****	***
Masons	*****	
McNeive Solicitors	****	
Nabarro Nathanson	**	
Olswang	******	****
Osborne Clarke	****	
Paisner & Co	***	
Rakisons		**
Robertson & Co, Technology Law Practice	**	
Rowe & Maw	***	**
Sidley & Austin		**
Simmons & Simmons	***	******
Slaughter and May	***	
Tarlo Lyons	***	
Taylor Joynson Garrett	***	**
Theodore Goddard	**	
Weil, Gotshal & Manges		**

South	Computer/IT	Telecoms
Anstey Sargent & Probert, Exeter	***	
Beachcroft Wansbroughs, Bristol	***	
Boyes Turner & Burrows, Reading	***	
Burges Salmon, Bristol	***	
Clark Holt, Swindon	*****	
Clyde & Co, Guildford	***	

	Computer/IT	Telecoms
Donne Mileham & Haddock, Brighton	****	
Garretts, Reading	*****	
Laytons, Bristol	****	
Lester Aldridge, Bournemouth	***	
Manches, Oxford	******	
Nabarro Nathanson, Reading	******	
Osborne Clarke, Bristol, Reading	*****	
Singletons, Pinner	**	
The Law Offices of Marcus J. O'Leary, Bracknell	******	
Wiggin & Co, Cheltenham		*
Willoughby & Partners, Oxford	*****	

Wales, Midlands & East Anglia	Computer/IT
Dibb Lupton Alsop, Birmingham	***
Edge Ellison, Birmingham	****
Edwards Geldard, Cardiff	****
Eversheds, Birmingham, Nottingham	*****
Eversheds, Cardiff	***
Hewitson Becke + Shaw, Cambridge, Northampton	*****
Morgan Cole, Cardiff	***
Pinsent Curtis, Birmingham	****
Wragge & Co, Birmingham	******

North	Computer/IT	Telecoms
Addleshaw Booth & Co, Leeds, Manchester	*****	
Dibb Lupton Alsop, Leeds, Manchester, Sheffield	***	
Eversheds, Leeds	****	**
Garretts, Leeds, Manchester	**	
Halliwell Landau, Manchester	****	
Irwin Mitchell, Leeds	**	
Masons, Leeds	******	
Masons, Manchester	**	
Oxley & Coward, Rotherham	******	
Pinsent Curtis, Leeds	****	

Firms and their star ratings are based on Chambers' Directory 1999–2000. Six stars represent a top-ranked firm, five stars a second-ranked firm, etc.

LITIGATION

Area of law

Litigation lawyers – usually known simply as litigators – act for clients involved in disputes. There are three ways in which disputes can be pursued. Litigation itself involves recourse to the courts. This can be an expensive and time-consuming process. For this reason, contracts often provide for disputes between the parties to be referred to binding arbitration, normally by an expert in the field. Unlike court proceedings, arbitrations are confidential. They are particularly common in the shipping, insurance and construction industries. Alternative Dispute Resolution (ADR) is a cheaper alternative to both litigation and arbitration. Although it can take various forms, ADR often involves structured negotiations between the parties directed by an independent mediator. This form of ADR is known as mediation. There are other less common forms such as neutral evaluation, expert determination and conciliation. The parties retain the right to litigate if they find it impossible to reach an agreement.

If you think that contentious work is all about court-room drama, think again. Many disputes settle before commencement of proceedings. If proceedings are commenced, the odds are that the case will never reach trial. Parties to commercial litigation are not, as a rule, interested in having their 'day in court' although there may be matters of principle which need to be determined. The emphasis, therefore, is on reaching a commercial settlement. "If you can keep your clients out of court, they will love you much more than if you get them into a scrap," says Neil Fagan, leading litigation partner at Lovells. "Most of our work involves trying to stop people litigating."

Type of work

General commercial litigators handle a variety of business disputes. Most cases will be contractual – everything from a dispute over the sale of a multi-million pound business, to an argument over the meaning of a term in a photocopier maintenance contract. They might also deal with negligence claims by companies against their professional advisors. Some litigators specialise in certain industry sectors – for example, construction, shipping, insurance, property or media. But most of the litigator's skills are common to all areas of commercial litigation, according to Christopher Style of Linklaters. "The procedure in running a court action or an arbitration, and the skill in negotiating an agreement is the same, whether you're talking about a dispute between the manufacturers of widgets or between accountants, stockbrokers or bankers," he says.

Litigation is a process. Once a case has been commenced, it follows a pre-determined course laid down by the rules of court – statement of case, disclosure of documents, various procedural applications and, in a small number of cases, trial. In a major case, this process can take several years. The mutual disclosure of relevant documents can be a particularly protracted and expensive affair, although new rules which came into force in April 1999 are intended to limit this process.

Managing this process is the litigator's primary role. This requires not only a mastery of the rules of court, but also a keen appreciation of tactics. If you're acting for a defendant, for example, you might ask the claimant for more information about its claim by means of a request for further information. Obtaining the information might not be your primary aim. You might know perfectly well the main thrust of the claim. But your request may expose weaknesses in the claimant's case. It also has a nuisance value, forcing the claimant to spend time and money in providing you with further information. If you're lucky, the request may persuade the claimant to settle a case. Disclosure can also be used as a tactical ruse, with parties taking advantage of their disclosure obligations to swamp their opponents with largely irrelevant documents. The Woolf reforms to the civil justice system, implemented in April 1999 have reduced the scope for such tactical games by simplifying procedures.

The range of the litigator's work has increased over the last few years, thanks largely to the extension of High Court rights of audience to solicitors. Although solicitors could always draft statements of case – the formal documents setting out the claimant's claim and the defendant's response – and act as advocates in High Court procedural hearings, they rarely did so. Instead, such work was normally referred to barristers. This is now changing. There hasn't been a flood of solicitor-advocates into the High Court. But the possibility of a career as an advocate, together with potential costs savings for the client, is encouraging solicitors to keep more work in-house. This phenomenon is particularly marked in the large City firms. Herbert Smith and Lovells for example have advocacy policies where solicitor advocates are used in all cases other than major hearings or full trials. The Woolf reforms are likely to accelerate this trend since they put a greater emphasis on written advocacy and have introduced the preliminary hearing – the case-management conference – which is dealt with by the solicitors with the day-to-day handling of the case.

As a trainee, a proportion of your time will be spent researching points of law and procedure. Depending on your firm, specialist group you sit in and timing, you could be involved on one massive case with an important role in running the organisation of all the documents to be disclosed. Or you could be running a caseload of small county court cases in which you may be making small applications before a district judge. In a large City firm, a qualified litigator may sometimes work on no more than two or three big cases at a time. The caseload will probably be more varied in smaller litigation departments.

Paul Williams, a five-year qualified litigator at Lovells, says his days can be quite varied. You might start your day preparing for a procedural hearing in the Commercial Court at which you will be the advocate, arriving at court to find you are opposed by an experienced barrister instructed by the other side. (Lovells has a policy of instructing counsel only in limited circumstances and litigators at Lovells are encouraged to undertake as much advocacy as possible.) After a discussion outside the court with the other side's counsel, you reach agreement on a number of points but there is one matter on which you cannot agree. Your opponent insists that his client is entitled to ask your client to produce certain documents. You disagree.

You enter court and the judge asks a number of questions about the conduct of the proceedings. You have to explain the reasons for delays in taking certain procedural steps. However, after some argument the judge agrees with you and refuses to order your client to produce the documents. After the judge has given directions dealing with the disclosure of documents and witness statements, the hearing ends. You look at your watch to see that the hearing has lasted over an hour, although it only felt like a few minutes.

You rush back to the office, listen to a number of voicemail messages from clients and other lawyers, check your e-mails, then see you have received a fax from a client requesting an urgent response. You are already running late for lunch with another client but have to stay to deal with the enquiry. After twenty minutes or so you arrive at the restaurant where the client and your supervising partner are having lunch to celebrate a successful mediation in which you were involved. The client, an insurer, is pleased because the mediation resulted in the settlement of a £7 million claim for less than £1 million and avoided the time and expense of a trial. "Mediation is a cost-effective and constructive way of resolving commercial disputes," says Williams "and clients favour it because they are fully involved in the process, unlike a trial, where the lawyers control what happens."

Back to the office after lunch for a meeting with a witness. You are preparing his witness statement. This is hard work because his recollection of events is poor. This is not surprising because the events in question happened over 5 years ago. This is not uncommon in litigation. Luckily you are able to use the firm's document database to locate a letter written by the witness which jogs his memory. "Computer databasing of documents is the way forward in litigation," says Williams. "It allows you to view images of documents on screen, and searches for documents which would have taken hours now take a matter of seconds. Trainees who would previously have carried out manual searches can do something more productive."

Finally it is time for a conference call with clients in the USA. Due to the time difference the call is arranged for 6pm. You and your supervising partner update the clients on procedural matters. The client wants to discuss strategy and the possibility of bringing other parties into existing litigation. After discussing this you raise the question of mediation. The client, a US insurer, has participated in numerous mediations and expects you to be familiar with the mediation process. Luckily your recent mediation experience allows you to discuss the different approaches to mediation in the UK and the USA. The client is clearly impressed by your experience. By 7.30pm the conference call is over. The client has asked for a letter of advice. You consider whether to start this now but decide instead to write it first thing the next morning when you can approach the matter fresh. Your department is having drinks at the local wine bar and, after a busy day, you are only too glad to join them at 8pm.

Skills needed

Litigators require drive, commercial-mindedness, a grasp of tactics and a certain natural toughness and competitiveness. "You need to like to win," says Linklaters' Christopher Style. "You have to have that drive. It's no use being some academic who sits back thinking clever thoughts. You have to be able to roll up your sleeves and really get stuck in."

The sheer scale and complexity of many commercial disputes, usually involving a huge volume of documentary evidence, places a premium on the ability to assimilate information quickly and see the big picture. "The best litigators are those with strong commercial awareness and an ability to think laterally around the immediate dispute," says Anthony Bourne of Glovers. "They must be able to spot the salient points early and allow more trivial matters to drop." And while litigators will fight their client's corner, they must also know when discretion is the better part of valour. "If, as proceedings progress, the client's case is looking bad, you have to work out how much can be salvaged. Knowing which points are worth pursuing and which can be negotiated away requires a detailed understanding of arguments for and against your client."

Negotiating skills are essential. 'Verve and panache' are important when getting your view across. However, litigators also need a hard edge. "Charm takes you a long way," says Paul Bowden of Freshfields. "But clients and opponents need to know that you can bite."

Career options

All commercial practices in London and the provinces have litigation departments. Law Society rules require that all trainees do a contentious element in their training contract. Herbert Smith has the leading general commercial litigation practice in the City, followed by Freshfields, Clifford Chance and Lovells. Among the specialist industry sectors, Masons leads the field in construction litigation. The insurance and shipping firms such as Barlow Lyde & Gilbert, Clyde & Co, Ince & Co and Davies Arnold Cooper are strong, not only in insurance litigation, but also in professional negligence work and shipping litigation.

In-house opportunities are less common than for corporate lawyers. Banks, insurance, construction and shipping companies sometimes employ specialist litigators. Only the very largest in-house departments need general commercial litigators.

The firms

Large-scale commercial litigation cases can only really be handled by the big City firms. The sheer logistics of these cases, where disclosure alone can take years, mean that huge teams of lawyers are required (increasingly supplemented with large numbers of short-term contract paralegals).

Herbert Smith fields a huge team of 50 partners and 100 assistants. They are known for their highly skilled and aggressive approach. They routinely handle cases worth millions of pounds and recently acted for BSkyB on the £37.5m claim against Carlton. On a slightly different note the team is acting for the Democratic Government of Chile in the proceedings surrounding the extradition of Pinochet.

Medium-sized City firms with good practices include Barlow Lyde & Gilbert, SJ Berwin & Co, DJ Freeman, Macfarlanes and Stephenson Harwood. They also handle major commercial cases. SJ Berwin acted for American Express against the BCCI liquidators. Stephenson Harwood represented Wang (UK) Ltd in a multi-million pound computer dispute. Barlow Lyde & Gilbert acted for McDonalds in the McLibel trial.

Smaller London firms with good departments include Reynolds Porter Chamberlain, Warner Cranston, Glovers and Goodman Derrick.

In the regions, Pinsent Curtis and Wragge & Co lead the field in the Midlands. The former acted for Nottingham County Council in a £10m claim for misfeasance in public office and the latter for 125 farmers against the NFU for compensation for loss of milk quota. In the north, Dibb Lupton Alsop in Liverpool and Leeds; and Eversheds, Addleshaw Booth & Co and Hammond Suddards in Manchester and Leeds are the leaders. Eversheds in Manchester successfully recovered £8m for 236 investors against a stockbroker regarding the collapse of an investment scheme. Addleshaws in Leeds obtained a £20m "retrospective taxation" case in the European Court of Human Rights on behalf of Yorkshire Building Society. In East Anglia, Eversheds and Mills & Reeve lead the field and in the south, Bond Pearce in Plymouth, Burges Salmon and Osborne Clarke in Bristol, Donne Mileham & Haddock in Brighton and Blake Lapthorn in Fareham are the major practices.

Leading Firms

London	Number of Litigators			
	100+	40-99	10-39	Under 10
Allen & Overy		*****		
Ashurst Morris Crisp		****		
Baker & McKenzie			***	
Barlow Lyde & Gilbert	***			
Berrymans Lace Mawer				***
S J Berwin & Co			**	
Berwin Leighton		**		
Biddle			**	
Bower Cotton				**
Clifford Chance	*****			
Clyde & Co	**			
CMS Cameron McKenna	***			
D J Freeman		**		
Denton Hall		**		
Dibb Lupton Alsop	*			
Eversheds		*		
Field Fisher Waterhouse			**	
Fladgate Fielder			**	

London	Number of Litigators 100+	40-99	10-39	Under 10
Freshfields	*****			
Glovers				***
Goodman Derrick			**	
Gouldens			***	
Hamlins			**	
Hammond Suddards			**	
Harbottle & Lewis			**	
Herbert Smith	******			
Holman Fenwick & Willan			**	
Howard Kennedy			**	
Jeffrey Green Russell			*	
Kennedys		*		
Kingsford Stacey Blackwell			*	
Lane & Partners				**
Lawrence Graham		*		
LeBoeuf, Lamb, Greene & McCrae, LLP				**
Lewis Silkin			**	
Linklaters		******		
Lovells	*****			
Macfarlanes			***	
Mackrell Turner Garrett				**
Manches			**	
Masons		*		
Memery Crystal			**	
Mishcon de Reya			**	
Nabarro Nathanson			***	
Nicholson Graham & Jones			**	
Norton Rose	****			
Pinsent Curtis				***
Radcliffes			*	
Reynolds Porter Chamberlain			**	
Richards Butler		**		
Rosling King			*	
Rowe & Maw			**	
Seddons				**
Sheridans				**
Simmons & Simmons	***			
Sinclair Roche & Temperley			**	
Slaughter and May		****		
Stephenson Harwood		***		
Taylor Joynson Garrett		*		
Theodore Goddard			**	
Titmuss Sainer Dechert			**	
Travers Smith Braithwaite				***
Warner Cranston				***
Wedlake Bell				***
Wilde Sapte		*		

East Anglia	Litigation
Birketts, Ipswich	*****
Eversheds, Ipswich, Norwich	******
Greenwoods, Peterborough	*****
Hewitson Becke + Shaw, Cambridge	*****

East Anglia	Litigation
Howes Percival, Norwich	***
Mills & Reeve, Cambridge, Norwich	******
Prettys, Ipswich	****
Taylor Vinters, Cambridge	****

Midlands	Litigation
Bell Lax Litigation, Birmingham	**
Browne Jacobson, Nottingham	****
Dibb Lupton Alsop, Birmingham	**
Edge Ellison, Birmingham	****
Eversheds, Birmingham, Nottingham	*****
Freeth Cartwright Hunt Dickins, Nott'm	***
Gateley Wareing, Birmingham	***
George Green & Co, Cradley Heath	**
Hewitson Becke + Shaw, N'hampton	**

Midlands	Litigation
Kent Jones & Done, Stoke-on-Trent	***
Knight & Sons, N'castle-under-Lyme	***
Lee Crowder, Birmingham	***
Martineau Johnson, Birmingham	****
Pinsent Curtis, Birmingham	******
Shakespeares, Birmingham	**
Shoosmiths, Northampton	**
The Wilkes Partnership, Birmingham	**
Wragge & Co, Birmingham	******

North East	Litigation
Addleshaw Booth & Co, Leeds	******
Andrew M. Jackson & Co, Hull	***
Beachcroft Wansbroughs, Leeds	***
Brooke North, Leeds	**
Dibb Lupton Alsop, Leeds	******
Dickinson Dees, Newcastle	****
Eversheds, Leeds	******
Eversheds, Newcastle upon Tyne	***
Ford & Warren, Leeds	**
Gordons Wright & Wright, Bradford	*
Gosschalks, Hull	**
Hammond Suddards, Leeds	******
Hay & Kilner, Newcastle	**

North East	Litigation
Irwin Mitchell, Sheffield	****
Linsley & Mortimer, Newcastle	*
Lupton Fawcett, Leeds	***
McCormicks, Leeds	**
Pinsent Curtis, Leeds	*****
Read Hind Stewart, Leeds	*
Robert Muckle, Newcastle	**
Rollit Farrell & Bladon, Hull	***
Shulmans, Leeds	*
Walker Morris, Leeds	*****
Ward Hadaway, Newcastle	***
Watson Burton, Newcastle	**

North West	Litigation
Addleshaw Booth & Co, Manchester	******
Beachcroft Wansbroughs, Manchester	**
Berg & Co, Manchester	***
Berrymans Lace Mawer, Liverpool, Manchester	**
Brabner Holden Banks Wilson, L'pool	**
Brabner Holden Banks Wilson, Preston	**
Chaffe Street, Manchester	**
Cobbetts, Manchester	*****
Cuff Roberts, Liverpool	**

North West	Litigation
Davies Wallis Foyster, Liverpool	****
Dibb Lupton Alsop, Liverpool, Manc	*****
Eversheds, Manchester	******
Halliwell Landau, Manchester	*****
Hammond Suddards, Manchester	*****
Hill Dickinson, Liverpool	****
Mace & Jones, Liverpool	*
Pannone & Partners, Manchester	***
Turner Parkinson, Manchester	*
Weightmans, Liverpool	**

South East	Litigation
Barlows, Guildford	**
Blake Lapthorn, Fareham	******
Bond Pearce, Southampton	***
Brachers, Maidstone	**
Burstows, Crawley	**
Clarks, Reading	***
Cripps Harries Hall, Tunbridge Wells	***
Donne Mileham & Haddock, Brighton	******
Furley Page Fielding & Barton, C'bury	**
Lamport Bassitt, Southampton	*
Matthew Arnold & Baldwin, Watford	**

South East	Litigation
Morgan Cole, Oxford, Reading	******
Paris Smith & Randall, Southampton	***
Pitmans, Reading	***
Rawlison & Butler, Crawley	**
Shoosmiths, Reading, Solent	*
Stevens & Bolton, Guildford	**
T'mas Eggar Church Adams, Chich	***
T'mas Eggar Church Adams, Worth	***
Thomson Snell & Passmore, T. Wells	***
Wollastons, Chelmsford	*

South West	Litigation
Anstey Sargent & Probert, Exeter	**
Beachcroft Wansbroughs, Bristol	***
Bevan Ashford, Bristol	***
Bond Pearce, Plymouth	*****
Burges Salmon, Bristol	******
Cartwrights, Bristol	**
Clarke Willmott & Clarke, Yeovil	**
Davies and Partners, Gloucester	**
Eversheds, Bristol	***
Foot & Bowden, Plymouth	**
Lawrence Tucketts, Bristol	**

South West	Litigation
Laytons, Bristol	**
Lester Aldridge, Bournemouth	**
Lyons Davidson, Bristol	**
Osborne Clarke, Bristol	******
Rickerby Watterson, Cheltenham	**
Stephens & Scown, Exeter	*
Townsends, Swindon	*
Trumps, Bristol	**
Veale Wasbrough, Bristol	***
Wilsons Solicitors, Salisbury	*
Wolferstans, Plymouth	**

Wales	Litigation
Edwards Geldard, Cardiff	*****
Eversheds, Cardiff	*****
Hugh James Ford Simey, Cardiff	******

Wales	Litigation
Morgan Cole, Cardiff, Swansea	******
Palser Grossman, Cardiff Bay	**

Firms and their star ratings are based on Chambers' Directory 1999–2000. Six stars represent a top-ranked firm, five stars a second-ranked firm, etc.

MEDIA

(Including Advertising & Marketing, Defamation, Film & Broadcasting, Digital Media, Music, Theatre and Publishing)

We have divided this chapter into three categories: Advertising and Marketing, Defamation and Entertainment law. Entertainment is further subdivided into Film and Broadcasting, Digital Media, Music, Theatre and Publishing. According to Nigel Bennett, partner in the Film & Television Department at leading media firm The Simkins Partnership, students should ask themselves one fundamental question. Do you want to be in the world of money or the world of ideas? If you want the former then join a big City firm. If you want something more flexible and less institutionalised, then entertainment law may just be for you.

Advertising & Marketing

Area of law and type of work

Firms with advertising and marketing clients specialise in both 'pure' and general advertising law. 'Pure' advertising law is copy clearance for ad agencies, marketing, PR, advertisers and other media clients. It requires a knowledge of broadcasting and publishing self regulatory codes such as the Advertising Standards Authority code and the Independent Television Commission code as well as statutes such as the Obscene Publications Act. An understanding of defamation and intellectual property law is also required.

General advertising law means advising your advertising client base on commercial contracts with suppliers, clients and the rest of the media, employment issues, corporate transactions and litigation. It is more likely that having gone to a firm with a client base in this industry you will tend to specialise one way or the other. The complete all-rounder is a rare creature.

Dominic Farnsworth is an assistant at West End firm Lewis Silkin, specialising in pure advertising advice to a number of agencies. "At 2pm I might get a call from an agency with a legal problem for an ad with a 5pm print deadline. They need immediate and robust copy clearance advice. The key legal risks that I have to assess are trademark and copyright infringement, passing off issues, defamation, regulatory codes, whether or not any consents are required from personalities, whether the ad is misleading and whether or not there are comparative advertising considerations. You've got to think really fast to identify the problems." He then has to find a way to minimise these. Any letter of advice has to be written with the agency's own clients in mind as his advice will normally be passed on to the advertiser as well and needs to be diplomatically presented.

'Talent contracts' are a specialism in themselves and require a depth of industry knowledge to do well. This is where an advertising lawyer acts on behalf of an ad agency client to negotiate a contract for the 'talent' to appear in a magazine, radio or TV ad. Clients will deal with the more routine ones themselves, but lawyers get called in for the bigger stars when the contracts become more complex.

Skills needed

You have to have a fast, practical and commercial mind for this type of work. "If all you can do is identify a problem you're not going to be instructed for very long" says Dominic Farnsworth. "You have to be able to find a way through the problem." Advertising clients like to work with lawyers who understand the pressures they are under. New creative concepts often test the boundaries of the law so as their lawyer you have to be prepared to respond to this. For example a client may wish to use music in an advert which sounds very much like something protected by copyright. An advertising lawyer will need to give guidance on how closely the music used can resemble the original without infringing it. A detailed knowledge of copyright is therefore essential. "It's not a document intensive area of law," Dominic told us "it's more of a mind game. You simply don't have the time to do hours of research....it's fast in and fast out. That keeps it fresh and fun."

Defamation

Area of law and type of work

Defamation is one of the most high-profile and arguably most 'glamorous' areas of legal practice. A person can be defamed by written word, which is libel, or by spoken word, which is slander. The majority of actions taken are for libel. On the contentious side, lawyers act for either individuals or companies (claimants) seeking to sue publishers or broadcasters for damaging their reputation or for the individuals or companies being sued (defendants). On the non-contentious side, work includes pre-publication or pre-broadcast advice to authors, editors and TV companies.

Defamation is a fascinating field of law to work in, hinging as it does on questions of personal honour and the right to freedom of expression. Clients can range from high profile politicians or popstars to unknown businessmen. A libel lawyer will therefore gain experience of people from all walks of life and numerous different professions. Client contact is likely to begin at a much more junior level than in the corporate sector. Many see it as 'critical to career progression' to build up personal links to clients and in-house lawyers as quickly as possible. A typical day might involve a client meeting – hearing a claimant's story for the first time and giving advice on the best course of action; planning how to run an action; making an application to court on a procedural matter; persuading a reluctant witness to give evidence in court and possibly investigating an obstruse point of law. Many people think libel is all about trials, but in fact most libel lawyers have only one or two full trials per year. Trainees will probably spend more time in court than qualified solicitors, because they are encouraged to shadow barristers on short hearings and they may also undertake advocacy themselves. Up and coming libel star Katherine Rimell of Theodore Goddard sees it as "a very interesting career, especially as it relates to freedom of expression. And it certainly has its glamorous moments!"

Skills needed

According to Katherine Rimell, "people skills are vital: you need to know what makes people tick." Peter Carter-Ruck and Partners' Andrew Stephenson emphasises the importance of "an interest in language and current affairs." The importance of a keen understanding of human nature is obvious in a practice area dominated by such personal issues as principles and reputation. Given that a libel generally rests on the interpretation of language, many defamation lawyers are English graduates or former journalists. Libel lawyers must be flexible enough to deal with clients from a wide variety of backgrounds and sensitive enough to understand their motives. Consequently an understanding of psychology, along with a sharp, analytical mind and a creative approach, are much valued in the field. Finally, defamation lawyers need a working knowledge of other areas of the law relevant to the media, in particular copyright, confidentiality and contempt of court as well as the relevant industry codes of practice.

Unlike most areas of law principles or public image often matter more than money. This means that clients may insist on taking a case to court for reasons of personal 'honour' even where they have a near hopeless case. "Principles are awfully expensive," said Rupert Grey of Crockers Oswald Hickson, "but they drive the whole game."

Entertainment

Area of law and type of work

We divide entertainment law into Film and Broadcasting, Digital Media, Music, Theatre and Publishing. Clients range from film studios and television production companies to theatre groups and individual artists. Work varies from the financing of West End productions to clearance and classification advice for the British

Board of Film Classification. Equally, clients of all types will need contract, employment and litigation advice. Key to almost everything is an understanding of commercial law and intellectual property and how these apply to the entertainment industry.

According to Nigel Bennett of The Simkins Partnership, the entertainment lawyer often fulfills a traditional role as a general commercial advisor, as well as providing technical legal services. "You are providing solutions to a whole range of problems. Someone may require a co-producer in Spain. Another client may wish to buy the film rights to John Le Carré's latest novel. Another may ask you to find the finance for a project. You have a broader brief. It is fascinating work."

As opposed to a lot of City work, entertainment law is not mainly a matter of standard form procedures. In the early stage of your career you must learn quickly how the industry works. Clients value experience and want lawyers who have done it before. You play a prominent role and are much more than a small cog in a huge corporate wheel.

You therefore need the confidence to stand up and be counted.

Film & Broadcasting

According to Nigel Bennett, from a lawyer's point of view, you can look at a film or a television programme as any other commercial product. First you have to develop the product, then you have to finance it, then you have to produce it and then you have to sell it. All of these elements require legal advice of one kind or another. The work can be roughly summarised as a combination of commercial contract law (with an element of banking and secured lending) and the law of copyright. The film lawyer would normally see the process through from start to finish.

Digital Media

An increasingly important aspect of media law which relates to information disseminated in a digitised format. This is a heavily internet-oriented practice area sometimes dubbed 'multimedia.' A dynamic (even 'fun') new area of practice, with both regulatory and transactional aspects, digital media is at the very forefront of 'convergence' issues. Most digital media lawyers originally hailed from an IP/Copyright background, though others started out in telecommunications (principally on the regulatory side) and data protection. However a basic understanding of copyright matters is considered pretty much indispensable. Clients are very varied, including internet service providers, internet industry bodies, software developers, games designers and banks providing on-line services. Naturally enough the nature of the work requires an up to date understanding of the ever-changing world of cyberspace, both technically and in terms of the industry as a whole. Flexibility to clients' needs and a "sensible approach to risk" are also said to be of prime importance, – understandably, given how many 'e-businesses' have come from nowhere to net hundreds of millions of pounds. Niche media firm The Simkins Partnership has advised NTL on 'internet liability' (whether a provider is responsible for illegal material accessible via their search vehicle) and is currently advising Sony on setting up a 'digital dance site.' IP/media boutique Henry Hepworth is acting for Ulster unionist leader David Trimble in his defamation suit against Amazon.com, the first libel action against an internet web-based bookshop.

Music

Clients come from all sectors of the music industry including record labels, production companies, managers and the artists themselves. Some firms lean more towards acting for talent, others to the record labels. Central to the work of each type of practice is contract work. High profile litigation sometimes arises when there is a dispute over contract terms or ownership of rights in compositions. Sometimes when band members split with each other or with their management, as happened with the Spice Girls and Take That, lawyers find that they are brought in to fight their client's corner in the process of sorting out who is entitled to what.

Whether specialising in contentious or non-contentious work, music lawyers have to be fully versed in all aspects of copyright as well as contract law. Specialist music firms may also advise on the incorporation and development of new record labels and joint venture agreements between larger and smaller labels.

Theatre

There are a few practitioners in London who thrive off the theatrical world. Some work with broader media firms, others attract clients by virtue of their own reputation. Clients include theatre and opera companies, producers, theatrical agents and actors. Theatre lawyers will spend a lot of time in contract negotiations for their clients. Relationships between the constituent parties to a new production all need to be established and regulated through these contracts. A lawyer will usually find himself involved from the inception of the idea for a production right through to the opening curtain and beyond. Increasingly, lawyers will become involved in arrangements for the funding of a new production.

Publishing

Work in this sector includes contractual, licensing, copyright and libel work for publishing houses. Most of this work is carried out in-house or by libel lawyers, so there are only a few London firms who can be said to specialise in publishing law. As with libel, an interest in language and literature are obvious requirements.

Skills needed

Media lawyers are assumed to have a glamorous working life and certainly there are elements to it that provide for a little more glitz than most other areas of the profession. Attending a client function might mean partying with the great and good of the pop world or going along to the opening night of a play or a film premiere. For most of you reading this, the idea of a business trip to the Cannes Film Festival probably doesn't sound like much of a hardship. Entertainment lawyers are expected to go out and win new clients the same as any other lawyer.

Social skills are vital; media clients can be charismatic individuals and they will want lawyers who share the some outlook and have an understanding of the industry and the way in which it operates. You need to be able to fit in with some very quirky clients and talk their language. An understanding of the way creative people work is vital.

Don't make the mistake of thinking that an encyclopaedic knowledge of the entertainment industry is all it takes to land a job in the field. A star-struck lawyer is a very unattractive proposition for the firms who specialise in entertainment law. Sean Egan, partner at Bates, Wells & Braithwaite warns that students getting into this area of the law need to be very clear that they want to be a lawyer rather than, say, a film or theatre producer. "It is important to see the line between what it is that you do as a lawyer and what your client does. You must want to be on the right side of that line." However, he went on to tell us about his fascination for his clients' work. " It's no good just standing on the touchline, you've got to be prepared to immerse yourself in the business."

Sean confirms that an entertainment lawyer's basic skills must include a "a thorough working knowledge of contract and copyright law." Communication skills, creativity in problem solving and commercial aptitude need to be there to back up the academics. According to Nigel Bennett, the skills involved are not dissimilar to those needed for any other area of commercial law. "You need to be patient, methodical and inquistive."

Career options

Increasingly there is crossover between private practice and working in-house for media and entertainment organisations. Lawyers transfer between the two more readily than they did a few years ago. Money is generally perceived to be better in-house and the hours are considered more favourable – you do not need to go out looking for new clients, for example. However, one should remember that in recessionary times, in-house counsel are normally the first to go as their legal work can quite easily be outsourced.

Michael Griffiths works for the legal department of Paramount Home Entertainment International, having initially been in private practice. His colleagues have come from a variety of places, both specialist media firms and general commercial firms. Mike's workload is very varied and all manner of things land on his desk. In addition to the film work, the company requires its lawyers to give them a range of advice, just like any other large organisation.

Working in-house can have distinct advantages over private practice. A lack of stiffness and formality is characteristic of the entertainment industry generally and Mike says that this translates through to his working environment. Casual dress, less hierarchy and involvement in a fair degree of non-legal business management tasks can make for a refreshing contrast to the usual experience of a commercial lawyer. Just after we interviewed him Mike was going to the screening of a film for two hours. Just part of the job!

The Firms

Advertising & Marketing

Most advertising lawyers are London-based. Lewis Silkin and Macfarlanes are the long established leaders, but close behind are Osborne Clarke and The Simkins Partnership. Outside of London, Edge Ellison in Leicester, Eversheds in Birmingham and Leicester Aldridge in Bournemouth are regarded highly.

Defamation

The London defamation scene continues to be dominated by the heavyweight triumvirate consisting of leading media firm Olswang, Farrer & Co and the well-known Peter Carter-Ruck and Partners. Olswang, which as a firm focuses on 'new media' in the entertainment and communications industries, has a small but strong defendant practice with an excellent reputation. They act for a number of major newspapers and can count Tom Cruise and Nicole Kidman amongst their clients. Farrer & Co have a practice evenly split between defendant and claimant work and are greatly appreciated by their clients for their discretion. Defendant clients include publishers and newspaper groups. Peter Carter-Ruck and Partners is arguably one of the best known firms in the country, thanks to several high profile celebrity cases (the great man himself however is now a part-time consultant). Work is evenly divided between claimants and defendants, with clients including Michael Winner, Hello Magazine and Express Newspapers. Other leaders include niche firm Schilling & Lom and Partners who have a reputation for celebrity claimant work and can count Liam Neeson and Natasha Richardson as clients. City heavyweights such as Clifford Chance and Lovells continue to dominate the scene when it comes to large corporate libels, while mid-sized City firms such as Theodore Goddard and DJ Freeman have maintained their strong reputations in the field. The former counts The Times, Givenchy and Alexander McQueen as clients, while the latter, which has a superb understanding of the television industry, acts for Channel 4 and BSkyB.

Outside of London, defamation practices are limited to say the least. Cheltenham-based Wiggin and Co and Exeter's Foot & Bowden are the best regional practices in England and Wales. The latter conducts both defendant and claimant work for clients including regional newspapers, while the former act principally for defendants drawn from the publishing industry. North of the border, the battlefield is dominated by Glasgow firms Bird Semple and Levy & McRae. The former's practice is defendant orientated, while the latter, happy to own up to an "aggressive" character, acts for principally for newspapers and television companies on both sides of the defamation equation. Clients include both English and Scottish newspapers and international information purveyors Reuters.

Entertainment

Almost all the leading entertainment firms are in London.

For film finance SJ Berwin and Richards Butler lead, whilst on the film production side Olswang and Marriott Harrison are seen to be heading a strong field. Olswang also appears as a leader for broadcasting work together with Denton Hall (soon to merge with Wilde Sapte).

In music law, the best regarded firms are a mix of small niche specialists and larger, broader media practices. The top dog is London firm Russells, but fellow London specialist Clintons is now seen to be snapping at its heels. Harbottle & Lewis, Lee & Thompson and Statham Gill all come in as leading firms.

Theatre practices are few and far between in the UK but in London, amongst the best regarded are those of sole practitioner Barry Shaw, and firms Tarlo Lyons, Campbell Hooper and Clintons.

Publishing leaders can be found in both large corporate firms such as Denton Hall and Taylor Joynson Garrett and in smaller niche practices like Henry Hepworth and that of sole practitioner B M Nyman.

In the regions, media work is not that common but some firms have overcome the London bias and are seen as players. Wiggin & Co in Cheltenham, Manches in Oxford and Morgan Cole's Cardiff and Swansea offices lead the field. In the Midlands, media leaders include Edge Ellison, Evershed, Wragge & Co and Frances Anderson, all of Birmingham. Moving further north, the leading firms include Leeds firms Dibb Lupton Alsop and McCormicks and Eversheds in Manchester.

Well-regarded Scots media lawyers are to be found at a number of Edinburgh and Glasgow firms including Dundas and Wilson CS, McGrigor Donald and Tods Murray WS.

London	Advertising & Marketing	Defamation	Film & Broadcasting	Theatre	Music	Publishing	Digital
Ashurst Morris Crisp							
Babbington & Bray						****	
Baker & McKenzie							***
Barry Shaw				******			
Bates, Wells & Braithwaite				***			
Beachcroft Wansbroughs	*						
Berwin Leighton			****				
S J Berwin & Co			****				
Biddle		*****					
Bindman & Partners		***					
Campbell Hooper				*****			
Clifford Chance	*	***					
Clintons				*****	******		
CMS Cameron McKenna	***						
Crockers Oswald Hickson		*****					
D J Freeman		****					
Davenport Lyons		*****	****		**		
David Price & Co		****					
Davies Arnold Cooper		**					
Denton Hall	*		****		**	***	
Eatons					****		
Edge Ellison	***						

Leading Firms

London	Advertising & Marketing	Defamation	Film & Broadcasting	Theatre	Music	Publishing	Digital
Eversheds					**		
Farrer & Co		******					
Field Fisher Waterhouse	***						
Finers Stephens Innocent		***					
Gentle Jayes					**		
Goodman Derrick		****				**	
Hamlins					***		
Harbottle & Lewis	*	***	*****	***	*****	**	
Harrison Curtis			***	****	**		
Henry Hepworth		****	***			**	
Lawrence Graham	**						
Lee & Thompson			****		*****		
Lewis Silkin	******	***					
Lovells	**	***				**	
Macfarlanes	******						
Manches	*	***					
Marriott Harrison			******				
Mishcon de Reya		**					
B. M. Nyman & Co						**	
Olswang	*	******	******				
Osborne Clarke	*****						
Peter Carter-Ruck and Partners	******						
Reynolds Porter Chamberlain	**						
Richards Butler			*****				
Rowe & Maw	*						
Russell Jones & Walker		***					
Russells					******		
Schilling & Lom and Partners	*****	***					
Searles					**		
Sheridans					****		
Simons Muirhead & Burton		***					
Spraggon Stennett Brabyn					**		
Statham Gill Davies					*****		
Swepstone Walsh		****					
Tarlo Lyons				******			
Taylor Joynson Garrett	**					***	
The Simkins Partnership	*****		****	***	****	**	
Theodore Goddard	***	*****	*****		****		
Townleys	*						
Wiggin & Co							

Midlands & East Anglia	Advertising & Marketing	Defamation	Entertainment
Edge Ellison, Birmingham			**
Edge Ellison, Leicester	**		
Eversheds, Birmingham	**		**
Frances Anderson, Birmingham			**
Leathes Prior, Norwich			*
Wragge & Co, Birmingham		*	**

North	Defamation	Entertainment
Brabner Holden Banks Wilson, Liverpool	**	
Cobbetts, Manchester	**	
Dibb Lupton Alsop, Leeds		**
Eversheds, Leeds		**
Eversheds, Manchester		**
Hart-Jackson & Hall, Newcastle upon Tyne		**
Lea & Company, Stockport		**
McCormicks, Leeds		**
Pannone & Partners, Manchester	*	
Ramsbottom & Co, Blackburn		**

South and Wales	Advertising & Marketing	Defamation	Entertainment
Bevan Ashford, Bristol		**	
Foot & Bowden, Exeter		***	
Knights, Tunbridge Wells		**	
Lester Aldridge, Bournemouth	**		
Manches, Oxford			*
Morgan Cole, Cardiff, Swansea			**
Wiggin & Co, Cheltenham		***	***

Firms and their star ratings are based on Chambers' Directory 1999–2000. Six stars represent a top-ranked firm, five stars a second-ranked firm, etc.

PERSONAL INJURY & CLINICAL NEGLIGENCE

Area of law

Being related areas of practice, personal injury and clinical negligence work are often undertaken in the same department or by specialist firms. Claimant firms are instructed by private individuals, legal expenses insurers and trade unions. Clients of defendant firms include private individuals, health authorities, hospitals, trusts, insurance companies, public bodies and self-insuring companies. Firms acting for both claimants and defendants are on the decrease, mainly as a result of major insurers shrinking their panels of firms which represent them.

Personal injury cases range from simple "slip and trip" cases (such as falling over uneven paving stones) to fatal accidents, major disaster litigation (the Paddington Rail crash) and complex group ("multi-party") actions, often in the environmental or industrial disease context. Examples of these include the asbestos-related disease actions brought on behalf of the South African miners, the tobacco litigation and the Gulf War Syndrome cases.

Clinical negligence actions include those arising from treatment of medical conditions or injuries. Among the most complex and serious cases which carry the highest potential amount of compensation are those arising from birth, such as brain-damaged babies.

Type of work

PI and clinical negligence lawyers spend the majority of their time gathering information from clients as evidence to support their cases, obtaining expert evidence, researching the technicalities of their cases and generally preparing for litigation. Pre-litigation advice includes advising the client on the strength of their case, and if it is strong enough to take forward, taking the client through aspects of funding the case and general case strategy. Only a very small percentage of cases reach trial as most settlements are reached out of court to avoid unecessary costs - an imperative objective under the new reforms to the legal system (commonly referred to as "the Woolf reforms").

Personal Injury

Road traffic accident ("RTA") claims are generally routine in nature ("high volume, low value claims") but are the staple diet of many high street and general practices. The most efficient practices will have dedicated IT resources to deal with the substantial amount of standard documentation and paperwork generated by this type of work. Other claimant firms which are more specialist in nature have lawyers with expertise in a variety of niche areas. Leigh, Day & Co specialises in multi-party actions with an environmental aspect such as asbestos-related diseases work and gas poisonings. They also have expertise in aviation disasters and horse-riding accidents. Russell Jones & Walker handle deafness cases, for example, representing police officers deafened by motorcycle and gunfire noise, and an office worker deafened by a faulty fire alarm. They also have a special unit for victims of sexual assault.

Defendant firms are often instructed by insurers, but they require as much specialist knowledge as their claimant counterparts. "Shortly after qualifying I bought myself a Teach Yourself Anatomy book and read it from cover to cover," says Steve Daykin, head of defendant PI at Nabarro Nathanson in Sheffield. He is has been defending British Coal in the "Vibration White Finger" (a condition where vibrating machinery causes fingers to turn white and go numb) litigation in the Court of Appeal, and in a group respiratory disease claim. He obviously needs to be fully aware of the medical conditions allegedly suffered by the claimants.

This type of work takes lawyers from the factory floor to the coal mine, from the scene of an accident to the hospital, and from the home to the sports field. They become mini-experts in a number of activities. Terry Lee, partner with Evill & Coleman, had to learn the ins and outs of the rules of rugby as well as draw on his knowledge of head and spinal injuries, when he represented the rugby player, Ben Smolden, in his ground-breaking action against two rugby referees. Smolden sustained severe injuries during a match and one of the referees was held liable for those injuries.

Clinical Negligence

Like PI, clinical negligence work ranges from simple injuries to actions worth millions of pounds in damages. The more complex cases require an in-depth knowledge of medical technicalities. Katie Hay, a consultant with the defendant firm, Capsticks, explains that the doctors and experts can tell you much of what you need to know, but that with most specialist cases, "you just have to sit down and learn it for yourself."

Hay defended Merton, Sutton and Wandsworth Health Authority in an action brought by a patient who became pregnant after she had supposedly been sterilised. Following detailed gynaecological, histological and video evidence, it was established that the doctor who performed the sterilisation had not been at fault. The lawyers knew as much about the medical complications as the doctors by the end of the trial.

An awareness of mental as well as physical illness is often required by the lawyers. Specialist claimant firm, Pritchard Englefield, acted for Mr and Mrs Tredget in their test case against Bexley Health Authority, which established that a father who witnessed the mismanaged birth of his son (who died shortly afterwards) could recover damages for his own psychological injury.

Magi Young, partner with claimant firm, Parlett Kent, recently achieved a settlement of £1.2 million for a psychiatric patient who managed to take an overdose while under one-to-one observation. For 12 hours, the hospital failed to realise that she had lapsed into a coma.

These cases are at the top end of the scale and a trainee or recently qualified solicitor would obviously play only a junior role in such matters. Nevertheless, this role could still involve liaising with clients and doctors. As a trainee with Parlett Kent points out: "I already have a lot of client contact, and give advice and support on the 'phone, as well as taking witness statements and attending consultations with counsel." He also undertakes advocacy for his firm and sometimes finds himself up against a partner on the other side.

Clinical negligence and PI are intense and absorbing fields and require hard work and long hours just to keep up to speed with advances in medicine and technology. According to Steve Daykin, those at the top of the profession routinely work a 60-70 hour week.

Skills needed

It goes without saying that lawyers entering these fields must be interested in medical issues. They need a knowledge of anatomy and medical conditions, and an understanding of how the NHS works so they can ask relevant questions about hospital forms and records. An awareness of the professional relationships between doctors, nurses, managers and patients is also essential. It is not surprising then that many clinical negligence lawyers have worked in the medical profession prior to practising law. The leading firms contain a number of doctors, nurses, dentists, medical secretaries and registrars. "We are here to carry out the day-to-day procedures of the law," says Katie Hay, "but a number of us come here with some sort of medical background and many people have wanted to be a doctor at some time." Bedtime reading will include not only legal updates, but also the latest issues of GP News, Health Service Journal and Healthcare Management.

An interest in medical issues must be accompanied by a "non-squeamish" nature. Most firms send their lawyers to hospitals to observe surgical procedures. As one partner commented, "Witnessing first hand what a hysterectomy involves can be pretty useful."

Good communication skills are essential for translating complicated medical issues into simple terms for clients, or for giving detailed accounts to increasingly cost-conscious health service bodies.

A sensitive and sympathetic approach, coupled with great strength of character are required in what can quite literally be life or death situations. As one trainee said: "You have to be able to empathise with people who have suffered a great deal. The fact that they may be badly treated by institutions which they see as powerful and secretive can add insult to injury."

Defendant solicitors must also employ tact and sensitivity. "We have to calm down agitated doctors as much as claimant solicitors have to calm down their clients," says Katie Hay. "Our job is no less stressful and we have to be reassuring and assertive at the same time. We must also weigh up the commercial considerations involved in conducting this type of litigation. A good defendant lawyer must have the ability to form an early view on whether a case should be settled or fought."

With so much emphasis on medical issues, it would be easy to forget that at the end of the day, the tactics of litigation are obviously at the forefront of this field, as with any contentious area. The usual qualities of confidence, tenacity and common sense (for knowing when to back down) are required.

Above all, successful lawyers in this field show an emotional commitment and dedication to their work, not often witnessed in drier areas of law. There are a lot of enthusiastic PI and clinical negligence lawyers, comments Magi Young. She herself finds the work "phenomenally interesting," "very rewarding" and is "totally committed."

On a day-to-day basis, the lawyers stress that they appreciate a partner or opponent who is "reasonable, practical and easy to deal with."

Career options

Magi Young has always acted for claimants. She trained in a small legal aid practice where she tackled personal injury, clinical negligence, mental health, housing, immigration, crime and family law. She then moved to Pannone Napier (now Pannone & Partners), where she immediately specialised in personal injury and clinical negligence and became a partner after four years. She has been a partner with Parlett Kent for the past eight years and recently set up a branch of the firm in Exeter.

After training with Robert Muckle, Steve Daykin joined British Coal as an assistant solicitor to experience the public sector. In 1986, he became British Coal's area solicitor for the north east and was in charge of 20 lawyers. In 1990, Nabarro Nathanson took over part of British Coal's legal department and Daykin moved to join the firm. He now heads their PI department. He had this to say of his field: "You talk to commercial lawyers who think their jobs are more demanding because they earn more money, but acting for defendants in PI is a hell of a challenge and no less intellectually demanding."

There are very few in-house options for lawyers in this field. When pressed, Steve Daykin suggested that there may be openings for defendant solicitors with health authorities and the Post Office, but commented that "such opportunities are getting rarer all the time, with the majority of work being referred to specialist practices." Magi Young knows of no in-house lawyers in this field and stressed that as it is such a demanding and highly-focused area. "It is only for those whose commitment is total and career changes on the inside are extremely rare." Katie Hay agrees: "This is a popular area of law as it involves commercial decision-making in a human context. Those who succeed in breaking into it tend to be here to stay."

Their advice is to make focused applications to specialist firms, because the trend within private practice is towards increasing specialisation in a small number of niche firms.

The Firms

Personal Injury

Many specialist personal injury firms, particularly in London, act either for claimants or defendants. Leading claimant firms include Leigh, Day & Co, Thompsons and Russell Jones & Walker. Leigh, Day & Co are renowned for their expertise in complex personal injury matters and multi-party actions (e.g. tobacco litigation); Thompsons are known for industrial disease cases, acting for union clients and Russell Jones & Walker were involved in Page v Sheerness, the leading House of Lords case on damages and collateral benefits. All these firms also have offices around the country.

Other regional claimant firms include Osborne Morris & Morgan in Leighton Buzzard, who have a particular specialism in neurological injuries; Rowley Ashworth in Exeter and Leeds (another firm acting for union clients, particularly in industrial disease cases); and Irwin Mitchell in Leeds, Birmingham and Sheffield, who have been involved in the miners' respiratory disease litigation against British Coal.

The leading defendant firms in London are all insurance/healthcare practices. Beachcroft Wansbroughs have defended a case for a South African company in relation to alleged mercury exposure suffered by miners, while Kennedys were instructed by the British Railways Board in two test actions involving claims for industrial diseases.

Defendant firms outside London include Davies Lavery in Maidstone, Morgan Cole in Reading, Buller Jeffries in Birmingham, Mills & Reeve in Norwich, Keogh Ritson in Bolton and Sinton & Co in Newcastle.

Several regional firms act for both claimants and defendants. They include Bond Pearce in Plymouth, Newsome Vaughan in Coventry, Colemans in Manchester and Hay & Kilner in Newcastle.

Clinical Negligence

There is a trend in clinical negligence work towards increasing specialisation in a small number of firms. It is particularly difficult for new defendant firms to break into this area because NHS Trusts select their legal adviser from a small panel of established firms.

Leigh, Day & Co are the leading London firm for claimant work, acting for all types of claimant, but particularly children with brain injuries. On the defendant side Capsticks, Hempsons and Beachcroft Wansbroughs lead the field.

Firms with leading reputations for PI work are often highly rated for clinical negligence as well. Osborne Morris & Morgan on the claimant side and Morgan Cole on the defendant side in the south east, for example. In the south west and Wales, Bevan Ashford are the clear leaders for defendant work, and are acknowledged as having one of the best defence practices in the country. Other noteworthy firms include Alexander Harris in Altrincham and London who specialise exclusively in health related work on behalf of claimants and have one of the largest clinical negligence teams in the country; and Freeth Cartwright Hunt Dickins (Nottingham and Derby) who cover a range of claimant work, with particular specialisms in obstetrics, gynaecology, cancer cases and pharmaceutical product liability.

▶

Leading Firms

London	PI Claimant	PI Defendant	Med. Neg Claimant	Med. Neg Defendant
Alexander Harris			****	
Anthony Gold, Lerman & Muirhead	**			
Barlow Lyde & Gilbert		******		
Beachcroft Wansbroughs		******		*****
Berrymans Lace Mawer		******		
Bindman & Partners			****	
Bolt Burdon	**			
Capsticks				******
Charles Russell			***	
CMS Cameron McKenna		**		
Davies Arnold Cooper		******		
E. Edwards Son & Noice		**		
Evill and Coleman	***		****	
Field Fisher Waterhouse	**		*****	
Finers Stephens Innocent	*			
G.L. Hockfield & Co	*			
Greenwoods		**		
Hempsons				******
Hextall Erskine		***		
Hodge Jones & Allen	***			
Irwin Mitchell	*			
Kennedys		***		
Kingsley Napley			*****	
Lawford & Co	*			
Lawrence Graham		**		
Le Brasseur J Tickle		**		*****
Leigh, Day & Co	*****		******	
O.H. Parsons & Partners	**			
Parlett Kent	*		*****	
Pattinson & Brewer	***		*	
Prince Evans	**			
Pritchard Englefield	*			
Rowley Ashworth	***			
Russell Jones & Walker	******			
Simmonds Church Smiles	*			
Thompsons McClure	******			
Vizards, Staples & Bannisters		***		
Watmores		***		
Wedlake Saint		*		

Firms and their star ratings are based on Chambers' Directory 1999–2000. Six stars represent a top-ranked firm, five stars a second-ranked firm, etc.

South East	**PI Claimant**	**PI Defendant**	**Med. Neg Claimant**	**Med. Neg Defendant**
A.E. Wyeth & Co, Dartford		*****		
Amery-Parkes, Basingstoke	*****			
Argles Stoneham Burstows, Maidstone	**	**		
Beachcroft Wansbroughs, Winchester				******
Blake Lapthorn, Portsmouth	*****		*****	
Bond Pearce, Southampton		*****		
Boyes Turner & Burrows, Reading	****		******	
Brachers, Maidstone		*****		*****
Buss Murton, Tunbridge Wells	**	**		
Clarkson Wright & Jakes, Orpington	***			
Cripps Harries Hall, Tunbridge Wells	**	**		
Darbys Mallam Lewis, Oxford	***			
Davies Lavery, Maidstone		******		
Donne Mileham & Haddock, Brighton	**	**		
E. Edwards Son & Noice, Ilford	**	**		
Ensor Byfield, Southampton		*****		
Fennemores, Milton Keynes	****			
Gadsby Wicks, Chelmsford			****	
George Ide, Phillips, Chichester	****			
Harris & Cartwright, Slough	**	**		
Henmans, Oxford	***	***		
Iliffes Booth Bennett, Uxbridge	*	*		
Kennedys, Brentwood		*****		
Lamport Bassitt, Southampton	***	***		
Marshall & Galpin, Oxford	***	***		
Merricks, Chelmsford		***		
Morgan Cole, Reading		******		
Osborne Morris & Morgan, Buzzard	******		******	
Pattinson & Brewer, Chatham	*****			
Penningtons, Godalming	***	***	****	
Peter Richbell & Co, Chelmsford	***			
Shoosmiths, Reading	*****			
T.G. Baynes & Sons, Bexleyheath	***			
Thompsons McClure, Ilford	*****			
Thomson Snell & Passmore, Tunbridge Wells	*****		*****	
Warner Goodman & Streat, Fareham	*****			
Wynne Baxter Godfree, Brighton				****

South West	**PI Claimant**	**PI Defendant**	**Med. Neg Claimant**	**Med. Neg Defendant**
Amery-Parkes, Bristol	**	**		
Barcan Woodward, Bristol			******	
Battens (with Poole & Co), Yeovil	**			
Beachcroft Wansbroughs, Bristol		******		*****
Bevan Ashford, Bristol		***		******
Bishop Longbotham & Bagnall, Trowbridge	***			
Bond Pearce, Plymouth	******	******		

Boyce Hatton, Torquay	*	*		
Burroughs Day, Bristol	****			
Cartwrights, Bristol		*****		
Crosse & Crosse, Exeter	**	**		
David Gist & Co, Bristol	***			
Davies and Partners, Gloucester	**	**		
Faulkners, Frome	**			
Frank & Caffin, Truro		**		
Hugh James Ford Simey, Exeter		***		
John Hodge & Co, Weston-super-Mare			*****	
Kirby Simcox, Bristol	*	*		
Lyons Davidson, Bristol	*****	*****		
Metcalfes, Bristol	**	**		
Nash & Co, Plymouth	***	***		
Over Taylor Biggs, Exeter	***		******	
Palser Grossman, Bristol		*		
Pardoes, Bridgwater	***			
Pattinson & Brewer, Bristol	*****			
Preston Goldburn, Falmouth			******	
Rowley Ashworth, Exeter	******			
Russell Jones & Walker, Bristol	******		******	
Sansbury Hill, Bristol		******		
Stephens & Scown, Exeter	*****	*****		
Stones, Exeter	***	***		
Tayntons, Gloucester	***	***		
Thompsons McClure, Bristol	******			
Townsends, Swindon	*****	*****		
Tozers, Exeter			******	
Trobridges, Plymouth	*	*		
Trumps, Bristol	***			
Veale Wasbrough, Bristol	*****	*****	*****	
Veitch Penny, Exeter	****	****		
Withy King, Bath			*****	
Wolferstans, Plymouth	*****	*****	*****	
Woollcombe Beer Watts, Newton Abbot	**	**	*****	

Wales	**PI Claimant**	**PI Defendant**	**Med. Neg Claimant**	**Med. Neg Defendant**
Bevan Ashford, Cardiff				******
Dolmans, Cardiff		***		
Douglas-Jones Mercer, Swansea	***	***		
Edwards Geldard, Cardiff			****	
Eversheds, Cardiff		**		
Graham Evans & Partners, Swansea	***	***		
Hugh James Ford Simey, Cardiff		******	*****	
Hugh James Ford Simey, Merthyr Tydfil	***			
Huttons, Cardiff	**		******	
John Collins & Partners, Swansea	***	***		

Leo Abse & Cohen, Cardiff	******			
Loosemores, Cardiff	**			
Morgan Cole, Cardiff		******		
Palser Grossman, Cardiff Bay		***		
Smith Llewelyn Partnership, Swansea	**		*****	
Thompsons McClure, Cardiff	******			
Walker Smith & Way, Wrexham	***		****	

Midlands	**PI Claimant**	**PI Defendant**	**Med. Neg Claimant**	**Med. Neg Defendant**
Amery-Parkes, Birmingham	**	**		
Anthony Collins Solicitors, Birmingham			*****	
Barratt Goff & Tomlinson, Nottingham	***			
Beachcroft Wansbroughs, Birmingham		******		**
Browne Jacobson, Nottingham		******		
Buller Jeffries, Birmingham		******		
Cartwright & Lewis, Birmingham		****		
Challinors Lyon Clark, Birmingham			*****	
Chapman Everatt, Birmingham		****		
Edge Ellison, Birmingham		****		
Everatt & Company, Evesham		******		
Flint, Bishop & Barnett, Derby	**	**		
Freeth Cartwright Hunt Dickins, Derby			******	
Freeth Cartwright Hunt Dickins, Nottingham	***		******	
Irwin Mitchell, Birmingham	******		****	
Keogh Ritson, Coventry		***		
Langleys, Lincoln	*	*		
Mills & Reeve, Birmingham				***
Nelsons, Nottingham	***			
Newsome Vaughan, Coventry	**	**		
Rowley Ashworth, Birmingham	******			
Rowley Dickinson, Birmingham		****		
Russell Jones & Walker, Birmingham	******			
Shakespeares, Birmingham		***	*****	
Shoosmiths, Northampton		***		
Thompsons McClure, Birmingham	******		****	
Thompsons McClure, Nottingham	******			
Weightmans, Birmingham		******		
Willcox Lane Clutterbuck, Birmingham		***		

East Anglia	**PI Claimant**	**PI Defendant**	**Med. Neg Claimant**	**Med. Neg Defendant**
Bates, Wells & Braithwaite, Ipswich	****			
Birketts, Ipswich	***	***		
Buckle Mellows, Peterborough	***	***		
Cunningham John, Thetford	******		******	
Dawbarns, Wisbech	*****			
Eversheds, Norwich		*****		
Greenwoods, Peterborough	***	***		

Hewitson Becke + Shaw, Cambridge		****		
Leathes Prior, Norwich	******			
Merricks, Ipswich		****		
Metcalfe Copeman & Pettefar, Wisbech	*****			
Mills & Reeve, Cambridge				*****
Mills & Reeve, Norwich		******		*****
Morgan Jones & Pett, Great Yarmouth	****		****	
Prettys, Ipswich	******	******	*****	
Rogers and Norton, Norwich	**	**		
Scrivenger Seabrook, St. Neots				*****
Taylor Vinters, Cambridge	****			
Ward Gethin, King's Lynn	*****			

North West	**PI Claimant**	**PI Defendant**	**Med. Neg Claimant**	**Med. Neg Defendant**
Abson Hall, Stockport	*			
Alexander Harris, Altrincham	****		******	
Beachcroft Wansbroughs, Manchester		****		
Berrymans Lace Mawer, Liverpool, Manc		*****		
Betesh Fox & Co, Manchester	***			
Blackhurst Parker + Yates, Preston	***	***		
Colemans Solicitors, Manchester	******	******		
Davies Arnold Cooper, Manchester		***		
Davies Wallis Foyster, Liverpool, Manc		****		
Donns Solicitors, Manchester	*****			
E. Rex Makin & Co, Liverpool	*			
Elliotts, Manchester		**		
Geoffrey Warhurst, Manchester		***		
George Davies & Co, Manchester				*****
Goldsmith Williams, Liverpool	*			
Halliwell Landau, Manchester		***		
Hammond Suddards, Manchester		***		
Hempsons, Manchester				******
Hill Dickinson, Liverpool		****		*****
Hill Dickinson, Manchester		****		
Horwich Farrelly, Manchester	****	****		
Hugh Potter & Company, Manchester	*			
Jack Thornley, Manchester	*****			
Jackson & Canter, Liverpool	**			
James Chapman & Co, Manchester		*****		
John Pickering & Partners, Oldham	******			
Jones Maidment Wilson, Manchester			***	
Keogh Ritson, Bolton		******		
Lawford & Co, Manchester	***			
Leigh, Day & Co, Manchester	******		***	
Linder Myers, Manchester	****		****	
Lonsdales, Blackpool			***	
Mace & Jones, Liverpool	***			
Maxwell Entwistle & Byrne, Kirkby			***	

Pannone & Partners, Manchester	******		******	
Percy Hughes & Roberts, Birkenhead		****		
Perkins & Co, Manchester	****	****		
Peter Rickson and Partners, Preston		****		
Ramsbottom & Co, Blackburn	**			
Russell Jones & Walker, Manchester	*****			
Silverbeck Rymer, Liverpool	****	****		
The Paul Rooney Partnership, Liverpool	***			
Thompsons McClure, Liverpool	*****			
Walker Smith & Way, Chester	*****			
Weightmans, Liverpool, Manchester		*****		
Whittles, Manchester	******			

North East	**PI Claimant**	**PI Defendant**	**Med. Neg Claimant**	**Med. Neg Defendant**
Beachcroft Wansbroughs, Leeds		***		
Beachcroft Wansbroughs, Sheffield				******
Beecham Peacock, Newcastle	**			
Browell Smith & Goodyear, Newcastle		**		
Crutes, Newcastle-upon-Tyne		**		******
Deas Mallen Souter, Newcastle		**		
Dibb Lupton Alsop, Bradford, Leeds, Sheffield		***		
Eversheds, Newcastle				******
Hammond Suddards, Leeds		**		
Hay & Kilner, Newcastle	******	******	*	
Hempsons, Harrogate				*****
Heptonstalls, Goole			****	
Irwin Mitchell, Leeds	******	*****		
Irwin Mitchell, Sheffield	******	*****	******	
Jacksons, Stockton-on-Tees		**		
Le Brasseur J Tickle, Leeds				*****
Linsley & Mortimer, Newcastle		**		
Lupton Fawcett, Leeds	*****	*****		
Marrons, Newcastle upon Tyne	****			
Nabarro Nathanson, Sheffield		**		
Pattinson & Brewer, York	****			
Peter Maughan & Co, Gateshead			*****	
Philip Hamer & Co, Hull	***			
Rollit Farrell & Bladon, Hull		*		
Rowley Ashworth, Leeds	*****			
Russell Jones & Walker, Leeds, Newcastle-upon-Tyne, Sheffield	*****			
Samuel Phillips & Co, Newcastle	*****	*****		*
Sinton & Co, Newcastle upon Tyne		***		
Smith & Graham, Hartlepool	**			
Stamp Jackson and Procter, Hull	*****	*****	****	
Thompsons McClure, Leeds, Newcastle		*****		
Ward Hadaway, Newcastle upon Tyne				**
Whittles, Leeds	**			

PRIVATE CLIENT

(Including Trusts & Personal Tax, Agriculture & Bloodstock and Charities)

Area of Law

'Private clients' are private individuals as opposed to corporate entities. The definition of 'private client' work really depends on what sort of firm you're thinking of applying to. In a commercial practice, the term generally refers to advice on tax and trusts to high net worth individuals who are prepared to pay hundreds of pounds an hour for top specialist advice and personal service. For a high street firm it could mean any member of the public, wealthy or otherwise and would include advice on divorce, conveyancing and drawing up wills. In this chapter we refer to the work carried out in commercial firms.

Private client work has become synonymous with certain services provided to individuals. These include trusts, tax and probate advice and associated services connected with the acquisition, disposal and management of personal assets.

There is often a cross-over between the work and clients of agricultural law specialists and private client practitioners. Ownership of farms is commonly by way of family trusts. Both specialisms draw heavily on land law. Similarly, those solicitors who have developed a niche in trust law may find that their expertise is sought after by charitable organisations so need an understanding of the rules governing charities. Work is generally purely advisory and non-contentious although litigation is always a possibility.

Type of work

Trusts and Personal Tax

Any solicitor must respect client confidentiality. With private clients the reasons for doing so are more acutely apparent. The solicitor is often drawn into a very detailed examination of a client's family life and finances. The solicitor has to respect the client's privacy whilst maintaining impartiality and giving the best possible practical advice. The solicitor must also hear the most private details of family circumstances and financial arrangements with understanding but without judgment.

David Long, partner at City firm Charles Russell, sees UK trusts law as a very portable product internationally. He is confident that firms will find their private client lawyers becoming more in demand in the future by foreign clients. "The beauty of our English language is that it is world-wide, and English corporate and commercial law is world-wide, ranking with New York law as the dominant law. Trusts and the tax planning work is also an important invisible export. The trust is a wonderfully flexible tool for planning." Surprisingly, Andrew Young of Lawrence Graham sees the trust as a fashionable tool for the international seriously rich. "Rich people in foreign countries know that their friends have trusts so they want one too. The trust is becoming the ultimate fashion accessory for the seriously rich."

Trusts are a very popular way of holding assets and avoiding tax (rather than evading tax, which is illegal) often by holding funds in off-shore jurisdictions. Trusts allow family members access to funds whilst also allowing the donor a degree of control over the manner in which the funds are accessed.

The creation of trusts in other jurisdictions often means that the lawyer will have to spend time ensuring that his client understands the system of law behind the setting up of a trust. David Long told us, "In the off-shore world you get a culture clash between people brought up in Napoleonic Code countries which have certain heirship rights for children which don't fit at all well with our common law system. So you get rich men in Italy or Spain taking their money to the Bahamas or Bermuda and creating trusts. Then you may have litigation in the original country to determine whether the trust works to defeat the interest of the children who would otherwise have inherited." A lawyer must be very careful to apprise the client of all the possible foreign law implications.

As well as handling off-shore trusts in conjunction with overseas lawyers and trust companies, private client lawyers find that they advise an increasing number of overseas clients seeking to invest in the UK. Off-shore and private banks may also need advice about their clients' UK interests.

A private client lawyer will be consulted on a range of different issues from immigration and employment questions through to share transactions and property deals. The most experienced individuals have the breadth of experience to give an answer to these diverse questions. However, in a large multi-service law firm there is plenty of opportunity to turn to the expertise of colleagues.

Agriculture and bloodstock

Agriculture and bloodstock lawyers advise on the law relating to agricultural holdings and to livestock and bloodstock. John Moore, head of Macfarlane's agricultural department, is well known for his work for private clients with landed estates or farms. He also does commercial work, but prefers agriculture. "It's a much smaller world with a friendly atmosphere - there are only ten top land agents so you are always dealing with the same people."

Charities

A related area of practice is charities law, where clients range from well known national charities to low profile local private charitable trusts. Work consists of charity registration and reorganisation, Charity Commission investigations, the development of trading subsidiaries and advising charitable clients on any other issues necessary such as tax, trust or property matters. Many firms, especially the smaller ones, frequently specialise in advising particular types of charity, for example religious or environmental charities.

Skills needed

Although primarily a tax specialist, you'll need to be a good all round lawyer as many clients will view you as their primary legal adviser and consult you on a range of issues. You should have a good 'bedside manner' and facilitation skills. If you bring colleagues on board for issues such as matrimonial matters or conveyancing, for example, you will need to monitor their relationship with your client. Client relationships are key. Says David Long: "Some private clients get very close to you and don't do anything major without asking or discussing it with you. You are often a trustee or executor looking after their money for the next generation and that's tremendous. It's very flattering to be asked to be a trustee." He likes the fact that aside from having some money the clients are all very diverse. "I would not wish my practice to have only rich farmers or aristocrats or businessmen. I like the variety because human beings are so different all the time. That's the beauty of it! And you do get to know them quite well when you're advising them on this sort of thing." The lawyer must be flexible enough to deal with all kinds of individual and, as Martyn Gowar of Lawrence Graham points out, they must have "enormous tolerance."

Obviously a strong grounding in trusts and tax is vital, but you will need to keep up to date with the law in relation to a variety of areas. Innovative yet well-organised thinkers do well. The client needs a smart lawyer who is capable of seeing the bigger picture and assessing how best to manage a portfolio of assets over a long period of time.

Career options

Training at an established private client firm such as Withers, Farrers and Boodle Hatfield will give the best possible start. Rare City firms such as Allen & Overy and Macfarlanes still offer these services to their clients, allowing trainees to combine private client work with a corporate training. However there has been a recent trend for the larger London commercial firms to hive off their private client departments, sending the work and the specialists to smaller practices, such as Charles Russell, or to regional firms.

In-house opportunities are limited although some off-shore trust companies and private banks do have in house legal advisers. For those who fancy working abroad, banks in the Bahamas, Cayman Islands and Jersey may employ lawyers in advisory or risk control positions.

For agriculture or charities specialists there is less scope in terms of law firms specialising in this area, but with the opportunity to make strong contacts with clients there is always the possibility of moving into a more general role within the industry.

The firms

Trusts and personal tax

For private client work in London the top firms are Allen & Overy, Boodle Hatfield, Charles Russell, Farrer & Co, Lawrence Graham, Macfarlanes and Withers.

In the regions there are plenty of strong practices. In the south west these are Anstey Sargent & Probert of Exeter, Bond Pearce in Plymouth, in Bristol Osborne Clarke and Burges Salmon, in Cheltenham Charles Russell and Wiggin & Co as well as Wilsons of Salisbury. In the south east, Boodle Hatfield's Oxford branch, Cripps Harries Hall and Thomson Snell & Passmore in Tunbridge Wells and Thomas Eggar Church Adams of Chichester lead the field. The top Welsh practices are Bevan Ashford's Cardiff office and Edwards Geldard also in Cardiff. In East Anglia, Hewitson Becke + Shaw in Cambridge lead with two Norwich practices, Eversheds and Mills & Reeve.

The Midlands leading players are Hewitson Becke + Shaw's Northampton office and Birmingham's Martineau Johnson. In the north, Liverpool firms Berrymans Lace Mawer and Brabner Holden Banks Wilson are top with Manchester firms Cobbetts and Halliwell Landau plus north eastern leaders Dickinson Dees of Newcastle upon Tyne. Heading the Scots firms are Brodies WS, Turcan Connell, Murray Beith Murray and Tods Murray WS all in Edinburgh, plus Maclay Murray & Spens in Glasgow. In Northern Ireland, two Belfast firms - Cleaver Fulton & Rankin and Johnsons have the largest teams in a tightly packed group of leading firms.

Agriculture and bloodstock

Agriculture and bloodstock specialists are widespread across the country. In London, Withers and Farrer & Co lead with Macfarlanes. In the south, Wales and East Anglia the top firms are Brachers of Maidstone, Burges Salmon in Bristol, Margraves of Llandrindod Wells, Mills & Reeve in Norwich, Thomas Eggar Church Adams in Chichester and White & Bowker in Winchester. In the Midlands, Roythorne & Co of Spalding and in the north, Dickinson Dees of Newcastle upon Tyne and Cartmell Shepherd in Carlisle are the leaders. Brodies WS of Edinburgh are the most well regarded in Scotland.

Charities

For charities work, the out and out leader in London is Bates, Wells & Braithwaite, followed by Allen & Overy, Farrer & Co and Paisner & Co In the regions the most respected practices are those of Stone King in Bath and Malcolm Lynch in Leeds.

Leading Firms

London	Agriculture & Bloodstock	Trusts & Personal Tax	Charities
Alexanders	*		
Allen & Overy		******	*****
Badhams Thompson	***		
Bates, Wells & Braithwaite			******
S J Berwin & Co			*
Bircham & Co.		****	****
Boodle Hatfield		******	
Bristows			*
Campbell Hooper	***		
Charles Russell		******	****
Claricoat Phillips			***
Collyer-Bristow		**	
Cumberland Ellis Peirs		*	
Currey & Co		*****	
Dawson & Co	***	**	
Denton Hall			**
Edwin Coe		*	
Ellis Wood			**
Farrer & Co	******	******	*****
Field Fisher Waterhouse			**
Fladgate Fielder		*	
Forsters	**	***	
Goodman Derrick			**
Gouldens		*	
Gregory, Rowcliffe & Milners		*	*
Harbottle & Lewis			**
Herbert Smith			*
Hunters		***	*
Lawrence Graham		******	*
Lee & Pembertons	**	***	**
Lee Bolton & Lee			**
Linklaters		*	***
Macfarlanes	******	******	*
Masons		*	
Maxwell Batley		*	
May, May & Merrimans	**	*	
Nabarro Nathanson			**
Nicholson Graham & Jones		****	
Paisner & Co		**	*****
Park Nelson		*	
Payne Hicks Beach	***	****	**
Radcliffes		**	**
Rooks Rider		*	
Russell-Cooke, Potter & Chapman		*	

Simmonds Church Smiles		*	
Simmons & Simmons		**	*
Sinclair Taylor & Martin			***
Smyth Barkham		*	
Speechly Bircham		*****	***
Taylor Joynson Garrett		****	
Titmuss Sainer Dechert	*	**	
Trowers & Hamlins	*	**	***
Tweedie & Prideaux			*
Vizard Oldham			*
Wedlake Bell		**	
Winckworth Sherwood		**	***
Witham Weld		*	**
Withers	******	******	****

South East	**Agriculture & Bloodstock**	**Trusts & Personal Tax**	**Charities**
Adams & Remers, Lewes		*****	
Argles Stoneham Burstows, Crawley		***	
B.P. Collins & Co, Gerrards Cross		***	
Barlows, Guildford		***	*
Blake Lapthorn, Portsmouth		****	*
Blandy & Blandy, Reading		*****	
Boodle Hatfield, Oxford		******	
Brachers, Maidstone	******	***	
BrookStreet Des Roches, Witney			**
Burley & Geach, Petersfield		***	
Buss Murton, Tunbridge Wells		****	
Chalk Smith Brooks, Swindon	******		
Charles Lucas & Marshall, Newbury			*
Charles Russell, Guildford		***	
Clarks, Reading		***	
Cripps Harries Hall, Tunbridge Wells	*****	******	*
Donne Mileham & Haddock, Brighton		****	
Elizabeth Cairns, Maidstone			***
Furley Page Fielding & Barton, Canterbury			*
George Ide, Phillips, Chichester		***	
Girlings, Herne Bay		**	
Griffith Smith, Brighton		***	**
Hallett & Co, Ashford	***	***	
Henmans, Oxford	*	***	
Iliffes Booth Bennett, Uxbridge		****	*
Knights, Tunbridge Wells	***		
Lamport Bassitt, Southampton		***	
Linnells, Oxford	*		*
Manches, Oxford			***
Matthew Arnold & Baldwin, Watford		***	
Matthew McCloy & Partners, Newbury	****		

Mayo & Perkins, Eastbourne		**	
Moore & Blatch, Lymington		*****	
Morgan Cole, Oxford	*****	*****	
Nabarro Nathanson, Reading			***
Paris Smith & Randall, Southampton		****	
Parrott & Coales, Aylesbury	*		
Penningtons, Basingstoke	***		
Pictons, St. Albans		***	
Pryce & Co, Abingdon	***		
Rawlison & Butler, Crawley		**	
Sharman & Trethewy, Bedford	*		
Sparling Benham & Brough, Colchester		***	
Staffurth & Bray, Bognor Regis		***	
Stanley Tee & Company, Bishop's Stortford	****	***	
Stevens & Bolton, Guildford		***	
Thomas Eggar Church Adams, Chichester	******	******	**
Thomson Snell & Passmore, Tunbridge Wells		******	***
Turbervilles with Nelson Cuff, Uxbridge		***	
White & Bowker, Winchester	******	***	
Whitehead Monckton, Maidstone		***	
Winckworth Sherwood, Oxford			***

South West	**Agriculture & Bloodstock**	**Trusts & Personal Tax**	**Charities**
Anstey Sargent & Probert, Exeter		******	
Battens (with Poole & Co), Yeovil	***		
Bevan Ashford, Bristol	**		
Bevirs, Swindon	*		
Beviss & Beckingsale, Chard	*		
Bond Pearce, Exeter	***		***
Bond Pearce, Plymouth	***	******	
Burges Salmon, Bristol	******	******	***
Cartwrights, Bristol		****	
Charles Russell, Cheltenham		******	
Clarke Willmott & Clarke, Taunton	****	*****	**
Coodes, St. Austell		*****	
Eastleys, Paignton		****	
Every & Phillips, Honiton	**		
Foot & Bowden, Plymouth		****	
Harris & Harris, Wells	*		
Hooper & Wollen, Torquay		*****	
Humphries Kirk, Wareham	*		
Lawrence Tucketts, Bristol		*****	
Lester Aldridge, Bournemouth		*****	*
Meade-King, Bristol		*****	
Michelmores, Exeter		*****	**
Osborne Clarke, Bristol	*	******	***
Pardoes, Bridgwater	**		

Parker Bullen, Salisbury			**
Peter, Peter & Wright, Holsworthy	**		
Porter Dodson, Yeovil	***		
Rickerby Watterson, Cheltenham			*
Slee Blackwell, Barnstaple	*		
A.E. Smith & Son, Stroud	*	****	
Steele Raymond, Bournemouth		*****	
Stephens & Scown, Exeter	****		
Stone King, Bath			******
Stones, Exeter	**	*****	
Thrings & Long, Bath	****		**
Tozers, Exeter			***
Veale Wasbrough, Bristol		*****	*
Wiggin & Co, Cheltenham		******	
Wilsons Solicitors, Salisbury	*****	******	***
Woollcombe Beer Watts, Chagford	*		
Woollcombe Beer Watts, Newton Abbot	*	****	

Wales	**Agriculture & Bloodstock**	**Trusts & Personal Tax**	**Charities**
Beor Wilson & Lloyd, Swansea		*****	
Bevan Ashford, Cardiff		******	
Edward Harris & Son, Swansea	*****		
Edwards Geldard, Cardiff		******	
Eversheds, Cardiff		*****	**
Gabb & Co, Abergavenny	**		
Greathead & Whitelock, Pembroke	*		
Jeffreys & Powell, Brecon	***		
Jonathan Stephens & Co, Usk	*****		
Margraves, Llandrindod Wells	******		
Price & Son, Haverfordwest	****		
Ungoed Thomas & King, Carmarthen	***		

Midlands	**Agriculture & Bloodstock**	**Trusts & Personal Tax**	**Charities**
Anthony Collins Solicitors, Birmingham			***
Arnold Thomson, Towcester	****		
Blythe Liggins, Leamington Spa		****	
Brethertons, Rugby	**	****	
Chattertons, Horncastle	**		
Freeth Cartwright Hunt Dickins, Nottingham		****	
Gabb & Co, Hereford	**		
Gateley Wareing, Birmingham			**
R. Gwynne & Sons, Wellington	**	****	
Harvey Ingram Owston, Leicester			***
Hewitson Becke + Shaw, Northampton	***	******	**
Higgs & Sons, Brierley Hill		****	
Knight & Sons, Newcastle-under-Lyme	**		

	Agriculture & Bloodstock	Trusts & Personal Tax	Charities
Lanyon Bowdler, Shrewsbury	***		
Lee Crowder, Birmingham		*****	
Manby & Steward, Wolverhampton	**		
Mander Hadley & Co, Coventry			**
Martineau Johnson, Birmingham	**	******	***
Morton Fisher, Worcester	***		
Roythorne & Co, Spalding	******	****	
Shakespeares, Birmingham		****	***
Tallents Godfrey & Co, Newark-on-Trent	**		**
The Wilkes Partnership, Birmingham		****	
Thursfields, Kidderminster	**		
Wace Morgan, Shrewsbury	**		
Wilkin Chapman, Louth	**		
Willcox Lane Clutterbuck, Birmingham		****	
Wragge & Co, Birmingham		*****	***
Wright Hassall, Leamington Spa	*****		

East Anglia	Agriculture & Bloodstock	Trusts & Personal Tax	Charities
Ashton Graham, Bury St Edmunds	***	*****	
Barker Gotelee, Ipswich	*****		
Birketts, Ipswich	****		
Cozens-Hardy & Jewson, Norwich		***	***
Edmondson Hall, Newmarket	******		
Eversheds, Cambridge	*****		**
Eversheds, Norwich	*****	******	**
Greene & Greene, Bury St. Edmunds	*	*****	
Greenwoods, Peterborough	*		**
Hewitson Becke + Shaw, Cambridge	***	******	**
Hood Vores & Allwood, Dereham		***	
Howes Percival, Norwich	***		
Leathes Prior, Norwich			**
Mills & Reeve, Norwich	******	******	***
Prettys, Ipswich	*	*****	
Rustons & Lloyd, Newmarket	******		
Steele & Co, Norwich		***	
Taylor Vinters, Cambridge	******	*****	***
Ward Gethin, King's Lynn		***	
Willcox & Lewis, Norwich		***	

North West	Agriculture & Bloodstock	Trusts & Personal Tax	Charities
Berrymans Lace Mawer, Liverpool		******	
Birch Cullimore, Chester	**	*****	***
Brabner Holden Banks Wilson, Liverpool		******	***
Cartmell Shepherd, Carlisle	******		
Cobbetts, Manchester		******	
Halliwell Landau, Manchester		******	*

Jones Maidment Wilson, Manchester		*****	
Lees Lloyd Whitley, Liverpool		*****	
Mason & Moore Dutton, Chester	***		
Oglethorpe Sturton & Gillibrand, Lancaster	*****		
Oswald Goodier & Co, Preston			**
Pannone & Partners, Manchester			*
Senior Calveley & Hardy, Lytham St. Annes	**		
Walker Smith & Way, Chester	*****		

North East	**Agriculture & Bloodstock**	**Trusts & Personal Tax**	**Charities**
Addleshaw Booth & Co, Leeds	*****	*****	**
Andrew M. Jackson & Co, Hull	**	*****	
Armitage Sykes Hall Norton, Huddersfield		***	
Askews, Redcar		***	
Brooke North, Leeds		****	
Denison Till, York	*		
Dickinson Dees, Newcastle upon Tyne	******	******	**
Eversheds, Leeds	*****	*****	
Eversheds, Newcastle upon Tyne			*
Ford & Warren, Leeds	*		
Gordons Wright & Wright, Bradford		****	
Grays, York	*		***
Harrowell Shaftoe, York		***	
Heptonstalls, Goole	*		
Irwin Mitchell, Sheffield		****	*
Keeble Hawson Moorhouse, Sheffield			**
Latimer Hinks, Darlington	**	***	
Lupton Fawcett, Leeds		*****	
Malcolm Lynch, Leeds			****
McCormicks, Leeds			*
Pinsent Curtis, Leeds		*****	**
Rollit Farrell & Bladon, Hull	*****	***	
Walker Morris, Leeds		***	
Ward Hadaway, Newcastle upon Tyne	******	****	
Wilkin Chapman, Grimsby	*		
Wrigleys, Leeds	*	*****	***

Firms and their star ratings are based on Chambers' Directory 1999–2000. Six stars represent a top-ranked firm, five stars a second-ranked firm, etc.

PROJECTS

Area of law

Project Finance

Project finance – the structuring, financing, construction and operation of infrastructure developments such as roads, power stations, bridges and telecommunications networks – is now considered a 'sexy' area for many of the UK's leading law firms. Several of these now have stand-alone project groups. Certainly, the high profile, international nature of the work attracts many of the most talented lawyers in the UK and overseas. Projects are located throughout the world and projects lawyers hail from every major jurisdiction. However, the major projects are dominated by a few City firms and the largest US practices.

PFI/PPP

In the UK, the Private Finance Initiative (PFI), a part of the Public Private Partnerships (PPP) introduced under the Labour Government, has provided an important source of work. The objective of PFI is to introduce private funding and management into areas which were previously the domain of government, such as the building and operation of roads and hospitals. Through PFI, many smaller London firms and regional practices have become involved in projects work for the first time.

Energy

Some energy projects fall within the heading 'Project Finance' – e.g. the development of the Manah power plant in Oman – but 'energy' is a much wider field. Examples of general energy work include CMS Cameron McKenna advising several Indian states on the restructuring and privatisation of their electricity boards and Lovells conducting specialist international joint venture work on production-sharing contracts to secure exploration rights in North Africa and Russia.

Construction

The physical building of infrastructure projects is only a small, if vital, part of project finance. Similarly, for most construction departments, project finance developments are only one of several sources of work. There are two aspects to construction work: developing the contractual arrangements prior to building work starting (negotiating the contracts between the employer, the contractor, sub-contractors, architects, engineers, surveyors, interior designers, etc.) and litigating when it all goes horribly wrong. Most construction practices do both contentious and non-contentious work. Some, however, are better known for one or the other. Fenwick Elliott is renowned for litigating when buildings are defective or late, while CMS Cameron McKenna's reputation rests on its building work.

Type of work

Projects vary from telecoms links in Tanzania, oil pipelines in the Caucasus and Sahel, power projects in China and India, port developments in Yemen and Oman, toll roads in Israel and gold mines in Indonesia, to PFI hospital projects in Greenwich and sewage plants in Birmingham. The exact nature of the work depends on the type, size and location of the project. However, almost all the major infrastructure projects in which regional firms are involved will be PFI projects of one sort or another. In addition to PFI and PPP other common acronyms include BOO (Build, own and operate), BOOT (Build, own, operate, transfer) and DBFO (Design, build, finance, operate) to name but a few.

Projects work also varies depending on the type of client a firm is acting for. There are a number of parties in a project finance development. There is the project company – usually a special purpose company established to build, own and operate (hence BOO) the power station or whatever the project is. Often the project company is a joint venture between a number of project sponsors who contribute equity to part-fund the project. Project sponsors could include the manufacturer of the gas turbines to be installed in the power station, the construction company that will erect the plant, and the power company that will buy the electricity produced. The company could also be partially owned by a government body or banks.

The project promoter is the organisation that commissions the project. It could be an NHS Trust that wants a new hospital built, or a host government which thinks a privately financed motorway would be a great idea. Funders provide the finance to build the project. Funders include banks, guarantors, export credit agencies, governments, and international funding agencies and they operate in consortiums and individually. Other categories of client are the contractors, operators, and so on. Each party requires its own legal representation.

A common feature of most major projects is the tender process. A public authority or major corporation (the procurer) will invite interested parties (bidders) to tender on the design, building, financing and operation (i.e. DBFO) of a project. At the end of this tender process – which can last up to two years – the winning company or consortium will be selected to manage the project. This company will then have to secure the finance, obtain the necessary planning permission and agree construction, service and employment contracts. Lawyers advising on any of these contracts must understand the big picture. They have to see how changing one contractual term will have a knock-on effect throughout the entire transaction.

Charles Robson, a partner in Lovells' projects department, acted for the banks in one of the PFI's flagship hospital projects, the £300m Norfolk and Norwich. "A commercial deal was struck between the project company and the NHS Trust. In the deal, the Trust promised to pay for the delivery of a new building and the services within it." says Robson. "There were two main parts to our role. We assessed how the principal parties had apportioned the risk in the project, and advised the bank on any amendments to their documents." This can sometimes include a renegotiation of the deal. The firm's other primary function was drafting the credit agreement between the project company and the banks, and the security documentation that supports it. PFI's comparative youth means there is still a lot of groundbreaking negotiation to be done. "It's certainly interesting, but can be pretty exhausting at times," says Robson.

International transactions are generally larger, more complex and can appear more glamorous. Jeremy Gewirtz of Linklaters recently advised the project sponsors financing an LNG tanker to transport gas from Muscat to the Dhabol power station in Maharashtra, India. Though the tanker financing was stand alone, it was also intimately linked to the complex and high profile Dhabol Power Project. The most complex issue involved the co-ordination of arrangements between the lenders to the tanker project and the lenders to Dhabol.

Skills needed

Traditionally, most projects lawyers used to have a background and specialism in another area of law such as banking, corporate, construction or property, and broadened this specialism into an understanding of the range of issues that face projects clients. This is no longer invariably the case, and most younger projects lawyers now go fresh into the field. The diverse nature of projects work means that good projects lawyers need to have an all-round "commercial awareness," harking back, according to Gewirtz, to the "old golden age of the generalist." Indeed he feels that project finance probably now provides a trainee with "the best all-round grounding in a wide variety of skills that you can get in a big City law firm." Projects lawyers should be able to recognise when there is a deal there to be done and need the patience and resilience to see that deal through without getting bogged down in details or in the mountains of paper produced by the project. This is particularly important given the long-term nature of projects transactions and the very close relationships that consequently develop between counsel and client. After all, even if the client is also using other specialist practitioners, the projects lawyer will remain the main "interphase" point. Tact and diplomacy are vital, especially when negotiating risk and favourable terms for the client. Finally, given that they operate in a truly multi-disciplinary practice area, projects lawyers are "expected to know everything. This can be dangerous!"

Lawyers advising on major international projects must be prepared to travel overseas several times a year, or even to live abroad for protracted periods. Before deciding to specialise in this type of work, personal circumstances should be considered. Trips abroad may sound glamorous, and there may be time to sample the local culture, but they won't be sightseeing tours. Client offices and big city hotels tend to look the same all over the world, even if they take 10 hours and a series of unpleasant innoculations to get to. Indeed, for some, overseas work is "frankly a pain." For those unwilling to travel overseas, a firm that specialises in domestic PFI work would be more suitable.

Career Options

Lawyers used to specialise in major projects after gaining several years' experience in a relevant discipline. Whilst a lot of people continue to enter projects work via this route, many take a more direct approach. It is now possible to specialise in projects work on qualification.

Nearly all international projects are governed (to varying degrees) by English law or New York law, so experience in this field is internationally marketable. American law firms in particular are recruiting experienced English lawyers, which has forced up salaries to make international projects work one of the highest paid specialisms in the legal world. Four year qualified assistants can expect anything up to £70k.

The Firms

Project Finance

International project finance is essentially a game for the largest of firms. Firms need an international presence, ideally with offices in the regions where the projects are located and in the financial markets where the funding is raised. Only a handful of English firms are significant players in the international market, however these – especially Allen & Overy, Clifford Chance, Linklaters and Freshfields – are among the very best. Other well known firms are Ashurst Morris Crisp, Denton Hall, Norton Rose and CMS Cameron McKenna. All these firms have large teams working all over the world. A number of American firms undertake projects work from London. Best known are Millbank, Tweed, Hadley & McCoy, White & Case and Shearman & Sterling. Allen & Overy has worked on power/gas projects in China and Oman, the largest of which was the massive US$2.2bn Shandong Zhonghua Power Project. Clifford Chance, which has reportedly been focusing of late on the Americas and Africa (and was also involved in the Shandong Zhonghua project) worked on the US$1.3bn Mozal Aluminium Smelter Project in Mozambique. For Linklaters, a real highlight was the US$1.8bn Dabhol II Power Project, one of few to reach financial close in India, while Freshfields was yet another party to the Shandong Zhonghua jamboree.

PFI

PFI is essentially project finance in the UK. Unsurprisingly, the same firms that feature in project finance also undertake PFI. Some City firms, however, have a higher profile in PFI than they do in international project finance. Herbert Smith got involved in PFI when many firms were still unsure whether it would work. In consequence, it is now one of the market leaders. Other firms which don't undertake international work have reputations in PFI. Bird & Bird is well known for IT and telecoms PFIs, Berwin

Leighton for property projects and Beachcroft Wansbrough for NHS projects. All the usual suspects, Allen & Overy, Freshfields, Linklaters and Clifford Chance are also big guns in the domestic PFI arena.

Regional firms feature highly in PFI, usually acting for the public sector. Masons' Bristol office tops the rankings in the south west, while Morgan Cole dominates the Welsh scene. In Birmingham and the Midlands, Dibb Lupton Alsop and Pinsent Curtis are the heavyweight contenders. Up north, Pinsents also rules the roost in Leeds alongside Eversheds, which is also, with Addleshaw Booth & Co, the leader in Manchester and the north west. North of the border, Dundas & Wilson CS and MacRoberts are the names to conjure with.

Energy

The City firms have a strong hold over energy work. Denton Hall is particularly good for oil and gas work, the Oman LNG project being a real highlight, and can count such giants as BP Amoco, BG and Thames Water as clients. Herbert Smith has a real niche specialism in electricity, with clients including Severn Trent, Anglia Water and BP Amoco. Of the regional firms, Martineau Johnson in Birmingham acts for the National Grid on regulatory issues and is, with Wragge & Co, the leading firm in the Midlands. In the south west, Bond Pearce in Plymouth is well known for its niche specialisms in renewable energy projects and green electricity trading. In the north, Nabarro Nathanson's Sheffield office is one of the UK's leading coal practices, while Eversheds' Leeds outpost is best known for its corporate finance work in the energy sector.

Construction

A large number of firms get involved in both contentious and non-contentious construction. Masons leads the field in London and has offices around both the country and the world. CMS Cameron McKenna has an impressive client roster and a dedicated construction group spanning all aspects of the industry. Many other firms, especially Rowe & Maw, also have strong reputations in the construction arena. There are also a number of niche construction practices with national, and even international, reputations. These include Fenwick Elliott (London), Shadbolt & Co (Reigate) and Neil F. Jones (Birmingham).

Leading Firms

London	Projects	PFI	Construction	Energy
Allen & Overy	******	******	*	*****
Ashurst Morris Crisp	****	****	***	*****
Baker & McKenzie	**		*	**
Barlow Lyde & Gilbert			*	
Barnett Alexander Chart		*		
Beachcroft Wansbroughs		**		*
Beale and Company			*	
Berrymans Lace Mawer			**	
Berwin Leighton		****	***	
S J Berwin & Co	**	**	**	
Bird & Bird		***		
Clifford Chance	******	*****	**	*****
Clyde & Co				***
CMS Cameron McKenna	****	*****	****	*****
Corbett & Co			*	

Coudert Brothers	**			***
Davies Arnold Cooper			***	
Denton Hall	****	*****	*	******
Edge Ellison			**	*
Eversheds				**
Fenwick Elliott			***	
Field Fisher Waterhouse				**
Freshfields	*****	*****	**	*****
Glovers			**	
Hammond Suddards			***	
Herbert Smith	****	*****	***	******
Holman Fenwick & Willan				**
Ince & Co				**
Lawrence Graham		*		***
LeBoeuf, Lamb, Greene & McCrae, LLP				***
Lewis Silkin			*	
Linklaters	******	******	**	*****
Lovells	***	*****	**	****
Macfarlanes		*		
Manches			*	
Masons	**	***	******	**
Milbank, Tweed, Hadley & McCloy	****			
Nabarro Nathanson		**	*	****
Nicholson Graham & Jones			***	
Norton Rose	****	***	**	****
Richards Butler				*
Rowe & Maw		*	***	
Shearman & Sterling	***			
Simmons & Simmons	***	***	*	***
Slaughter and May	***	***		****
Speechly Bircham			*	
Taylor Joynson Garrett	**		***	
Trowers & Hamlins	**		**	*
Warner Cranston			**	
Watson, Farley & Williams				*
Wedlake Bell			**	
White & Case LLP	****			
Wilde Sapte	***	***		
Winward Fearon			***	

South East	Construction	Energy
Blake Lapthorn, Portsmouth	***	
Clarks, Reading	**	
Cripps Harries Hall, Tunbridge Wells	***	
Deborah Mills Associates, Marlow		*
Linnells, Oxford	**	
Morgan Cole, Oxford	***	
Shadbolt & Co, Reigate	***	

South West	Projects	Construction	Energy
Beachcroft Wansbroughs, Bristol		****	
Bevan Ashford, Bristol	****	****	
Bond Pearce, Plymouth		***	***
Burges Salmon, Bristol	****	****	
Foot & Bowden, Plymouth			*
Laytons, Bristol		******	
Masons, Bristol	*****	******	
Stephens & Scown, Exeter			*
Stones, Exeter		**	
Veale Wasbrough, Bristol	****	****	**

Wales	Projects	Construction
Eversheds, Cardiff		***
Hugh James Ford Simey, Cardiff		***
Morgan Cole, Cardiff	*****	***

Midlands	Projects	Construction	Energy
Crane & Walton, Leicester			*
Dibb Lupton Alsop, Birmingham	******	*****	
Edge Ellison, Birmingham	***	*****	**
Edwards Geldard, Derby			**
Eversheds, Birmingham		**	**
Eversheds, Derby		**	
Eversheds, Nottingham	*****	**	
Freeth Cartwright Hunt Dickins, Nottingham		*	
Gateley Wareing, Birmingham		****	
Hacking Ashton, Newcastle-under-Lyme		**	
Kent Jones and Done, Stoke-on-Trent			*
Knight & Sons, Newcastle-under-Lyme			*
Martineau Johnson, Birmingham			***
Merricks, Birmingham		**	
Neil F. Jones, Birmingham		******	
Pinsent Curtis, Birmingham	******	****	**
Wragge & Co, Birmingham	****	******	***

East Anglia	Projects	Construction
Birketts, Ipswich		***
Eversheds, Norwich		***
Greenwoods, Peterborough		*****
Hewitson Becke + Shaw, Cambridge		*****
Merricks, Ipswich		***
Mills & Reeve, Cambridge	****	******
Prettys, Ipswich		**
Taylor Vinters, Cambridge		**

North West	Projects	Construction	Energy
Aaron & Partners, Chester			*
Addleshaw Booth & Co, Manchester	******	****	
Beachcroft Wansbroughs, Manchester	***		
Dibb Lupton Alsop, Liverpool, Manchester		***	
Elliotts, Manchester		**	
Eversheds, Manchester	******		
Halliwell Landau, Manchester		***	
Hammond Suddards, Manchester		*****	
Hill Dickinson, Liverpool		**	
Kirk Jackson, Manchester		****	
Masons, Manchester	****	******	
Pannone & Partners, Manchester		***	
Wake Dyne Lawton, Chester			*

North East	Projects	Construction	Energy
Addleshaw Booth & Co, Leeds	******	******	
Beachcroft Wansbroughs, Sheffield	***		
Denison Till, Leeds		***	
Dibb Lupton Alsop, Sheffield		*****	
Dickinson Dees, Newcastle upon Tyne	*****	*****	**
Eversheds, Leeds	******	******	***
Eversheds, Newcastle upon Tyne		******	
Garretts, Leeds	***		
Hammond Suddards, Leeds		*****	
Hay & Kilner, Newcastle-upon-Tyne		**	
Irwin Mitchell, Sheffield	***		
Malcolm Lynch, Leeds			*
Masons, Leeds	****	******	
Nabarro Nathanson, Sheffield		***	***
Pinsent Curtis, Leeds	******		*
Robert Muckle, Newcastle-upon-Tyne		****	
Walker Morris, Leeds		****	
Ward Hadaway, Newcastle upon Tyne		**	
Watson Burton, Newcastle upon Tyne		****	

Firms and their star ratings are based on Chambers' Directory 1999–2000. Six stars represent a top-ranked firm, five stars a second-ranked firm, etc.

PROPERTY
(including Social Housing)

Area of Law

A property lawyer's tools are land law and contract law. Most work involves a blend of the two. The acquisition and disposal of land and the creation and termination of relationships between investors, land owners and land users are, in the main, contractual issues. Add to this a body of common law and a swathe of statutes and you have the nuts and bolts of property law. Overlaying all of this is the property market, the most significant ingredient of all.

Clients vary widely in terms of their level of involvement with the property market. At one end of the scale is the residential conveyancing client who may only be involved in one property transaction in his whole life. At the other is the large institution whose representative is a property professional himself. In between are the users and owners of property. Each client requires a different style of service. The one-off user may need plenty of hand-holding, whilst the professional may simply need action without detailed explanation.

The firm you choose will determine what type of client base you'll be working with and increasingly the type of transaction you'll encounter. Some in the City believe that commercial property work is going through a sea change and that at the largest firms routine lease drafting and more conventional property work has had its day. Clients will look to smaller and medium sized firms and to the regions for this kind of service. The big City property practices will concentrate on the newer ways of investing in property through joint ventures, limited partnerships and investment trusts. The City firms will specialise in complex property finance and become more like corporate lawyers whose deals have a property asset base.

The work of the property solicitor leans against other disciplines - company law, finance, revenue law and trusts to name but three. You may encounter areas such as liquor licensing, health and safety, telecommunications, environmental law, agricultural law, insolvency, project finance and planning. You will come to learn about the role of surveyors and property agents. You will interact with the Inland Revenue, local authorities, the Land Registry, Companies House, property agents, building surveyors, architects, banks and mortgage lenders, brokers, designers and the list goes on. Think about how much real property there is in this country and how many different relationships there are between owners, users, investors, sellers and buyers. You will see how much property work there is and how varied it is.

Type of work

Property work is basically transaction driven and involves a huge amount of documentation to be considered and amended. In an average day you'll spend a considerable amount of time in negotiations either on the phone or in meetings with clients, other lawyers and property professionals in related areas.

An example of a standard piece of commercial property work would be the business lease. Typically you might receive instructions for a new lease from a client who has negotiated the basics with the help of a commercial agent. The main structure of the deal will be established but many points require further negotiation. A fifteen year lease of one floor in an office block, for example, could involve a provision for one party to bring the lease to an end after a certain number of years. It could involve the right for the tenant to sub-let or transfer the lease to a third party. It could involve a major re-fit of the premises or a period which is rent free. During the lease period major issues between the parties include the review of rent at set times and the level of annual service charge payments to cover the costs of maintenance and services to the building. All of these issues must be dealt with before the lease is signed and the parties commit to the long-term relationship. Clients always want certainty from you; it's your job to give them the nearest possible thing to that. They expect you, the experienced professional, to anticipate what might go wrong and to protect them ahead of time. Whilst a property lawyer generally works on a deal in which both sides have the same goal, the trick is to get the very best deal for your client and to get it done within the time scale that the client sets for you.

Victoria Sutcliffe is an assistant solicitor at Lovells. Property took her by surprise - as it does for a good majority of those who end up making a career of it. She liked the fact that, from her first day as a trainee she felt she was productive, in control and running her own files. "From day one the phone was ringing. As I walked in the door a client rang to say they were ready to complete and from then on the telephone didn't stop ringing. The clients don't stop asking lots of questions so you build up a very good relationship with them. More than in almost any other department you are responsible for your own destiny at a very junior level. There is an end product which you can see. You can drive through any city centre and say I bought that, I sold that, I leased that."

Skills needed

Certain qualities are universal to all good property lawyers, irrespective of their client base, such as verbal and written negotiating skills, attention to detail and the ability to think through a potential problem and give clear advice to clients as to the significance of each possible outcome. You must also be a pro-active time and case manager. You might have several important deals running at any one time. Each will need to be pushed forward to a conclusion. A missed deadline will be disastrous for your client. Sometimes it feels like juggling and it can be stressful trying to keep all the balls in the air at once. At times you will have to work very long hours when big deals coincide or if you are part of a team working on a large corporate project. It is a people-intensive area of the law and you need to be able to communicate well and forge professional relationships. Better to have others 'playing the game' with you rather than fighting against you. But you can't be a push over when you come up against a resistant opponent. Victoria Sutcliffe told us "On the tube on the way in you're thinking about what you've got to do and you're making a mental list. All of that totally flies out of the window in property." She explained how an urgent matter can crop up and require all of your attention so that you didn't even get to start your scheduled work until the end of the day. "I once had an airline ring me. They said 'We have a flight coming down this afternoon, people will be queuing up at ticket desk 5 at Gatwick to board the plane. Firstly we have no right to have a ticket desk there. Secondly, we have no right to let the airplane park on the runway.' So I had to strike some informal arrangements with Gatwick Airport over the telephone. Otherwise the plane would have been up there somewhere circling!"

The good solicitor knows his client's business, be this an investment fund with a large commercial property portfolio, a chain of restaurants or retail outlets, a registered Social Landlord or a maverick property speculator with a penchant for listed buildings.

Career Options

Just as the fortunes of the property market have been cyclical, the fortunes of property lawyers rise and fall accordingly. A decade ago, the market dealt a serious blow to this part of the legal profession and it is only in more recent years that there has been a strong demand for property lawyers. For those qualifying into and gaining experience in commercial property work during the leaner years, the present up turn in the market has put them in a strong position and the salaries commanded have begun to match those in other core commercial areas.

After a while in private practice or perhaps as a result of other commitments, some lawyers look for change. In-house jobs in industry and commerce are popular. Such positions offer the chance to work for a single 'client' on essentially the same types of transactions as contemporaries in private practice.

The Land Registry or the Law Commission provide career options for those with a more academic bent and, increasingly, know-how lawyers play a prominent role in the education and ongoing training of property lawyers in larger practices. In addition to keeping their teams up to speed on developments in the law the know-how specialist would be responsible for periodically updating the firm's standard documentation and producing news updates for clients.

The Firms

Commercial Property

In London the large City firms with broad commercial practices are at the top of the pile. Linklaters holds on to the very best reputation. Other top practices include Berwin Leighton, Clifford Chance, Herbert Smith, Lovells, Nabarro Nathanson and SJ Berwin & Co.

The strongest firms in the South include Bond Pearce in the West Country and Burges Salmon and Osborne Clarke in Bristol. The Welsh leaders are Eversheds, Edwards Geldard and Morgan Cole all of Cardiff, plus Morgan Cole's Swansea office. Birmingham firms Wragge & Co. and Eversheds lead in the Midlands. In the North the leading practices are those of Addleshaw Booth & Co. (Leeds and Manchester), Dibb Lupton Alsop (Liverpool and Manchester) together with Eversheds, Cobbetts and Halliwell Landau in Manchester.

Scottish property is led by Dundas & Wilson CS, Maclay Murray & Spens, McGrigor Donald and Shepherd & Wedderburn. Each has offices in both Glasgow and Edinburgh. In Northern Ireland, five Belfast firms top the ranks; Carson & McDowell, Elliott Duffy Garrett, L'Estrange & Brett, Johns Elliot and Tughan & Co.

In London, the most highly rated property litigation practices are those of Nabarro Nathanson and Linklaters. Out in the regions there are a score of top firms. In the south, and East Anglia the leaders are Burges Salmon in Bristol, Donne Mileham & Haddock in Brighton, Eversheds in Ipswich and Norwich and Mills & Reeve's Norwich office. In Wales, Morgan Cole's Cardiff and Swansea offices compete at the top with Eversheds and Hugh James Ford Simey in Cardiff. The Midlands' leader is Wragge & Co. whilst in the north there is tough competition at the top between firms such as Addleshaw Booth & Co. and Eversheds in both Leeds and Manchester, Cobbetts and Dibb Lupton Alsop in Manchester and Pinsent Curtis in Leeds.

In Scotland Dundas & Wilson CS and Steedman Ramage WS are the strongest Edinburgh firms and Maclay Murray & Spens is at the top in Glasgow. Seven Northern Irish firms are equally highly rated in Belfast.

Social Housing

Social housing is a growth area. Trowers & Hamlins offices in London, Manchester and Exeter are leaders in the field. Established leaders also include London firms Devonshires, Prince Evans, Lewis Silkin, Lawrence Graham and Winckworth Sherwood together with some strong regional firms. In the south, the Midlands and Wales noted firms are Anthony Collins Solicitors and Irwin Mitchell in Birmingham, Burges Salmon in Bristol, Coffin Mew & Clover in Portsmouth, Owen White in Slough and Eversheds, Morgan Cole and Hugh James Ford Simey in Cardiff.

In the north we highlight Brabner Holden Banks Wilson of Liverpool, Cobbetts and Howarth Goodman of Manchester, Dickinson Dees in Newcastle upon Tyne, Rollit Farrell & Bladon in Hull and Walker Charlesworth & Foster.

Leading Firms

London	Commercial Property	Social Housing
Allen & Overy	**	******
Anderson & Co		***
Ashurst Morris Crisp	****	
S J Berwin & Co	****	
Berwin Leighton	*****	
Boodle Hatfield	*	
Charles Russell	*	
Clifford Chance	*****	******
CMS Cameron McKenna	***	
Coudert Brothers	**	***
D J Freeman	***	
Dawson & Co		**
Denton Hall	***	
Devonshires		*****
Dewar Hogan		
Dibb Lupton Alsop	**	
Druces & Attlee		
Evans Butler Wade		***
Eversheds	**	
Fenners	*	
Field Fisher Waterhouse	**	
Finers Stephens Innocent	*	
Fladgate Fielder	*	
Forsters	**	
Freshfields	***	
G.L. Hockfield & Co		**
Glovers	*	
Gouldens	***	
Hamlins	*	
Herbert Smith	*****	
Hodge Jones & Allen		**
Jenkins & Hand		****
Julian Holy	*	
Lawrence Graham	**	****
Lewis Silkin		****
Linklaters	******	
Lovells	*****	
Macfarlanes	**	
Maclay Murray & Spens		***
Manches	**	
Maples Teesdale		
Masons		
Maxwell Batley	**	

McGuinness Finch	**	
Nabarro Nathanson	*****	
Nicholson Graham & Jones	***	
Norton Rose	***	
Olswang	**	
Paisner & Co	*	
Park Nelson	*	
Prince Evans		****
Radcliffes		
Richards Butler	**	
Rowe & Maw	**	
Sharratts		***
Simmons & Simmons	**	
Slaughter and May	**	
Speechly Bircham	*	
Stephenson Harwood		
Stepien Lake Gilbert & Paling	**	
Teacher Stern Selby	*	
Thomas Eggar Church Adams	*	
Titmuss Sainer Dechert	***	
Travers Smith Braithwaite	**	
Trowers & Hamlins	*	******
Wilde Sapte	**	*****
Winckworth Sherwood		****

South East Firms	**Commercial Property**	**Social Housing**
Argles Stoneham Burstows, Crawley		
B.P. Collins & Co, Gerrards Cross	**	
Blake Lapthorn, Fareham	***	
Bond Pearce, Southampton	***	
Brachers, Maidstone	*	
BrookStreet Des Roches, Witney	**	
Clarks, Reading	**	
Coffin Mew & Clover, Portsmouth	*	******
Colemans, Maidenhead	*	
Cripps Harries Hall, Tunbridge Wells	**	****
Dean Wilson Laing, Brighton	*	
Denton Hall, Milton Keynes	***	
Donne Mileham & Haddock, Brighton	***	***
Ellison & Co, Colchester	*	
Fitzhugh Gates, Brighton		****
H. Montlake & Co, Ilford	**	
Harold Benjamin & Collins, Harrow	*	
Hawkins Russell Jones, Hitchin	*	
Iliffes Booth Bennett, Slough	*	
Kenneth Elliott & Rowe, Romford	***	
Laytons, Hampton Court	*	
Linnells, Oxford	*	

Manches, Oxford		*****
Marsons Solicitors, Bromley		***
Moore & Blatch, Southampton	*	
Morgan Cole, Oxford	**	
Owen White, Slough		******
Paris Smith & Randall, Southampton	***	
Penningtons, Basingstoke	*	
Penningtons, Godalming	*	
Penningtons, Newbury	*	*****
Pictons, St. Albans	*	
Pitmans, Reading	**	
Rawlison & Butler, Crawley	**	
Sherrards, St. Albans		****
Sherwin Oliver Solicitors, Portsmouth	**	
Shoosmiths, Solent	**	
Stevens & Bolton, Guildford	***	
Thomas Eggar Church Adams, Chichester	***	
Thomas Eggar Church Adams, Horsham	***	
Thomas Eggar Church Adams, Reigate	***	
Thomas Eggar Church Adams, Worthing	***	
Thomson Snell & Passmore, Tonbridge		
Thomson Snell & Passmore, Tunbridge Wells	**	
Tolhurst Fisher, Southend-on-Sea	*	
Willmett & Co, Windsor	*	
Wollastons, Chelmsford	***	

South West Firms	**Commercial Property**	**Social Housing**
Beachcroft Wansbroughs, Bristol	***	
Bevan Ashford, Bristol	****	*****
Bobbetts Mackan, Bristol		
Bond Pearce, Plymouth	*****	
Bretherton Price Elgoods, Cheltenham	**	
Burges Salmon, Bristol	*****	******
Cartwrights, Bristol	***	
Charles Russell, Cheltenham	**	
Clarke Willmott & Clarke, Taunton	****	
Crawford Owen, Bristol	****	
Davies and Partners, Gloucester	**	
Eversheds, Bristol		
Foot & Bowden, Plymouth	**	
Laceys, Bournemouth	**	
Lawrence Tucketts, Bristol	***	
Lester Aldridge, Bournemouth	***	
Lyons Davidson, Bristol	***	
Michelmores, Exeter	****	
Osborne Clarke, Bristol	*****	
Rickerby Watterson, Cheltenham	**	
Steele Raymond, Bournemouth	**	

Stones, Exeter		****
Townsends, Swindon	**	
Trethowan Woodford, Salisbury	**	
Trowers & Hamlins, Exeter		******
Trumps, Bristol	***	
Veale Wasbrough, Bristol	****	
Wolferstans, Plymouth	**	

East Anglia	**Commercial Property**
Birketts, Ipswich	***
Eversheds, Cambridge	****
Eversheds, Ipswich, Norwich	****
Gotelee & Goldsmith, Ipswich	*
Greenwoods, Peterborough	**
Hewitson Becke + Shaw, Cambridge	***
Leathes Prior, Norwich	*
Mills & Reeve, Cambridge	****
Mills & Reeve, Norwich	****
Prettys, Ipswich	**
Taylor Vinters, Cambridge	***

Midlands	**Commercial Property**	**Social Housing**
Anthony Collins Solicitors, Birmingham		******
Band Hatton, Coventry	*	
Browne Jacobson, Nottingham		*****
Dibb Lupton Alsop, Birmingham	**	
Edge Ellison, Birmingham	*****	
Edge Ellison, Leicester	*****	
Eversheds, Birmingham	******	
Eversheds, Derby		
Eversheds, Nottingham		
Freeth Cartwright Hunt Dickins, Nottingham	*	****
Harvey Ingram Owston, Leicester	*	****
Higgs & Sons, Brierley Hill	*	
Irwin Mitchell, Birmingham		******
Knight & Sons, Newcastle-under-Lyme	**	
Lee Crowder, Birmingham	***	****
Manby & Steward, Wolverhampton	*	
Martineau Johnson, Birmingham	***	
Needham & James, Stratford upon Avon		****
Pinsent Curtis, Birmingham	*****	
Shakespeares, Birmingham		***
Shoosmiths, Northampton	*	
Shoosmiths, Nottingham	*	
Wragge & Co, Birmingham	******	
Wright Hassall, Leamington Spa	*	*****

Wales	Commercial Property	Social Housing
Berry Smith, Cardiff	****	
Edwards Geldard, Cardiff	******	
Eversheds, Cardiff	******	******
Hugh James Ford Simey, Cardiff	***	******
Morgan Cole, Cardiff	******	******
Morgan Cole, Swansea	******	
Palser Grossman, Cardiff Bay	****	
Robertsons, Cardiff	**	

North West	Commercial Property	Social Housing
A. Halsall & Co, Birkenhead		****
Aaron & Partners, Chester	**	
Addleshaw Booth & Co, Manchester	******	
Barker, Booth & Eastwood, Blackpool	**	
Beachcroft Wansbroughs, Manchester	****	
Bell Lamb & Joynson, Liverpool		**
Bermans, Liverpool	***	
Berrymans Lace Mawer, Liverpool	***	
Brabner Holden Banks Wilson, Liverpool	**	*****
Bremner Sons & Corlett, Liverpool	**	*
Bullivant Jones & Company, Liverpool	*****	
Chaffe Street, Manchester	**	
Cobbetts, Manchester	******	*****
Croftons, Manchester		****
Cuff Roberts, Liverpool	***	
Davies Wallis Foyster, Liverpool	*****	
Dibb Lupton Alsop, Liverpool	******	
Dibb Lupton Alsop, Manchester	******	
Elliotts, Manchester	**	
Eversheds, Manchester	******	***
Field Cunningham & Co, Manchester	*****	
Gorna & Co, Manchester	**	***
Halliwell Landau, Manchester	******	
Hammond Suddards, Manchester	****	
Hill Dickinson, Liverpool	***	
Howarth Goodman, Manchester		*****
Jones Maidment Wilson, Manchester	***	
Kuit Steinart Levy, Manchester	**	
Napthen Houghton Craven, Preston	***	
Pannone & Partners, Manchester	**	
Trowers & Hamlins, Manchester		******
Walker Smith & Way, Chester	**	
Weightmans, Liverpool	***	
Weightmans, Manchester	***	

North East	Commercial Property	Social Housing
Addleshaw Booth & Co, Leeds	******	*****
Andrew M. Jackson & Co, Hull	***	
Archers, Stockton-on-Tees	*	
Attey Bower & Jones with Dibb and Clegg, Doncaster		*
Cranswick Watson, Leeds	*	
Denison Till, Leeds	*	
Dibb Lupton Alsop, Leeds	*****	
Dickinson Dees, Newcastle upon Tyne	*****	*****
Eversheds, Leeds	*****	
Eversheds, Newcastle upon Tyne	***	
Garretts, Leeds	***	
Gordons Wright & Wright, Bradford	**	
Gosschalks, Hull	**	
Hammond Suddards, Leeds	***	
Irwin Mitchell, Sheffield	***	
Jacksons, Stockton-on-Tees	*	
Keeble Hawson Moorhouse, Sheffield	*	
McGuinness Finch, Leeds	**	
Nabarro Nathanson, Sheffield	***	
Oxley & Coward, Rotherham	*	
Pinsent Curtis, Leeds	*****	
Read Hind Stewart, Leeds	***	
Robert Muckle, Newcastle-upon-Tyne	**	
Rollit Farrell & Bladon, Hull	**	*****
Rollit Farrell & Bladon, York		*****
Savage Crangle, Skipton		***
Stamp Jackson and Procter, Hull	*	
Wake Smith, Sheffield	*	
Walker Charlesworth & Foster, Leeds		*****
Walker Morris, Leeds	*****	
Ward Hadaway, Newcastle upon Tyne	**	****
Watson Burton, Newcastle upon Tyne	**	

Firms and their star ratings are based on Chambers' Directory 1999–2000. Six stars represent a top-ranked firm, five stars a second-ranked firm, etc.

PUBLIC INTEREST LAW
(including Civil Liberties, Immigration, Local Government and Education)

Area of law
The fundamental concern of public interest law is the relationship between state and citizen. Thus, while each area of law grouped under this heading is a separate subject in its own right, requiring particular skills and personal qualities, they all concern the activities of public bodies, and in particular whether their actions are lawful. Challenging their decisions by way of judicial review is an important thread in civil liberties, immigration and education work while lawyers involved in local government law see the other side of the coin by advising public authorities on their powers and defending their decisions.

Each area is likely to be heavily affected by the implementation of the Human Rights Act, which enshrines the European Convention of Human Rights in British law. Thus all legislation and court judgments will have to be read in the light of provisions of the Act such as the right to privacy and family life, the right to a fair trial and freedom of expression. There are likely to be exciting times ahead for lawyers in these fields.

Civil Liberties

Type of work
Civil liberties is a broad concept covering suspected miscarriages of justice, actions against the police, prisoners' rights, public order, discrimination and free speech issues. Redress will often be sought by judicial review, and there is considerable cross-over between civil liberties and areas such as crime and immigration.

As all these areas are covered under provisions of the new Human Rights Act, the volume of judicial review is likely to increase at pace over the next few years. Several lawyers and campaign groups who practice in this field are at present engaged in training fellow lawyers and professionals in the implications of the Act for other areas of law, including the commercial arena.

At Bindman & Partners, Stephen Grosz's work is characterised by its variety. A morning's work might include studying a European directive on freedom of access to information on the environment, advising a client on a school closure, meeting a student who failed exams because of insufficient provision for dyslexia, and considering new instructions from a homosexual naval officer.

An imaginative legal mind, an ability to adapt to different areas of law and an interest in using the law creatively and strategically are all important qualities in a civil liberties lawyer, according to Stephen Grosz. "You need to try and push back the boundaries, and if you're working with campaigning organisations, as you frequently are, you have to understand their needs and priorities." Grosz also looks for a sympathetic and understanding nature and a broad world view, as opposed to a narrow legalistic outlook.

Career options
It need hardly be mentioned that places at the few firms which do civil liberties work and offer training are incredibly competitive. Such firms often prefer older trainees who have worked in relevant fields to students fresh from university. It is vital, then, to get involved in voluntary or campaign work at an early stage if you wish to train in this area.

Four major organisations which are particularly known for their campaigning work in civil liberties and human rights are listed below. All can be joined, for a fee, and amongst other benefits will send you newsletters with up to date information about their campaigns and recent changes in the law. For hands-on experience, it is best to contact your local Law Centre or relevant voluntary organisations.

A career as a civil liberties lawyer may be interesting, but is unlikely to be lucrative. Law Centres, campaigning groups and voluntary organisations offer alternatives to private practice.

Campaigning Organisations

Organisation	What they do	Contact
Liberty	Conducts human rights test cases, lobbying and research.	21 Tabard Street, London SE1 4LA Tel. 0207 403 3888 E-mail liberty@gn.apc.org
Amnesty International	Lobbies governments, monitors countries and researches human rights abuses around the world.	99-119 Rosebery Avenue, London EC1R 4RE Tel. 0207 814 6200 E-mail info@amnesty.org.uk
Justice	Carries out research, audits legislation and publishes reports into human rights and access to justice issues.	59 Carter Lane, London EC4V SAQ Tel. 0207 329 5100 E-mail admin@justice.org.uk
Legal Action Group	Supports, campaigns and trains lawyers and advisers to promote access to justice.	242 Pentonville Road, London N1 9UN Tel.0207 8332931 E-mail lag.org.uk

Immigration

Type of work

There are two types of immigration work: personal and business. Personal immigration work includes political asylum cases, nationality issues, marriage applications and family reunion cases. Much of this work is legally aided and is carried out by small firms. Business or corporate immigration includes advising national and multinational corporations on work permits and investor applications and advising employers on avoiding criminal liability under the Immigration and Asylum Act 1996. Large and medium-sized commercial firms undertake this work.

A typical day, says Peter Alfandary, head of Corporate Immigration at Warner Cranston, might involve advising the English arm of a foreign company wanting to bring staff from New York to work in the UK, drafting an application for a work permit on behalf of a multi-national client, advising a foreign investor on setting up a business in the UK, advising a human resources department on whether a potential employee has a legal right to work in the UK and telephoning the British Embassy in Beijing to sort out entry clearance for the wife of a Chinese executive.

A typical day for personal immigration expert Wesley Gryk could involve encounters with a whole range of clients. He may spend the morning with a lesbian couple advising them on same sex immigration issues, followed by an emergency meeting with a foreign wife abandoned by her husband. The afternoon could involve simple work permit advice to someone who is not likely to have a problem, then more complicated advice to someone who has virtually no right to be in the country and has been "underground" for twenty years. A junior lawyer's day may be just as varied - they may start the morning filing, but then be sent off on their own for a five hour interview at Gatwick airport or the Home Office, in sole charge of looking after the interests of an asylum seeker.

Skills needed

"Communication skills are of overriding importance" emphasises Peter Alfandary. "They are an absolute prerequisite. There is an enormous amount of client contact and a lot of telephone work, and if you can't communicate effectively you won't get past first base." Communicating with senior executives, government departments and embassies requires tact, diplomacy and patience. Good drafting and advocacy skills are also essential if you are to present a convincing case on behalf of your client.

In personal immigration, Wesley Gryk looks for an interest in current affairs and politics, liberalism (with a small "L"), but also a healthy scepticism. "You're not doing clients any favours by assuming that everything they tell you is true and repeating it verbatim to the Home Office," he says. "In some ways you need to do a tougher cross-examining job than the government to get to the core of their true story so you can present it well to the authorities. It's not good enough to be well-intentioned and to offer a cup of tea and sympathy." Personal immigration lawyers must also be true team players - the offices are often small and busy and there is no standing on ceremony - everyone has to be prepared to chip in.

Career options

Personal immigration, like civil liberties work, doesn't offer the financial rewards enjoyed by those in more commercial disciplines, including those specialising in business immigration. But would-be personal immigration specialists are unlikely to be motivated by financial gain anyway. Alternatives to private practice include working for a Law Centre or bodies such as the UN or the Joint Council for the Welfare of Immigrants. Leading immigration lawyer Alison Stanley, for example, was articled at Winstanley Burgess, then spent several years as the solicitor to the JWCI before returning to private practice with Bindman & Partners. It is also possible to come to this type of work from a more commercial background. Wesley Gryk began his career as a corporate lawyer with large US firm Shearman and Sterling.

Local Government

Type of work

Law firms act for local authorities on a whole range of matters, from development and urban regeneration projects, to new methods of service delivery through third parties. Berwin Leighton recently acted for the City and Council of Swansea on the redevelopment of Morfa Stadium, and that of Castle Quays for retail purposes. Lawrence Graham have recently advised the London Borough of Enfield on the £200 million regeneration of Edmonton Town Centre.

Other work includes housing stock transfers, advising on local authority finance and vires (powers), and acting in relation to planning appeals and judicial reviews. Rowe and Maw, for example, acted for the Westminster City Council Auditor in the 'homes for votes' case. A variety of different types of decisions of local authorities may be judicially reviewed, such as childcare, education, healthcare etc.

A typical day for Tony Curnow, head of the Public Sector Group at Ashurst Morris Crisp, might include drafting heads of terms for a local authority regeneration project, meeting with clients to discuss a housing transfer agreement, reviewing a compulsory purchase order case and chasing the Department of Transport for the issue of a draft road closure order.

Skills needed

To succeed as a local government lawyer, says Tony Curnow, you need "an ability to get on with people at all levels, from chief executives to lowly officers." You need to be flexible and modulate your approach depending on who you're dealing with. Furthermore, you need to be politically aware, and understand the relationship between central and local government. A head for statutory interpretation and an ability to master a complex regulatory regime are essential. Self-motivation and a common sense approach are also vital attributes.

Career options

The obvious starting point for someone wishing to specialise in local government law is to apply for a training contract with a local authority legal department. You then have the option to stay at the authority or move into private practice. "Somebody who'd done their training in a local authority, stayed on for a year or so, and then applied to us would be an attractive package" says Tony Curnow. "They might be more attractive than someone who'd been solely in the private sector, but it depends on the individual."

On the other hand, firms like Nabarros, Eversheds or Ashursts may be able to offer broader commercial experience during training, as well as good quality local government work. A wider range of options may then remain open on qualification. You could continue in a commercial private practice, transfer into more general public law work or move into a local authority.

Salaries are generally higher in private practice, but hours are often longer to match. The good news about local authorities is that pay and conditions are perceived to be improving.

Education

Type of work

Type of work depends on type of client and there are two kinds of client: institutions and individuals. Commercial firms tend to act for institutions including universities, schools, colleges and funding organisations. Smaller, niche firms act for individuals, including pupils and their parents, university students and special needs children.

Advice to institutional clients covers more than just education law. Eversheds, for example, advises universities and colleges on employment law, industrial relations, constitutional issues, funding matters, student relations and discipline. At Beachcroft Wansbroughs, Julian Gizzi was involved in the Dearing Committee inquiry into the running of Further Education colleges and is also involved in funding and franchising issues.

David Ruebain, meanwhile, at David Levene & Co, might spend his morning with the parents of a disabled child trying to sort out funding for transport to school. His afternoon could be spent on the telephone arguing against an examining board on behalf of a special needs pupil. Jack Rabinowicz at Teacher Stern Selby may have to deal with the parents of a child bully one day and the parents of a child who has been bullied the next.

Skills needed

Julian Gizzi emphasises the importance of a commercial outlook when acting for educational institutions. "Universities are businesses like any other business these days. The people we're dealing with have their feet firmly on the ground and expect to receive commercial advice like any other organisation." An aptitude for statutory interpretation is important in the public law side of the work he says, and because education law is a fast changing area, with new legislation every year, "having the self-confidence to stick your neck out and take a view" is vital.

"I don't think there's any point in doing this work if you don't take a rights-based perspective" says David Ruebain of education work for individuals. "And you've got to have decided that earning as much money as possible is not your priority, otherwise you'd be acting for institutions." As for particular skills, it's important to have a head for statute and case law, but "it's not sufficient to have an encyclopaedic knowledge of rules and regulations if you don't have an instinct for when judges will consider certain behaviour unacceptable, even though there isn't a rule that says it's unacceptable." A feel for the way public policy is developing is also important.

Career options

There are a number of opportunities to practice education law outside private practice. Joining a local authority legal department is one obvious option - a significant part of local authority legal work involves educational institutions. There are also posts within the Department for Education, and some universities now have their own legal units.

The Firms

Civil liberties

Bindman & Partners are widely acknowledged as the leading firm acting for applicants in civil liberties and human rights judicial review. Notable recent work includes acting for Amnesty International in the landmark Pinochet case, winning damages for Winston Silcott for false imprisonment and malicious prosecution, and acting for applicants in the gay rights cases on the age of consent and gays in the military. Bhatt Murphy and Birnberg Peirce & Partners are London firms with expertise in miscarriages of justice, actions against the police and prisoners' issues. Tyndallwoods is the leading Midlands civil liberties firm, with particular strengths in immigration, criminal, discrimination and prisoners' rights issues. In the north, Liverpool's AS Law and Harrison Bundey & Co in Leeds are well-known outfits. The latter has a stand alone department dealing with prisoners' rights and actions against the police, and recent work includes the case of Christopher Alder, whose death in custody was caught on video camera.

Immigration

CMS Cameron McKenna is the acknowledged leader of the few large City firms who undertake business immigration work, and advises corporate clients and high net worth individuals. Kingsley Napley, who recently took on Simmons & Simmons' entire immigration team, are another large player in this market. Bates, Wells & Braithwaite does business and personal immigration work, and its clients include corporations such as Shell and Cellnet, and self-employed artists. Warner Cranston is also strong in the business field.

Winstanley Burgess has a longstanding reputation in personal immigration with a human rights element. Wesley Gryk is particularly known for refugee law and gay rights cases. Outside London, Darbys Mallam Lewis and Linnells in Oxford have strong reputations in both personal and business immigration, while McGrath & Co in Birmingham and David Gray & Company in Newcastle have leading status in asylum and legal aid work.

Local Government

Sharpe Pritchard are the pre-eminent firm in London for judicial reviews and statutory and planning appeals on behalf of public and local authorities. Nabarro Nathanson advise a large number of local authority and other public sector clients on their powers and duties, as well as how to avoid being the subject of judicial review proceedings.

TV Edwards handle a large number of community care and mental health cases involving judicial review of the policies of local authorities.

Eversheds in Leeds and Manchester dominate the North and the firm represents over 300 local authorities nationally. Pinsent Curtis are strong in the Midlands, where 50% of the firm's workload is advising for or against local authorities.

Education

In this area, a distinction can be made between firms which act for individuals, and those which represent institutions. Teacher Selby Stern are well known for bringing education judicial review actions on behalf of individuals and David Levene & Co have a similar reputation. On the institutional side, Winckworth Sherwood have an impressive institutional client base which includes schools and higher education colleges. Eversheds' London office is particularly skilled in this type of work with many institutional clients and a strong reputation in advising on mergers and governance.

Outside London, Martineau Johnson (Birmingham) are known for their education work. The firm acts for grant maintained schools and new universities in matters involving academic performance and disciplinary procedures. The Leeds and Manchester offices of Eversheds also handle a variety of administrative and public law questions relating to education bodies.

▶

Leading Firms

London	Civil Liberties	Education	Immigration	Local Government
Ashurst Morris Crisp				****
Baker & McKenzie			***	
Bartram & Co, Hounslow			****	
Bates, Wells & Braithwaite			*****	
Beachcroft Wansbroughs		*****		
Berwin Leighton				*****
Bhatt Murphy	*****			
Bindman & Partners	******	*****	******	
Birnberg Peirce & Partners	*****		*****	
Campbell Hooper			**	
Christian Fisher	***		****	
Clifford Chance				***
CMS Cameron McKenna			******	
Coker Vis Partnership			*****	
D J Freeman				***
D J Webb & Co			*	
David Levene & Co		*****		
Deighton Guedalla	***		******	
Denton Hall				****
Eversheds		******	****	
Finers Stephens Innocent	*			
Fisher Meredith	*			
Fox Williams			**	
Gherson & Co			*****	
Gills, Southall		*****		
Glazer Delmar			****	
Gulbenkian Harris Andonian			***	
Harbottle & Lewis			*	
Herbert Smith				**
Hickman & Rose	**			
Irwin Mitchell	**			
Jenkins & Hand				***
John Ford Solicitors		****		
Kingsley Napley			******	
Lawford & Co		*****		
Lawrence Graham				****
Lee Bolton & Lee		****		
Léonie Cowen & Associates				****
Magrath & Co			*****	
Mishcon de Reya			*	
Nabarro Nathanson				******
Norton Rose			****	**
Penningtons			*	
Powell & Co			****	

Pullig & Co			***	
Radcliffes			*	
Reynolds Porter Chamberlain		*****		
Rowe & Maw				*****
Sharpe Pritchard				****
Simons Muirhead & Burton	**			
Stuart Miller			****	
Sturtivant & Co			*****	
Teacher Stern Selby		******		
Titmuss Sainer Dechert				**
Trowers & Hamlins				****
Warner Cranston			*****	
Wesley Gryk			******	
Wilson & Co			****	
Winckworth Sherwood		*****		*
Winstanley-Burgess	***		******	
Witham Weld		****		

South East	**Education**	**Immigration**	**Local Government**
Birkett Long, Colchester	***		
Blake Lapthorn, Fareham			*
Darbys Mallam Lewis, Oxford		******	
Donne Mileham & Haddock, Brighton	***		
Eric Robinson & Co, Southampton		*****	
Linnells, Oxford		******	
Manches, Oxford	***		
Morgan Cole, Oxford	***		
Peter Liell, Potters Bar	******		
Thomas Eggar Church Adams, Chichester	***		
Trethowan Woodford, Southampton		******	
Winckworth Sherwood, Oxford	***		
Wollastons, Chelmsford	***	*****	

South West	**Education**	**Immigration**	**Local Government**
A.E. Smith & Son, Stroud	****		
Bevan Ashford, Bristol	***		
Bevan Ashford, Exeter			***
Bobbetts Mackan, Bristol		*****	
Bond Pearce, Plymouth	***		
Michelmores, Exeter	*****		
Osborne Clarke, Bristol	***		
Rickerby Watterson, Cheltenham	*****		
Steele Raymond, Bournemouth	***		
Stone King, Bath	*****		
Tozers, Exeter	*****		
Veale Wasbrough, Bristol	******		*

Wales	Education	Immigration	Local Government
Dolmans, Cardiff			*
Edwards Geldard, Cardiff			**
Eversheds, Cardiff	*****	*****	**
Hugh James Ford Simey, Cardiff	*****		
Morgan Cole, Cardiff	*****		**

Midlands	Civil Liberties	Education	Immigration	Local Government
Anthony Collins Solicitors, B'ham				*****
Browne Jacobson, Nottingham				*
Dibb Lupton Alsop, Birmingham				******
Eversheds, Birmingham				***
Eversheds, Derby, Nottingham		*****		***
George, Jonas & Co, Birmingham	***			
Glaisyers, Birmingham	***			
Martineau Johnson, Birmingham		******		
McGrath & Co, Birmingham	***		******	
Nelsons, Nottingham			*****	
Pinsent Curtis, Birmingham				******
Shakespeares, Birmingham		*****		
Tyndallwoods, Birmingham	******		******	
Wragge & Co, Birmingham		*****		****
Young & Lee, Birmingham		****		

East Anglia	Education	Immigration	Local Government
Eversheds, Ipswich, Norwich	******		
Gross & Co., Bury St. Edmunds		*****	
Leathes Prior, Norwich		*****	
Mills & Reeve, Cambridge	******		
Mills & Reeve, Norwich	******		*
Steele & Co, Norwich			*

North West	Civil Liberties	Education	Immigration	Local Government
A S Law, Liverpool	***		*****	
Addleshaw Booth & Co, Manchester		****		
Burnetts, Carlisle		*		
Davis Blank Furniss, Manchester			***	
Dibb Lupton Alsop, Liverpool		***		
Elaine Maxwell & Co, Lancaster		***		
Eversheds, Manchester		*****		
Jackson & Canter, Liverpool			*****	
Pannone & Partners, Manchester				***
Robert Lizar, Manchester	***			
Thornhill Ince, Manchester			***	

North East	Civil Liberties	Education	Immigration	Local Government
David Gray & Company, Newcastle upon Tyne		**		******
Eversheds, Leeds		*****		******
Eversheds, Middlesbrough		****		
Eversheds, Newcastle upon Tyne		****		
Ford & Warren, Leeds		***		
Garretts, Leeds		**		
Grays, York		*		
Harrison Bundey & Co., Leeds	***		******	
Howells, Sheffield	***		******	
Irwin Mitchell, Sheffield	**			
James & Co, Bradford			******	
Masons, Leeds				***
Pinsent Curtis, Leeds		***		***
Samuel Phillips & Co, Newcastle upon Tyne				***

Firms and their star ratings are based on Chambers' Directory 1999–2000. Six stars represent a top-ranked firm, five stars a second-ranked firm, etc.

SHIPPING

DEFINITION OF TERMS

P&I Club - 'Protection and indemnity' Club: a marine insurance club run mutually by and for ship-owners.

Charter-party - Commercial instrument, essentially a contract for the hire of an entire ship for the purpose of import or export of goods.

Bill of Lading - a certificate of undertaking by the master of a ship to deliver goods on payment of the named sum to a named party.

Salvage - reward payable by owners of ships and goods saved at sea by 'salvors.'

Underwriter - an individual who agrees to indemnify an assured person against losses under a policy of insurance.

MOA - Memorandum of Agreement.

Area of law

Suggest shipping law as a practice area to the majority of law students and you may well be met by a glazed look and a swift exit. At best you will call to mind images of Greek shipping magnates chewing on vast Havanas and news coverage of dramatic collisions at sea. In fact shipping law is an exciting, complex and unpredictable area of practice, involving many cutting edge principles of law.

Shipping law can be defined as "the law relating to all aspects of carriage by sea and international trade". It involves both contentious and non-contentious work.

Contentious work is divided into 'Wet' and 'Dry'. The difference, in essence, is that "Wet" (traditionally known as Admiralty) work concerns disputes arising from mishaps at sea, ie. collision, salvage, total loss etc. whilst "Dry" (traditionally known as Marine) arises from disputes over contracts made on dry land; charter-parties, bills of lading, cargo and sale of goods contracts. Non-contentious includes registration of ships and re-flagging yet mainly relates to ship finance advice, which is essentially corporate in nature.

Other niche practice areas include yachting and fishing (often regulatory advice).

Type of work

Shipping lawyers have a choice of non-contentious and contentious work available to them on qualification. On the non-contentious side advice is given on shipbuilding contracts, sale and purchase agreements, ship finance, contracts of employment for crew members and contracts of affreightment etc. Contentious work includes ad hoc 'consultancy' advice on day to day matters for regular clients, arrest of ships, together with conduct of High Court and arbitration cases from the time of the initial dispute through issuing of pleadings and interlocutory proceedings to final hearing and enforcement. Clients range from owners, operators, traders and charterers to P&I Clubs, other insurers and hull underwriters.

Very few lawyers will advise on both sides and those that do are generally located in smaller overseas offices where they are often required to turn their hands to most shipping related matters. Moreover, the type of firm you train with will normally pre-determine your eventual specialism.

There are a number of specialist firms in London such as Ince & Co, Holman Fenwick & Willan and Clyde & Co. where you will concentrate to a large degree on contentious shipping work for the duration of your training contract. Other corporate firms such as Norton Rose and Watson Farley Williams are known predominantly for their non-contentious work (namely ship finance) yet will also offer seats in other practice areas. Gina Power, four years qualified shipping lawyer at Lawrence Graham, started her career at medium sized City firm Penningtons precisely because she was not entirely sure which area of law she intended to specialise in. She was immediately attracted to commercial litigation and had a chance to do a six month seat in shipping. A broad choice of seats may prove vital if a trainee decides after six months that shipping is not for them.

Clare Matthews, shipping lawyer at AUS P&I in Sydney, urges prospective trainees to obtain vacation work placements prior to deciding which firms to apply to. She decided to commence her training at Ince & Co after taking a placement there one summer. If you are unable to obtain work experience then try to talk to lawyers at the firms. They will invariably be happy to discuss any queries you may have and will largely welcome your interest and initiative.

Trainees at the bigger London firms are occasionally offered the chance to take a seat abroad and this is definitely something you should consider. Don't despair if this is not the policy of your chosen firm or if they do not actually have any overseas offices. Gina Power, for example, speaks fluent Greek, and pestered her partners at Penningtons to be allowed to do a 3 month stint with a Greek shipping firm. It was up to her to arrange this, yet she managed to gain valuable international experience with a top firm in the port of Piraeus.

All shipping lawyers interviewed baulked at the idea of describing a typical day; nothing about this area of law is typical - 'expect the unexpected' is the catchphrase. Due to the global nature of your client base you are acutely aware of all the different time zones that you are working to on any one day. "Organisation is the key", says Power, who admits it is sometimes difficult for shipping lawyers to juggle their day. Oliver Weiss from leading firm Ince & Co. describes how on one occasion he recieved a call from a client to say that a barge had capsized in the South China Sea leaving many casualties. By 10 that night he was on a flight to Singapore (with a team including trainees) to take statements from all surviving crew members. This may not be a run of the mill occurrence for trainees but it is not unusual for shipping lawyers at a senior level.

Many cases are high profile, attracting media interest for both their factual and legal content. Consider the shipping casualties which have hit the headlines over the last 10 years; The Marchioness, Herald of Free Enterprise, the Braer oil spillage and the Sea Empress - all have involved lawyers in various capacities. Consider too, the cases you learn in contract law - many of the leading cases are complex shipping matters.

Skills needed

"Shipping is a very different area of law", says Clare Matthews, "you meet some very charismatic people and it is not a place for shrinking violets." Your multi-cultural clients are invariably extremely 'clued up' on the law and expect their lawyers to be likewise. "You are getting to know a whole industry and it is very important to keep abreast of both legal developments and industry trends," says Matthews. The need for an in-depth familiarity with the laws of contract, tort and court procedure goes without saying. If you don't enjoy learning the cases then shipping may not be for you.

Shipping lawyers also need to be extremely flexible in terms of hours and availability to travel at short notice. Home and mobile phone numbers are automatically put on business cards and weekend working is not uncommon. Shipping is not a 9-5 job.

Prospective trainees also need to be good communicators - English is invariably not your client's first language. You must be clear and concise in both a written and oral sense and not be prone to over-elaboration. Tony Vlasto at Clifford Chance maintains that although "shipping law is a more legally intensive area of law than many others - the problems which confront us are immediate and practical and require prompt handling." He looks for good humour, common sense, team spirit and self motivation.

Most interviewees agreed that the shipping industry is still, on the whole, dominated by men. Many cultures are still male oriented when it comes to business and prefer to deal 'man to man.' Indeed, within shipping law there is still quite a high drop-out rate amongst women and most of the top shipping partners are male. Nonetheless, all lawyers interviewed agreed that this should not dissuade female applicants. Many top female shipping lawyers are now coming through the ranks and achieving partnership staus at a relatively young age. According to Gina Power, "although some shipping clients can be difficult at first, they all show enormous respect once they realise you are as effective, hard working and persistent as your male counterparts."

For those specialising in wet work, previous knowledge of sea life is very useful. Many wet lawyers are ex-mariners or naval officers who have converted to the law. There is a steep learning curve in the first six months of a shipping seat and a trainee who was a mariner in his/her previous incarnation will have a head-start in terms of shipping regulations and terminology. Steve Mackin of Eversheds (Newcastle) was second officer aboard a Shell supertanker until 1987 when he came ashore to take a degree in Maritime Studies. A course on Maritime Law fascinated him early on and he decided to study for the CPE on graduation. "People who have worked at sea tend to be categorised on the wet side" he comments. "My seafaring background gave me a good feel for what is right or wrong and it means I can explain things to counsel more easily than non-mariners. It also helps to talk on the same level as your clients."

Career Options

Those interested in shipping law should be aware that jobs outside London are relatively few and far between. Shipping work is limited to towns with ports. After London, Plymouth, Liverpool and Newcastle are most important. In the larger firms with overseas offices there are opportunities for assistants to gain experience working abroad for a few years or even permanently. All interviewees considered this to be a good career move, particularly with regard to future partnership prospects back home. According to Gina Power, you are likely to undertake greater responsibility in a smaller overseas office where you are working in the same time zone and culture as your clients. This immediacy of contact is great for personal PR and you could end up returning to London with a host of new clients which you would not have otherwise obtained. Oliver Weiss is now based in the Greek port of Piraeus after lengthy stints in the firm's London and Hong Kong offices.

If, after qualification, you decide that shipping is not for you then your skills and solid grounding as a commercial litigator should allow you to qualify into another contentious department within or outside your present firm.

If private practice does not appeal, there is of course the possibility of going in-house. Ship owners, P&I clubs, operators and marine insurers all have openings for specialist lawyers. Clare Matthews, for example, completed her training at Ince & Co. before joining Watson Farley & Williams as a shipping lawyer in Singapore. She now works for AUS P&I Club in Sydney, Australia as a correspondent for many of the major international P&I Clubs. She feels that her knowledge of the day to day running of the shipping industry has increased substantially since working in-house. "The advice is more immediate and quite exciting," she says, "although in the long term you are not likely to make as much money as a top London partner." The hours and working conditions are widely perceived to be much more attractive than life in private practice. The predominance of English law in international shipping matters also make it relatively easy for in-house shipping lawyers to return to private practice in the future.

Some shipping lawyers choose to go it alone as sole practitioners or are setting up niche firms. One such lawyer is Nicola Ellis (Plymouth) who set up on her own in 1994. Her background was in general litigation, but she 'fell into' marine work on qualification after a spell at Clyde & Co. in Guildford during which she handled some cargo claims. Having gained that experience she found herself handling similar work in subsequent jobs and being encouraged to specialise by one particular yacht-building client. She now deals with mainly yachting work, representing the insured rather than the insurer in the majority of cases.

The Firms

The most well-known shipping firms in London are Clyde & Co., Holman Fenwick & Willan and Ince & Co. Holman Fenwick's workload is 50% shipping. The firm has offices in London, Paris, Rouen, Nantes, Piraeus, Hong Kong and Singapore and is particularly well respected for its wet work. Ince & Co. is an international commercial law firm with an unusual structure being non-departmentalised. All work stems from its origins as a shipping and commercial firm; shipping and international trade constitute about 40% of its workload and well over half the fee-earners handle shipping work. Because of its unusual structure trainees at this firm do not sit in different seats. Instead they sit with different partners and compete for work from all parts of the firm. Ex-trainee Clare Matthews, comments that "you are a file handler from day one which is both exciting and daunting." The firm has offices in London, Singapore, Piraeus and Hong Kong. Clyde & Co. has a similar structure and is particularly rated for its cargo expertise. The firm has over 270 lawyers, who are qualified in 17 jurisdictions. It has nine offices worldwide covering Europe, Asia and the Gulf.

The large City firms with shipping capability include Norton Rose, particularly active in non-contentious work, and litigation specialists Herbert Smith. Richards Butler also has a well respected shipping group with both contentious and non-contentious expertise.

Respected niche firms include Curtis Davis Garrard, a relaxed outfit of ex-City lawyers who wanted out of the rat-race and have a dress-down policy and encourage home working. Their choice of location at Heathrow reflects a focus on off-shore work. Thomas Cooper & Stibbard is a long-established shipping firm with a particularly successful marine personal injury team and a branch office in Singapore.

The main shipping centres outside of London are Plymouth, Liverpool and Newcastle. Hill Dickinson are highly respected in the north, as are Dibb Lupton Alsop. Both firms have a large presence in Liverpool. In Newcastle, Eversheds retain a superb reputation for wet work, acting on a number of high profile collisions. Plymouth based firms Bond Pearce and Davies Johnson & Co. undertake a broad spread of shipping work.

▶

Leading Firms

London	Shipping	Shipping (Admirality)
Barlow Lyde & Gilbert	**	
Bentleys, Stokes & Lowless	***	**
Clifford Chance	****	***
Clyde & Co	*****	*****
Constant & Constant	***	**
Curtis Davis Garrard, Staines	**	
Fishers	*	
Hill Taylor Dickinson	****	****
Holman Fenwick & Willan	*****	******
Holmes Hardingham	***	***
Ince & Co	******	******
Jackson Parton	***	
Lawrence Graham	***	
Middleton Potts	**	
More Fisher Brown	***	
Norton Rose	****	***
Richards Butler	****	***
Shaw and Croft	**	**
Sinclair Roche & Temperley	****	***
Stephenson Harwood	****	***
Stockler Charity	*	
Thomas Cooper & Stibbard	***	
Waltons & Morse		**
Waterson Hicks	*	
Watson, Farley & Williams	***	

South & East Anglia	Shipping
Bond Pearce, Plymouth, Southampton	*****
Dale & Co Solicitors, Felixstowe	****
Davies, Johnson & Co, Plymouth	*****
Donne Mileham & Haddock, Brighton	*****
Eversheds, Ipswich	****
Foot & Bowden, Plymouth	*****
Grant & Horton Marine Solicitors, Plymouth	*****
Hayes, Exeter	****
John Weston & Co, Felixstowe	****

North	Shipping	Shipping (Admirality)
Andrew M. Jackson & Co, Hull	*****	***
Dibb Lupton Alsop, Liverpool	*****	
Eversheds, Newcastle upon Tyne	*****	
Hill Dickinson, Liverpool	******	***
Mills & Co, Newcastle-upon-Tyne	******	
Rayfield Mills, Newcastle-upon-Tyne	******	***

SPORTS LAW

Area of law

Initially the term "sports law" was a convenient umbrella denoting an amalgam of separate legal disciplines both contentious and non-contentious for sporting clients. The job for the lawyer was to apply these general legal principles within a sporting context. However, whilst this definition still holds strong in many respects, all lawyers interviewed agreed that a separate body of law relating to specific sports-related issues is now developing at an ever-increasing pace.

According to Andy Korman, Head of Sponsorship at sports specialists Townleys, this is best illustrated when national law and particular sports regulations collide. He gives the example of the well known Bosman Case, in which football regulation governing the transfer of players were at odds with European employment legislation. Regulatory bodies are increasingly being taken to court for imposing rules which are at odds with the prevailing laws of the land. Parul Patel, assistant solicitor at Clarke Willmott & Clarke, agrees and comments that increased professionalism and the globalisation of sporting concerns will inevitably lead to increased legislation nationally and across Europe. She points to the creation of a Minister for Sport and the fact that sport is now such a major global industry as an indication of the inevitability of further specific industry regulation.

The areas of law which retain particular importance in sports-related work remain intellectual property (the protection and exploitation of rights); EU and competition law (looking at the sports industry to see whether it is restrictive of competition); media and entertainment law (covering broadcasting, sponsorship, advertising); commercial/corporate law; crime & personal injury.

Type of work

The area we call "sports law" can be divided into three main aspects:

1. The regulatory, disciplinary, criminal and personal injury advice given to individuals, teams and ruling bodies.

2. Media/sponsorship and advertising.

3. Corporate and commercial advice, eg the stock market listing of a football club.

In addition, students should also determine whether they envisage a career in litigation or as a non-contentious lawyer. There is increasingly a greater willingness to litigate among sporting clients.

However one defines sports law it is obvious that prospective trainees should think carefully before deciding which firms to approach. Firms fall broadly into one category or another although most handle a cross-section of sports-related work as required by their clients.

Townleys advise exclusively on sports law matters and offer trainees four sports-related seats to be chosen from the areas of broadcasting, commercial, New Media, dispute resolution, governance, IP and sponsorship. The team works on sports as varied as triathlon, squash, football, rugby and bob-sleigh and last year worked on the sponsorship of the Rugby World Cup legal programme; Fulham FC's Commercial and player matters; Six Nations merchandising and Formula One brand protection work.

Denton Hall, meanwhile, has a strong media bias to their sports work advising individuals on their intellectual property rights and sponsorship. They recently advised Tracey Edwards (skipper of the first all-woman crew attempting to sail round the world) on various trademark registrations, on a publishing deal and on setting up her own website. The team are also involved in regulatory and disciplinary issues and recently defended Restrictive Practices Court proceedings brought by the Director General of

Fair Trading regarding Premier League Rules and broadcast agreements.

Another firm known for regulatory and disciplinary work is Farrer & Co. Karena Vleck advised the British Athletics Federation in the long running Diane Modahl case and is a non-executive director of UK Athletics. As well as dealing with constitutional issues she has been negotiating TV rights and sponsorship, agency and event agreements.

Nicholson Graham & Jones was probably the first City firm to establish a sports department and to approach the sector from a corporate angle. Many sporting disciplines are covered by their client base, including football, rugby and cricket as well as minor sports such as greyhound racing and snow boarding. Their involvement in acquisitions of businesses, competition law, property, insolvency, sponsorship agreements, players' contracts and constitutional advice shows the breadth of the team's work.

'Sporadic' is the description most used by practitioners to describe the nature of the job. A typical day for rugby specialist Parul Patel might involve a lengthy contract negotiation for a player, advising a major international name on personal injury litigation and attempting to find clubs for out of contract clients. All agreed that, although their chosen field was considered by most to be a 'sexy' area to work in, sports law is by no means a soft option. The day to day legal work is as exhausting (and at times mundane) as any other specialism. Nonetheless, the high profile nature of the job was viewed favourably by all sport lawyers interviewed. Andy Korman, for example, gets a "kick" when watching a football team whose shirt sponsorship he has negotiated. Moreover, if commenting on your cases for television, fending off newspaper reporters and watching major events from the comfort of the directors' box interests you then you are likely to enjoy the discipline.

Skills needed

"It is not enough to be passionate about sport" claims Andy Korman. "You need to be able to grasp many aspects of law quickly, and to understand how they impact on each other." Particularly important is a good commercial grounding, a knowledge of contract, media and intellectual property law and an awareness of EU and competition law. He cites the example of a trainee at Townleys whose Masters in intellectual property law and IT law made him particularly suited to the firm's New Media department.

However it is vital to show a proven track record of interest in the area. If students are offered the chance to do a dissertation at University then they should pick a topic with a relevance to sport. Trainees who can relate to the sporting issues of the day and understand the inherent legal implications are precisely what Townleys are looking for.

Parul Patel, meanwhile, considered language skills important, and pointed to the increasing globalisation of sport in this respect. Her ability to speak French and Italian is proving invaluable in her negotiations with European clubs on behalf of her rugby playing clients.

Personal skills are as important as legal skills in this people-driven industry. You must be "outgoing, definitely not shy" says Patel. "You need the confidence to go it alone if necessary." It is not an industry for shrinking violets. However, neither is it an industry for publicity craving, starstruck graduates. Clients hire sports lawyers because they know the law. "We don't want prima donnas" says Warren Phelops, head of sport at Nicholson, Graham & Jones. He looks for "people skills as well as paper skills," vibrant team players with energy and a determination to succeed.

All sports lawyers interviewed agreed that it is not enough to say, "I want to be a lawyer and I really like playing football." You also need to know the business of sport and nothing will show you up more in a meeting than ignorance of the game. A legendary example of this is the lawyer who, in front of a client, repeatedly confused St. James' Park, Newcastle (the world renowned football stadium) with St. James' Park, London (the world renowned royal park).

"The nuts and bolts of a particular contract are usually quite basic" says Andy Korman. "What is important is tailoring the deal and approach to the style of the client and the way the structure of the sport fits together. A technical appreciation of the sport is, therefore, extremely important.

Unfortunately, for the majority of people, this is an area where good contacts can easily sway job interviews. A sports department will be much more likely to look at you if you have played rugby for your country or if your father is a premiership football manager. Jonny Searle, lawyer with Ashurst Morris Crisp and Olympic oarsman, also suggests that clients tend to treat you with less suspicion when they know you can empathise with them as a sports player. Despite increased professionalism many sportsmen and women are still cynical about lawyers and the business of making money out of sport.

Students should not despair if they fail to get a training contract offering a sports law seat. Andy Korman, for example, trained at a well known corporate firm in the City before joining Townleys on qualification. Likewise, Parul Patel joined Clarke, Willmott & Clarke as a sports lawyer after qualification from leading regional firm Eversheds. Although Eversheds was not known for its sporting client base she harassed the partners for anything sports-related that came in, managing to build up her own portfolio of experience. "You will only get work if you ask for it" she says. "Be persistent, use your initiative and be up front about your interest in sport from day one."

Career Options

In private practice, sports specialists move into this area both by accident and design. Sports lovers often try to steer their careers in this direction, while corporate, litigation, intellectual property or personal injury lawyers who have acquired a sporting clientele may suddenly find themselves referred to as sports lawyers.

There are various in-house opportunities in the the sports world. Brian Clarke (ex-Nabarro Nathanson) is the European head of sports management agency IMG. You could work for a governing body such as the FA or the the RFU; for a sports broadcaster negotiating rights, or as an agent for individual sports personalities or teams. Lawyer Mel Stein has made a name for himself in this respect with his work for Paul Gascoigne.

The Firms

Townleys in London remains the only law firm in the country specialising exclusively in sport. The practice has expanded and now boasts 5 partners and 17 assistants. Much of their work concerns the commercial exploitation of sporting and cultural events. During 1999 they worked on events such as the Five Nations Championship, the Rugby World Cup 1999, the Commonwealth Games 2002, the Boat Race 1999 and Formula One motor racing. Much of their work is international and foreign language skills are useful. Some of the staff are former professional sports people.

Denton Hall is an example of a large commercial firm with a well-developed sports practice. Five partners and three assistants handle sports-related work. There are overlaps with the firm's entertainment practice and with the planning department whose clients include Chelsea Football Club.

Medium-sized firms such as Farrer & Co and Bird & Bird have respected sports departments. Bird & Bird advises major international stars on matters ranging from sponsorship to tax planning.

Large City firms are increasingly marketing their advice on sports-related work as a specialism. Herbert Smith maintains a strong reputation for commercial, broadcasting, litigation and disciplinary matters. Their client portfolio is drawn from football, motor racing and rugby league and union. They count Tottenham Hotspur as a major client. Freshfields benefits from its European branches allowing it to act for Portuguese, Spanish and Italian clubs on proposed listings and international offering of shares. The work is largely corporate in nature. Charles Russell is primarily an equine practice and its profile is restricted to the spheres of horse racing and polo.The practice advises on varied matters from race fixing and constitutional matters to copyright and health and safety. Nicholson Graham & Jones have a corporate bias to their work. They acted on behalf of Mohammed Al Fayed in his investment in Fulham F.C.

Outside London a variety of firms handle sports-related work. In Bristol, Osborne Clark is appointed by the Professional Cricketers Association as regional solicitors for South West England. Fellow Bristol firm, Clarke Willmott & Clarke represents the current Bath and England Rugby Union squads. In St Albans Pickworths continues to be involved in the Ayrton Senna manslaughter trial, whilst in Exeter, Stones has a niche practice handling ski-ing injuries. In the Midlands, Edge Ellison are involved in well publicised contentious work including the Diane Modahl litigation. James Chapman & Co in Manchester and McCormicks in Leeds are two of the best known sports firms in the north, while larger firms like Addleshaw Booth & Co and Walker Morris also handle sports work. The former was appointed legal adviser to both the Manchester 2002 Commonwealth Games and Rugby Football League; the latter counts David Batty and Superleague Europe among its clients.

Leading Firms

London	Sports
Ashurst Morris Crisp	**
S J Berwin & Co	*
Bird & Bird	*****
Charles Russell	***
Clintons	**
Collyer-Bristow	***
Davies Arnold Cooper	*
Denton Hall	******
Farrer & Co	*****
Field Fisher Waterhouse	*
Freshfields	***
Grower Freeman & Goldberg	**
Hammond Suddards	*
Harbottle & Lewis	***
Herbert Smith	****
John Bowden Trainer & Co	*

London	Sports
Keene Marsland	*
Lawrence Graham	**
Lovells	*
Max Bitel, Greene	****
Memery Crystal	**
Mishcon de Reya	*
Moorhead James	**
Nicholson Graham & Jones	****
Payne Hicks Beach	*
Russell Jones & Walker	***
Simmons & Simmons	*
The Simkins Partnership	*
Theodore Goddard	*
Townleys	******
Wedlake Bell	**

South	Sports
Alsters, Bristol	***
David Jeacock & Co, Swindon	**
Matthew McCloy & Partners, Newbury	*

South	Sports
Osborne Clarke, Bristol	***
Pickworths, St. Albans	**
Stones, Exeter	**

Midlands	Sports
Edge Ellison, Birmingham	***

East Anglia	Sports
Greenland Houchen, Norwich	**

North	Sports
Addleshaw Booth & Co, Manchester	***
George Davies & Co, Manchester	*****
Gorna & Co, Manchester	*****
James Chapman & Co, Manchester	******

North	Sports
McCormicks, Leeds	******
Walker Morris, Leeds	*****
Zermansky & Partners, Leeds	***

TAX

(including Corporate Tax and VAT. For personal tax see Private Client section)

Area of law

Our tax section deals with the impact of revenue law on corporate business. The scope of the work covers taxes paid by businesses to the Inland Revenue - corporation tax, capital gains tax, stamp duty etc. and those paid to Customs & Excise, such as VAT.

A significant percentage of a company's income is paid out in tax, so it's not hard to see why tax lawyers are so valuable to their clients. Good advice can result in a tax saving that can reap enormous financial benefits for the client. Even the most costly lawyers' fees are money well spent. In a nutshell, it's the tax adviser's job to tell the client exactly how to structure its business activities so as to be most tax efficient.

Type of work

In the country's top corporate tax departments between 60-70% of the work is transaction based. Where companies are buying or selling businesses, tax lawyers advise on the revenue implications in conjunction with their colleagues from the corporate and property departments. Such involvement with merger and acquisition work is often seen within the law firm as a 'support' role. In fact, tax lawyers are often called upon to help structure deals from the outset so as to ensure that the most tax efficient approach is taken.

Corporate tax lawyers are widely seen as 'anoraks.' In fact they need to be extremely commercial animals. Tax law is not a refuge for those who want to screen themselves from client involvement behind towers of statute books. There's no room for those who want to theorise about technicalities of 'black letter law' in isolation from the real world for which it was written. That said, if it is the thrill of the chase you are after, and the adrenalin of the all-night meeting, you may be unfulfilled. Steve Edge, partner at Slaughter and May and probably the UK's most well-known tax lawyer comments: "Sometimes I'm the first lawyer to be involved on a big deal. But as the job is done, I'll see people who have been up all night on negotiations and have the tremendous satisfaction that they've moved mountains. More often than not the tax people will have been more remote in the latter stages of the deal unless a problem arises. When a problem does arise you have to react like the fire brigade and sort things out quickly!" No one then has any patience with tax advisers who make a meal of things. There is tremendous satisfaction in being able to come in and provide a positive solution under pressure in such circumstances and that obviously produces its own form of adrenalin. You certainly have to regard yourself as an ideas person and a problem solver, but you are unlikely to get the champagne and the glory for driving the deal to completion.

A good lawyer absorbs himself in the world of his clients. Be they corporate finance, banking or property-based he needs to understand these areas of law and the culture, constraints and regulations affecting the sector. So, as in all commercial areas of law, you need to be a business adviser, with a particular expertise in tax.

Most tax work is advisory. However litigation may follow after a dispute arises between a tax payer and the Revenue. Greg Sinfield, partner at Lovells, has made a career in contentious tax work. He tells us that his practice can involve anything from drafting a carefully-worded response to an Inland Revenue query, sitting with a client during an interview under caution by the Customs authorities to being the client's advocate at appeal hearings. Appeals often raise mixed questions of fact and law, so the advocate must be a skilled handler of evidence and witnesses as well as familiar with the minutiae of the relevant statutes. "Contentious tax work combines the intellectual challenge of a good crossword puzzle with the strategic and tactical challenge of a military campaign and just a dash of drama if the matter goes to appeal."

An increasing amount of tax consultancy work is now handled by solicitors. Traditionally the preserve of the accountancy professional, this consultancy or 'stand alone' work might involve the lawyer reviewing proposals for a new financial product or working to develop a tax saving scheme.

Skills needed

Steve Edge is amused by the anorak label that still attaches to tax lawyers. It is far removed from the reality of his job. Whilst the job involves a lot of law, it is light on procedure. As the subject matter is complex, it is vital to be able to communicate difficult ideas effectively in layman's language. Great pleasure can be derived from being able to convey complicated ideas to clients frustrated by their own lack of understanding of the concepts.

If the communication of complex concepts is what the client gets on the surface, there's a mass of rigorous investigation and activity going on underneath. The good tax lawyer is one who can understand how their client's activities are impacted by the tax regime and assess how those activities can be best carried out so as to optimise profitability and safeguard assets. You'll need a keen eye for detail and be driven to get to the heart of a problem. A forensic mind is often felt to be a hallmark of a good tax lawyer. There's no room for tax generalists in the profession, only true specialists. A deal can stand or fall on your advice, so it must be precise. You need to have absolute confidence in your judgment and to inspire the same level of confidence in others.

A by-product of working with conceptual ideas backed up by rigorous research is that you won't be swimming in documents all day, scratching red amendments onto the fifth draft of some lengthy contract. Steve Edge is thankful for this and likes the fact that there's a mutual respect between tax lawyers in different firms. "People in tax spend less time pushing paper and more time thinking about points, less time negotiating with stubborn people and more time trying to remove obduracy from a deal. Very often, you'll find the tax people on a deal are doing their own bit and negotiating with equals on the other side. Everybody is sensible because we all have a common enemy."

Career options

Specialist tax lawyers are not two-a-penny so after just a few years of bedding down into the practice area you will become a very marketable commodity. In the last few years there has been a degree of movement of senior figures between tax departments in banks, accountancy firms, law firms and also to the Bar and to and from the Inland Revenue or Customs and Excise.

Some of the most respected tax barristers have only been called to the bar for a couple of years but had previously been successful solicitors. The knowledge and skills developed in practice are so transferable that you then become free to select the context in which you deliver a service to clients or advise those who make policy decisions concerning tax legislation.

Nigel Popplewell joined Bristol's Burges Salmon last year to head up their corporate tax department. He thinks that prospects for tax lawyers in the regions are looking healthy with clients now following the trend in London and scrutinising their traditional habit of taking tax advice from accountants. Nigel thinks that the regional players are going to be "recruiting like crazy" in order to compete with the accountancy firms. "The million dollar question is who are the clients going to go to for the pro-active advice?" he asks. He feels lawyers are better suited to helping their clients assess risk and make difficult decisions. They can also implement tax planning strategies by drafting the appropriate documents. He also thinks that clients will see regional tax lawyers providing a service which is better value for money than many of the 'Big 5' accountants who are increasingly driven by global fee pressures. "You don't always need rocket science, just to know that it is available if you do."

The firms

A strong tax department goes hand in hand with a strong corporate department, so aim for the big commercial firms if this work interests you. In the main, corporate transactions are the bread and butter work of tax departments.

In London, the top five tax practices are seen to be streaks ahead of the rest of the pack. Not surprisingly, Freshfields, Linklaters and Slaughter and May each have superb reputations for corporate tax, as do Clifford Chance and Allen & Overy. The average size of their departments is around 10 partners and 25 assistants. The globalisation of commerce has led to an increase in cross-border transactions. Tax lawyers often work in tandem with colleagues in overseas offices or with allied firms in other jurisdictions. Linklaters advised BP and Freshfields were instructed by Amoco on the £110bn merger of the two multinationals last year.

In the regions, fewer firms field tax departments and they are usually considerably smaller units. Four or five tax specialists is the norm, although Leeds big-hitters Addleshaw Booth & Co have a team of eight. The pattern reflects that of London, with the strongest commercial firms being those with a significant tax capability.

In Bristol, the leading firms are Burges Salmon and Osborne Clarke. In the Midlands, Pinsent Curtis and Wragge & Co head the Birmingham firms. Pinsent Curtis' five-strong team in Leeds tops the northern league along with Addleshaw Booth & Co. In Scotland, McGrigor Donald's Glasgow-based lawyers lead in tax advice.

Leading Firms

London	Tax	London	Tax
Allen & Overy	*****	Linklaters	******
Ashurst Morris Crisp	***	Lovells	***
S J Berwin & Co	**	Macfarlanes	***
Berwin Leighton	*	Nabarro Nathanson	*
Clifford Chance	*****	Norton Rose	***
Clyde & Co	*	Olswang	*
CMS Cameron McKenna	**	Simmons & Simmons	**
Denton Hall	*	Slaughter and May	******
Dibb Lupton Alsop	*	Theodore Goddard	**
Field Fisher Waterhouse	*	Travers Smith Braithwaite	**
Freshfields	******	Watson, Farley & Williams	**
Hammond Suddards	*	Wilde Sapte	*
Herbert Smith	***		

South East/Wales	Tax	South East/Wales	Tax
Blake Lapthorn, Fareham	*	Mills & Reeve, Cambridge	**
Burges Salmon, Bristol	***	Osborne Clarke, Bristol	***
Eversheds, Norwich	*	Wiggin & Co, Cheltenham	***

Midlands	Tax	Midlands	Tax
Dibb Lupton Alsop, Birmingham	****	Pinsent Curtis, Birmingham	******
Eversheds, Nottingham	****	Wragge & Co, Birmingham	******

North	Tax	North	Tax
Addleshaw Booth & Co, Leeds, Manc	******	Hammond Suddards, Leeds, Manc	*****
Dickinson Dees, Newcastle upon Tyne	***	Pinsent Curtis, Leeds	******
Eversheds, Leeds, Manchester	***	Walker Morris, Leeds	***

a-z of Law Firms

INDEX TO FIRMS

ADDLESHAW BOOTH & CO

Sovereign House PO Box 8 Sovereign Street Leeds LS1 1HQ
Tel: (0113) 209 2000 Fax: (0113) 209 2060
100 Barbirolli Square Manchester M2 3AB
Tel :(0161) 934 6000 Fax: (0161) 934 6060
60 Cannon Street London EC4N 6NP
Tel: (020) 7982 5000 Fax: (020) 7982 5060
Email: grad@addleshaw-booth.co.uk
Website: www.addleshaw-booth.co.uk

Firm Profile
Addleshaw Booth & Co is a leading UK law firm, operating nationally and with an international capability. We provide commercial advice and legal solutions to a wide range of clients in the corporate, financial, public and private sectors.

Main Areas of Work
Banking and Financial Services; Commercial; Commercial Property; Corporate Finance; Litigation and Dispute Resolution; Private Client; Recoveries Management

Trainee Profile
Graduates of all disciplines who are capable of achieving a 2:1, can demonstrate commercial awareness, a flexible attitude and a willingness to learn. Non-academic interests and achievements will also be taken into account and applications from mature applicants are welcomed.

Training Environment
During each six-month seat, there will be regular two-way performance reviews with the supervising partner or solicitor. Trainees are given the opportunity to spend a seat in one of the other offices and there are also a number of secondments to the in-house legal departments of various clients such as Astra Zeneca, British Aerospace and Airtours. The on-the-job training received within teams is complemented by a programme of lectures and residential courses, many designed specifically for trainees. The firm has a reputation of being a friendly and pleasant place to work and particular emphasis is placed upon building relationships and valuing everybody's contribution towards the success of the business.

Benefits
Corporate membership of gyms, profit related pay, season ticket loan.

Vacation Placements
Places for 2000: 40; Duration: 2 weeks; Remuneration: £125 p.w.; Closing Date: 25 February 2000.

Sponsorship & Awards
CPE and LPC fees are paid, together with a maintenance award of £3,500.

Partners	100
Assistant Solicitors	398
Total Trainees	60

Contact
Joanna Rue, Graduate Manager

Method of Application
Application form

Selection Procedure
Interview, assessment day

Closing date for 2002
28 July 2000

Application

Training contracts p.a.	40 approx
Applications p.a.	2,000
% interviewed p.a.	6%
Required degree grade	2:1

Training

Salary: 1st year(2000)	£16,000–£16,500
Salary: 2nd year(2000)	£17,000 –£17,500
Holiday entitlement	25 days
% of trainees with a non-law degree p.a.	40%

Post-Qualification

Salary (2000)	£26,000
% of trainees offered job on qualification (1999)	85%

Other Offices
Birmingham, Bristol, Leeds, London, Manchester, Sheffield, Winchester

ALLEN & OVERY

One New Change London EC4M 9QQ
Tel: (020) 7330 3000 Fax: (020) 7330 9999
Website: www.allenovery.com

Firm Profile
Allen & Overy is one of the world's premier global law firms, with major strengths in banking, international capital markets and corporate work. All departments work closely together to meet the needs of clients which include governments, financial institutions, businesses and private individuals.

Main Areas of Work
Banking; International Capital Markets; Corporate; Litigation; Property; Private Client; Tax; Employment and related areas.

Trainee Profile
Intellectual ability is a prerequisite but as Allen & Overy is a commercial firm it also looks for people with a good level of business understanding. The firm looks for creative, problem solving people who can quickly identify salient points without losing sight of detail. You will need to be highly motivated, demonstrate initiative and the ability to alternate between leading and being part of a team.

Training Environment
Within a highly pressurised environment, trainees obtain a balance of practical and formal tuition. You will experience at least four different areas of work, but will spend a significant amount of time in at least two of the following departments: banking, corporate and international capital markets. Your preferences will be balanced with the firm's needs. Seminars provide practical advice and an introduction to each area of law. Placements abroad are available. A positive, open and co-operative culture is encouraged both professionally and socially. A range of sporting activities are available.

Benefits
PPP scheme, private medical insurance, season ticket loans, gym membership, subsidised restaurant, 6 weeks unpaid leave on qualification.

Vacation Placements
Places for 2000: 90; Duration: 3 weeks; Remuneration: £200 p.w.; Closing Date: 31 January 2000.

Sponsorship & Awards
CPE and LPC fees and £4,500 maintenance p.a. (£4,000 outside London and Guildford).

Partners	265*
Associates	900*
Total Trainees	282*

** denotes world-wide figures*

Contact
Mimi Lee-Denman

Method of Application
Application form

Selection Procedure
Assessment centre

Closing date for 2002
CPE candidates:
Early February 2000;
Law students: Early August, 2000

Application
Training contracts p.a.	120
Applications p.a.	4,000
% interviewed p.a.	10%
Required degree grade	2:1

Training
Salary: 1st year(2000)	£21,000
Salary: 2nd year(2000)	£24,000
Holiday entitlement	25 days
% of trainees with a non-law degree p.a.	40%
No. of seats available abroad p.a.	25

Post-Qualification
Salary (2000)	£33,000
% of trainees offered job on qualification (1999)	90%
% of partners (as at 1/9/98) who joined as trainees	60%

Overseas Offices
Amsterdam, Bangkok, Beijing, Brussels, Bratislava, Budapest, Dubai, Frankfurt, Hong Kong, Luxembourg, Madrid, Milan, Moscow, New York, Rome, Paris, Prague, Singapore, Tirana, Tokyo, Turin, Warsaw.

ANTHONY GOLD, LERMAN & MUIRHEAD

New London Bridge House 25 London Bridge Street
London SE1 9TW
Tel: (020) 7940 4000 Fax: (020) 7378 8025
Email: agold@agold.law.co.uk

Firm Profile

A progressive and expanding practice. Anthony Gold, Lerman & Muirhead take a creative approach to problem solving, working to achieve client's goals and offering imaginative funding arrangements. The firm provides a wide range of services for individuals and businesses. Its specialist Personal Injury, Family, Housing and Commercial Litigation teams, in particular, have high reputations.

Main Areas of Work

Family 20%; Personal Injury/Medical Negligence 30%; Conveyancing/Probate 10%; Corporate/Commercial 20%; Housing/Public Law 20%.

Trainee Profile

Trainees must possess a strong academic background, common sense and a commitment to the firm's work. They should display excellent written and oral communication skills and an ability to form effective interpersonal relationships.

Training Environment

Trainees will usually spend time in three of the five departments (to achieve a mix of contentious and non-contentious work). The firm aims to accommodate your areas of interest. You will be expected to deal professionally with clients and you will have the chance to manage your own casework. You will be expected to work as part of a team under the supervision of a Partner or senior solicitor. Your supervisor will conduct a three-month assessment and six-month review. There is a comprehensive in-house training programme and externally provided PSC. Trainees are encouraged to participate in social and sporting events and to contribute towards the marketing of the firm.

Benefits

A subsidised gym, Season Ticket Loan, PRP, private medical care, permanent health insurance.

Sponsorship & Awards

£1,000 paid for LPC fees and interest free loan.

Partners	11
Assistant Solicitors	11
Total Trainees	9

Contact

Kim Beatson

Method of Application

Handwritten letter and/or application form

Selection Procedure

One interview

Application

Training contracts p.a.	4
Applications p.a.	400
% interviewed p.a.	7.5%
Required degree grade	2:1

Training

Salary: 1st year(2000)	£16,500
Salary: 2nd year(2000)	£18,000
Holiday entitlement	20 days

Post-Qualification

Salary (2000)	£24,050
% of trainees offered job on qualification (1999)	100%
% of assistants (as at 1/9/99) who joined as trainees	63%
% of partners (as at 1/9/99) who joined as trainees	42%

ASHURST MORRIS CRISP

Broadwalk House 5 Appold St London EC2A 2HA
Tel: (020) 7638 1111 Fax: (020) 7972 7990
Email: jane.ahern@ashursts.com
Website: www.ashursts.com

Firm Profile
An international City practice, smaller than its principal competitors yet consistently ranked amongst the top few firms in the country in terms of the work in which it is involved and clients for whom it acts.

Main Areas of Work
Company 45%; Property 25%; Litigation 15%; Banking 10%; Tax 5%.

Trainee Profile
Candidates should want to be involved in the highest quality work that a City firm can offer. The firm wants high achievers academically as the work is intellectually demanding. Candidates should show common sense, good judgement, a willingness to take on responsibility, a sense of humour and an outgoing nature. Language skills and an international perspective on life will impress.

Training Environment
The training contract comprises four or five seats including six months in each of three of the principal departments. Opportunities exist to work in Brussels, Paris, Frankfurt, Milan, Singapore and Tokyo, or on secondment to a client. The firm runs the LPC and PSC in partnership with the College of Law. A fast-track two week course covers the compulsory core elements of the PSC and there is an extensive in-house training programme. The firm gives trainees as much responsibility as they can manage, and a full role in servising clients' needs. Trainees are encouraged to take on pro bono work.

Benefits
Season ticket loan, medical cover, life cover, membership of a gym/squash club, subsidised annual health check.

Vacation Placements
Places for 2000: 45–50; Duration: 3 weeks; Remuneration: £200 p.w.(1999); Closing Date: 1 January–29 February 2000.

Sponsorship & Awards
CPE and LPC funding and maintenance allowance.

Partners	91*
Assistant Solicitors	293*
Total Trainees	96

** denotes world-wide figures*

Contact
Jane Ahern

Method of Application
Handwritten or typed letter and CV

Selection Procedure
Interview with 2 partners

Closing date for 2002
31 August 2000

Application
Training contracts p.a.	45–50
Applications p.a.	3,000
% interviewed p.a.	13%
Required degree grade	n/a

Training
Salary: 2000

1st seat (First 6 months)	£21,000
2nd seat (6-12 months)	£22,000
3rd seat (12-18 months)	£23,000
4th seat (after 18 months)	£24,000
Holiday entitlement	25 days
% of trainees with a non-law degree p.a.	50%
No. of seats available abroad p.a.	14

Post-Qualification
Salary (2000)	£35,000
% of trainees offered job on qualification (1999)	95%

Overseas Offices
Brussels, Delhi, Frankfurt, Paris, Singapore, Tokyo; associated offices in Milan, Rome and Verona.

BAKER & MCKENZIE

100 New Bridge Street London EC4V 6JA
Tel: (020) 7919 1000 Fax: (020) 7919 1999
Email: london.graduate.recruit@bakernet.com
Website: www.bakerinfo.com

Firm Profile
Baker & McKenzie is the world's largest law firm. The London office is a leading City practice with a domestic and foreign client base. It provides business and financial legal services to corporations, financial institutions, governments and entrepreneurs.

Main Areas of Work
Corporate/Finance/EC/Tax/Commercial 47%; Litigation/Construction 23%; Employment/Pensions/Immigration 13%; Intellectual Property 10%; Commercial Property 7%.

Trainee Profile
Baker & McKenzie are looking for trainees who are stimulated by intellectual challenge and want to be 'the best' at what they do. Effective communication together with the ability to be creative but practical problem solvers, team players and to have a sense of humour are qualities which will help them stand out from the crowd. Language and IT skills are also valued. The firm encourages their trainees to take time out before commencing their training contract whether just to travel or undertake further studies.

Training Environment
Four six-month seats which include corporate and litigation together with the possibility of a secondment abroad or with a client. During each seat you will have formal and informal reviews to discuss your progress as well as subsequent seat preferences. Your training contract commences with a highly interactive and practical induction programme which focuses on key skills including practical problem solving, interviewing, presenting and the application of information technology. The firm's training programmes include important components on management and other business skills, as well as seminars and workshops on key legal topics for each practice area. They run the Professional Skills Course in-house – two modules of which are undertaken at the start of your training contract. There is a Trainee Solicitor Liaison Committee which acts as a forum for any new ideas or problems which may occur during the training contract. Trainees are actively encouraged to participate in a variety of pro bono issues and outside of office hours there is a varied sporting and social life.

Partners	68
Assistant Solicitors	149
Total Trainees	44

Contact
Joanna Darby / Natalie Stacey

Method of Application
Letter and application form

Selection Procedure
Candidates to give a short oral and written presentation, interview with 2 partners, meeting with a trainee

Closing date for 2002
Non-law: 18/2/00; Law: 28/7/00

Application
Training contracts p.a.	22-25
Applications p.a.	2,000
% interviewed p.a.	6%
Required degree grade	2:1

Training
Salary: 1st year(1999)	£21,000
Salary: 2nd year(1999)	£23,500
Holiday entitlement	25 days
% of trainees with a non-law degree p.a.	approx 50%
No. of seats available abroad p.a.	Variable

Post-Qualification
Salary (1999)	£35,000 – £36,000
% of trainees offered job on qualification (1999)	82%
% of partners (as at 1/9/99) who joined as trainees	40%

Overseas Offices
Almaty, Amsterdam, Bahrain, Baku, Bangkok, Barcelona, Beijing, Berlin, Bogotá, Brasilia, Brussels, Budapest, Buenos Aires, Cairo, Caracas, Chicago, Dallas, Frankfurt, Geneva, Hanoi, Ho Chi Minh City, Hong Kong, Houston, Hsinchu, Juarez, Kiev, Madrid, Manila, Melbourne, Mexico City, Miami,

▶

Benefits

Permanent health insurance, life insurance, private medical insurance, group personal pension plan, gym membership, luncheon vouchers, interest-free season ticket loan.

Vacation Placements

Places for 2000: 30; Duration: Summer (3 weeks); Remuneration: £250 p.w.; Closing Date: 31 January 2000

Sponsorship & Awards

CPE Funding: Fees paid + £4,500 maintenance.
LPC Funding: Fees paid + £4,500 maintenance.

Additional Information

As mentioned, trainees have the opportunity to spend three months working in one of our overseas offices. Trainees have already been seconded to our offices in Sydney, Palo Alto and Riyadh. In addition they also operate an Associate Training Programme which enables lawyers with 18–24 months pqe to spend between 6–24 months working in an overseas office. In recent years the firm has had associates spend time in Palo Alto, Chicago, Moscow, Hong Kong and Sydney. Baker & McKenzie have a very extensive know-how practice both in London and globally which is ably assisted by BakerWeb, the firm's intranet.

Trainee Comments

"I've only been working at Baker & McKenzie for a short while and I already feel part of the team. The work is both interesting and challenging and I have been given much more responsibility than I thought I would. In fact, I've not been near a photocopier yet!" (James Smith, first seat trainee, read Law at Jesus College, Oxford)

"Baker & McKenzie, with its emphasis on quality work and quality training, provides an interesting and challenging environment for a trainee solicitor to work in." (Allison Brown, first seat trainee, read German Studies at Warwick University)

"For me, the appeal of Baker & McKenzie encompassed the combined advantage of a truly global firm, with opportunities to be involved in high profile and often multi-jurisdictional transactions on a daily basis, and of a friendly and welcoming London office. I have not been disappointed." (Claire Collins, second seat trainee, read Law at Bristol University)

"I enjoy the friendly atmosphere at Baker & McKenzie, and the feeling that the individual matters. I have been involved in a variety of projects, and have learned a great deal in a short space of time. The firm has now given me the opportunity to go on a client secondment - this is another example of the way in which the firm looks to maximize their trainees' experience." (Sam Parr, second seat trainee, read Law at Glamorgan University)

Milan, Monterrey, Moscow, Munich, New York, Palo Alto, Paris, Prague, Rio de Janeiro, Riyadh, Rome, St Petersburg, San Diego, San Francisco, Santiago, São Paulo, Singapore, Stockholm, Sydney, Taipei, Tijuana, Tokyo, Toronto, Valencia, Warsaw, Washington DC, Zurich.

BARLOW LYDE & GILBERT

Beaufort House 15 St. Botolph Street London EC3A 7NJ
Tel: (020) 7247 2277 Fax: (020) 7643 8500
Email: grad.recruit@blg.co.uk or cwalsh@blg.co.uk
Website: www.blg.co.uk

Partners	70
Assistant Solicitors	135
Total Trainees	33

Contact
Caroline Walsh
Graduate Recruitment and Development Manager

Method of Application
Firm's application form

Closing date for 2002
31 July 2000

Training

Salary: 1st year(2000)	£21,000
Salary: 2nd year(2000)	£24,000
Holiday entitlement	4 weeks

Post-Qualification

Salary (2000)	£35,000

Overseas Offices
Hong Kong

Firm Profile

Barlow Lyde & Gilbert is a major commercial City practice and is a leader in commercial litigation and insurance and reinsurance law. The Corporate & Finance Division is the fastest growing area of the firm.

Main Areas of Work

Commercial Litigation; Corporate and Commercial; Banking; Tax; Property; Insurance and Reinsurance; Professional Indemnity; Aviation; Shipping; Construction; Environmental; Employment; Information Technology; Personal Injury and Medical Negligence.

Trainee Profile

Barlow Lyde & Gilbert recruit 16 trainees each year and the firm looks for intelligent and motivated graduates with good academic qualifications and with the social skills that will enable them to communicate effectively and get along with their colleagues and clients. Trainees must be able to work independently or in a team and are expected to display common sense and initiative. An appreciation of the client's commercial interests is essential.

Training Environment

Four six-month seats are divided between the litigation, corporate/commercial and property divisions. Every effort is made to accommodate a trainee's preference for a particular type of work and there may be opportunities to spend time in the Hong Kong office or on secondment with clients. A capable trainee will be given responsibility from an early stage in his or her training, subject of course to supervision, and will have to deal regularly with clients. All trainees are expected to undertake and assist in practice development and client care. Social activities play an important role for BLG and successful candidates can look forward to a variety of sporting and social events which ensure that people in different parts of the firm have a chance to meet and stay in contact with each other.

Barlow Lyde & Gilbert

Vacation Placements

There are a series of Open Days held over Easter which will lead to two week Vacation Schemes in the summer. The closing date for applications is 28 February.

Sponsorship & Awards

Financial assistance is available for both the CPE and LPC.

BEACHCROFT WANSBROUGHS

100 Fetter Lane London EC4A 1BN
Tel: (020) 7242 1011 Fax: (020) 7831 6630
Email: efalder@bwlaw.co.uk
Website: www.bwlaw.co.uk

Firm Profile
Beachcroft Wansbroughs is a dynamic and progressive national partnership providing a strong regional office network and offices in the City of London.

Main Areas of Work
Beachcroft Wansbroughs is structured into three market-focused divisions (Insurance, Health and Commercial) and six practice-based departments. These comprise Corporate Services, Commercial Property, Employment, Projects and PFI, Health Litigation and Insurance Litigation. The firm is recognised throughout the UK for its expertise in all aspects of defendant litigation and it is a leading adviser to the insurance and health sectors in this area. The Commercial Division looks after the needs and requirements of industry, financial and public and private sector clients across a wide range of disciplines. As well as being an integral member of European-wide legal networks, Beachcroft Wansbroughs also has a fully-integrated Brussels office which provides advice on competition law and all European issues.

Trainee Profile
The firm is happy to receive applications from graduates in all disciplines. Relevant commercial experience or sector experience is a real advantage. The firm also welcomes applications from mature students and those contemplating a second career.

Training Environment
The training offered provides a thorough grounding in the methodology and practicalities of law as well as in the firm's specialities. Formal in-house training is provided both in the form of the Professional Skills Course and other training events in a variety of areas. This is seen as complementary to the hands-on process of learning on the job. Beachcroft Wansbroughs has made a huge commitment to IT and trainees are trained in and expected to use the technology efficiently as a tool in the everyday practice of law.

Sponsorship & Awards
LPC Funding: Fees paid + £3,000 maintenance - London
£2,500 paid towards fees - Out of London

Partners	126
Assistant Solicitors	300
Total Trainees	64

Contact
Emma Falder
Graduate Recruitment Manager

Method of Application
Application form and CV

Selection Procedure
Assessment Centre & one interview with partners

Closing date for 2002
1 August 2000

Application
Training contracts p.a. 37

Training
Salary: 1st year(2000)
London - £21,000
Out of London - £15,000
Salary: 2nd year(2000)
London - £22,500
Out of London - £17,000
Holiday entitlement 21 days

Post-Qualification
Salary (2000) £30,000
% of trainees offered job on qualification (1999) 71%
% of assistants (as at 1/9/99) who joined as trainees 35%
% of partners (as at 1/9/99) who joined as trainees 45%

Overseas Offices
Brussels

Other Offices
Birmingham, Bristol, Leeds, London, Manchester, Sheffield, Winchester.

BEALE AND COMPANY

Garrick Hse 27-32 King St Covent Garden
London WC2E 8JD
Tel: (020) 7240 3474 Fax: (020) 7240 9111
Email: a.bruce@beale-law.com
Website: www.beale-law.com

Firm Profile

Beale and Company is a commercial practice, located in the heart of Covent Garden. The firm was founded in 1838. It provides a comprehensive range of services to commercial clients and has well developed niches in the following sectors: Construction, Insurance, IT, Company Commercial and International Business. The firm aims to develop and expand further these areas of its practice.

Main Areas of Work

Litigation; Company Commercial; other non-contentious (including Private Client and Property)

Trainee Profile

Trainees should have an excellent academic backgound and be eager to make their mark. Commercial awareness and an interest in Construction or IT will assist.

Training Environment

The firm offers excellent prospects to the right candidate. The training period generally consists of four six-month seats in a partner's room, two in litigation and the remainder in company commercial, private client or property. Each trainee is supervised on a daily basis by the partner for whom the trainee is working and progress is reviewed in regular meetings with another partner. There is a formal induction procedure and in-house lectures and seminars on legal matters relevant to the practice are given. The offices are fully computerised. The firm has a friendly working environment and regular social events.

Benefits

Season ticket loan (after 6 months), private health insurance (after 2 years), discretionary entertainment and social events.

Vacation Placements

N/A

Sponsorship & Awards

N/A

Partners	9
Assistant Solicitors	6
Total Trainees	6

Contact

Mrs Alexandra Bruce
Training Partner

Method of Application

CV with covering letter (typed or hand written) and SAE

Selection Procedure

Two interviews with partners

Closing date for 2002

Submit between 1 August 2000 and 31 October 2000

Application

Training contracts p.a.	3
Applications p.a.	1500
% interviewed p.a.	1.5%
Required degree grade	2:1

Training

Salary: 1st year(2002)
To be determined (not less than £18,500)
Salary: 2nd year(2003)
Discretionary review every six months

Holiday entitlement	23 days
% of trainees with a non-law degree p.a.	60%

Post-Qualification

Salary (2000)	£32,000
% of trainees offered job on qualification (1999)	60%
% of partners (as at 1/9/99) who joined as trainees	89%

Overseas Offices

N/A

BERG & CO

Scottish Mutual House 35 Peter Street
Manchester M2 5BG
Tel: (0161) 833 9211 Fax: (0161) 834 5566
Email: help@berg.co.uk
Website: www.berg.co.uk

Partners	9
Assistant Solicitors	6
Total Trainees	4

Contact
Stephanie Klass
Training Partner

Method of Application
Letter and CV

Selection Procedure
2 interviews with partners and written test

Closing date for 2002
December 2001

Application

Training contracts p.a.	2
Applications p.a.	500+
% interviewed p.a.	3%
Required degree grade	2:1

Training
Salary: 1st year(2000)
Law Society minimum
Holiday entitlement 20 days

Firm Profile
Founded in 1980, Berg & Co is now a well established medium-sized Manchester practice serving the needs of the business community. The firm's clients include international corporations, major public companies, owner-managed businesses and individual entrepreneurs. They are drawn from both the manufacturing and service industries and also from the public sector. In particular, the firm has many clients in technology-related industries and the textile and retailing sectors.

Main Areas of Work
Berg & Co aims to meet the needs of its clients on a wide range of corporate, commercial, litigation, human resources and property law issues. The firm is known for its expertise in the field of matrimonial finance.

Trainee Profile
Candidates need to show intelligence and common sense. Berg & Co welcomes applications from both law and non-law graduates. The firm seeks individuals who can demonstrate initiative, commercial acumen and an ability to work as a team with clients and other fee earners. The firm's aim is to employ trainees whom it can invite to be assistant solicitors and it is able to do so in a large percentage of cases.

Training Environment
Trainee solicitors gain experience by means of seats in commercial litigation; corporate/commercial; employment and commercial property. The firm believes that the longer nature of its seats enables trainees to obtain a thorough grounding in practical legal skills and to make a real contribution to each department's work. Trainees are encouraged to attend in-house training sessions, in addition to the compulsory Law Society professional skills course. Each trainee receives monthly reviews from his/her training partner. The firm is informal with an open-door policy, ensuring that trainees have ready access to partners.

Vacation Placements
Places for 2000: On application

S J BERWIN & CO

222 Grays Inn Road London WC1X 8HB
Tel: +44(0)20 7533 2222 Fax: +44(0)20 7533 2000
Email: info@sjberwin.com

Firm Profile

Since its formation in 1982, S J Berwin & Co has established a strong reputation in corporate finance. It also has a number of niche specialisms in areas such as film finance and private equity. Much work is international and clients range from major multi-national business corporations and financial institutions to high net worth individuals.

Main Areas of Work

Corporate 50%; Commercial Property 20%; Litigation 17%; EU/Competition 10%; Tax 3%.

Trainee Profile

The firm wants ambitious, commercially-minded individuals who seek a high level of involvement from day one. Candidates must be bright and determined to succeed. They should be likely to achieve a 2:1 or first.

Training Environment

Four seats of six months each will be completed, and the seats are set, ideally, to the needs of the trainee. At least one seat will be in corporate finance. The firm has a dedicated training department and weekly training schedules coupled with training designed specifically for trainees allows a good grounding in legal and non-legal skills and knowledge. Language tuition is available to those with a European language.

Benefits

PRP, corporate sports membership, free lunch, health insurance.

Vacation Placements

Places for 2000: 60; Duration: 2 weeks; Remuneration: £200 p.w.; Closing Date: 1 March 2000.

Sponsorship & Awards

CPE and LPC Fees paid and £3,750 maintenance p.a.

Partners	74
Assistant Solicitors	160
Total Trainees	56

Contact
Helen Turnbull

Method of Application
Handwritten letter and CV

Selection Procedure
Interview (early September)

Closing date for 2002
10 August 2000

Application

Training contracts p.a.	35
Applications p.a.	2,000
% interviewed p.a.	10%
Required degree grade	2:1

Training

Salary: 1st year(2000)	£22,000
Salary: 2nd year(2000)	£24,500
Holiday entitlement	41 days over 2 years
% of trainees with a non-law degree p.a.	40
No. of seats available abroad p.a.	2

Post-Qualification

Salary (2000)	£35,000
% of trainees offered job on qualification (1999)	82%
% of assistants (as at 1/9/99) who joined as trainees	25%
% of partners (as at 1/9/99) who joined as trainees	16%

Overseas Offices
Brussels, Frankfurt, Madrid.

BERWIN LEIGHTON

Adelaide House London Bridge London EC4R 9HA
Tel: (020) 7760 1000 Fax: (020) 7760 1111
Email: traineerecruit@berwinleighton.com
Website: www.berwinleighton.com

Firm Profile
Berwin Leighton is a top 20 City firm. Founded in 1970, the firm is a modern growing practice that puts a premium on commercial, as well as technical advice, client relations and quality transactional care. They are entrepreneurial, tenacious and innovative.

Main Areas of Work
The firm is highly regarded for their Corporate, Commercial Property, Finance and Litigation departments.

Trainee Profile
Berwin Leighton is looking for intelligent trainees who are motivated, creative, interested in business and demonstrate strong communication skills.

Training Environment
Training starts with an induction covering all the practical aspects of working in a law firm from billing to client care. Comprehensive technical education programmes have been developed for each department and trainees attend weekly seminars supplemented by trainee lunches and skill sessions. You will undertake a tailor made PSC course which the firm is accredited to run in-house. Trainees spend six months in four seats, and your progress will be reviewed every three months. The firm operates an open door policy and trainees can enjoy early responsibility secure in the knowledge that there is a safety net of supervision.

Benefits
Private health insurance, subsidised gym membership, season ticket loan, life assurance.

Vacation Placements
Places for 2000: Open Days in the Easter Vacation, application by CV and covering letter before 29 February 2000. Attendance at an Open Day could lead to a one week placement in the Summer Vacation.

Sponsorship & Awards
CPE funding: Fees paid + £4,000 maintenance LPC funding: Fees paid + £4,000 maintenance

Partners	69
Assistant Solicitors	131
Total Trainees	38

Contact
Claire Benson
Graduate Recruitment Manger

Method of Application
Firm application form

Selection Procedure
Assessment centre + partner interview

Closing date for 2002
31 July 2000

Application
Training contracts p.a.	20
Applications p.a.	2,000
% interviewed p.a.	5%
Required degree grade	2:1

Training
Salary: 1st year(2000)	£22,000
Salary: 2nd year(2000)	£24,000
Holiday entitlement	22 days
% of trainees with a non-law degree p.a.	40%
No. of seats available abroad p.a.	4

Post-Qualification
Salary (2000)	£34,000
% of trainees offered job on qualification (1999)	100%
% of assistants (as at 1/9/99) who joined as trainees	38%
% of partners (as at 1/9/99) who joined as trainees	22%

Overseas Offices
Brussels

BEVAN ASHFORD

35 Colston Avenue Bristol BS1 4TT
Tel: (0117) 923 0111 Fax: (0117) 929 1865
Email: j.brierley@bevanashford.co.uk
Website: www.bevanashford.co.uk

Firm Profile

Bevan Ashford is one of the largest regional practices in the UK with a network of 7 offices in Bristol, Cardiff, Exeter, London, Plymouth, Taunton and Tiverton. With 69 experienced partners, each of whom is a specialist in their field, and a total staff of over 500, the firm is able to provide clients with an efficient, professional and cost-effective service. Its national reputation means that the firm's client base ranges from multi-national corporations and institutions through to smaller businesses, partnerships and individuals. Its success in attracting and keeping quality clients is achieved by the firm's complete commitment to total client care. By recruiting, training and keeping top quality personnel the firm believes it can continue its culture of client care and offer its clients the individual standards of service they require.

Main Areas of Work

Healthcare 27%; Commercial Property 20%; Commercial Litigation 15%; Company & Commercial 16%; Private Client 17%; Other Work 5%.

Trainee Profile

Bevan Ashford is only as strong as its people. The firm's success is achieved by attracting and keeping enthusiastic, bright people with sound common sense, plenty of energy and the ability to work and communicate well with others plus a sense of humour! Language and IT skills are also desirable.

Training Environment

The core of your training will be practical work experience in conjunction with an extensive education programme consisting of talks, lectures and residential weekend seminars to back-up the practical work. The training is aimed at developing attitudes, skills and legal and commercial knowledge essential for your career success. Your practical work experience will be reviewed on a regular basis by your supervising partner and you will be encouraged to take on as much work, and responsibility, as you wish. The firm is friendly with an open door policy with a wide range of social, sporting and cultural activities plus an active social club.

Vacation Placements

Places for 2000: 75

Sponsorship & Awards

Available for LPC only

Partners	69
Assistant Solicitors	83
Total Trainees	40

Contact

Jean Brierley

Method of Application

Application form and covering letter

Closing date for 2002

31 July 2000

Application

Training contracts p.a.	19
Required degree grade	2:1

Post-Qualification

% of trainees offered job on qualification (1999)	90%

Other Offices

Bristol, Cardiff, Exeter, London, Plymouth, Taunton, Tiverton.

BIDDLE

1 Gresham St London EC2V 7BU
Tel: (020) 7606 9301 Fax: (020) 7606 3305
Email: gradrecruit@Biddle.co.uk
Website: www.Biddle.co.uk

Firm Profile

A progressive, medium-sized business law practice based in the City. Clients range from institutional investors, pension funds and international companies, to newspapers, publishers and new technology buinesses. They are a member of LOGOS, a group of law firms with offices throughout the European Union.

Main Areas of Work

Corporate/Commercial 33%; Litigation 20%; Pensions 14%; Media & IT 14%; Property 8%; Insolvency 4%; Employment 7%.

Trainee Profile

The firm values, above all, first-class intelligence, common-sense, willingness to learn and commercial awareness. They are not looking for specific character traits. Their aim is to build a team of varied yet complementary personalities where, for example, the more bookish are balanced by the charismatic. A second language is an asset but not essential.

Training Environment

On-the-job training is supplemented with in-house seminars and courses. Coaching in IT is also given. Trainees spend three to four six-month placements in varying departments: corporate/commercial, litigation, media and IT, pensions, property, taxation, private client, and employment law. The final seat is likely to be in the area in which you wish to specialise. Trainees sit with partners and progress during each seat is closely monitored by the relevant partner. The company culture is open-door and informal.

Benefits

BUPA, life assurance, season ticket loan.

Sponsorship & Awards

CPE and LPC fees paid and maintenance grant offered.

Additional Information

The firm's website has a special Graduate Section developed by current trainees. Find it at www.Biddle.co.uk.

Partners	32
Assistant Solicitors	33
Total Trainees	11

Contact

Martin Webster

Method of Application

2 page CV and covering letter

Selection Procedure

1 interview

Closing date for 2002

31 August 2000

Application

Training contracts p.a.	6
Applications p.a.	1,500
% interviewed p.a.	2.5%
Required degree grade	2:1

Training

Salary: 1st year (1999)	£22,500
Salary: 2nd year (1999)	£26,000
Holiday entitlement	4 weeks
% of trainees with a non-law degree p.a.	50%

Post-Qualification

Salary (1999)	£33,000
% of trainees offered job on qualification (1999)	80%
% of assistants (as at 1/9/99) who joined as trainees	54%
% of partners (as at 1/9/99) who joined as trainees	36%

BIRCHAM & CO.

1 Dean Farrar St Westminster London SW1H 0DY
Tel: (020) 7222 8044 Fax: (020) 7222 3480
Email: sarahstowell@bircham.co.uk

Firm Profile

Founded in 1834, the firm has particular strengths in private client, charity and property work together with thriving litigation and company commercial practices. It also comprises the leading parliamentary agency Dyson Bell Martin. A member of the Lexwork International group, it has associate offices in twenty European countries.

Main Areas of Work

Private Client/Charities; Parliamentary/Public Affairs; Litigation; Property; Company Commercial.

Trainee Profile

Beyond a high level of academic achievement, successful candidates are commercially aware, down-to earth, mature, adaptable and self-confident. Candidates who have taken a year out for work/life experience are strongly preferred. Languages are useful.

Training Environment

You will spend six months in four of the firm's five main departments: private client/charity, parliamentary/public affairs, property, company commercial and litigation. Bircham & Co is the right size to give you both responsibility and good supervision. The firm has a businesslike, friendly and informal atmosphere. There are regular social events and sporting activities.

Benefits

BUPA, Group Life Assurance

Partners	24
Assistant Solicitors	31
Total Trainees	7

Contact
Sarah Stowell

Method of Application
CV and handwritten letter

Selection Procedure
2 interviews

Closing date for 2002
End February 2000

Application

Training contracts p.a.	4
Required degree grade	2:1

Training

Salary: 1st year(2000)	£19,000
Salary: 2nd year(2000)	£20,000
Holiday entitlement	21 days
% of trainees with a non-law degree p.a.	70%

Post-Qualification

% of trainees offered job on qualification (1999)	66%
% of assistants (as at 1/9/99) who joined as trainees	30%
% of partners (as at 1/9/99) who joined as trainees	45%

BIRD & BIRD

90 Fetter Lane London EC4A 1JP
Tel: (020) 7415 6000 Fax: (020) 7415 6111
Website: www.twobirds.com

Firm Profile

Bird & Bird is an international commercial law firm, with offices in London, Hong Kong, Brussels and Paris. The firm has a growing international client base, regularly acting for leading European and global firms and is particularly specialised in the technology-based industry sectors. Highly regarded for its work in e-commerce, communications, information technology, digital media, sport, intellectual property and pharmaceuticals and biotechnology, the firm also provides advice to clients on corporate and commercial law, employment, banking, litigation and taxation.

Main Areas of Work

Company 46%; Intellectual Property 30%; Property 11%; Litigation 11%; Private Client 2%.

Trainee Profile

The firm looks for high calibre recruits – confident individuals capable of developing expert legal skills and commercial sense.

Training Environment

Following an introduction course, you will undertake four seats of six months, three of which are spent in company, litigation and property. The choice of final seat is yours. You will share an office with a partner or senior assistant who will guide and advise you. You will hone drafting and legal research skills and gain familiarity with legal procedures. The firm encourages you to make an early contribution to case work and to meet clients immediately. Internal seminars and external lectures are arranged to cover the PSC. Trainees are welcome to join the number of sports teams at the firm and to attend various social events and outings.

Benefits

BUPA, season ticket loan, subsidised sports club membership, life cover, PHI.

Vacation Placements

Places for 2000: 12; Duration: 3 weeks; Remuneration: £160 p.w.; Closing Date: March 2000.

Sponsorship & Awards

LPC and CPE fees paid and a yearly maintenance grant of £3,500.

Partners	54
Assistant Solicitors	125
Total Trainees	13

** denotes world-wide figures*

Contact

Lynne Walters

Method of Application

Application form

Selection Procedure

First Interview and Second Interview

Closing date for 2002

July 2000

Application

Training contracts p.a.	12
Applications p.a.	2,500
% interviewed p.a.	10%
Required degree grade	2:1

Training

Salary: 1st year(2000)	£21,000
Salary: 2nd year(2000)	£22,500
Holiday entitlement	20 days
% of trainees with a non-law degree p.a.	varies

Post-Qualification

Salary (2000)	£34,000
% of trainees offered job on qualification (1999)	100%
% of assistants (as at 1/9/99) who joined as trainees	20%
% of partners (as at 1/9/99) who joined as trainees	25%

Overseas Offices

Brussels, Hong Kong, Paris.

BLAKE LAPTHORN

Harbour Court Compass Road North Harbour
Portsmouth PO6 4ST
Tel: (01705) 221122 Fax: (01705) 221123
Website: www.blakelapthorn.co.uk

Partners	47
Assistant Solicitors	70
Total Trainees	22

Firm Profile
Founded in 1869 and one of the largest and most progressive regional law firms in the south of England, the firm's main activities are centred in two large purpose built out of town offices on the M27 – one providing commercial and litigation services and the other private client services. In addition there are offices in Southampton and London and all the offices are equipped with state of the art information technology. The size of the firm means that it is able to offer clients the same range and level of service expected from the best London firms. There are 47 partners, many of whom were trainees with the firm and a total staff of over 400.

Main Areas of Work
Company/Commercial 24%; Commercial Property 17%; Litigation 26%; Private Client (PI, Property, Family, Crime, Probate, Finance) 33%.

Trainee Profile
In addition to excellent academic achievements, the firm values previous experience, which has developed maturity and a wider perspective. Commercial awareness, teamworking and well-developed communication skills are also an advantage as well as familiarity with the use of IT.

Training Environment
Five trainees are recruited each year and have a minimum of four placements lasting three or six months. Trainees' preferences are taken into account as far as possible, but the firm believes in providing well-rounded training supplemented with in-house education and regular appraisals and reviews with the Training Principal.

Benefits
Trainee accommodation (first year).

Sponsorship & Awards
LPC: loan of £4,000 repayable from salary.

Contact
Ruth Kalinowicz
Director of Personnel & Training

Method of Application
Firm's Application form
(on website) plus c.v.

Selection Procedure
Interview with Partners, including giving a presentation plus group exercise.

Closing date for 2002
31 July 2000

Application

Training contracts p.a.	5
Applications p.a.	750
% interviewed p.a.	8/10%
Required degree grade	2.1

Training

Salary: 1st year(1999)	£13,000
Salary: 2nd year(1999)	£14,500
Holiday entitlement	22 days

Post-Qualification

Salary (1999)	£22,000
% of trainees offered job on qualification (1999)	80%

BOND PEARCE

Ballard House West Hoe Road Plymouth PL1 3AE
Tel: (01752) 266 633 Fax: (01752) 225 350
Email: tlh@bondpearce.com
Website: www.bondpearce.com

Firm Profile

Major commercial law firm. With offices in Bristol, Exeter, Plymouth and Southampton they are one of the largest commercial legal practices in southern England.

Main Areas of Work

The size of Bond Pearce and the full range of legal services provided ensures trainee solicitors gain unrivalled experience with training in four separate specialist seats. Specialist groups within Bond Pearce, backed up by effective support services, provide the highest quality of services to a broad range of clients: Commercial Group; (Corporate, Banking & Insolvency, Commercial Litigation); Insurance Group; Property Group (Commercial Property, Planning & Environment, Private Client); Personal Injury and Family Group.

Trainee Profile

Experience has shown that successful candidates have a 2:1 in their chosen subject, not necessarily law, together with a wide range of interests and an enthusiastic and energetic approach to work. Personal qualities are paramount – they look for individuals who can demonstrate initiative, commercial acumen, enthusiasm, team working skills and a sense of humour.

Training Environment

Trainee solicitors have their own desks in the same office as the partner, associate or senior solicitor with whom they are working. They become an integral part of each team, closely involved in the diversity of their work and whilst fully supervised, trainees are encouraged to take on as much responsibility as possible. Training enhances existing legal skills and teaches trainees to apply those skills in a practical and effective manner. Technology plays a vital role in Bond Pearce. Their offices are linked by a networked computer system, the accounts and time recording systems are fully computerised and all staff, including trainee solicitors, are equipped with a fully networked PC on their desks. There are close links between the firm's offices and trainee solicitors join together in all training and many social activities. Bond Pearce has a thriving sports and social club.

Sponsorship & Awards

LPC financial assistance.

Partners	56
Assistant Solicitors	99
Total Trainees	38

Contact

Tina Hosken

Method of Application

Application form, handwritten letter, CV and photograph

Selection Procedure

Interviews and selection day

Closing date for 2002

31 March 2000

Application

Training contracts p.a.	15-20
Applications p.a.	750
% interviewed p.a.	10%
Required degree grade	2:1

Training

Salary: 1st year(2000)	£14,250
Holiday entitlement	20 days
% of trainees with a non-law degree p.a.	25%

Post-Qualification

Salary (2000)	£21,000
% of trainees offered job on qualification (1999)	75%
% of assistants (as at 1/9/99) who joined as trainees	40%
% of partners (as at 1/9/99) who joined as trainees	38%

BOODLE HATFIELD

61 Brook Street London W1Y 2BL
Tel: (020) 7629 7411 Fax: (020) 7629 2621
Email: law@boodlehatfield.co.uk

Firm Profile

Founded over 275 years ago, Boodle Hatfield is a medium-sized firm based in the heart of Mayfair, with a second, fast-growing office in Oxford. Known originally for representing wealthy individuals and landed estates, and still outstanding in those fields, the firm now acts for a wide range of international corporate, commercial and private clients. In addition to the four main departments (Property, Tax & Financial Planning, Corporate and Litigation) the firm has created cross-departmental groups specialising in areas such as employment law, family law, private capital, construction, IT, agrochemicals, Anglo-German cross border transactions and inward investment.

Main Areas of Work

Property 45%; Tax & Financial Planning 20%; Corporate 20%; Litigation 15%

Trainee Profile

The firm looks for academic excellence, leadership qualities and good communications skills. Relevant work experience is also viewed favourably. Applicants should have a thorough knowledge of current affairs. Languages and IT skills are desirable but not essential.

Training Environment

Trainees spend 6 months in each of the firm's main departments. As an alternative to one of these seats, there are opportunities to spend 6 months on secondment to the legal departments of ICI and Shell International. There is a regular internal programme of seminars on a wide range of legal subjects.

Benefits

Season ticket loan, discretionary Christmas bonus.

Vacation Placements

Places for 2000: 10; Duration: 2 wks; Remuneration: £90 pw; Closing Date: 1 June 2000.

Sponsorship & Awards

CPE Funding: Fees paid + discretionary maintenance.
LPC Funding: Fees paid + discretionary maintenance.

Partners	35
Assistant Solicitors	24
Total Trainees	8

Contact

Christine Jones Personnel Administrator

Method of Application

Application form with photo

Selection Procedure

1 interview with 2 partners

Closing date for 2002

31 July 2000

Application

Training contracts p.a.	4 or 5
Applications p.a.	450
% interviewed p.a.	5%
Required degree grade	1st or 2.1

Training

Salary: 1st year(1999)	£21,000
Salary: 2nd year(1999)	£23,000
Holiday entitlement	20 days
% of trainees with a non-law degree p.a.	30%

Post-Qualification

Salary (1999)	£33,000
% of trainees offered job on qualification	varies (100% in 1999)
% of assistants (as at 1/9/99) who joined as trainees	50%
% of partners (as at 1/9/99) who joined as trainees	35%

BOYES TURNER & BURROWS

10 Duke St Reading RG1 4RX
Tel: (0118) 959 7711 Fax: (0118) 957 3257
Email: hbarnett@b-t-b.co.uk
Website: www.btb-solicitors.co.uk

Firm Profile

Boyes Turner & Burrows is a leading Thames Valley practice, renowned for its Insolvency and Medical Negligence work and well respected for Corporate and Commercial, Commercial Property, Intellectual Property, Employment, Personal Injury, Family Law and Private Client. While the focus for growth has been commercial work, the firm retains a commitment to acting for individuals and also to civil legal aid.

Main Areas of Work

Company / Commercial (including Employment) 20%; Commercial Property 20%; Medical Negligence / Personal Injury 20%; Litigation 15%; Insolvency 10%; Family 5%; Private Client 10%.

Trainee Profile

BTB regards its trainees of today as its assistant solicitors and beyond of tomorrow and expects a high level of commitment, hard work and resourcefulness. Trainees must be responsive to the firm's mission to provide an excellent quality of service to both commercial and individual clients and also contribute to the team-working philosophy.

Training Environment

The programme is structured so that trainees spend six months in each of four areas: property, litigation, private client and commercial. Work covers both individual and commercial clients, with as much client contact as possible, supervised by a partner or a senior solicitor. A training partner oversees all aspects of the programme, while each trainee is assigned a director (one of the partners) who reviews their progress monthly. This is on two levels – first in assessing how the trainee is developing as a lawyer and secondly how the trainee is developing as an individual, including communication and negotiating skills.

Benefits

Free medical insurance.

Sponsorship & Awards

CPE and LPC loan of £3,000 and only one loan per applicant. Interest free and re-paid over training contract.

Partners	14
Assistant Solicitors	15
Total Trainees	6

Contact
Helen Barnett

Method of Application
Letter and CV

Selection Procedure
2 interviews

Closing date for 2002
31 August 2000

Application

Training contracts p.a.	2/3
Applications p.a.	750
% interviewed p.a.	1%+
Required degree grade	2:2

Training

Salary: 1st year(2000)	£16,000
Salary: 2nd year(2000)	£17,000
Holiday entitlement	4 weeks
% of trainees with a non-law degree p.a.	Varies

Post-Qualification

Salary (2000)	£23,500
% of trainees offered job on qualification (1999)	100%
% of assistants (as at 1/9/99) who joined as trainees	33%
% of partners (as at 1/9/99) who joined as trainees	20%

BRISTOWS

3 Lincoln's Inn Fields London WC2A 3AA
Tel: (020) 7400 8000 Fax: (020) 7400 8050
Email: info@bristows.co.uk
Website: www.bristows.com

Firm Profile

Bristows is a leading commercial practice in Central London, pre-eminent in intellectual property law including IT, multimedia, brands and biotechnology. It has a substantial practice in company and commercial law with strong complementary practices in competition, environmental and property law.

Main Areas of Work

Intellectual Property 50%; Company/Corporate Finance/Commercial 15%; Computer and IT 10%; Commercial Litigation 10%; Commercial Property 10%; Charities/Professional Institutions/Partnership/Environmental 5%.

Trainee Profile

They recruit graduates of all disciplines. As well as academic ability, they look for practical intelligence, the capacity to communicate well and the ability to assimilate complex materials while still seeing the wood for the trees.

Training Environment

Trainees receive a high level of individual attention, spending each of their four seats with either a partner or senior fee-earner. This, plus the opportunity of secondments to leading clients, gives trainees closer involvement in cases and greater contact with partners and clients alike. Continuous and formal assessment by seat holders, regular counselling sessions with the training partner and a comprehensive in-house training programme all provide additional support for trainees to develop the skills gained from this excellent hands on experience. Working in small teams, with each team headed by a partner, trainees play an active role from very early on in their training, seeing assignments through from start to finish.

Benefits

Excellent career prospects, a competitive City package, firm pension scheme, life assurance and health insurance.

Vacation Placements

Places for 2000: 36; Duration: Summer – 2 weeks, Christmas/Easter – 1 week; Remuneration: £200 p.w.; Closing Date: Christmas – 15/11; Easter/Summer – 29/2.

Sponsorship & Awards

CPE/LPC fees plus £4,000 maintenance grant for each.

Partners	20
Assistant Solicitors	45
Total Trainees	12

Contact

Graduate Recruitment Officer

Method of Application

Application form

Selection Procedure

2 individual interviews

Closing date for 2002

31 January 2000 for February interviews, 31 August for September interviews

Application

Training contracts p.a.	8
Applications p.a.	1,000
% interviewed p.a.	6%
Required degree grade	2.1 (Preferred)

Training

Salary: 1st year(1999)	£21,000
Salary: 2nd year(1999)	£23,000
Holiday entitlement	4 weeks
% of trainees with a non-law degree p.a.	75%

Post-Qualification

Salary (1999)	£32,500
% of trainees offered job on qualification (1999)	72%
% of assistants (as at 1/9/99) who joined as trainees	50%
% of partners (as at 1/9/99) who joined as trainees	47%

BURGES SALMON

Narrow Quay House Narrow Quay Bristol BS1 4AH
Tel: (0117) 939 2000 Fax: (0117) 902 4400
Email: lisa.head@burges-salmon.com
Website: www.burges-salmon.co.uk

Firm Profile
Burges Salmon is one of the country's leading firms of solicitors. All staff are located in modern waterfront offices situated in the heart of Bristol's thriving commercial centre. Burges Salmon is a name recognised and respected internationally and the firm is enjoying sustained organic growth, with over 50% of its clients being located outside the South West. In addition, a facility has recently been established to service the firm's national clients.

Main Areas of Work
Working for both commercial and private clients, Burges Salmon provides specialist advice across a broad range of areas including company, commercial & corporate finance, property, commercial litigation and tax and trusts.

Trainee Profile
To be successful, candidates will have to demonstrate high levels of analytical ability, communication skills, resilience and a clear understanding of client service.

Training Environment
Training at Burges Salmon is a partnership between the individual and the firm. Trainees provide talent and commitment whilst the firm provides all necessary resources and support for the individual's success. The firm's record for retaining trainees is excellent and this success is, in part, due to an unusual trainee seat system consisting of four periods of four months in the main practice areas, allowing for an option seat and qualification seat. Trainees are not kept in the background on mundane tasks and are actively involved in setting the tempo and direction of their training contract, taking on responsibility and gaining expertise at a pace appropriate for them.

Benefits
Rates of pay are substantially in excess of the Law Society recommendations and reviewed on 1 November each year.

Vacation Placements
Places for 2000: 30; Duration: 2 weeks; Remuneration: £125 p.w.; Closing Date: 25 February 2000.

Sponsorship & Awards
In addition to CPE and LPC tuition fees, maintenance grants of £3,500 to LPC students and £4,000 to students studying for both CPE and LPC (£2,000 p.a.) are paid.

Partners	41
Assistant Solicitors	120
Total Trainees	28

Contact
Lisa Head
Graduate Recruitment & Development Manager

Method of Application
Employer's Application Form & covering letter

Selection Procedure
Penultimate year of law degree or final year of non-law degree, apply for open days and vacation placements.

Closing date for 2002
11 August 2000

Application

Training contracts p.a.	18
Applications p.a.	1,000
% interviewed p.a.	10.5%
Required degree grade	2:1

Training

Salary: 1st year(2000)	£16,000
Salary: 2nd year(2000)	£17,000
Holiday entitlement	24 days
% of trainees with a non-law degree p.a.	40%

Post-Qualification

Salary (2000)	£27,000
% of trainees offered job on qualification (1999)	100%
% of assistants (as at 1/9/99) who joined as trainees	35%
% of partners (as at 1/9/99) who joined as trainees	20%

CADWALADER, WICKERSHAM & TAFT

55 Gracechurch Street London EC3V 0EE
Tel: (020) 7456 8500 Fax: (020) 7456 8600
Website: www.cadwalader.com

Partners	7
Assistant Solicitors	18
Total Trainees	2

Firm Profile

Cadwalader, Wickersham & Taft was founded in New York in 1792. In 1997 the firm opened in London with the goal of building on the firm's pre-eminent US financial services practice and expanding the service to UK, European and Asian clients. Cadwalader specialises in servicing financial services clients with highly respected practices in capital markets, securities, finance, corporate, financial restructuring, real estate finance, project finance, litigation, tax and private client.

Main Areas of Work

Capital markets, Financial restructuring, Corporate finance, M&A, Project finance, Tax and private client, Real estate

Trainee Profile

Candidates need to demonstrate that they are intellectually bright and ambitious, good communications skills and a commitment to the law. The firm looks for well-rounded individuals with a desire to succeed and a robust and resilient personality.

Training Environment

Training consists of four six-month seats taking into account trainees' preferences. Responsibility and exposure to client meetings will take place at an early stage. Trainees share an office with a partner or associate, who supervise, review performance and provide feedback on a regular basis. Formal reviews will be carried out every six months. Elements of the PSC will occur at the start of the training contract; the remainder will take place over the following two years. The firm is friendly and supportive with an open door policy, operating a strict "dress down code" during the summer months and each Friday at other times. There is also a comprehensive sporting and social calendar.

Benefits

Permanent health insurance, season ticket loan and BUPA.

Vacation Placements

Places for 2000: 6; Duration: 4 wks (3 in London and 1 in New York); Remuneration: £225 p.w.; Closing Date: 18 Feb 2000.

Sponsorship & Awards

CPE Funding: Fees paid + £4000 maintenance LPC Funding: Fees paid + £4000 maintenance

Contact

Julie Bounden HR Manager

Method of Application

Hand-written letter and CV

Selection Procedure

2 interviews

Closing date for 2002

31 August 2000

Application

Training contracts p.a.	6
Applications p.a.	600
% interviewed p.a.	1-2%
Required degree grade	2:1

Training

Salary: 1st year(2000) (under review)	£21,000
Salary: 2nd year(2000) (under review)	£23,000
Holiday entitlement	20 days

Post-Qualification

Salary (2000)	£40,000
% of trainees offered job on qualification (1999)	100%

Overseas Offices

New York, Washington and Charlotte

CAPSTICKS

77-83 Upper Richmond Road London SW15 2TT
Tel: (020) 8780 2211 Fax: (020) 8780 4811
Email: career@capsticks.co.uk
Website: www.capsticks.com

Firm Profile
One of the leading legal advisers to the National Health Service, the firm handles litigation, administrative law, commercial and property work for NHS Trusts and health authorities, as well as other public sector bodies and their insurers.

Main Areas of Work
Clinical Negligence/Personal Injury 40%; Commercial and Property Transactions 25%; Commercial and Property Litigation 15%; Employment Law 10% Administrative Law 10%.

Trainee Profile
Successful candidates possess intellectual agility, good interpersonal skills and are capable of taking initiative.

Training Environment
Four six-month seats, which may include clinical negligence/personal injury; commercial property; contract and commercial; employment law and commercial/property litigation. Trainees take responsibility for their own caseload and are involved in client meetings from an early stage. There are also opportunities to contribute to the firm's marketing and management processes. There are numerous in-house lectures for all fee earners. There is an open door policy, and trainees receive informal feedback and supervision as well as regular appraisals. Despite the firm's rapid expansion, it has retained a friendly atmosphere and a relaxed working environment. There are numerous informal social and sporting activities.

Benefits
Bonus scheme, PHI, death in service cover.

Vacation Placements
Places for 2000: yes; Duration: 2 weeks; Closing Date: 31 March 2000.

Sponsorship & Awards
Scholarship contributions to CPE and LPC courses.

Partners	25
Assistant Solicitors	34
Total Trainees	12

Contact
Sue Laundy

Method of Application
Application form and CV

Selection Procedure
Candidates are encouraged to participate in the firm's summer placement scheme. Final selection is by interview with the Training Principal and other partners

Closing date for 2002
31 July 2000

Application
Training contracts p.a.	6–8
Applications p.a.	1000+
% interviewed p.a.	4%
Required degree grade	2:1 or above

Training
Salary: 1st year(2000) c. £21,000
Salary: 2nd year(2000) c. £23,000
Holiday entitlement 22 days p.a. (increased by 1 day p.a. to max 25 days)
% of trainees with a non-law degree p.a. 23%

Post-Qualification
Salary (1999) £28,000 + bonus scheme
% of trainees offered job on qualification (1999) 100%
% of assistants (as at 1/9/99) who joined as trainees 20%
% of partners (as at 1/9/99) who joined as trainees 6%

CARTWRIGHTS

Marsh House 11 Marsh Street Bristol BS99 7BB
Tel: (0117) 929 3601 Fax: (0117) 926 2403
Email: recruitment@cartwrights.com
Website: www.cartwrights.com

Firm Profile

This leading Bristol firm has a national reputation for leisure and licensing, insurance litigation, employment and transport law. Its clients range from major PLCs (including more than 20 of the FTSE 100) to sole traders and private individuals. Cartwrights offers a broad training with a quality of work normally associated with the City. The firm's hallmark is its detailed understanding of its clients' market sectors and their business needs. Further information is available from the firm's website.

Main Areas of Work

Commercial (including corporate, litigation, property, employment and transport) 38%; Insurance Litigation 30%; Licensing and Leisure 24%; Private Client 8%.

Trainee Profile

Good academic performance (2:1 degree, law or non-law), enthusiasm, motivation, commercial understanding, IT and teamworking skills. Relevant work experience and language skills an advantage. Non-academic achievement is also valued.

Training Environment

On arrival, trainees take part in a comprehensive induction programme and are then assigned to a six-month seat in company commercial, commercial litigation, commercial property or insurance. Thereafter, trainees are consulted on the allocation of their remaining three seats. You will share an office with other trainees, working under the supervision of a partner or senior fee-earner whom you will actively assist. In some departments you will conduct your own files, in others you will work as part of a team. Initiative and responsibility are encouraged. Progress is reviewed regularly. Social and sporting life is varied and trainees are active members of the Bristol Trainee solicitors group.

Vacation Placements

Places for 2000: 18; Duration: 1 week; Closing Date: 28 February 2000.

Sponsorship & Awards

Up to £5,000 paid towards LPC fees and £2,400 interest free loan.

Partners	15
Associates	4
Assistant Solicitors	22
Total Trainees	10

Contact

Christopher Eskell

Method of Application

Application form

Selection Procedure

Interviews and aptitude tests

Closing date for 2002

1 August 2000

Application

Training contracts p.a.	5
Applications p.a.	750
% interviewed p.a.	5%
Required degree grade	2:1

Training

Salary: 1st year(2000)	£14,750–£15,350
Salary: 2nd year(2000)	£15,950–£16,550
Holiday entitlement	20 days

Post-Qualification

Salary (1999)	£23,500
% of trainees offered job on qualification (average)	50%
% of assistants (as at 1/9/99) who joined as trainees	39%
% of partners (as at 1/9/99) who joined as trainees	29%

CHARLES RUSSELL

8–10 New Fetter Lane London EC4A 1RS
Tel: (020) 7203 5000 Fax: (020) 7203 0200
Graduate Recruitment Line: (020) 7203 5353
Website: www.cr-law.com

Firm Profile

Charles Russell is a progressive City law firm with regional offices in Cheltenham and Guildford and a network of close professional contacts throughout the world. One of the fastest growing law firms in the UK, it offers a wide range of legal services for both corporate and private clients. The firm recruits a small number of trainees for a firm of its size as it believes it enables them to provide the best possible training. The firm is committed to its clients and their demands. It also respects the fact that its staff need to have a life of their own.

Main Areas of Work

Whilst the commercial division offers the opportunity for involvement in major corporate transactions, the firm's commitment to private clients and charities remains unshaken. Charles Russell is particularly well known for media and communications, commercial property, company/commercial, charities, insurance and reinsurance and offers clients specialist expertise in employment and pensions, corporate finance, tax, intellectual property, family, computer law, sports regulation, planning and environmental law.

Trainee Profile

Trainees should be balanced, rounded achievers with a solid academic background. Outside interests are fundamental.

Training Environment

Trainees spend six months in four of the following training seats – litigation, company/commercial, property, private client, family, employment and intellectual property. Wherever possible the firm will accommodate an individual preference. You will be seated with a partner/senior solicitor. Regular appraisals are held to discuss progress and direction. Trainees are encouraged to attend the extensive in-house training courses. The PSC is taught both internally and externally. All trainees are expected to take on as much responsibility as possible. A social committee organises a range of activities from quiz nights through to sporting events.

Benefits

BUPA immediately, PHI and Life Assurance after 1 year's service, 23 days holiday (under review).

Sponsorship & Awards

CPE and LPC fees paid and annual maintenance (currently under review but no less than £3,500).

Partners	76
Assistant Solicitors	130
Total Trainees	22

Contact

Elaine Emmington
Graduate Recruitment Line:
020 7203 5353

Method of Application

Hand written letter and application form

Selection Procedure

Assessment days to include an interview and other exercises, designed to assess identified performance criteria

Closing date for 2002

31 July 2000

Application

Training contracts p.a.	10–12
Applications p.a.	1,500
% interviewed p.a.	3%
Required degree grade	2:1

Training

Salary: 1st year(1999)	£21,500
Salary: 2nd year(1999)	£23,500
Holiday entitlement	23 days

Post-Qualification

Salary (1999)	£34,000

Regional Offices

Also offer training contracts in its Cheltenham and Guildford offices. For further details, please telephone the graduate recruitment line.

CLEARY, GOTTLIEB, STEEN & HAMILTON

City Place House 55 Basinghall Street London EC2V 5EH
Tel: (020) 7614 2200 Fax: (020) 7600 1698
Website: www.cleary.com

Firm Profile

Founded in the United States in 1946, from its inception the firm has maintained a strong international presence. It now has over 550 lawyers in 10 offices worldwide with more than 150 lawyers in Europe with offices in Paris (opened 1949), Brussels (1961),Frankfurt (1991) and Rome (1998) in addition to London (1971). It is common for lawyers to spend time in offices other than their home office.

Main Areas of Work

Mergers and aquisitions (takeovers, cross-border mergers, joint-ventures), securities (equity offerings, debt offerings, bond issues, privatisations, global offerings, private placements), banking and finance, tax, EU and competition law.

Trainee Profile

Candidates must have an excellent academic background including at least a 2.1 law degree from a top U.K. university and have an open and outgoing personality. They must have a flexible approach to work, I.T. and language skills are an advantage.

Training Environment

There are no departments. Trainees sit with partners and senior solicitors and will do a mix of M&A, capital markets, tax and regulatory work. Seats change every six months. One seat will be in Brussels and there will be opportunities to travel and work in other offices. Ongoing legal training is provided by regular training talks covering all areas of law practised at the firm. I.T. training is also provided. Trainees will be required to take the New York bar exam. Assistance will be given with this. Trainees will work on a wide range of matters many governed by Laws other than English Law. Trainees will in most respects be fulfilling the same roles as first year lawyers do in our other offices.

Benefits

Pension, health insurance, long-term disability insurance, health club, employee assistance programme.

Sponsorship & Awards

LPC funding; Fees paid plus £4,500 maintenance award.

Partners	9
Assistants	32
Total Trainees	4

Contact
Andrew Curran

Method of Application
Letter and C.V.

Selection Procedure
2 interviews

Closing date for 2002
30 July 2000

Application

Training contracts p.a.	3
Required degree grade	2.1

Training

Salary: 1st year(2000)	£33,000
Salary: 2nd year(2000)	£39,000
Holiday entitlement	20 days

Post-Qualification
Salary varies from office to office

Overseas Offices
Brussels, Frankfurt, Hong Kong, Moscow, New York, Paris, Rome, Tokyo, Washington DC.

CLIFFORD CHANCE

200 Aldersgate Street London EC1A 4JJ
Tel: (020) 7600 1000 Fax: (020) 7600 5555
Email: graduaterecruitment.uk@cliffordchance.com
Website: www.cliffordchance.com

Firm Profile

Clifford Chance is a leading global law firm offering a full range of services to businesses, financiers and governments from 30 offices worldwide. The firm maintains a friendly working atmosphere. The firm's working style is characterised by a real sense of energy, enthusiasm and determination to provide the best possible service to their clients.

Main Areas of Work

Banking & Finance; Capital Markets; Corporate; Litigation & Dispute Resolution; Real Estate; Tax, Pensions & Employment.

Trainee Profile

Consistent strong academic profile, a broad range of interpersonal skills and extra-curricular activities and interests.

Training Environment

Four six month periods or "seats". Training seats are available in all areas of the firm's practice and about 75% of trainees will spend a seat on secondment in an international office or with a client. Practical experience is supplemented by formal training and courses to develop personal and business skills. Trainees are encouraged to use initiative to make the most of the expertise and resources available in the firm. Three monthly appraisals and monitoring in each seat ensure trainees gain a range of work and experience.

Benefits

Prize for first class degrees and distinction in LPC, interest free loan, private health insurance, subsidised restaurant, fitness centre, life assurance, occupational health service, and permanent health assurance.

Vacation Placements

Places for 2000: 80 placements - Easter and summer vacations. The scheme's aim is to give a broad understanding of how an integrated global law firm operates. The firm also organises seminars, case studies, visits to city institutions and a number of social and sporting events with trainee solicitors.;
Remuneration: £200 pw; Closing Date: 11 February 2000.

Sponsorship & Awards

CPE and LPC fees paid and £4,500 maintenance p.a. (£4,100 outside London and Guilford).

Partners	365
Assistant Solicitors	1285
Total Trainees	254

Contact

Katrina Thomas
Graduate Recruitment

Method of Application

Application form

Selection Procedure

First interview with partner and senior assistant, followed by assessment day and interview

Closing date for 2002

N/A

Application

Training contracts p.a.	130
Applications p.a.	2,000
% interviewed p.a.	30%
Required degree grade	2:1

Training

Salary: 1st year(2000)	£21,000
Salary: 2nd year(2000)	£24,000
Holiday entitlement	25 days
% of trainees with a non-law degree p.a.	40%
No. of seats available abroad p.a.	98

Post-Qualification

Salary (2000)	£33,500
% of trainees offered job on qualification (1999)	95%

Overseas Offices

Amsterdam, Bangkok, Barcelona, Beijing, Berlin, Brussels, Budapest, Dubai, Düsseldorf, Frankfurt, Hanoi, Ho Chi Minh City, Hong Kong, Leipzig, Madrid, Milan, Moscow, Munich, New York, Padua, Paris, Prague, Rome, São Paulo, Shanghai, Singapore, Tokyo, Warsaw, Washington DC.

CLYDE & CO

51 Eastcheap London EC3M 1JP
Tel: (020) 7648 1580 Fax: (020) 7623 5427
Email: careers@clyde.co.uk
Website: www.clydeco.com

Firm Profile
A major international firm with over 650 staff world-wide and a client base spanning more than 100 countries. It has particular strengths in international trade, insurance, reinsurance, shipping, energy, corporate and finance matters. It has UK offices in London, Guildford and Cardiff, with trainee solicitors recruited for London and Guildford.

Main Areas of Work
Marine 30%; Insurance/Reinsurance 30%; Company, Commercial, Banking, Property 20%; International Trade 10%; Other Commercial Litigation 10%.

Trainee Profile
The firm has no stereotypical trainee. Non-law graduates are welcome, especially those with modern languages or science degrees. The firm places as much importance on finding candidates with an outgoing, interesting personality as it does on academic credentials.

Training Environment
Trainees become immediate 'casehandlers' and usually have their own office. They are encouraged to take on as much responsibility and client contact as possible, and are involved in developing business relationships. The PSC is run in-house and there is a full programme of lectures, seminars, courses, workshops and educational visits.

Benefits
Subsidised sports club, interest free ticket loan, staff restaurant and weekly free bar (London); monthly staff lunch and monthly free bar (Guildford).

Legal Training Days
Legal training days: 64; Duration: 1 day; Remuneration: travel expenses; Closing Date: 28 February 2000.
Please telephone for further details.

Sponsorship & Awards
CPE and LPC Fees paid and maintenance grant. Sponsorship provided where no LEA funding available.

Partners	100
Assistant Solicitors	104
Total Trainees	36

Contact
Sharon Lithgow
Recruitment Officer

Method of Application
Application form and covering letter

Selection Procedure
Individual interview with recruitment officer, followed by interview with two partners

Closing date for 2002
31 August 2000

Application

Training contracts p.a.	16
Applications p.a.	2,000
% interviewed p.a.	varies
Required degree grade	2:1

Training

Salary: 1st year (1999)	£21,500
Salary: 2nd year(1999)	£23,000
Holiday entitlement	22 days
% of trainees with a non-law degree p.a.	varies
No. of seats available abroad p.a.	varies

Post-Qualification

Salary (1999)	£33,000
% of trainees offered job on qualification (1999)	100%

Overseas Offices
Caracas, Dubai, Hong Kong, Paris, Piraeus Singapore, Associate office – St Petersburg.

CMS CAMERON McKENNA

Mitre House 160 Aldersgate Street London EC1A 4DD
Tel: (0845) 3000 491 Fax: (01753) 608 005
Email: cameronmckenna@bnbi.com
Website: www.cmck.com

Firm Profile

Winner of 'The Law Firm of the Year' (Legal Business Awards, 1998), CMS Cameron McKenna is a major full service UK and international commercial firm advising businesses and governments on transactions and projects particularly in the UK, continental Europe, the Asia Pacific region, North America and Southern Africa. They have particular strengths in a number of industry sectors such as banking and finance, corporate, construction, projects, energy, healthcare, bioscience, insurance and property. The firm is modern, entrepreneurial and innovative and is strong on achievement. (They believe the key to success is clear communication and entrepreneurial flair.)

Main Areas of Work

Banking and International Finance; Commercial; Commercial Litigation/Dispute Resolution; Corporate; Energy, Projects & Construction; Property; Taxation & Employee Benefits; Insurance/Reinsurance.

Trainee Profile

The firm looks for high-achieving team players with good communication, analytical and organisational skills. You will need to show initiative and be able to accept personal responsibility, not only for your own work, but also for your career development. You will need to be resilient and focused on achieving results.

Training Environment

The firm is friendly and supportive and puts no limits on a trainee's progress. It offers four six month seats, three of which will be in the firm's main area of practice. In addition you may gain experience of a specialist area or opt for a secondment to national or international clients. In each seat you will be allocated high quality work on substantial transactions for a range of government and blue-chip clients. Regular appraisals will be held with your seat supervisor to assess your progress, skills and development needs. The three compulsory modules of the PSC will be completed before joining, allowing trainees to become effective and participate on a practical level as soon as possible. The Professional Skills Course is complemented by a comprehensive in-house training programme that continues up to qualification and beyond.

Partners	165
Assistant Solicitors	375
Total Trainees	104

Contact
Graduate Recruitment Team
0845 3000 491

Method of Application
Employer's application form

Selection Procedure
Two-stage selection procedure. Initial interview followed by assessment centre

Closing date for 2002
By September 2000

Application

Training contracts p.a.	80
Applications p.a.	1,500
% interviewed p.a.	27%
Required degree grade	2:1

Training

Salary: 1st year(2000)	£21,500
Salary: 2nd year(2000)	£24,000
Holiday entitlement	22 days

increasing to 24 days in second year

% of trainees with a non-law degree p.a.	40%
No. of seats available abroad p.a.	(currently) 12

Post-Qualification

Salary (2000)	£34,500
% of trainees offered job on qualification (1999)	87%

▶

CMS CAMERON McKENNA *continued*

Benefits
Private medical insurance, Corporate gym membership, Season ticket loan, Personal Health Insurance, Life assurance, 22 days holiday, Travel bursaries for future trainees.

Vacation Placements
Places for 2000: 55; Duration: 2 weeks; Remuneration: £200 p.w.; Closing Date: 11 February 2000.

Sponsorship & Awards
CPE and LPC Funding: Fees paid and a maintenance grant of £4,250 (London and Guildford), £4,000 (elsewhere).

Additional Information
Every trainee has a PC on their desk with email connection and access to legal and business databases. The firm financially supports trainees who wish to learn or improve a foreign language. There will be the opportunity to become involved in a number of sporting and social events.

Trainee Comments
"It's important to get to know your client's business. I've recently been involved at the fundraising stage of a new drug delivery system being developed in the pharmaceutical field. There's a lot of technical information to absorb but it's fascinating to be involved in cutting-edge developments and to work with businesses that are shaping the future." (Stuart Curbishley, ex-trainee, now lawyer, Corporate)

"I spent half of my second seat in Almaty, the capital of Kazakhstan, working with 30 others to establish companies to develop the country's oil, gas and gold reserves. In a previous seat, I had to complete and hand over title on a £10 million deal myself. It was an incredible amount of responsibility and a valuable experience." (Simon Mead, trainee solicitor)

"Compared to other firms where I have friends it's very friendly and unstuffy here. It has retained the smaller firm environment even though we're now a top ten firm. Some firms pay lip service to the 'open door' idea but it really happens here. My best moment so far was helping the team who pitched against four of the top ten City firms for one of two places to do work for the Post Office – and we were appointed." (Jamie Butler, trainee solicitor)

Branch Offices
Aberdeen, Almaty, Amsterdam, Arnhem, Beijing, Berlin, Bristol, Brussels, Bucharest, Budapest, Chemnitz, Dresden, Düsseldorf, Frankfurt, Hamburg, Hilversum, Hong Kong, Leipzig, Moscow, Munich, Prague, Singapore, Stockholm, Stuttgart, Tashkent, Toronto, Utrecht, Vienna, Warsaw, Washington DC.

cameron mcKenna

COBBETTS

Ship Canal House King Street Manchester M2 4WB
Tel: (0161) 833 3333 Fax: (0161) 833 3030
Email: lawyers@cobbetts.co.uk
Website: www.cobbetts.co.uk

Firm Profile

Cobbetts is one of Manchester's most long-established firms with a staff of 260 including 41 partners. The firm has successfully managed to remain at the forefront of commercial law practice without sacrificing the professionalism by which it earned its reputation.

Main Areas of Work

Corporate, commercial, intellectual property, IT, banking and private client. The commercial property division is one of the largest under one roof in the north including specialist expertise in enviromental law, planning, licensing, property litigation, housing associations, and construction. Cobbetts' client base includes both PLCs and owner-managed businesses, banks and financial institutions, public-sector organisations, property companies and retail and licensed operators.

Trainee profiles

Law and non-law graduates.

Training Environment

Four six-month seats are available. Typically, these include one property, one litigation and one commercial/corporate seats. There is an opportunity for one trainee each year to spend three months in Brussels.

Benefits

Social Club and Y Club.

Vacation Placements

Small number of placements available during July and August.

Sponsorship & Awards

CPC and LPC grant available.

Partners	41
Legal Personnel	60
Total Trainees	22

Contact

Simon Jones
Trainee Partner

Method of Application

Handwritten letter with application form (available on request)

Selection Procedure

Six half day assessments

Closing date for 2002

31 July 2000

Application

Training contracts p.a.	7
Applications p.a.	700
% interviewed p.a.	10%
Required degree grade	2:2

Training

Salary: 1st year (2000)	£15,000
Salary: 2nd year	£16,500
	Reviewed each year
Holiday entitlement	20 days
% of trainees with a non-law degree p.a.	30%
No. of seats available abroad p.a.	1

Post-Qualification

Salary (2000)	£15,000
% of trainees offered job on qualification (1999)	90%
% of assistants (as at 1/9/99) who joined as trainees	75%
% of partners (as at 1/9/99) who joined as trainees	60%

Overseas Offices

Brussels (Associated).

COUDERT BROTHERS

60 Cannon Street London EC4N 6JP
Tel: (020) 7248 3000 Fax: (020) 7248 3001
Email: info@london.coudert.com
Website: www.coudert.com

Firm Profile
Founded in 1853, Coudert Brothers is a global partnership with 27 offices in 16 countries worldwide. In London the firm was one of the first English multi-national partnerships of English solicitiors and registered foreign lawyers. The firm advises on all aspects of national and international business law.

Trainee Profile
The quality and complexity of legal work undertaken by the firm demands that it recruits only individuals of the highest calibre. It is essential that trainees are enthusiastic, confident and outward going individuals, able to perform in a fast-moving and challenging environment. Early responsibility is routine and broadbased experience guaranteed. Coudert Brothers accepts law and non-law graduates. Applicants should have at least three A-level passes at Grades A and B and a 2:1 degree. In view of the international nature of the firm's work and clients, languages are an advantage, but not essential.

Training Environment
The training at Coudert Brothers comprises four six-month placements. Three of these will be with the firm's core practices: corporate and commercial, banking and finance, litigation, and property. The fourth will be drawn from one of the firm's other disciplines: energy and utilities, telecommunications, tax and funds and competition law. There is an opportunity for a secondment to one of our foreign offices. Partners and senior assistants ensure that trainees gain practical experience in research, drafting, procedural and client-related skills by working closely with them during each placement. There are regular appraisals during the 2 year training contract. Legal and professional training is provided through an in-house training programme and external conferences.

Benefits
Pension, health insurance, subsidised gym membership, season ticket loan.

Sponsorship & Awards
CPE Funding: Fees paid + £3,750 p.a. maintenance
LPC Funding: Fees paid + £3,750 p.a. maintenance

Partners	15
Assistant Solicitors	19
Total Trainees	8

Contact
Christine de Ferrars Green
Graduate Recruitment Partner

Method of Application
Letter and CV

Selection Procedure
2 interviews with partners

Closing date for 2002
15 August 2000

Application
Training contracts p.a.	4
Required degree grade	2:1

Training
Salary: 1st year(2000)	£23,500-£24,000
Salary: 2nd year(2000)	£24,500-£25,000
Holiday entitlement	20 days

Post-Qualification
% of trainees offered job on qualification
Prospects are good as the firm only takes a small number of trainees each year

Overseas Offices
Almaty, Antwerp, Bangkok, Beijing, Berlin, Brussels, Denver, Frankfurt, Ghent, Hanoi, Hong Kong, Jakarta, Los Angeles, Montréal, Moscow, New York, Palo Alto, Paris, San Francisco, San José, Singapore, St Petersburg, Sydney, Tokyo, Washington DC.

Associated Offices:
Mexico City and Budapest

CRIPPS HARRIES HALL

Seymour House 11–13 Mount Ephraim Road
Tunbridge Wells Kent TN1 1EN
Tel: (01892) 515121 Fax: (01892) 506069
E-mail: aol@crippslaw.com
Website: www.e-cripps.co.uk

Firm Profile

Established almost 150 years ago, Cripps Harries Hall has grown steadily to become one of the largest firms in the South East. The firm is progressing steadily towards being regarded as the leading law firm in the South East outside London. It is an innovative and young firm; most of the partners are in their thirties or forties and the atmosphere is friendly and outgoing. Their headquarters are in Tunbridge Wells. In addition, they have an office in London and one in Crowborough, East Sussex.

Main Areas of Work

Commercial Litigation: 25% Corporate & Commercial Property: 24%; Finance and Investment Services: 21% Private Client: 14%; Residential conveyancing and agriculture: 11%; General Litigation: 5%.

Trainee Profile

Cripps Harries Hall is looking for talented, confident, capable people who want to make a contribution during their period of training and who will want to stay with us as assistant solicitors and potential partners. You will be expected to integrate expert legal advice with a highly developed use of information technology.

Training Environment

The two year training contract is divided into six periods, each spent in a different department or division where you will receive a thorough grounding in the relevant practice. You will usually share a room with a partner, and work as an integral member of a small team. At the end of each period in a department, monitored monthly by the partner, there is a more formal review with the Managing Partner and the Personnel Manager. The Director of Education will arrange your continuing education. In addition to the Professional Skills Course, you will attend seminars and courses and receive training in business, presentation, IT and marketing skills.

Benefits

PPP, DIS, PHI.

Sponsorship & Awards

Discretionary LPC Funding: Fees – 50% interest free loan, 50% bursary.

Partners	31
Assistant Solicitors	43
Total Trainees	13

Contact

Annabelle Lawrence
Personnel Manager

Method of Application

Handwritten letter and firm's application form, available on website.

Selection Procedure

1 interview with Managing Partner and Personnel Manager

Closing date for 2002

31 July 2000

Application

Training contracts p.a.	8
Applications p.a.	Up to 1,000
% interviewed p.a.	5%
Required degree grade	2.1

Training

Salary: 1st year(2000)	£13,500
Salary: 2nd year(2000)	£15,500
Holiday entitlement	20 days
% of trainees with a non-law degree p.a.	25%

Post-Qualification

Salary (2000)	£22,250
% of trainees offered job on qualification (1999)	100%
% of assistants (as at 1/9/99) who joined as trainees	42%
% of partners (as at 1/9/99) who joined as trainees	30%

Associated Firms

Berlin, Frankfurt, Madrid, Munich, Paris, Rotterdam.

CROCKERS OSWALD HICKSON

10 Gough Square London EC4A 3NJ
Tel: (020) 7353 0311 Fax: (020) 7353 0743
Email: lawyers@c-o-h.co.uk
Website: www.c-o-h.co.uk

Firm Profile

Crockers Oswald Hickson is a City Firm, whose history dates back to the early 1900's. The Firm's offices are near Fleet Street. The Firm is particularly well known for its media practice (defamation, intellectual property etc) and acts for a large number of national and local newspapers and for several major publishing groups. The Firm is also known for its long standing connections with the insurance industry, particularly the Lloyd's Market.

Main Areas of Work

Media 45%; Personal Injury Litigation 30%; Property 10%; Company-Commercial 10%; Private Client 5%.

Trainee Profile

The Firm seeks to recruit trainees who have a strong academic background, are practical, hardworking and good team players. The Firm has a friendly atmosphere and looks for trainees who will get on well with staff throughout the Firm and clients.

Training Environment

The training is usually divided into four six-month seats (Media, Personal Injury, Property and Company-Commercial). Sometimes special arrangements are made to accommodate trainees from particular backgrounds (e.g. a trainee who is an ex-journalist will spend longer in the Media Department). Trainees are closely supervised and supported.

Partners	9
Assistant Solicitors	15
Total Trainees	4

Contact

The Head of Recruitment

Method of Application

Letter and CV

Selection Procedure

2 Interviews

Closing date for 2002

31 August 2000

Application

Training contracts p.a.	2-3
Applications p.a.	1000
% interviewed p.a.	2.5%
Required degree grade	2:1

Training

Salary: 1st year(1999)	£18,000
Salary: 2nd year(1999)	£19,000
Holiday entitlement	20 days
% of trainees with a non-law degree p.a.	variable

Post-Qualification

Salary (1999)	£27,500
% of trainees offered job on qualification (1999)	50%
% of assistants (as at 1/9/99) who joined as trainees	30%
% of partners (as at 1/9/99) who joined as trainees	45%

CUMBERLAND ELLIS PEIRS

Columbia House 69 Aldwych London WC2B 4RW
Tel: (020) 7242 0422 Fax: (020) 7831 9081
Email: cep@cep-law.co.uk
Website: www.cep-law.co.uk

Firm Profile
A Central London firm of solicitors with a varied practice. The firm has a broad base of commercial and institutional clients including those involved in the media and information technology, quasi government councils, sporting associations, charities, City Livery companies, housing associations and landed estates, as well as having an established reputation for its private client services.

Main Areas of Work
Company/Commercial; Commercial Property; Litigation; Private Client and Financial Services.

Trainee Profile
Law and non-law graduates who have a consistently strong academic record. Individuals who can work with and relate well to others; who are commercially aware, with an ability to think creatively and to make a contribution to the firm. The firm is looking for candidates who have presence and enthusiasm, who are outgoing and articulate and who have a broad range of outside interests. IT skills are important.

Training Environment
Trainees spend six months in each of the Company Commercial, Litigation, Private Client and Property departments under the supervision of a Partner or Senior Assistant. Trainees are fully invloved in all aspects of the work of the department. Client contact and early responsibility for handling your own caseload are encouraged, subject to necessary guidance and supervision. There are a number of social, sporting and marketing activities going on during the course of the year and life outside the office is encouraged. An open door policy applies and the firm has a friendly and infomal environment. Where possible the firm aims to recruit its trainees at the end of the training contract. The PSC is taught externally at the College of Law.

Benefits
Season ticket loan, luncheon vouchers.

Sponsorship & Awards
It is not the firm's policy to offer vacation placements or sponsorship.

Partners	12
Assistant Solicitors	9
Total Trainees	3

Contact
Nicola Waldman

Method of Application
Handwritten letter and covering CV (adding reference to 'Chambers')

Selection Procedure
Two interviews with partners

Closing date for 2002
To be submitted between 1 July and 30 September 2000

Application

Training contracts p.a.	1 or 2
Applications p.a.	600
% interviewed p.a.	3%
Required degree grade	2:1

Training

Holiday entitlement	20 days

DAVENPORT LYONS

1 Old Burlington Street London W1X 2NL
Tel: (020) 7468 2600 Fax: (020) 7437 8216
Email: dl@davenportlyons.com
Website: www.davenportlyons.com

Firm Profile
Davenport Lyons is a leading entertainment and media law practice and combines this work with strong company/commercial, (including IP/IT), litigation, property and private client departments. The firm adopts a keen commercial and practical partner-led approach and builds on long-term partnerships with its clients.

Main Areas of Work
Litigation 23%; Company Commercial 25%; Entertainment/ Media 22%; Commercial Property 18%; Private Client 12%

Trainee Profile
Upper Second plus; interesting background; business acumen; sociability; knowledge of foreign languages an advantage. Scope for being the extra piece in the jigsaw.

Training Environment
Four seats of six months each. Six monthly assessments. Supervision from within departments. Ongoing programme of in-house lectures and professional skills training. Davenport Lyons offers interesting hands-on training. Trainees are treated as junior fee earners and are encouraged to develop their own client relationships and to handle their own matters under appropriate supervision.

Benefits
Season ticket loans. Client introduction bonuses. Contributions to gym membership.

Vacation Placements - Easter, Summer and Christmas
Places for 2000: 10; Duration: 2–3 weeks; Remuneration: £150 p.w.; Closing Date: None fixed.

Sponsorship & Awards
The firm does not generally offer financial assistance other than in exceptional circumstances.

Partners	24
Assistant Solicitors	19
Total Trainees	6

Contacts
Michael Hatchwell
Training Partner
Ann Goldie
HR/Training Manager

Method of Application
Letter and CV

Selection Process
Interviews

Closing date for 2002
Late 2000

Application
Training contracts p.a.	4
Applications p.a.	1,500
% interviewed p.a.	20%
Required degree grade	2:1

Training
Salary: 1st year(2000)	£20,500
Salary: 2nd year(2000)	£21,500
Holiday entitlement	4 weeks+
% of trainees with a non-law degree p.a.	60–70%

Post-Qualification
Salary (1999)	£30,000
% of trainees offered job on qualification (1999)	66%
% of assistants (as at 1999) who joined as trainees	15%
% of partners (as at 1999) who joined as trainees	5%

DAVIES ARNOLD COOPER

6–8 Bouverie Street London EC4Y 8DD
Tel: (020) 7936 2222 Fax: (020) 7936 2020
Email: daclon@dac.co.uk
Website: www.dac.co.uk

Partners	44*
Total Fee-earners	215*
Total Trainees	34

** denotes world-wide figures*

Contact
Graduate Recruitment

Method of Application
DAC application form

Selection Procedure
Open days and individual interviews

Closing date for 2002/2001
30 June 2000

Required degree grade
2:1 capability

Firm Profile
Davies Arnold Cooper's clear strategic vision will ensure the firm maintains and increases its competitive advantage into the millennium. It has other offices in London Market, Manchester, Newcastle and Madrid as well as strong contacts with leading foreign firms throughout the world. The firm focuses on its core strengths; it is a leading practice in Dispute Resolution (including all forms of litigation, arbitration and alternative dispute resolution) and has a growing reputation in Commercial Property and Secured Lending. The firm identifies and addresses the issues of the future and has recently been at the forefront of the Woolf Reforms, Y2K issues, Health and Safety and the use of paperless litigation. It has taken a lead in its firm wide usage of ADR and remains the number one choice for multi-party actions arising in the UK and internationally relating to product liability or physical disasters and accidents.

Main Areas of Work
Insurance, financial services, construction, commercial property, pharmaceutical and healthcare.

Trainee Profile
Davies Arnold Cooper look for people who can demonstrate a strong intellect combined with analytical and problem solving skills. Well organised, flexible and self motivated you must be a strong communicator and able to work effectively with a variety of different people. You will thrive in a fast moving, commercial environment with plenty of opportunity for early responsibility. The firm welcomes applications from all age groups and backgrounds, from people who want to make a positive difference.

Training Environment
One of the only two law firms listed in the 'Britain's Best Employers' Directory. Their induction and training schemes are widely admired and trainees receive a comprehensive grounding in core legal skills. As a medium-sized firm they offer a flexible training programme with the opportunity for early responsibility within a supportive environment. Their aim is to recruit for the future of the firm and they select to ensure positions will be available on qualification.

Sponsorship & Awards
CPE and LPC: grants covering course and examination fees. Discretionary interest-free loans for maintenance up to £4,000.

DAVIES WALLIS FOYSTER

Harvester House 37 Peter Street Manchester M2 5GB
Tel: (0161) 228 3702 Fax: (0161) 835 2407
5 Castle Street Liverpool L2 4XE
Tel: (0151) 236 6226 Fax: (0151) 236 3088
Email: trainees@dwf-law.com
Website: www.dwf.law.co.uk

Firm Profile

Davies Wallis Foyster is a leading North West law firm providing Corporate and Commercial Services and Insurance Claims Services to a substantial number of successful and growing businesses in most market sectors. With over 130 lawyers across its two offices the firm has an exceptionally strong team and a reputation for the style, enthusiasm and energy of its people.

Main Areas of Work

Corporate and Commercial Services 65%; Insurance Claims Services 35%.

Trainee Profile

DWF wants trainees to play a part in building on its success. The firm is looking for trainees who enjoy working as part of a busy team, who respond positively to a challenge and think they have what it takes to hugely impress a client. The firm is looking for its partners of the future and in 1999 all its qualifying trainees were offered jobs.

Training Environment

All trainees commence life at DWF with a welcome programme designed to provide a clear picture of the firm and its services before moving to their first seat. The firm provides a flexible seat rotation including corporate, property, commercial litigation and insurance with agreed options which focus on post-qualification aspirations. This is supplemented by general training as well as specific training relevant to the particular seat which may be run in-house or using external courses. Appraisals are carried out during each seat to review progress and development. Trainees will have the opportunity to join in the busy social life within the office and with local trainee solicitors' groups.

Vacation Placements

Places for 2000: Individual arrangements may be made.

Sponsorship & Awards

LPC funding.

Partners	41
Assistant Solicitors	85
Total Trainees	9

Contact

Mrs Lynn Davies
Training Administrator
(Manchester address)

Method of Application

Handwritten letter and C.V. or DWF application form

Selection Procedure

Two interviews with partners

Closing date for 2002

31 July 2000

Application

Training contracts p.a. at least 6
Applications p.a. 1000
% interviewed p.a. 5%
Required degree grade 2:1 in any subject preferred

Training

Salary: 1st year(1999) £14,000
Holiday entitlement 20 days p.a. minimum

Post-Qualification

% of trainees offered job on qualification (1999) 100%

DAWSON & CO

2 New Square Lincoln's Inn London WC2A 3RZ
Tel: (020) 7421 4800 Fax: (020) 7421 4848
Email: legal@dawson-and-co.co.uk

Firm Profile
Dawson & Co is a medium-sized Lincoln's Inn firm, advising both business and private clients. Its strengths are in litigation, property, trusts and personal tax. It has a progressive outlook and most of the partners are under 40.

Main Areas of Work
Tax planning, Trusts & Probate 37%; Property 28%; Litigation and Family 28%; Company/Commercial 7%.

Trainee Profile
Candidates need to show excellent intellectual capabilities, a keen interest in the firm's areas of expertise, and a practical approach to problem-solving.

Training Environment
Training usually consists of three six-month seats in the following departments: property, trusts and personal tax, and litigation. The final seat is usually intended to be in the department in which you will hope to work after qualification, subject always to the availability of places. You will share an office with a partner, who will assist you and formally review your progress at the end of your seat. The PSC is taught externally. The firm is friendly with an open-door policy and there are various sporting and social events.

Benefits
Season ticket loan

Vacation Placements
Places for 2000: 2; Duration: 2 weeks; Remuneration: £150 p.w.; Closing Date: 28 February 2000.

Sponsorship & Awards
Discretionary. On application.

Partners	18
Assistant Solicitors	12
Total Trainees	7

Contact
Tim Robinson
Practice Director

Method of Application
Handwritten letter and CV

Selection Procedure
2 interviews with partners + oral test

Closing date for 2002
31 July 2000

Application

Training contracts p.a.	2/3
Applications p.a.	1000
% interviewed p.a.	2%
Required degree grade	2:1

Training

Salary: 1st year(2000)	£20,000
Salary: 2nd year(2000)	£22,000
Holiday entitlement	20 days
% of trainees with a non-law degree p.a.	40%

Post-Qualification

Salary (2000)	£28,000
% of trainees offered job on qualification (1999)	90%
% of assistants (as at 1/9/99) who joined as trainees	60%
% of partners (as at 1/9/99) who joined as trainees	50%

DENTON HALL

Five Chancery Lane Clifford's Inn London EC4A 1BU
Tel: (020) 7242 1212 Fax: (020) 7404 0087
Email: info@dentonhall.com
Website: www.dentonhall.com

Firm Profile

Denton Hall is one of the largest firms in the City, with particular strengths in the media/entertainment/telecommuncations industries and in the energy/infrastructure sectors as well as in corporate, project finance, banking/financial services, property and planning, litigation, arbitratrion, IP and IT. It has an international outlook, including an extensive Asian network, offices in the Middle East and a European network of associated offices. In February 2000, the firm will join forces with Wilde Sapte to form Denton Wilde Sapte. Please see Wilde Sapte's entry and refer to both websites for any further procedural change.

Main Areas of Work

Company and commercial 38%; Litigation and arbitration 26%; Property and planning 22%; Media and technology 14%

Trainee Profile

The firm looks for candidates with high academic ability and ambition. They should be commercially aware, self-motivated, determined and should show flair and precision. Languages are an advantage, but not essential.

Training Environment

Four six-month seats. Three of the seats are likely to be spent in company/commercial or media/technology and in the property and litigation departments. In the fourth seat, you may decide to specialise within a main seat. For example, company/commercial includes energy and infrastructure, corporate finance, tax, competition, banking & financial markets and insolvency. Trainees sit with a partner/senior solicitor who supervises their work. Seats abroad or client secondments are sometimes available. There are a range of sporting and social activities.

Benefits

Holiday entitlement rises by 1 day after each full year served, luncheon vouchers, private health cover, season ticket loan, gym membership

Sponsorship & Awards

CPE and LPC funding: fees and a maintenance grant of £3,750 for an outer London institution, and £4,000 for a London or Guildford institution.

Partners	138
Assistant Solicitors	240
Total Trainees	62

Contact
Howard Morris, Partner

Method of Application
Application form and handwritten letter

Selection Procedure
Interview

Closing date for 2002
no offficial closing date, accept from 1 June 2000

Application

Training contracts p.a.	approx 30
Applications p.a.	2,500
% interviewed p.a.	8%
Required degree grade	2:1

Training

Salary: 1st year(1999)	£21,000-£22,000
Salary: 2nd year(1999)	£23,000-£24,000
Holiday entitlement	21 days
% of trainees with a non-law degree p.a.	50% max.
No. of seats available abroad p.a.	Sometimes available

Post-Qualification

Salary (1999)	£34,000
% of trainees offered job on qualification (1999)	85% approx.

Overseas Offices
Almaty, Beijing, Brussels, Cairo, Dubai, Gibraltar, Hong Kong, Istanbul, Moscow, Singapore, Tokyo and associated offices at Barcelona, Berlin, Chemnitz, Cologne, Copenhagen, Dresden, Düsseldorf, Frankfurt, Gothenburg, Hamburg, Madrid, Malmö, Munich, Oslo, Paris,

DIBB LUPTON ALSOP

125 London Wall London EC2Y 5AE
Tel: (020) 7796 6677 Fax: (0121) 212 5792

Firm Profile

This ambitious firm thinks of itself as a business as much as a law firm. Its expansion has been meteoric. In 1989, it was below the top 35 UK firms in terms of size – it is now the seventh largest. It has offices in six major cities in the UK, but still operates as one partnership. The full range of corporate and commercial services are offered.

Main Areas of Work

Corporate 25%, Insurance 9%, Property & Construction 17%, Litigation 17%, Business Support & Restructuring 6%, Human Resources 7%, Business Services 6%, Banking 7%

Trainee Profile

The firm only wants exceptional people. Good academic ability is no longer sufficient. It wants people with different backgrounds and skills. The successful candidates will believe in themselves, relate well to other people, have an appetite for life and a desire to succeed in business.

Training Environment

The firm deliberately takes on a relatively small number of trainees for its size. This enables it to offer in-depth experience and excellent prospects. Trainees will be assigned a mentor to guide them through their contract. They will spend four six month seats in different commercial areas. They will sit with a partner or assistant and learn through practice and observation. There is an ongoing commercial skills training programme and the PSC is run in-house. Good sports and social facilities.

Benefits

Pension, health insurance, life assurance, 23 days holiday.

Vacation Placements

Places for 2000: 180; Duration: 1 week; Remuneration (1999): £175 p.w. London, £125 p.w. regions; Closing Date: 28 February 2000.

Sponsorship & Awards

CPE and LPC fees paid and a maintenance for grant for both years.

Partners	217*
Assistant Solicitors	365*
Total Trainees	100

* denotes world-wide figures

Contact

Sally Carthy

Method of Application

Application form

Selection Procedure

First interview, assessment afternoon including second interview with 2 partners

Closing date for 2002

31 July 2000

Application

Training contracts p.a.	60
Applications p.a.	2,200
% interviewed p.a.	10%
Required degree grade	2:1

Training

Salary: 1st year(1999) £21,500 (London) £16,000 (regions)
Salary: 2nd year(1999) £24,000 (London) £17,500 (regions)
Holiday entitlement 23 days
% of trainees with a non-law degree p.a. 40%

Post-Qualification

Salary (1999) £34,000 (London) £26,500 (regions)
% of trainees offered job on qualification (1999) 90%

▶

DIBB LUPTON ALSOP *continued*

Trainee Comments

"Growing up in Liverpool and having spent all my academic life here, it was not a question of where I wanted to start my professional career but who I wanted to start it with. I applied to a number of firms in Liverpool but it was Dibb Lupton Alsop which impressed me the most. Dibb Lupton Alsop provided an opportunity to do high quality commercial work in my home town and showed commitment and dedication to my training and future career which was second to none." (Clare Tickle, second year trainee in the Liverpool office, read law at Liverpool University)

"I had lived in London for three years on and off before starting work and I had long wanted to work in a City firm. I chose Dibb Lupton Alsop for their obvious ambition - particularly evidenced around the time I applied for a training contract by the well documented merger and their expansionist ideas. I was influenced greatly by the unstuffy attitude I perceived at interview. This was a marked difference from some other firms who interviewed me." (Guy Sheppard, second year trainee in the London office, read Latin at Exeter University)

"As a truly national firm Dibb Lupton Alsop offers me a City reputation, excellent quality of work and a commitment to training without being in London. As a trainee with a past 'non legal life' Dibb Lupton Alsop is a firm with a modern culture that recognises the added value that alternative disciplines can offer. As business lawyers with a reputation for being pro-active, ambitious and competitive in the market, Dibb Lupton Alsop are always looking to be better and committed to be the best." (Joely Richardson, newly qualified in the Birmingham office, studied Business Studies at Leeds Business School)

"Once I started applying for training contracts it became obvious that Dibb Lupton Alsop, as a truly national firm, would be able to offer me the best quality work and training. However, the main factor that influenced me was that despite rapid growth in the last decade, the firm were still very ambitions and had such clear objectives of the position they wanted to be in in the near future and how they planned to achieve it. This expansion was something that I wanted to be a part of." (Jamie Gamble, first year trainee in the Sheffield office, studied law at Nottingham University)

Overseas Offices
Brussels, Hong Kong

Associated Offices (DLA & Partners)
Paris, Barcelona, Brussels

DICKINSON DEES

St. Ann's Wharf 112 Quayside
Newcastle-upon-Tyne NE99 1SB
Tel: (0191) 279 9000 Fax: (0191) 279 9100
Email: law@dickinson-dees.co.uk
Website: www.dickinson-dees.com

Firm Profile
The largest firm in the north east, Dickinson Dees offers both commercial and private client services. The firm has new premises on the Quayside in Newcastle. The firm has an associated office in Brussels with opportunities for trainees to spend time on secondment there.

Main Areas of Work
Corporate 30%; Property 30%; Private Client 20%; Litigation 20%.

Trainee Profile
Good academic and analytical ability. Good commercial and business sense. Confident, personable and adaptable with good communication skills. Able to fit into a team.

Training Environment
Trainees are relatively few for the size of the practice. You are fully integrated into the firm and involved in all aspects of firm business. The training contract consists of four seats. One seat is spent in each of the commercial property, company/commercial and litigation departments. You are able to specialise for the fourth seat. This is encouraged so that personnel rise through the firm rather than being recruited from outside. Trainees sit with partners or associates and training is reviewed every three months. The firm has its own Training & Development Manager. There are in-house induction courses on each move of department and opportunities for trainees to get involved in the in-house training programme. The professional skills course is run in conjunction with Northumbria University and the firm has played a key role in the development and implementation of this course. The working environment at Dickinson Dees is supportive and friendly. You will lead a busy life with sporting and social events organised by the office.

Vacation Placements
Places for 2000: 20; Duration: 1 week; Remuneration: £50 p.w.; Closing Date: 28 February 2000. Application forms are available.

Open Days
Open days will be held in the summer of 2000. Application forms are available on request. Closing date: 30 April 2000.

Partners	46
Assistant Solicitors	98
Total Trainees	18

Contact
Jen Smurthwaite

Method of Application
Application form and handwritten letter

Selection Procedure
Interview

Closing date for 2002
31 July 2000

Application
Training contracts p.a.	8-10
Applications p.a.	700
% interviewed p.a.	10%
Required degree grade	2:1

Training
Salary: 1st year(1999)	£15,250
Salary: 2nd year(1999)	£16,250
Holiday entitlement	4 weeks
% of trainees with a non-law degree p.a.	50%
No. of seats available abroad p.a.	2

Post-Qualification
Salary (2000)	£23,250
% of trainees offered job on qualification (1999)	100%
% of assistants (as at 1/9/99) who joined as trainees	60%
% of partners (as at 1/9/99) who joined as trainees	29%

Branch Office
Rond Point Schuman 9 - Box 13
B-1040 Brussels
Tel: +32 2 233 3747
Fax: +32 2 233 3740

▶

DICKINSON DEES *continued*

Sponsorship & Awards

LPC fees paid and £2,000 interest free loan.

Trainee Comments

"Dickinson Dees, as well as being a firm with an impressive range of clients and work, immediately struck me as being a friendly employer – a heady mix!" (Oliver Bennett, first year trainee, read Law at Durham University)

"I wanted to work for a leading commercial firm with a progressive outlook and an excellent training record; Dickinson Dees is the law firm that fulfils all their criteria." (Elizabeth Allen, first year trainee, read English at University of London and LLB at Northumbria University)

"I wanted to work for an expanding and developing commercial firm that invested time and effort in its trainees. Dickinson Dees offers all of the above with an enthusiastic and friendly approach." (Edward Meikle, second year trainee, read Art History at University of East Anglia)

"After completing a week of work experience at Dickinson Dees I felt that I would get a thorough training at a leading commercial firm and great future prospects." (Sara Brody, first year trainee, read law at Hull University)

"Dickinson Dees offered exposure to a wide range of work and clients and a positive approach to trainees. What stood out was a keenness to involve and develop trainees: the firm's culture is certainly progressive, but also supportive and friendly. You never feel the 'typical' trainee solicitor; your work is valued." (Kevin Mercer, second year trainee, read Geography at Nottingham University)

"Dickinson Dees offers trainees the highest level of training. Trainees are involved at all levels and have a high degree of client contact. Overall a great place to work in a friendly and relaxed environment." (Ian Hornby, first year trainee, read Law at Newcastle Univesity)

D J FREEMAN

43 Fetter Lane London EC4A 1JU
Tel: (020) 7583 4055 Fax: (020) 7353 7377
Email: aem@djfreeman.co.uk
Website: djfreeman.co.uk

Firm Profile

An innovative firm whose lawyers work in multi-disciplinary teams concentrating on specific business sectors. It is one of the leading firms in the property, insurance and media/ communications industries, and has a strong commercial litigation department. It also has more women partners than any other City law firm.

Main Areas of Work

Property Services 42%; Insurance Services 26%; Commercial Litigation 20%; Media & Communications 12%.

Trainee Profile

Clear and creative thinkers who work well under pressure and as part of a team.

Training Environment

Trainees spend six months in the firm's major practice areas, and once a month are able to discuss their progress in each seat with a partner. Believing supervised experience to be the best training, the firm soon gives trainees the chance to meet clients, be responsible for their own work and join in marketing and client development activities. Regular workshops in each seat help develop basic skills in the different departments. Any suggestions or concerns can be voiced at a trainee solicitors' committee. The firm has an active social committee which organises events from quiz evenings to wine tasting, as well as a theatre club.

Benefits

Subsidised meals in staff restaurant; BUPA after three months; a variety of social and sporting events.

Vacation Placements

Places for 2000: 16; Duration: 3 weeks; Remuneration: £150 p.w.; Closing Date: 14 March 2000.

Sponsorship & Awards

CPE or LPC Funding.

Partners	56
Assistant Solicitors	71
Total Trainees	25

Contact

Anne Mellars

Method of Application

Application form

Selection Procedure

Interview

Closing date for 2002

16 July 2000

Application

Training contracts p.a.	12–15
Applications p.a.	600
% interviewed p.a.	10%
Required degree grade	2:1

Training

Salary (2000)	
1st six months	£20,000
2nd six months	£21,000
3rd six months	£22,500
4th six months	£23,500
Holiday entitlement	20 days

Post-Qualification

Salary (2000)	£34,000

DONNE MILEHAM & HADDOCK

100 Queens Road Brighton BN1 3YB
Tel: (01273) 744 340 Fax:(01273) 744 404
Email: admin@dmh.co.uk
Website: www.dmh.co.uk

Firm Profile
Donne Mileham & Haddock aims to offer expertise and service comparable to City firms. Its main commercial offices are at Brighton and Crawley where the firm continues its rapid expansion. The firm also undertakes international work. Client focused, the firm is open, approachable and innovative.

Main Areas of Work
Corporate Finance; Commercial Property; Employment; Intellectual Property/IT; Private Client.

Trainee Profile
The firm looks for trainees with a sound academic background, enthusiasm, good communication and interpersonal skills and external interests. Local connections are also of value.

Training Environment
Usually four six-month seats taken from the following areas: Employment, Intellectual Property/IT, Commercial, Corporate Finance, Planning, Commercial Property, Construction Litigation, Personal Injury, Civil Litigation and Private Client work. Trainees are closely supervised by the partner to whom they are attached but have every opportunity to work as part of the team and deal directly with clients. The majority of seats are in Brighton and Crawley.

Vacation Placements
Places for 2000: limited number, priority given to trainee interviewees and Sussex University. Duration: 1–2 weeks; Remuneration: £100.00 p.w. expenses; Closing Date: 31 March 2000.

Partners	29
Associates	14
Assistant Solicitors	13
Total Trainees	9

Contact
Jean Clack

Method of Application
CV and covering letter

Closing date for 2002
December 2000

Application
Training contracts p.a.	4–5
Applications p.a.	350–450
% interviewed p.a.	3%
Required degree grade	2:1

Training
Salary: 1st year(2000)	£13,000
Salary: 2nd year(2000)	£15,500
Holiday entitlement	20 days
% of trainees with a non-law degree p.a.	50%

Post-Qualification
Salary	£21,000
% of trainees offered job on qualification	100%
% of assistants) who joined as trainees	33%
% of partners who joined as trainees	52%

EDGE ELLISON

Rutland House 148 Edmund St Birmingham B3 2JR
Tel: (0870) 513 4441 Fax: (0121) 214 2617
18 Southampton Place London WC1A 2AJ
Regent Court, Regent Street Leicester LE1 7BR
Email: graduates@edge.co.uk
Website: www.edge.co.uk/graduates

Firm Profile

One of the largest national commercial legal practices with offices in Birmingham, London and Leicester. Its fresh approach to winning business and training & recruiting resulted in the Firm receiving "The Most Enterprising Law Firm of the Year" award from Legal Business last year.

Main Areas of Work

Commercial 9.5%; Corporate 16%; Litigation 18%; Property 25.5%; Finance Law 12%; Construction & Engineering 7%; Pensions 6%; Employment 6%.

Trainee Profile

Trainees are recruited to be retained and there are excellent propects. The Firm is acknowledged to be one of the most innovative and progressive firms in the UK and seeks to recruit motivated, ambitious and creative people. The Firm provides a training environment for trainees to use their skills and intelligence to solve problems, exploit opportunities and develop legal solutions for a high profile national and international client list. Along the way, you will attain job satisfaction, a considerable degree of personal fulfilment and a high level of responsibility.

Training Environment

Six months is spent in each of the four main areas (litigation, commercial, corporate and property) with the fourth seat in an area of your choice. In each department you will be fully involved in the work of your supervisor: attending client interviews and meetings from an early stage. In certain seats, you will soon be responsible for your own files but guidance will always be on hand. The PSC is integrated into a structured programme which includes seminars, workshops and skills development. A full social and sports programme is on offer.

Benefits

Private health cover, pension (post qualification/25 years of age).

Vacation Placements

Places for 2000: 75; Duration: 2 weeks; Remuneration: £100 Midlands £120 London p.w.; Closing Date: 11 February 2000.

Sponsorship & Awards

CPE Funding: Fees paid.
LPC Funding: Fees paid & £3,500 maintenance.

Partners	83
Assistant Solicitors	136
Total Trainees	38

Contact

Helen Thomas
Recruitment & Coaching Manager

Method of Application

Download application form from website or direct from Firm

Selection Procedure

Selection day, including group exercises and interview

Closing date for 2002

28 July 2000

Application

Training contracts p.a.	25+
Applications p.a.	1200
% interviewed p.a.	10%
Required degree grade	2:1

Training

Salary: 1st year(2000)	
London	£19,500
Midlands	£15,500
Salary: 2nd year(2000)	
London	£21,000
Midlands	£17,000
Holiday entitlement	20 days
% of trainees with a non-law degree p.a.	30%

Post-Qualification

Salary (2000)	
London	£31,500
Midlands	£26,500
% of trainees offered job on qualification (1999)	95%
% of assistants (as at 1/9/99) who joined as trainees	35%
% of partners (as at 1/9/99) who joined as trainees	37%

Offices

Birmingham, Leicester, London

▶

EDGE ELLISON *continued*

Additional Information

edge ellison offers its trainees one to one coaching facilities that sharpen up mind mapping, brainstorming, photo reading and lateral thinking abilities. They'll also instruct you in the art of techniques like self management and delegation. Led by a core group of Coaching Pioneers, our dynamic approach is helping individuals and teams alike to realise their full potential. At the same time it creates the capacity within the organisation to design, develop and deliver outstanding services for the future.

Trainee Comments

"I saw genuine teamwork within the offices. The Firm has the dynamism, resource and commitment to expand, providing a wide variety of legal and commmercial challenges working for 'household name' clients." (Craig Armstrong, first year trainee, read Law at Cardiff University)

"It was obvious that trainees' contributions were really valued and responsibility was given. I liked the well structured training programme encompassing a broad range of good quality work; both of these created an atmosphere which encourage legal skills to develop. I also liked the opportunities to get to know colleagues through activities as diverse as women's football to legal advice work at the CAB!" (Claire Mortimer, second year trainee, read Law at Nottingham University)

"edge ellison attracted me for two reasons. Its size means it attracts major clients and offers 'real work' for trainees. Secondly, the biggest attraction is the people. Everyone seems willing to help from trainees to partners and two months into my training contract, my opinion hasn't changed." (Stuart James, second year trainee, read Politics, Philosophy & Economics at Oxford University)

"The main reason for my choosing edge ellison for my training contract was the friendly, sociable and supportive atmosphere which everyone seems to contribute to. This was evident immediately from talking to edge ellison trainees at my univesity law careers fair, and remains an important part of my working life here. The balance between responsibility and support is excellent and really helps to build self-confidence." (Andrew Digwood, 1st year trainee, read Law at Durham University)

"Life here at edges seems to be what you make it, a trait that I think many law firms simply can't offer. Everyone has gone out of their way to make me feel welcome and part of the team. Whilst there are always deadlines to be met and letters to be sent, there is a defined ethos within edge ellison which encourages a relaxed and friendly working environmnet. The emphasis here is as much on quality of life as it is on quality of work." (Ramez Moussa, 1st year trainee, read Law at Manchester University)

EVERSHEDS

Senator House 85 Queen Victoria Street London EC4V 4JL
Tel: (020) 7919 4500 Fax: (020) 7919 4919
Email: gradrec@eversheds.com
Website: www.eversheds.com

Firm Profile
A European law firm, Eversheds has over 1,500 legal and business advisers in 19 locations. Its distinctive approach gives clients access to a large team of lawyers who combine local market knowledge with an international perspective.

Main Areas of Work
Corporate, commercial, litigation and dispute management, commercial, property and employment. In addition to these core areas each office provides expertise in a further 30 business and industry sectors.

Trainee Profile
Eversheds' people are valued for being straightforward, enterprising and effective. The firm listens to its clients and simplifies rather than complicates. It expects its trainees to be business-like, unstuffy and down-to-earth. You will need to display commercial acumen, imagination and drive, and above all you will need to be results-driven.

Training Environment
You will be encouraged to play a major part in the direction your training and development takes, with advice and supervision always available. In each department you will sit with a partner or a senior assistant and participate from an early stage in varied, complex and high-value work. Eversheds aims to retain as many trainees as possible on qualifying, and many of the partners were trainees with the firm. A steep learning curve begins with a month of basic training followed by departmental seats - three of which will cover the firm's main practice areas. During your training you will also complete an Eversheds-designed Professional Skills Course, and, on qualification, follow a progressive career structure.

Benefits
Regional variations

Vacation Placements
Places for 2000: 120; Duration: 2 weeks; Remuneration: regional variations; Closing Date: 31 January 2000.

Sponsorship & Awards
CPE/LPC fees and maintenance grants.

Partners	340+
Assistant Solicitors	621
Total Trainees	210

Contact
Mr Andrew M Looney

Method of Application
Application form and handwritten covering letter to be returned to London address

Selection Procedure
Selection days include group and written exercises plus interview.

Closing date for 2002
31 July 2000

Application
Training contracts p.a.	100-110
Applications p.a.	3,000
% interviewed p.a.	15%
Required degree grade	2:1

Training
Salary: 1st year(2000)	£15,000 to £21,000
Salary: 2nd year(2000)	£16,000 to £23,000
Holiday entitlement	21 days
% of trainees with a non-law degree p.a.	45%
No. of seats available abroad p.a.	Up to 12

Post-Qualification
Salary (2000)	Regional variations
% of trainees offered job on qualification (1999)	93%

Overseas Offices
Birmingham, Bristol, Brussels, Cambridge, Cardiff, Copenhagen*, Derby, Ipswich, Leeds, London, Manchester, Monaco, Moscow, Newcastle, Norwich, Nottingham, Paris, Sofia*, Teesside.
(*Associate offices)

FARRER & CO

66 Lincoln's Inn Fields London WC2A 3LH
Tel: (020) 7242 2022 Fax: (020) 7831 9748
Email: trainees@farrer.co.uk
Website: www.farrer.co.uk

Firm Profile

Farrer & Co is one of the UK's leading law practices. It provides a range of specialist advice to private, institutional and corporate clients.

Main Areas of Work

The firm's breadth of expertise is reflected by the fact that it has an outstanding reputation in fields as diverse as matrimonial law, offshore tax planning, employment, heritage work, charity law and defamation.

Trainee Profile

Trainees are expected to be highly motivated individuals with keen intellects and interesting and engaging personalities. Those applicants who appear to break the mould – as shown by their initiative for organisation, leadership, exploration, or enterprise – are far more likely to get an interview than the erudite, but otherwise unimpressive, student.

Training Environment

The training programme involves each trainee in the widest range of cases, clients and issues possible in a single law firm. This provides a broad foundation of knowledge and experience and the opportunity to make an informed choice about the area of law in which to specialise. A high degree of involvement is encouraged under the direct supervision of solicitors and partners. Trainees attend an induction programme and regular internal lectures. The training principal reviews trainees' progress at the end of each seat and extensive feedback is given. The firm has a very friendly atmosphere and regular sporting and social events.

Benefits

Health and life insurance, subsidised gym membership, season ticket loan.

Vacation Placements

Places for 2000: 18; Duration: 2 weeks at Easter, 3 weeks in summer; Remuneration: £190 p.w.; Closing Date: 31 January 2000.

Sponsorship & Awards

CPE Funding: Fees paid + £4,000 maintenance.
LPC Funding: Fees paid + £4,000 maintenance.

Partners	39
Assistant Solicitors	48
Total Trainees	12

Contact

Graduate Recruitment Manager

Method of Application

Firm's application form and covering letter

Selection Procedure

Interviews with Graduate Recruitment Manager and Partners

Closing date for 2002

31 July 2000

Application

Training contracts p.a.	6
Applications p.a.	1,500
% interviewed p.a.	2.5%
Required degree grade	2:1

Training

Salary: 1st year(2000)	£21,000
Salary: 2nd year(2000)	£23,000
Holiday entitlement	20 days
% of trainees with non-law degrees p.a.	46%

Post-Qualification

Salary (2000)	£33,500
trainees offered job on qualification (1999)	100%
% of assistants (as at 1/9/99) who joined as trainees	66%
% of partners (as at 1/9/99) who joined as trainees	70%

FENNERS

15 New Bridge Street London EC4V 6AV
Tel: (020) 7936 8000 Fax: (020) 7936 8100
Email: info@fenners.co.uk

Firm Profile

Fenners is a City based firm specialising in company/commercial law, corporate finance, commercial property, town planning and residential property development. The firm has a broad client base, including listed and unquoted companies, financial advisers, brokers, banks and other institutions.

Main Areas of Work

Commercial Property 50%; Corporate/Commercial 50%.

Trainee Profile

Candidates will demonstrate academic exellence combined with commitment and motivation to pursuing a career in a niche City firm. In addition, extra curricular activities and interests are highly regarded as evidence of a balanced and well rounded candidate.

Training Environment

Training consists of seats within the firm's commercial property and corporate/commercial departments, with an option for a further contentious seat. You will sit with a Partner or an experienced solicitor who will provide you with daily tasks and support. In addition, you will have an opportunity to receive feedback and discuss your progress with your training principal every three months. Fenners' trainees are highly valued and their development within the firm is encouraged by providing a challenging, supportive and enjoyable environment in which to work.

Benefits

Health insurance, season ticket loan.

Vacation Placements

Places for 2000: 10; Duration: 2 weeks; Remuneration: competitive rates; Closing Date: 30 April 2000.

Sponsorship & Awards

CPE and LPC funding to be discussed with candidates.

Partners	4
Assistant Solicitors	5
Total Trainees	2

Contact

Robert Fenner

Method of Application

Handwritten letter and CV.
Brochures available on request

Selection Procedure

2 interviews with partners. The firm does not require completion of an application form. Candidates should submit CVs

Closing date for 2002

Applications should preferably be received by November 2000.

Application

Training contracts p.a.	3
Applications p.a.	400
% interviewed p.a.	10%
Required degree grade	2:1

Training

Salary: 1st year(2000)	Market for city
Salary: 2nd year(2000)	Market for city
Holiday entitlement	22 days
% of trainees with a non-law degree p.a.	0%

Post-Qualification

Salary	Market for city

FIELD FISHER WATERHOUSE

35 Vine Street London EC3N 2AA
Tel: (020) 7861 4000 Fax: (020) 7488 0084
Email: kmd@ffwlaw.com
Website: www.ffwlaw.com

Firm Profile
Field Fisher Waterhouse is a City firm with a reputation for providing an excellent all-round service to an impressive list of UK and international clients. The firm has particular strengths in its core practice areas of Corporate/Finance, Property, Litigation and IP/IT. It is also highly regarded for its expertise in specialist areas such as travel & tourism, communications & media, e-commerce and medical litigation. The firm prides itself on its collegiate atmosphere, its creative and commercial approach to the law and its constructive approach to career development.

Main Areas of Work
Company/Commercial 25%; Commercial Property 22%; IP/IT 15%; Litigation 13%; Banking & Finance 11%; Professional Regulation 9%; Employment 5%

Trainee Profile
The firm is looking to recruit ambitious individuals with ability, enthusiasm and determination, who will be able to respond creatively and commercially to its clients' needs. It values strong personal qualities as well as academic achievement and welcomes applications from both law and non-law students.

Training Environment
Four of your five seats will be in the firm's core practice areas and you will be able to choose your final seat in the department which interests you most. In each seat you will work with several partners and assistants to gain a broad experience of the department. You will receive a formal assessment at the end of each seat. The firm aims to develop your grasp of legal principles and to foster your commercial awarness. It offers a comprehensive training programme with in-house lectures given by partners and outside speakers as well as a thriving sports and social committee that organises many events throughout the year.

Benefits
25 days annual holiday, season ticket loans, health insurance, private medical healthcare.

Vacation Placements
Placements available for Summer 2000. Application by CV and covering letter.

Sponsorship & Awards
Tuition fees and maintenance grant paid for CPE and LPC.

Partners	67
Assistant Solicitors	77
Total Trainees	20

Contact
Karen Danker

Method of Application
Firm's own application form and covering letter

Selection Procedure
Interview

Closing date for 2002
31 August 2000

Application
Training contracts p.a.	10
Applications p.a.	2,500
Required degree grade	2:1

Training
Salary: 1st year(2000)	£21,600
Salary: 2nd year(2000)	£23,600
Holiday entitlement	25 days
% of trainees with a non-law degree p.a.	50%

Post-Qualification
Salary (2000)	£31,500
% of trainees offered job on qualification (1999)	80%
% of assistants (as at 1/9/99) who joined as trainees	40%
% of partners (as at 1/9/99) who joined as trainees	40%

Overseas Offices
Brussels

FINERS STEPHENS INNOCENT

179 Great Portland St London W1N 6LS
Tel: (020) 7323 4000 Fax: (020) 7580 7069
Email: admin@fsilaw.co.uk
Website: www.finersstephensinnocent.co.uk

Firm Profile
Finers Stephens Innocent was formed in 1999 by the merger of West End property and commercial practice Finers with City niche media and litigation practice Stephens Innocent. The environment of the firm is friendly and forward thinking, and it is known for being client focussed and having an entrepreneurial and practical approach to its work. The firm is a member of the Network of Leading Law Firms and of LAWROPE, a European network of law firms.

Main Areas of Work
Commercial Property, Litigation, Media, Family, Defamation, Company/Commercial. Private Client. See the firm's website for further details.

Trainee Profile
The firm looks for academic excellence in applicants and prefers those with a law degree. It also looks for maturity, an interesting personality, strong communication skills, ability to think like a lawyer and an indefinable 'it' which shows that you have the potential to become a long-term member of the firm's team.

Training Environment
After your induction programme, you will complete four six-month seats, sharing a room with either a Partner or Senior Assistant. The firm has two Training Partners who keep a close eye on the welfare and progress of trainees. There are regular group meetings of trainees and an appraisal process which enables you to know how you are progressing as well as giving you a chance to provide feedback on your view of your training.

Benefits
20 days holiday, private medical insurance, death in service insurance, long term disability insurance, subsidised gym membership, season ticket loan.

Open Day
Held in June/July 2000 for 2002 training contract applicants. For further details, please write during May 2000 with an up to date CV including your most recent exam results.

Sponsorship & Awards
Contribution of £1,000 towards LPC course fees.

Partners	33
Assistant Solicitors	25
Total Trainees	11

Contact
Sandra Jackson
Personnel Director

Method of Application
CV and covering letter, including details of latest exam results.

Selection Procedure
Two interviews, each with two Partners usually including one of the Training Partners, Robert Craig and Carolyn Brown.

Closing date for 2002
31 July 2000

Application

Training contracts p.a.	3-6
Applications p.a.	1000
% interviewed p.a.	5%
Required degree grade	2:1

Training

Salary: 1st year(2000)	£19,000
Salary: 2nd year(2000)	£20,000
Holiday entitlement	20 days
% of trainees with a non-law degree p.a.	0-33%

Post-Qualification

Salary (2000)	£31,500
% of trainees offered job on qualification (1999)	75%

FRESHFIELDS

65 Fleet Street London EC4Y 1HS
Tel: (020) 7936 4000 Fax: (020) 7832 7001
Email: graduaterecruitment@freshfields.com
Website: www.freshfields.com

Firm Profile
Freshfields is a major international law firm providing a comprehensive worldwide service to corporations, financial institutions and governments all over the world through its offices in Europe, Asia and the US.

Main Areas of Work
Corporate; M&A; Banking; Litigation; Arbitration; Joint Ventures; Employment, Pensions and Benefits; Asset Finance; Comm Property; Tax; Capital Markets; Intellectual Property and Information Technology; Project Finance; Private Finance Initiative; US securities; EU/Competition; Communications and Media; Construction and Engineering; Energy; Environment; Financial Services; Restructuring and Insolvency; Insurance; International Tax; Investment Funds.

Trainee Profile
Good academic qualifications, good record of achievement in other areas, common sense and creative thinking. Linguistic and computer skills also an advantage.

Training Environment
At least three months in each of the corporate, finance and litigation departments. Seats in the property, intellectual property/information technology, employment and tax departments also available. Trainees may also have the option of spending 6 months in another office or in the legal department of a client. High priority is given to trainees' preferences. A comprehensive programme of technical legal training and skills training, as well as the PSC, is provided.

Benefits
Life Ass; permanent health ins; group personal pension; interest-free loan for a season travel ticket, after six months free membership to the firm's private medical ins scheme; loan scheme; subsidised staff restaurant; gym.

Vacation Placements
Places for 2000: 100; Duration: 2 weeks; Remuneration: £450 (total); Closing Date: 14 February 2000 but apply as quickly as possible after 1 December 1999. There may not be places left by the deadline.

Sponsorship & Awards
CPE and LPC fees paid and £4,500 maintenance p.a. (£4,000 outside London and Guildford).

Partners	277*
Assistant Solicitors	972*
London-based Trainees	138

** denotes world-wide figures*

Contact
Maia Lawson

Method of Application
Application form

Selection Procedure
1 interview with 2 partners

Closing date for 2002
24 August 2000

Application
Training contracts p.a.	90
Applications p.a.	c.3,000
% interviewed p.a.	c.11%
Required degree grade	2:1

Training
Salary: 1st year(2000)	£21,000
Salary: 2nd year(2000)	£24,000
Holiday entitlement	25 days
% of trainees with a non-law degree p.a.	c.40%
No. of seats available abroad p.a.	c.40

Post-Qualification
Salary (2000)	£33,000
% of trainees offered job on qualification (1999)	98%

Overseas Offices
Amsterdam, Bangkok, Barcelona, Beijing, Berlin, Brussels, Cologne, Frankfurt, Hanoi, Ho Chi Minh City, Hong Kong, Madrid, Milan, Moscow, New York, Paris, Rome, Singapore, Tokyo, Washington DC.

GARRETTS

180 Strand London WC2R 2NN
Tel: (020) 7344 0344 Fax: (020) 7438 2518

Firm Profile
Garretts is a nationwide practice, with an office in London and five further offices around the country. It is also associated with Andersen Legal, a global legal network associated with Andersen Worldwide S.C. Current strengths lie in corporate and IT work.

Main Areas of Work
Corporate; Intellectual Property/Info Technology; Property; Employment & Benefits; Litigation; Pensions & Tax.

Trainee Profile
Successful candidates will have a strong academic background, outgoing personality, relevant work experience and an interest in extra-curricular activities.

Training Environment
Trainees spend six months in four different seats, in a variety of departments. You will have the opportunity to choose your fourth seat which could also be spent in one of their associated offices overseas. Formal training consists of a residential induction course, two day courses at the start of each new placement and professional in-house lectures. Social and sporting activities are encouraged.

Benefits
BUPA; subsidized gym membership; S.T.L.

Vacation Placements
Places for 2000: 60 throughout the UK; Duration: 3 weeks; Remuneration: up to £200 p.w. (1999); Closing Date: n/a.

Sponsorship & Awards
CPE + LPC fees paid and £3,750–£4,000 grant p.a.

Partners	51
Assistant Solicitors	129
Total Trainees	50

Contact
Kate Henry

Method of Application
Application form

Selection Procedure
1 hour interview in London, second interview held in regional office of choice

Closing date for 2002
N/A

Application

Training contracts p.a.	40
Applications p.a.	2,000
% interviewed p.a.	c.20%
Required degree grade	2:1

Training

Salary: 1st year(1999) (London)	£21,000
Holiday entitlement	20 days

GOODMAN DERRICK

90 Fetter Lane London EC4A 1PT
Tel: (020) 7404 0606 Fax: (020) 7831 6407

Firm Profile

Founded in 1954 by Lord Goodman, the firm now has a broad commercial practice and is well known for its media and defamation work, particularly relating to television.

Main Areas of Work

Media 35%; Commercial and General Litigation 25%; Corporate 20%; Property 15%; Charities/Private Client 5%.

Trainee Profile

Candidates must show that they will quickly be able to handle responsibility and deal directly with clients. They must be suited to the firm's work environment, present themselves confidently and be quick thinking and practically-minded.

Training Environment

Training at the firm is based on direct and active involvement with the work of the practice. The PSC is partly carried out at the start of the training contract, with some courses taking place over the following two years, coupled with the firm's general training programme. Trainees are in addition expected to initiate personal research if specialist knowledge needs to be gained for a particular piece of work. Four periods of six months are spent in litigation, property, media (contentious and non-contentious) and company/commercial law. Work groups within these main departments allow you to experience further specialist fields. For example, litigation includes employment work. Your own preferences and aptitude will be monitored by your supervising partner and discussed at monthly meetings and at three-monthly appraisals. The firm has a very friendly and informal environment.

Benefits

Medical Health Insurance, season ticket loan.

Sponsorship & Awards

LPC fees plus maintenance grant.

Partners	15
Assistant Solicitors	16
Total Trainees	5

Contact

Nicholas Armstrong

Method of Application

CV and covering letter

Selection Procedure

2 interviews

Closing date for 2002

End August 2000

Application

Training contracts p.a.	3
Applications p.a.	1200
% interviewed p.a.	2%
Required degree grade	min. 2:1

Training

Salary: 1st year (1999)	£18,500
Salary: 2nd year (1999)	£19,500
Holiday entitlement	20 days
% of trainees with a non-law degree p.a.	0%

Post-Qualification

Salary (1999)	£30,500
% of trainees offered job on qualification (1999)	100%
% of assistants (as at 1/9/99) who joined as trainees	40%
% of partners (as at 1/9/99) who joined as trainees	26%

GOULDENS

10 Old Bailey, London, EC4M 7NG
Tel: (020) 7583 7777 Fax: (020) 7583 6777
Email: recruit@gouldens.com
Website: www.gouldens.com

Firm Profile

Gouldens is a leading commercial firm based in the City of London with a high quality client base in the UK and abroad. It provides a full range of legal services to major commercial clients from the UK and overseas.

Main Areas of Work

Company/Commercial (incl Corporate Tax) 42%; Property (inc. Planning) 23%; Litigation (incl IP) 20%; Banking/Capital Markets 12%; Personal/International Tax Planning 3%.

Trainee Profile

Candidates should have obtained or are predicted a 2:1 degree in any discipline. They should be willing to accept the challenge of responsibility in an atmosphere where not only technical expertise but flair, originality and enthusiasm are rewarded.

Training Environment

The firm operates a non-rotational system of training which is unique in the City. Trainees receive work simultaneously from all departments in the firm and see matters through from start to finish. They are encouraged to assume their own workload which allows for early responsibility and development of potential at a faster rate than might otherwise be the case, and more extensive client contact. Work will vary from small cases which you may handle alone (with appropriate supervision) to larger matters where you will assist a partner or an assistant solicitor. Practical experience is supported by a full training programme, including twice-weekly seminars as well as regular sessions. Provided performance during training has been good, the firm aims to offer jobs to all trainees on qualification.

Benefits

BUPA, season ticket loan, subsidised sports club membership, group life cover.

Vacation Placements

Places for 2000:
Summer (law): 35 : 2 weeks: £225 : closing date 28/2
Easter (non-law): 7 : 2 weeks : £225 : closing date 28/2
Christmas (non-law): 14 : 2 weeks : £225 : closing date 30/10

Sponsorship & Awards

CPE and LPC fees paid and £4,500 maintenance p.a.

Partners	37
Assistant Solicitors	75
Total Trainees	26

Contact

Jeanette Ryan

Method of Application

Letter and CV

Selection Procedure

2 interviews with partners

Closing date for 2002

30 October 2000

Application

Training contracts p.a.	20
Applications p.a.	2,500
% interviewed p.a.	10%
Required degree grade	2.1

Training

Salary: 1st year(2000)	£25,000
Salary: 2nd year(2000)	£27,000
Holiday entitlement	4 weeks
% of trainees with a non-law degree p.a.	25%

Post-Qualification

Salary (2000)	£40,000
% of trainees offered job on qualification (1999)	100%
% of assistants (as at 1/9/99) who joined as trainees	55%
% of partners (as at 1/9/99) who joined as trainees	52%

HALLIWELL LANDAU

St. James's Court Brown St Manchester M2 2JF
Tel: (0161) 835 3003 Fax: (0161) 835 2994
Email: info@halliwells.com

Firm Profile

Halliwell Landau is one of Manchester's largest commercial law firms. Over the last few years the firm has increased substantially in both size and turnover and now has in excess of 120 fee earners. This development leads to a continuing requirement for solicitors and has given rise to more internal promotions to partnerships.

Main Areas of Work

Corporate/Banking 24%; Commercial Litigation 20%; Commercial Property 17%; Insolvency 12%; Insurance Litigation 12%; Planning/Environmental law 4%; Trust and Estate Planning 4%; Intellectual Property 4%; Employment 3%.

Trainee Profile

Candidates need to show a good academic ability but do not necessarily need to have studied law at University. They should demonstrate an ability to fit into a hardworking team. In particular Halliwell Landau is looking for candidates who will develop with the firm after their initial training.

Training Environment

Each trainee will spend six months in at least three separate departments. These will usually include commercial litigation, corporate and property. So far as possible if an individual trainee has a particular request for experience in one of the more specialist departments then that will be accommodated. In each department the trainee will work as a member of one of the teams within that department as well as being able to assist other teams. Specific training appropriate to each department will be given and in addition trainees are strongly encouraged to attend the firm's regular seminars on legal and related subjects. There is also a specific training programme for trainees. Each trainee will be assessed both mid-seat and at the end of each seat.

Benefits

A subsidised gym membership is available.

Vacation Placements

Places for 2000: 25; Duration: 2 weeks; Remuneration: £100 p.w.; Closing Date: 31 March 2000.

Sponsorship & Awards

A contribution will be made to either CPE or LPC fees.

Partners	52
Assistant Solicitors	90
Total Trainees	14

Contact
Paul Rose

Method of Application
CV and application form

Selection Procedure
Open days or summer placements

Closing date for 2002
31 July 2000

Application

Training contracts p.a.	8
Applications p.a.	600
% interviewed p.a.	5%
Required degree grade	2:1

Training

Salary: 1st year(2000)	£15,750
Salary: 2nd year(2000)	£16,750

Post-Qualification

Salary (2000)	£26,000
% of trainees offered job on qualification (1999)	100%
% of assistants (as at 1/9/99) who joined as trainees	12%
% of partners (as at 1/9/99) who joined as trainees	9%

HAMMOND SUDDARDS

7 Devonshire Square Cutlers Gardens London EC2M 4YH
2 Park Lane Leeds LS3 1ES
Trinity Court 16 Dalton Street Manchester M6O 8HS
Tel: (020) 7655 1000 Fax: (020) 7655 1001
Website: www.hammondsuddards.co.uk

Firm Profile
Hammond Suddards is a leading commercial law firm with offices in London, Leeds, Manchester and Brussels. They have over 1,300 staff, including 105 partners, 220 solicitors and 45 trainees, and are regarded as innovative, opportunistic and highly successful in the markets in which they operate. The firm's rapid growth has meant they have doubled in size during the last four years.

Main Areas of Work
Banking; Corporate Finance; Commercial Dispute Resolution; Construction; Employment; Financial Services & Corporate Tax; Insolvency; Intellectual Property; Insurance; Pensions; Property.

Trainee Profile
Hammond Suddards seek applications from all disciplines for both vacation work and training contracts. They look for three characteristics: strong academic performance, work experience in the legal sector and significant achievement in non-academic pursuits.

Training Environment
Around 25 trainee solicitors are recruited each year who each carry out six four-month seats during their training contract. All trainees are required to move around the offices during their training and subsidised trainee accommodation is provided in all our locations to facilitate this process. Trainees can choose their seats as they progress through the training contract.

Benefits
Subsidised accommodation in all locations. Flexible benefits scheme which allows trainees to choose their own benefits from a range of options.

Vacation Placements
Places for 2000: 35; Duration: 3 weeks; Remuneration: £220 p.w. (London), £170 pw (Leeds and Manchester); Closing Date: 29 February 2000.

Sponsorship & Awards
CPE and LPC fees paid and maintenance grant of £4,100 p.a.

Partners	105
Assistant Solicitors	620
Total Trainees	45

Contact
Alison Archer
Graduate Recruitment Manager
(London office)

Method of Application
Application form

Selection Procedure
Two Interviews

Closing date for 2002
31 July 2000

Application
Training contracts p.a.	25
Applications p.a.	2,000
% interviewed p.a.	3%
Required degree grade	2:1

Training
Salary: 1st year(2000)	£17,000 + accommodation
Salary: 2nd year(2000)	£19,000+ accommodation
Holiday entitlement	23 days
% of trainees with a non-law degree p.a.	25%
No. of seats available abroad p.a.	6

Post-Qualification
Salary (1999) London	£33,500
Other	£25,500
% of trainees accepting job on qualification (1999)	95%

Overseas Offices
Brussels; plus secondment opportunities to Hong Kong.

HARBOTTLE & LEWIS

Hanover House 14 Hanover Square London W1R 0BE
Tel: (020) 7667 5000 Fax: (020) 7667 5100
Email: kbeilby@harbottle.co.uk
Website: www.harbottle.co.uk

Firm Profile
Harbottle & Lewis is recognised for the unique breadth of its practice in the entertainment, media, travel (including aviation) and leisure industries. It undertakes significant corporate commercial and contentious work for clients within these industries including newer industries such as digital mixed media.

Main Areas of Work
Music, film and television production, theatre, broadcasting, computer games and publishing, sport, sponsorship and advertising, aviation, property investment and leisure.

Trainee Profile
Trainees will have demonstrated the high academic abilities, commercial awareness, and initiative necessary to become part of a team advising clients in dynamic and demanding industries.

Training Environment
The two year training contract is divided into four six months seats where trainees will be given experience in a variety of legal skills including company commercial, litigation, intellectual property and real property working within teams focused on the firm's core industries. The firm has a policy of accepting a small number of trainees to ensure they are given relevant and challenging work and are exposed to and have responsibility for a full range of legal tasks. The firm has its own lecture and seminars programme in both legal topics and industry know-how. An open door policy and a pragmatic entrepreneurial approach to legal practice provides a stimulating working environment.

Benefits
Lunch provided; season ticket loans.

Sponsorship & Awards
LPC fees paid and interest free loans towards maintenance.

Partners	17
Assistant Solicitors	55
Total Trainees	10

Contact
Kathy Beilby

Method of Application
CV and letter

Selection Procedure
Interview

Closing date for 2002
31 July 2000

Application

Training contracts p.a.	5
Applications p.a.	800
% interviewed p.a.	5%
Required degree grade	2:1

Training

Salary: 1st year(2000)	£20,000
Salary: 2nd year(2000)	£21,000

Holiday entitlement
in the first year - 21 days
in the second year - 26 days

% of trainees with a non-law degree p.a.	40%

Post-Qualification

Salary (2000)	£31,500
% of trainees offered job on qualification (1999)	75%

HARVEY INGRAM OWSTON

20 New Walk Leicester LE1 6TX
Tel: (0116) 254 5454 Fax: (0116) 255 4559
Email: cvf@hio.co.uk

Partners	26
Assistant Solicitors	30
Total Trainees	6

Contact
Mr Chris Finlay

Method of Application
CV followed by application form

Closing date for 2002
31 August 2000

Firm Profile
Located in Leicester, Harvey Ingram Owston is one of the East Midlands' leading commercial law firms. They are ambitious and forward-looking in their approach and committed to providing all their clients with an efficient and friendly service.

Main Areas of Work
The firm is divided into four main departments – Company and Commercial, Property, Litigation and Probate and Trust.

Trainee Profile
Harvey Ingram Owston looks for applicants with a good academic record. Successful applicants have a practical and disciplined approach to their work together with the virtues of common sense, flexibility, strong communication skills and a sense of humour.

Training Environment
Harvey Ingram Owston places great emphasis on training and career development. Trainee Solicitors usually spend at least five months in each of the firm's main departments and thus gain a broad experience in all the different aspects of legal work. Trainees are encourageed to take on responsibility at an early stage but support and supervision is always on hand. Trainee Solicitors have regular individual meetings with the training partner to discuss the progress of the trainee. Salaries are competitive and are generally increased during the training contract. The long term prospects are very good for successful applicants for training contracts.

Sponsorship & Awards
Assistance with LPC funding is considered on application.

HEMPSONS

33 Henrietta Street Covent Garden London WC2E 8NH
Tel: (020) 7836 0011 Fax: (020) 7836 2783
Email: london-hempsons@btinternet.com

Firm Profile

With offices in London, Manchester and Harrogate, Hempsons is recognised as a leading national practice in the provision of legal services to the NHS, hospital trusts and healthcare professionals. The firm also provides specialist legal services to a range of charity clients. The practice has expanded considerably in the recent past and now totals more than 300 members.

Main Areas of Work

Medical Litigation 38%; Healthcare 15%; Partnership 15%; Commercial Property 12%; Commercial Litigation/ Defamation 10%; Charity 10%.

Trainee Profile

The firm looks for intellectual rigour and a sound academic record together with emotional maturity and evidence of an ability to empathise with clients' needs. Genuinely open-minded about a candidate's age and degree discipline, they are not searching for one particular type of personality as they recognise the importance of a varied team. Relevant work experience is useful and preference is sometimes given to candidates seeking to become dually qualified in law and a medical discipline.

Training Environment

The trainee typically undertakes four six-month seats. Depending on the office in which the trainee is based, these will be drawn from a combination of some of the following: healthcare litigation; employment; partnership; PFI; defamation; commercial property; commercial litigation; crime; probate and trusts; charities. The trainee is allocated to a team and sits with a partner or senior solicitor in each seat. A local partner has reponsibility for the trainees in that office (typically four) and meets regularly with each trainee to review progress and deal with any problems arising. A senior partner monitors consistency, progress and development across the three offices. An open door policy applies and trainees are regarded very much as an integral part of the team to which they have been allocated. The atmosphere is friendly and forward thinking.

Benefits

Non-contributory pension. Season ticket loan for London based trainees. Holiday entitlement: 20 Days. Life cover.

Partners	28
Assistant Solicitors	74
Total Trainees	10

Contact

Trainee Solicitor Co-ordinator, London office

Method of Application

Application form and covering letter.

Selection Procedure

2 interviews. Second interviews held in London.

Closing date for 2002

To be decided

Application

Training contracts p.a.	6

HERBERT SMITH

Exchange House Primrose Street London EC2A 2HS
Tel: (020) 7374 8000 Fax: (020) 7374 0888
Email: herbertsmith@dial.pipex.com
Website: www.herbertsmith.com

Firm Profile

A major City firm with an international dimension, Herbert Smith has particular strengths in international M&A, corporate finance and international projects with a strong profile in litigation and arbitration. The working environment is strongly team-orientated, friendly and informal, probably as a result of the diverse backgrounds of the firm's partners and staff.

Main Areas of Work

International M&A; Corporate Finance and Banking (including Capital Markets); Energy; Projects and Project Finance; Competition; Property; International Litigation; Arbitration.

Trainee Profile

Trainees need common sense, self-confidence and intelligence to make their own way in a large firm. They are typically high-achieving and intelligent, numerate and literate with general and legal work experience.

Training Environment

Structured training and supervision are designed to allow trainees to experience a unique range of both contentious and non-contentious work and take on responsibilities as soon as they can. You will work within partner-led teams and have your own role. Individual strengths will be monitored, developed and utilised. On-the-job training is divided into four six-month seats: three in the firm's major areas of practice and one abroad or in a specialist area. Lectures and case studies will take up 30 days of the contract and the firm runs its own legal development programme. There are good social and sporting activities and a life outside work is positively encouraged.

Benefits

PRP, gym, private health insurance, season ticket loan, life assurance.

Vacation Placements

Places for 2000: 90; Duration: 1x1 week; 1x2 weeks; 3x3 weeks; Remuneration: £200 p.w.; Closing Date: Mid-February.

Sponsorship & Awards

CPE and LPC fees paid and £4,500 maintenance p.a. (£4,000 outside London).

Partners	148*
Assistant Solicitors	370*
Total Trainees	150

** denotes world-wide figures*

Contact
Sharon Stelling

Method of Application
Application form

Selection Procedure
Interview

Closing date for 2002
31 October 2000

Application

Training contracts p.a.	90
Applications p.a.	2,000
% interviewed p.a.	10%
Required degree grade	2:2

Training

Salary: 1st year(2000)	£21,000
Salary: 2nd year(2000)	£24,000
Holiday entitlement	23 days
% of trainees with a non-law degree p.a.	c. 40%

Post-Qualification

Salary (2000)	£33,000
% of trainees offered job on qualification (1999)	93%

Overseas Offices
Bangkok, Beijing, Brussels, Hong Kong, Moscow, Paris, Singapore.

HEWITSON BECKE + SHAW

42 Newmarket Road Cambridge CB5 8EP
Tel: (01604) 233 233 Fax: (01223) 316511
Email: mail@hewitsons.com (for all offices)
Website: www.hbslaw.co.uk (for all offices)

Firm Profile
Established in 1865, the firm handles mostly company and commercial work, but has a growing body of public sector clients. The firm has three offices: Cambridge, Northampton and Saffron Walden.

Main Areas of Work
Four sections: Corporate, Technology, Property and Private Client.

Trainee Profile
The firm is interested in applications from candidates who have achieved a high degree of success in academic studies and who are bright, personable and able to take the initiative.

Training Environment
The firm offers four six-month seats.

Benefits
The PSC is provided by the College of Law during the first year of the Training Contract. This is coupled with an extensive programme of Trainee Solicitor Seminars provided by specialist in-house lawyers.

Vacation Placements
Places for 2000: a few placements are available, application is by way of letter and CV to Caroline Lewis; Duration: 1–2 weeks.

Sponsorship & Awards
Funding for the CPE and/or LPC is not provided.

Partners	52
Assistant Solicitors	44
Total Trainees	19

Contact
Caroline Lewis
7 Spencer Parade
Northampton NN1 5AB

Method of Application
Firm's application form

Selection Procedure
Interview

Closing date for 2002
End of August 2000

Application
Training contracts p.a.	15
Applications p.a.	1,400
% interviewed p.a.	10%
Required degree grade	2:1 min

Training
Salary: 1st year(1999)	£14,500
Salary: 2nd year(1999)	£15,500
Holiday entitlement	22 days
% of trainees with a non-law degree p.a.	50%

Post-Qualification
Salary (2000)	Under review
% of trainees offered job on qualification (1998)	57%
% of assistants (as at 1/9/98) who joined as trainees	31%
% of partners (as at 1/9/98) who joined as trainees	13%

HOLMAN FENWICK & WILLAN

Marlow House Lloyds Avenue London EC3N 3AL
Tel: (020) 7488 2300 Fax: (020) 7481 0316
Email: grad.recruitment@hfw.co.uk

Partners	74
Assistant Solicitors	90
Total Trainees	17

Firm Profile

Holman, Fenwick & Willan is an international law firm and one of the world's leading specialists in maritime transportation, insurance, reinsurance and trade. The firm is a leader in the field of commercial litigation and arbitration and also offers comprehensive commercial and financial advice. Founded in 1883, the firm is one of the largest operating in its chosen fields with a team of over 200 lawyers worldwide, and a reputation for excellence and innovation.

Main Areas of Work

Their range of services include marine, admiralty and crisis management, insurance and reinsurance, commercial litigation and arbitration, international trade and commodities, energy, corporate and financial.

Trainee Profile

Applications are invited from commercially minded undergraduates and graduates of all disciplines with good A-levels and who have, or expect to receive, a IIi degree. Good foreign languages or a scientific or maritime background are an advantage.

Training Environment

During your training period they will ensure that you gain valuable experience in a wide range of areas. They also organise formal training supplemented by a programme of in-house seminars and ship visits in addition to the PSC. Your training development as an effective lawyer will be managed by our Recruitment & Training Partner, Ottilie Sefton, who will ensure that your training is both successful and enjoyable.

Benefits

Private medical insurance, permanent health and accident insurance, subsidised gym membership, season ticket loan.

Vacation Placements

Places for 2000: 12; Duration: 2 weeks.
Dates: 26 June – 7 July/ 17 July – 28 July; Remuneration: £200 p.w.;
Closing Date: Applications accepted 1 Jan – 14 Feb.

Sponsorship & Awards

CPE Funding: Fees paid + £4,000 maintenance.
LPC Funding: Fees paid + £4,000 maintenance.

Contact

Graduate Recruitment Officer

Method of Application

Handwritten letter and typed CV

Selection Procedure

Two interviews with partners

Closing date for 2002

31 July 2000

Application

Training contracts p.a.	7
Applications p.a.	1,000
% interviewed p.a.	2%
Required degree grade	2:1

Training

Salary: 1st year(1999)

1st six months	£21,500
2nd six months	£22,000
3rd six months	£22,500
4th six months	£23,000
Holiday entitlement	20 days
% of trainees with a non-law degree p.a.	30%

Post-Qualification

Salary (1999)	£33,000
% of trainees offered job on qualification (1999)	100%

Overseas Offices

Hong Kong, Nantes, Paris, Piraeus, Rouen, Shanghai and Singapore.

HOLMES HARDINGHAM

22–23 Great Tower Street London EC3R 5AQ
Tel: (020) 7283 0222 Fax: (020) 7283 0768
Email: HoHa@Compuserve.com

Firm Profile

Holmes Hardingham specialises in shipping law and provides a full range of maritime and commercial services, including international road transport matters.

Main Areas of Work

Sale/Purchase Commodities; Salvage; Collision; Cargo Claims: road, rail, air, charter party, bills of lading, yacht matters.

Trainee Profile

A law degree is preferred, though the firm will make exceptions in cases with a strong technical or maritime background. Academic excellence is a pre-requisite in all cases.

Training Environment

Four seats of six-months are spent in shipping, cargo claim (dealing with road, marine and air transport), marine and commodities. The first seat is pre-selected but you are able to choose the order of the following three seats. In every department you will work for a partner and have either your own office or share with a fee earner. Formal training is covered by an externally provided PSC course and by in-house seminars covering the firm's specialist areas of practice. The firm maintains a sociable atmosphere. This is aided by a communal lunch every Monday and Friday.

Benefits

Private health and insurance, interest free season ticket loan.

Vacation Placements

Duration: 1–2 weeks; Remuneration: £250 p.w.;
Closing Date: May 2000.

Sponsorship & Awards

Discretionary funding for LPC.

Partners	12
Assistant Solicitors	9
Total Trainees	4

Contact

Glenn Winter

Method of Application

Letter and CV

Selection Procedure

2 interviews

Closing date for 2002

None

Application

Training contracts p.a.	2
Applications p.a.	500
% interviewed p.a.	10
Required degree grade	2:1

Training

Salary: 1st year(2000)	t.b.a. (currently £21,000)
Salary: 2nd year(2000)	t.b.a. (currently £23,000)
Holiday entitlement	21 days
% of trainees with a non-law degree p.a.	0%
No. of seats available abroad p.a.	1

Post-Qualification

Salary (2000)	t.b.a (currently) £31,000
% of trainees offered job on qualification (1999)	100%
% of assistants (as at 1/9/99) who joined as trainees	42%
% of partners (as at 1/9/99) who joined as trainees	50%

HOWES PERCIVAL

Oxford House Cliftonville Northampton NN1 5PN
Tel: (01604) 230400 Fax: (01604) 620956
Email: law@howes-percival.co.uk
Website: www.howes-percival.co.uk

Firm Profile

The firm is a 27 partner commercial law firm with a committed view to exceeding clients' expectations well into the 21st century. It has four offices throughout the East Midlands and East Anglia. Areas of outstanding strength within the firm include: company commercial (with particular emphasis on corporate finance), commercial property, commercial litigation, employment, tax and private client. The client profile is to be envied by any city firm.

Main Areas of Work

Company Commercial 30%; Commercial Property 25%; Commercial Litigation 20%, Insolvency 10%; Employment 10%; Private Client 5%.

Trainee Profile

Beyond excellent academic qualifications and technical and professional skills, the firm is looking for those with a proven track record in team working, who are commercially aware, innovative, adaptable to change and high on conceptual thinking, analysis and decision making. In addition candidates will be able to demonstrate excellent interpersonal skills.

Training Environment

As the practice is departmentalised, trainees will spend a maximum of six months in four departments (see "Main Areas of Work"). At the Norwich office trainees may also gain experience in agriculture and licensing. Trainees are assigned a departmental training supervisor who, in addition to providing day to day guidance' will formally assess the trainee at three and six month intervals. In addition to PSC training, trainees will receive a tailored in-house training programme, including CPD accredited courses, the firm's own Client Care Programme and IT training.

Benefits

Payment of PSC course fees.

Partners	27
Assistant Solicitors	27
Total Trainees	9

Contact

Mrs K Collyer

Method of Application

Letter and firm's form

Selection Procedure

Assessment centres including second interview with training principal and partner

Closing date for 2002

31 July 2000

Application

Training contracts p.a.	6
Applications p.a.	300
% interviewed p.a.	13%
Required degree grade	2:1

Training

Salary: 1st year(2000)	£15,500
Salary: 2nd year(2000)	£16,750
Holiday entitlement	23 days

Post-Qualification

% of trainees offered job on qualification (1999)	66%
% of assistants (as at 1/9/99) who joined as trainees	6%
% of partners (as at 1/9/99) who joined as trainees	7.5%

INCE & CO

Knollys House 11 Byward Street London EC3R 5EN
Tel: (020) 7623 2011 Fax: (020) 7623 3225
Email: sarah.bosley@ince.co.uk

Firm Profile
Since its foundation in 1870, Ince & Co has specialised in international commercial law and is best known for its shipping and insurance work.

Main Areas of Work
Shipping & International Trade 40%; Insurance/Reinsurance 40%; Professional Indemnity 10%; Company, Commercial Property 10%.

Trainee Profile
Hard-working competitive individuals with initiative who relish challenge and responsibility within a team environment. Academic achievements, positions of responsibility, sport and travel are all taken into account.

Training Environment
Trainees sit with four different partners for six months at a time throughout their training. Under close supervision, they are encouraged from an early stage to meet and visit clients, interview witnesses, liaise with counsel, deal with technical experts and handle opposing lawyers. They will quickly build up a portfolio of cases from a number of partners involved in a cross-section of the firm's practice and will see their cases through from start to finish. They will also attend in-house and outside lectures, conferences and seminars on practical and legal topics.

Benefits
STL, corporate health cover, PHI, Discretionary Bonus.

Vacation Placements
Places for 2000: 16; Duration: 2 weeks; Remuneration: £200 p.w.; Closing Date: 18th February 2000.

Sponsorship & Awards
LPC fees, £4,000 grant for study in London, £3,500 grant for study elsewhere.

Partners	54*
Assistant Solicitors	72*
Total Trainees	23

** denotes world-wide figures*

Contact
Sarah Bosley

Method of Application
Typed/handwritten letter and CV

Selection Procedure
Interview with 2 partners from Recruitment Committee and a written test

Closing date for 2002
1 September 2000

Application
Training contracts p.a.	10
Applications p.a.	1,200
% interviewed p.a.	5%
Required degree grade	2:1

Training
Salary: 1st year(2000)	£21,000
Salary: 2nd year(2000)	£23,000
Holiday entitlement	22 days
% of trainees with a non-law degree p.a.	55%

Post-Qualification
Salary (2000)	£32,000
% of trainees offered job on qualification (1999)	91%
% of assistants (as at 1999) who joined as trainees	65%
% of partners (as at 1999) who joined as trainees	76%

Overseas Offices
Hong Kong, Singapore, Piraeus (consultancy)

IRWIN MITCHELL

St. Peter's House Hartshead Sheffield S1 2EL
Recruitment line: (0114) 274 4580 Fax: (0114) 272 9346
Email: enquiries@irwinmitchell.co.uk
Website: www.irwinmitchell.co.uk

Firm Profile

Irwin Mitchell is a rapidly expanding 76 partner practice with over 1300 employees and offices in Sheffield, Leeds, Birmingham and London. The firm is particularly well known for commercial law, commercial litigation, insurance law, business crime and plaintiff personal injury litigation. Their strong reputation for dealing with novel and complex areas of law and handling developmental cases (such as the vibration white finger and CJD cases and the Matrix-Churchill 'arms to Iraq' affair) means that they can offer a broad range of experience within each of their specialist departments, giving trainees a high standard of training.

Main Areas of Work

Corporate Services 37%; Plaintiff Personal Injury 28%; Insurance Litigation 17%; Private Client 12%; Police Prosecutions 6%.

Trainee Profile

Irwin Mitchell is looking for well motivated individuals with a real commitment to the law and who can demonstrate above average academic and social ability. Law and non-law graduates are recruited. Foreign languages and IT skills are an asset. The firm believes that trainees are an investment for the future and as such they prefer to keep their trainees once they qualify.

Training Environment

The two-year Training Contract consists of 4 seats. Our trainees also benefit from an Induction programme, monthly training meetings and the Professional Skills Course which is organised and financed by the firm. Each trainee has a review every 3 months with their supervising partner. There are numerous other activities in which trainees are encouraged to participate, eg. team skills challenges, conferences, mock trials.

Vacation Placements

Places for 2000: 30; Duration: 2 weeks; Remuneration: £75 p.w.; Closing Date: 1 March 2000.

Sponsorship & Awards

CPE and LPC fees paid and £3,000 maintenance grant.

Partners	76
Assistant Solicitors	132
Total Trainees	30

Contact

Sue Lenkowski/Tracey Easton

Method of Application

Brochures and application forms are available from the Human Resources Dept. Call the recruitment line between 1 March and 30 July

Selection Procedure

Assessment centres and interviews are held in late August and early September and successful candidates are invited to a second interview with 2 partners

Closing date for 2002

31 July 2000

Application

Training contracts p.a.	15
Applications p.a.	1,000
% interviewed p.a.	6%

Training

Salary: 1st year(2000)	£15,500
Salary: 2nd year(2000)	£17,500
Holiday entitlement	23 days
% of trainees with a non-law degree p.a.	44.5%

Post-Qualification

% of trainees offered job on qualification (1999)	64%
% of assistants (as at 1/9/99) who joined as trainees	32%
% of partners (as at 1/9/99) who joined as trainees	16%

JEFFREY GREEN RUSSELL

Apollo House 56 New Bond Street London W1Y OSX
Tel: (020) 7339 7000 Fax: (020) 7339 7001
Email: jgr@jgrlaw.co.uk
Website: www.jgrweb.com

Partners	26
Assistant Solicitors	20
Total Trainees	4

Firm Profile
Jeffrey Green Russell is a medium-sized commercial law firm with strong international connections based in New Bond Street, London. The firm is determined to excel on its clients behalf. It works hard to find the best and most cost effective solutions to their problems. The firm tries to be innovators not imitators, providing a rapid and constructive response to its clients' increasingly specialised needs. JGR is a founder member of ACL International, an association of commercial lawyers, providing members with access to an effective global legal service, beneficial for international business requirements.

Main Areas of Work
JGR has a diverse client base and specialises in company/commercial and taxation, litigation, white-collar crime, insurance litigation, property, gaming, licensing and leisure, and private client. Most of its clients are in commerce, finance and industry, and range in size from small businesses to multinational corporations. Their activities are wide-ranging and include banking, finance, technology, leisure and the licensed trade, insurance, and property.

Trainee Profile
The firm welcomes intelligent, enthusiatic, and ambitious individuals, who are not afraid of responsibility, and are keen to learn from experienced lawyers who will guide them through their training period. Not only should they undertake work with dilligence and care, and strive to develop negotiating skills, but should consider the variety of needs of both individual and corporate clients.

Training Environment
Trainees are supervised through the various departments, including company/commercial. litigation, property, and licensing. To maxamise our efficiency and productivity, and to provide cost effective services, the firm has for many years been making major investments in sophisticated office technology. Accordingly trainees should have a keen interest in utilising office technology and be willing to develop these skills alongside their legal training to encourage the highest-quality service with speed. Visit the firm's website for further information.

Contact
Mark Spragg

Method of Application
CV with covering letter

Selection Procedure
Room will be made available for exceptional candidates.

Closing date for 2002
No time limits because the firm has no specific vacancies to fill.

Application
Training contracts p.a. 4

KENNEDYS

Longbow House 14-20 Chiswell Street London EC1Y 4TW
Tel: (020) 7614 3681 Fax: (020) 7614 3861
Email: personnel@kennedys-law.com
Website: www.kennedys-law.com

Firm Profile
Kennedys is a medium-sized international City firm which has grown considerably in recent years. The firm is primarily known as an insurance-driven commercial litigation practice, although it is also recognised for its skills in the non-contentious commercial field. The firm has 45 partners and over 300 staff located in four offices in the UK, including two in London. The firm's associated offices in New York, San Francisco, Paris, New Delhi, Karachi and Hong Kong, together with its in-house European lawyers in London, ensure that it can advise its clients on all their commercial problems within most jurisdictions.

Main Areas of Work
Insurance Litigation 83%; Company/Commercial 6%; Employment 6%; Construction (non-contentious) 3%; Commercial Property 2%.

Trainee Profile
Kennedys are looking for ambitious people with creative practical, problem-solving skills. Successful candidates will be those who combine independence of thought with the ability to work as part of a team. Requirements are a minium 2:1 degree which may or may not be in law. Fluency in a major European langauge is a positive asset.

Training Environment
At Kennedys the emphasis will be on commercial litigation but trainees will also undertake non-contentious work in company/commercial and commercial departments. Trainees may also spend some time in the construction, medical negligence, personal injury, banking and employment teams. There may also be opportunities for training abroad, particularly France and Germany.

Benefits
Life assurance, PHI, private medical insurance, season ticket loan, subsidised gym membership.

Vacation Placements
Places for 2000: 10

Sponsorship & Awards
£9,000 towards fees and assistance for LPC only.

Partners	45
Assistant Solicitors	45
Total Trainees	14

Contact
Gina Suleyman

Method of Application
Handwritten letter, CV and application form.

Selection Procedure
Minimum of one interview with two Partners and Director of Personnel

Closing date for 2002
12 August 2000

Application
Training contracts p.a.	10
Applications p.a.	1500
% interviewed p.a.	3%
Required degree grade	2:1

Training
Salary: 1st year(1999)	£19,000
Salary: 2nd year(1999)	£20,000
Holiday entitlement	25 days

Post-Qualification
Salary (1999)	£30,500
% of trainees offered job on qualification (1999)	95%

Overseas Offices
Hong Kong

Associated Offices
New York, San Francisco, Paris, New Delhi, Karachi.

KNIGHT & SONS

The Brampton, Newcastle under Lyme ST5 0QW
Tel: (01782) 619 225 Fax: (01782) 717 260
Email: ttpc@knightandsons.co.uk
2nd Floor, 75 Mosley Street, Manchester M2 3HR
Tel: (0161) 281 4000 Fax: (0161) 281 4010
Email: man@knightandsons.co.uk
Website: www.knightandsons.co.uk

Firm Profile

Knight & Sons is a medium sized, commercially orientated firm with a strong private client department. The firm was founded in 1767 and it has 14 partners and approximately 120 members of staff. The firm has recently expanded, opening an office in Manchester and is committed to taking full advantage of legal and technological developments.

Main Areas of Work

The firm's main areas of work are Commercial Property 30%; Corporate and Commercial 27%; Commercial Litigation 26%; Tax, Trust and Private Client 11%; Brewery and Licensing 6%.

Trainee Profile

The firm is keen to recruit trainees who will stay on once they have qualified. Successful candidates are commercially aware, proactive and outgoing in character. Languages, computer literacy and outstanding academic achievement are desirable.

Training Environment

Trainees generally spend six months in each of the four main departments (litgation, commercial property, company commercial and tax, trusts and private client), but may also gain experience in the specialist units such as planning and environmental, employment, personal injury, agriculture and charity. The firm runs in-house skills-based programmes designed to enhance business and client care skills for all fee-earners. The atmosphere is lively and a social committee organises events throughout the year ranging from a summer ball to a quiz night.

Benefits

Subsidised gym membership.

Vacation Placements

Applications to be received by :
31 October for the following Christmas
28 February for the following Easter
30 April for the following Summer

Sponsorship and Awards

Interest free loans may be available but are strictly subject to individual negotiation.

Trainees	7
Partners	14

Contact
Zoe Theofilopoulos

Method of Application
Please make a handwritten application supported by CV.

Closing date for 2002
By 31 July each year to begin two years hence.

Application
Training contracts p.a. 3-4

Starting salary
Above Law Society minimum with a review each six months

Minimum qualifications
2.1 degree

Offices
Newcastle under Lyme, Manchester

LANDWELL

St Andrew's House 20 St Andrew Street
London EC4A 3TL
Tel: (020) 7212 1616 Fax: (020) 7212 1570
Email: gr.landwell@uk.pwcglobal.com
Website: www.landwell.co.uk

Firm Profile

Landwell in the UK is one of the fastest growing law firms in the City. It is the UK correspondent law firm for PricewaterhouseCoopers, the world's largest professional services organisation. The firm works with specialists in corporate finance, management consulting and tax to provide integrated solutions. The firm is a member of the PwC international law practice, which has over 1,400 lawyers in over 40 jurisdictions.

Main Areas of Work

Full range of legal services across the business spectrum including corporate, E-business, intellectual property, financial services, employment, immigration, pensions, real estate, competition, international trade and regulation.

Trainee Profile

A strong academic record, with excellent interpersonal skills and awareness and interest in the main issues affecting the business world.

Training Environment

The firm was established in 1998 and has a dynamic and open culture. Trainee lawyers will have experience in at least four areas of law, including corporate and they are actively encouraged to take early responsibility, with appropriate supervision and support. The firm will develop your technical expertise, business and interpersonal skills and on qualification, aim to accommodate all trainees in their preferred area of specialisation.

Benefits

Interest-free season ticket loan, permanent health insurance, life assurance, private medical cover, subsidised restaurant and fitness centre.

Vacation Placements

Places for 2000: up to 20; Duration: Two week scheme. 19-30 June and 3-14 July 2000; Closing Date: 25 February 2000.

Sponsorship & Awards

CPE and LPC: fees and £4,500 maintenance.

Partners	16
Assistant Solicitors	77
Total Trainees	3

Contact
Graduate Recruitment

Method of Application
Firm's application form

Selection Procedure
Interview and written test

Closing date for 2002
31 August 2000

Application

Training contracts p.a.	45
Required degree grade	2:1

Training

Salary: 1st year(1999)	1st seat £21,000
Salary: 2nd year(1999)	4th seat £24,000
Holiday entitlement	22 days

Post-Qualification

Salary (1999)	£35,000

LAWRENCE GRAHAM

190 Strand London WC2R 1JN
Tel: (020) 7759 6694 Fax: (020) 7379 6854
Email: graduate@lawgram.com
Website: www.lawgram.com

Partners	78
Assistant Solicitors	97
Total Trainees	29

Firm Profile

Lawrence Graham is a growing firm with a broad client base, which includes many UK and international public and private companies, pension funds, financial institutions, shipping companies, small businesses and private individuals. The firm's business is divided into four main practice areas: Commercial Property, Company & Commercial, Litigation and Tax & Financial Management. Each of the four main practice areas is organised into specialised teams. The firm has associations with many law firms throughout the world, including North America, Europe and the Far East. It also has an office in the Ukraine where the firm has had clients since the 1920s.

Main Areas of Work

Property 36%; Company & Commercial 29%, Litigation 17%, Tax & Financial Management 12%, Shipping 6%.

Trainee Profile

Trainees, who are normally of 2.1 calibre, should demonstrate strong technical and interpersonal skills, the ability to understand a client's commercial priorities and objectives and the judgement to deal with complex problems.

Training Environment

Trainees are given the opportunity to learn both formally and practically. Seminars are regularly held throughout the two years. Training consits of four six-month seats including a position in each of the Company & Commercial, Litigation and Property departments. The fourth seat can be in either one of the main departments or with Tax & Financial Management. Each trainee is assigned a mentor. All work is supervised but independence and responsibility increases with experience. Social events including sporting events are also organized.

Benefits

Season ticket loan, on-site gym.

Vacation Placements

Places for 2000: 20-24; Duration: 2 weeks during Easter break and 3x2 weeks between June-August; Remuneration: £200 p.w.; Closing Date: 28 February 2000.

Sponsorship & Awards

CPE Funding: Course Fees and £3,750 maintenance grant.
LPC Funding: Course Fees and £3,750 maintenance grant.

Contact

The Graduate Recruitment Officer

Method of Application

Firm's application form.
For Law: After 2nd year results
For Non-Law: After final results

Selection Procedure

Interview and written exercise

Closing date for 2002

12 August 2000

Application

Training contracts(2002)	15
Applications p.a.	1,500
Required degree grade	2:1

Training

Salary: 1st year(2000)	£21,000
Salary: 2nd year(2000)	£24,000
% of trainees with a non-law degree p.a.	Varies

Post-Qualification

Salary (2000)	£34,000
% of trainees offered job on qualification (1999)	90%
% of assistants (as at 1/9/99) who joined as trainees	42%
% of partners (as at 1/9/99) who joined as trainees	32%

LAWRENCE TUCKETTS

Bush House 72 Prince Street Bristol BS99 7JZ
Tel: (0117) 929 5252 Fax: (0117) 929 8313
Email: connect@lawrence-tucketts.co.uk

Partners	19
Assistant Solicitors	33
Total Trainees	9

Firm Profile
A progressive, expanding commercial practice advising business and private clients. Particular strengths are in Company & Commercial, Property & Planning, Environmental and Dispute Resolution.

Main Areas of Work
Dispute Resolution 38%; Commercial and Corporate 35%; Commercial Property and Planning 25%.

Trainee Profile
A strong academic background is preferred, but the firm appreciates that this is not the only indicator of intelligence, and a resourceful personality is also a consideration. Any other interesting responsibilities/experiences are also considered.

Training Environment
Trainees indicate their preference for three or four seats of six months each, which the firm tries to match. Although it is not essential for trainees to specialise in their first year, they are encouraged to develop their chosen field in the second. Trainees will be allocated a dedicated supervisor in each department. All trainees sit with another lawyer, but in every case their work is drawn from all parts of the team or department so that they gain as much experience as possible. Review meetings are held regularly. Lawrence Tucketts strives to give you a high level of responsibility and involvement, while ongoing lectures are designed to extend your knowledge. Sports and social activities are available.

Benefits
Subsidised health insurance, subsidised sports and health club facility.

Vacation Placements
A minimum of 8 places each year.

Sponsorship & Awards
Interest paid on loan for LPC up to £6,000.

Contact
Human Resources

Method of Application
Firm's application form

Selection Procedure
Assessment Day

Closing date for 2002
31 July 2000

Application

Training contracts p.a.	8
Applications p.a.	900
% interviewed p.a.	1.5%
Required degree grade	n/a

Training

Holiday entitlement	4 weeks
% of trainees with a non-law degree p.a.	50%

Post-Qualification

Salary (2000)	market rate
% of trainees offered job on qualification (1999)	100%
% of assistants (as at 1/9/99) who joined as trainees	25%
% of partners (as at 1/9/99) who joined as trainees	25%

LAWRENCE TUCKETTS
Solicitors

LAYTONS

Carmelite 50 Victoria Embankment Blackfriars
London EC4Y 0LS
Tel: (020) 7842 8000 Fax: (020) 7842 8080
Email: laytonsl@laytons.com

Partners	29
Assistant Solicitors	42
Total Trainees	14

Firm Profile

Laytons works closely with clients in long term relationships. The firm combines a range of complementary fields of focused legal expertise with knowledge of the client and its business and a creative, energetic approach to achieving objectives and adding value. High service quality and client care, together with the provision of advice which is technically and commercially effective, are of paramount importance.

Main Areas of Work

Company/Commercial 33%; Commercial Property/Land Development 20%; General Litigation 19%; Building Litigation 11%; Employment 8%; Private Client 5%; Insolvency 4%.

Trainee Profile

Trainees form part of the professional team immediately they start and gain early client contact alongside qualified lawyers. Working closely with a partner, trainees are encouraged to take progressive responsibility whilst undergoing their training programme. Requirements are a first or 2:1 hons degree from a good university, together with a commitment to achieve excellent results and a sense of humour.

Training Environment

Trainees are placed in four six-month seats in each of the firm's principal departments: Company Commercial, Property, Litigation and Private Client.

Vacation Placements

Places for 2000: 6; Duration: 1 week; Closing Date: March 2000.

Sponsorship & Awards

CPE and LPC Funding.

Contact
Ian Burman

Method of Application
Application form

Selection Procedure
2 interviews

Closing date for 2002
31 August 2000

Application
Training contracts p.a. 2
Applications p.a. 2,000
% interviewed p.a. 5%
Required degree grade 1 or 2:1

Training
Salary: 1st year(2000) Market rate
Salary: 2nd year(2000) Market rate
Holiday entitlement 22 days

Post-Qualification
Salary (2000) Market rate
% of trainees offered job on qualification (1999) 83%
% of assistants (as at 1999) who joined as trainees 73%
% of partners (as at 1999) who joined as trainees 22%

LE BRASSEUR J TICKLE

Drury House 34–43 Russell Street London WC2B 5HA
Tel: (020) 7836 0099 Fax: (020) 7831 2215
Email: enquiries@lbjt.co.uk
6–7 Park Place Leeds LS1 2RU
Tel: (0113) 234 1220 Fax: (0113) 234 1573

Firm Profile

Le Brasseur J Tickle has an enviable reputation for tradition and excellence. The firm has 24 partners and approximately 135 members of staff. The firm is located in two major commercial and legal centres, London and Leeds, from which legal expertise is provided to all types of clients from multinational corporations to individuals.

Main Areas of Work

Health Care: 40%; Personal Injury: 10%; Employment: 10%; Company Commercial: 15%; Commercial Property: 10%; Commercial Litigation: 15%.

Trainee Profile

Le Brasseur J Tickle looks to recruit trainees from a broad academic background with good intellectual ability and an assured outgoing personality who will prove to be responsive to the needs of the firm's clients. When recruiting trainees, the partners look to the future and to appointing trainees as assistant solicitors following qualification. Indeed a significant number of partners trained with the firm.

Training Environment

The firm provides an extensive legal and skills training programme for trainee solicitors and other qualified staff in addition to on-the-job training. Trainees are introduced to the firm with an indication programme covering the work of the firm's departments, the major clients, procedural matters and professional conduct. Training consists of four six-month seats in the following areas: Company Commercial; Commercial Property; Health Care Law; and General Litigation. Every endeavour is made to allocate the final seat following discussion in to the area of law in which the trainee wishes to specialise after qualification. You will share an office with a partner, who will assist you and formally review your progress at the end of your seat. The PSC is taught externally. The firm is friendly with an open-door policy and there are various sporting and social events organised throughout the year.

Partners	24
Assistant Solicitors	30
Total Trainees	8

Contact
Training Partner

Method of Application
Letter and CV

Selection Procedure
2 interviews

Closing date for 2002
31 July 2000

Application

Training contracts p.a.	4
Applications p.a.	1,500
% interviewed p.a.	1%

Training

Salary: 1st year(2000)	
(London)	£18,000
(Leeds)	£13,500
Salary: 2nd year(2000)	
(London)	£20,000
(Leeds)	£14,250
Holiday entitlement	4 weeks
% of trainees with a non-law degree p.a.	50%

Post-Qualification

Salary (2000)	
(London)	£30,000
(Leeds)	£22,500
% of trainees offered job on qualification (1999)	100%
% of assistants (as at 1/9/99) who joined as trainees	60%
% of partners (as at 1/9/99) who joined as trainees	50%

LEE BOLTON & LEE

1 The Sanctuary Westminster London SW1P 3JT
Tel: (020) 7222 5381 Fax: (020) 7222 7502
Email: enquiries@1thesanctuary.com

Firm Profile

Founded in 1855 Lee Bolton & Lee is a successful medium sized firm based in Westminster. It is closely associated with parliamentary agents and solicitors, Rees and Freres, who provide a specialist service in parliamentary, public and administrative law.

Main Areas of Work

Commercial; Property; Private Client; Litigation; Charity; Education Work.

Trainee Profile

They seek to recruit trainees with a good degree (2:1 or above), first class communication skills, motivation, professionalism, initiative, enthusiasm, and a sense of humour.

Training Environment

Trainees spend six months in each of four seats: Private Client, Property, Litigation and Commercial Property, sitting with either a senior solicitor or a Partner. Training is comprehensive and covers a full induction programme, participation in internal seminars and training sessions and attendance at external courses, including the Professional Skills Course. Trainees are given responsibility for their own files from the beginning, and whilst this might at first seem daunting, the firm operates an open door policy and help is never far away. Progress is reviewed monthly by your elected Supervisor and every three months by the Training Principal. There are various sporting and social events.

Benefits

Season ticket loan, non-guaranteed bonus.

Sponsorship & Awards

A contribution towards LPC funding but dependent upon being offered a training contract.

Partners	15
Assistant Solicitors	9
Total Trainees	4

Contact

Susie Hust

Method of Application

Letter and CV

Selection Procedure

Panel interview

Closing date for 2002

End July 2000

Application

Training contracts p.a.	2
Applications p.a.	800
% interviewed p.a.	3%
Required degree grade	2:1

Training

Salary: 1st year	£18,000
Salary: 2nd year	£19,000
Holiday entitlement	22 days
% of trainees with a non-law degree p.a.	50%

Post-Qualification

Salary (1999)	£29,000
% of trainees offered job on qualification (1999)	100%
% of assistants (as at 1/9/99) who joined as trainees	33%
% of partners (as at 1/9/99) who joined as trainees	20%

LESTER ALDRIDGE

Russell House Oxford Road Bournemouth BH8 8EX
Tel: (01202) 786161 Fax: (01202) 786110
Email: enquiries@lester-aldridge.co.uk

Partners	30
Assistant Solicitors	17
Total Trainees	8

Firm Profile

Lester Aldridge is one of the largest law firms in central Southern England. It is a progressive and innovative practice, which has adopted a corporate style mangement structure. The firm is market led with an emphasis on the development of specialist units offering expert advice on specific aspects of the law from lawyers who are familiar with a particular industry. Lawyers are encouraged and trained to adopt a commercial approach, seeking legal solutions to business problems. The firm has taken the innovative step of employing non-solicitors e.g. accountants to develop certain areas of the business.

Main Areas of Work

Litigation: 34%; Corporate & Banking and Finance: 26%; Private Client Services: 19%; Commercial Property: 15%; Investment Services: 6%.

Trainee Profile

Candidates should have strong intellectual capabilities, be resourceful and be able to relate easily to other people. IT skills and a team approach are also required.

Training Environment

Trainees receive an extended version of the firm's induction procedure which covers the firm's aims, values and structure, administration and support. Training consisits of four six month seats in the private client, banking and finance, commercial and litigation departments, and trainees are fully integrated menbers of the units they work within. About half way through each seat, trainees discuss their preferences for the next seat with the partner responsible for allocations and every attempt is made to match aspirations to the needs of the firm. Trainees have a training principal for the duration of the contract who will discuss progress every month. They receive a comprehensive formal appraisal from their unit section head towards the end of each seat, and the managing partner also meets all trainees as a group every three months.

Benefits

Life assurance scheme.

Vacation Placements

Places for 2000: 8; Duration: 2 weeks; Remuneration: £60 pw; Closing Date: 31 March 2000.

Sponsorship & Awards

Discretionary

Contact

Ms Juliet Milne

Method of Application

Letter, CV and completed application form

Selection Procedure

Interview by a panel of partners

Closing date for 2002

31 August 2000

Application

Training contracts p.a.	5
Applications p.a.	300
% interviewed p.a.	5%
Required degree grade	2:1

Training

Salary: 1st year(2000)	£14,000
Salary: 2nd year(2000)	£15,000
Holiday entitlement	20 days
% of trainees with a non-law degree p.a.	20%

Post-Qualification

Salary (2000)	£23,500
% of trainees offered job on qualification (1999)	100%
% of assistants (as at 1/9/99) who joined as trainees	30%
% of partners (as at 1/9/99) who joined as trainees	25%

LEWIS SILKIN

Windsor House 50 Victoria Street London SW1H 0NW
Tel: (020) 7227 8000 Fax: (020) 7222 4633
Email: info@lewissilkin.com

Firm Profile
Lewis Silkin places the highest priority on its relationship with clients, excellent technical ability and the commercial thinking of our lawyers. As a result, it is a profitable and distinctive firm, with a friendly and lively style.

Main Areas of Work
The firm has a wide range of corporate clients and provides services through three main departments: corporate, litigation and property. The major work areas are: corporate services, which includes company, commercial and corporate finance; commercial litigation and dispute resolution; employment; marketing services, embracing advertising and marketing law; technology and communications, which includes IT, media and telecommunications; property, construction and project finance.

Trainee Profile
The firm looks for trainees with keen minds and personality, who will fit into a professional but informal team. Law and non-law degrees considered.

Training Environment
Lewis Silkin provides a comprehensive induction and training programme, with practical "hands-on" experience in four six-month seats, three of which will be in one of the main departments. The fourth seat can be in one of the specialist areas. Trainees usually sit with a partner who can give on-going feedback and guidance and progress is formally reviewed every three months. Trainees have the opportunity to get involved in the firm's social and marketing events and also to represent the firm at local trainee solicitors' groups and Law Centres.

Benefits
Life assurance, critical illness cover, health insurance, season ticket loan, subsidised conveyancing costs.

Vacation Placements
Places for 2000: None.

Sponsorship & Awards
Full fees paid for LPC.

Partners	25
Assistant Solicitors	35
Total Trainees	12

Contact
Ruth Willis
Personnel and Training Manger

Method of Application
Covering letter and C.V.

Selection Procedure
Assessment day, including an interview with two partners and an analytical exercise.

Closing date for 2002
31 July 2000

Application
Training contracts p.a.	6
Applications p.a.	1,000
Required degree grade	2:1

Training
Salary: 1st year(2000)	£21,000
Salary: 2nd year(2000)	£22,000
Holiday entitlement	22 days

Post-Qualification
Salary (2000)	£32,000

LINKLATERS

One Silk Street London EC2Y 8HQ
Tel: (020) 7456 2000 Fax: (020) 7456 2222
Email: grecruit@linklaters.com
Website: www.linklaters.com

Firm Profile
Linklaters has developed into one of the largest law firms in the world with over 1,300 fee earners which includes 237 partners and 261 trainee solicitors. In total, staff numbers are over 2500. The firm is a member of Linklaters & Alliance which comprises some of Europe's leading law firms (De Bandt, van Hecke & Lagae, De Brauw Blackstone Westbroek N.V., Gianni, Origoni & Partners, Lagerlöf & Leman, Linklaters and Oppenhoff & Rädler). Linklaters & Alliance operates from 35 offices in 21 countries covering the world's key commercial and business centres globally.

Main Areas of Work
Core businesses include corporate, international finance, project and asset finance, commercial property and litigation. The firm also has specialist groups advising on UK and offshore investment funds, regulatory compliance, insurance, EU and competition and regulation, corporate recovery and insolvency, and employment and employee benefits.

Trainee Profile
The firm looks for high academic achievers with a variety of outside interests. Confidence and commitment to thrive in the strong client centred, commercial environment is vital as is the desire for involvement and responsibility early on in your training. The firm welcomes applications from students of all disciplines. Any language skills are considered advantageous.

Training Environment
From the start of the LPC we want you to feel part of the firm. Therefore we have designed a unique programme to keep in touch and to give you an early understanding of our business and the different practice areas within it. Training begins with a 3 week induction course, incorporating the Professional Skills Course. This is supplemented with many more courses throughout to support your practical experience. Trainees are involved in transactions for blue chip companies from the outset, contributing as a group resource in their chosen departments. Your on-the job training is planned around your preferred practice areas, allowing you to get fully involved in client work and to take on responsibility from your first day. If your preference/interests change at any stage we work with you to develop a new training plan to suit.

Partners	238*
Assistant Solicitors	706*
Total Trainees	261

** denotes world-wide figures*

Contact
Jane Leader

Method of Application
Application form

Selection Procedure
2 Interviews (same day)

Application
Training contracts p.a.	125
Applications p.a.	2,500
% interviewed p.a.	20%
Required degree grade	2:1

Training
Salary: 1st year(2000)	£21,000
Salary: 2nd year(2000)	£24,000
Holiday entitlement	25 days
% of trainees with a non-law degree p.a.	approx. 45%
No. of seats available abroad p.a.	100

Post-Qualification
Salary (2000)	£33,000
% of trainees offered job on qualification (1999)	100%

Overseas Offices
Alicante, Amsterdam, Antwerp, Bangkok, Berlin, Bratislava, Brussels, Bucharest, Budapest, Cologne, Frankfurt, Gothenburg, The Hague, Hong Kong, Leipzig, London, Luxembourg, Madrid, Malmö, Milan, Moscow, Munich, New York, Paris, Prague, Rome, Rotterdam, São Paulo, Shanghai, Singapore, Stockholm, St Petersburg, Tokyo, Washington D.C.

▶

LINKLATERS *continued*

By the end of your training you will have had in-depth experience in your chosen practice area, and a variety of experience in other departments (including offices outside the UK and client secondments) that complements that practice, so the transition to qualification is seamless. The firm's mentoring scheme enables any issues to be discussed openly with colleagues in any department. Trainees are also encouraged to volunteer for pro bono activities supported by the firm and to get involved in the various sporting and social opportunities.

Benefits

PPP medical insurance, life assurance, pension, season ticket loan, in-house gym as well as corporate membership to Holmes Place, in-house dentist, doctor and physiotherapist, 24 hour subsidised staff restaurant.

Vacation Placements

Places for 2000/2001: 80;
Duration: Christmas – 2 weeks.
Easter – 2 weeks.
Summer (2 intakes) – 4 weeks.
Remuneration: £200 p.w. (1999)

Sponsorship & Awards

CPE and LPC fees paid in full. A maintenance grant is also provided of £4,500 for London and £4,000 for outside of London. Language bursaries are also offered, upon completion of the LPC.

LINKLATERS
& ALLIANCE

LOVELLS

White Durrant.

65 Holborn Viaduct London EC1A 2DY
Tel: (020) 7236 0066 Fax: (020) 7248 4212
Email: recruit@lovells.com
Website: www.lovells.com

Firm Profile

One of the largest firms of solicitors based in the City of London with a recognised international practice. Lovells has 12 offices located across North America, Europe and Asia. The breadth of the practice, and a pre-eminence in so many practice areas sets the firm apart from most of its competitors.

Main Areas of Work

Corporate Finance; Banking; EC and Competition Law; Insurance; Litigation; Intellectual Property; Insolvency; Commercial Property.

Trainee Profile

Individualists, not clones, whose keen intelligence extends beyond an excellent degree. A practical and commercial mind is vital, and so is a talent for analytical thinking.

Training Environment

Six-month seats in the four key sectors: corporate, litigation, property and one other specialised commercial sector. In each department you will be assigned a partner or senior solicitor. During each seat, you will have formal and informal reviews to discuss your progress and preferences for subsequent seats. The third seat can be spent in an overseas office or on secondment to the in-house legal department of a major client. Trainees can help with Lovells' pro bono work such as part-time work at law centres or in a Citizens Advice Bureau. Numerous social and sporting activities help staff unwind together.

Benefits

PPP, PHI, season ticket loan, gym membership, staff restaurant, life assurance.

Vacation Placements

Places for 2000: 80; Duration: 2–3 weeks; Remuneration: £200 p.w.; Closing Date: 19/2/00 for Easter and summer, 10/11/00 for Christmas.

Sponsorship & Awards

CPE and LPC course fees are paid, as well as a maintenance grant (in 1999/00) of £4,500 for London and Guildford and £4,000 elsewhere.

Additional Information

Lovells has a number of support systems which ensure you are getting the help you need. You are assigned a 'contact partner'

Partners	172*
Assistant Solicitors	495*
Total Trainees	120

** denotes world-wide figures*

Contact

Clare Walton

Method of Application

Application form

Selection Procedure

Assessment day: interview, group exercise, critical reasoning test

Closing date for 2002

End of October 2000

Application

Training contracts p.a.	80
Applications p.a.	1,800
% interviewed p.a.	30%
Required degree grade	2:1 or better

Training

Salary: 1st year(2000)	£21,000
rising every six months reviewed each May	
Holiday entitlement	25 days
% of trainees with a non-law degree p.a.	30%
No. of seats available abroad p.a.	20

Post-Qualification

Salary (2000)	£33,000

Overseas Offices

Beijing, Brussels, Chicago, Ho Chi Minh City, Hong Kong, Moscow, New York, Paris, Prague, Singapore, Tokyo, Washington DC.

▶

LOVELLS *continued*

during training, who will meet with you regularly, to monitor your progress and help you plan your future. Formal training is also vital during your Training Contract because you will be working in specialised areas. You will also gain an overview of the numerous areas of Lovells' practice. The courses are given by a combination of external and in-house training and have been adapted for, or developed by, the firm. You will also participate in the Professional Skills Course.

Trainee Comments

"I chose to accept a Training Contract from Lovells on the basis of my interest in litigation, the friendliness of the people, and the knowledge of the firm that I had gained during the summer placement." (Julian Craughan, second year trainee, read law at University College London)

"The variety of the work and the amount of client contact really appealed to me – as did Lovells' culture." (Paul Brown, qualified lawyer, read law at Nottingham)

"Despite its size, Lovells constantly impresses me with the remarkable level of efficiency and speed with which it goes about its business." (Tom Harding, first year trainee, read Archaeology and Anthropology, at Peterhouse, Cambridge)

"Lovells views its employees as individuals, and has the foresight to invest in its trainees for the future benefit of the firm." (Rachel Cunningham, second year trainee, read Biological Sciences at Magdalen College, Oxford)

MACE & JONES

19 Water Street Liverpool L2 0RP
Tel: (0151) 236 8989 Fax: (0151) 227 5010
Email: donalbannon@maceandjones.co.uk
14 Oxford Court, Bishopsgate, Manchester M2 3WQ
Tel: (0161) 236 2244 Fax: (0161) 228 7285
Email: philfarrelly@maceandjones.co.uk
Website: www.maceandjones.co.uk

Firm Profile

Mace & Jones is a leading regional practice in the North West and remains a full service firm while enjoying a national reputation for its commercial expertise, especially in employment, litigation/insolvency, corporate and property. The firm's clients range from national and multinational companies and public sector bodies to owner managed businesses and private individuals, reflecting the broad nature of the work undertaken. Sound practical advice is given always on a value for money basis.

Main Areas of Work

Commercial Litigation/Insolvency 20%; Commercial Property 20%; Company/Commercial 20%; Employment 20%; Personal Injury/Private Client/Family 20%.

Trainee Profile

The firm seeks to recruit highly motivated trainees with above average ability and the determination to succeed. The right calibre of trainee will assume responsibility early in their career. The firm provides a comprehensive internal and external training programme.

Training Environment

Trainees complete an induction course to familiarise themselves with the work carried out by the firm's main departments, administration and professional conduct. Training consists of four six month seats in the following departments: Company/Commercial, Employment, Commercial Litigation/Personal Injury Litigation, Property Law, Family Law. Strenuous efforts are made to ensure that trainees are able to select the training seat of their choice. A trainee will normally be required to share an office with a partner who will supervise their work and review the trainee's progress at the end of the seat. The PSC is taught externally. The firm operates an open door policy and has various social events.

Benefits

Health Insurance

Partners	26
Assistant Solicitors	35
Total Trainees	12

Contact

Liverpool office: Donal Bannon
Manchester Office: Phil Farrelly

Method of Application

Handwritten letter and typed C.V. which should indicate individual degree subject results

Selection Procedure

Interview with partners

Closing date for 2002

31 March 2002

Application

Training contracts p.a.	12
Applications p.a.	1500
% interviewed p.a.	1%
Required degree grade	2:1

Training

Salary: 1st year(2000)	£11,000
Salary: 2nd year(2000)	£11,500
Holiday entitlement	20 days
% of trainees with a non-law degree p.a.	40%

Post-Qualification

Salary (2000)	negotiable
% of trainees offered job on qualification (1999)	50%
% of assistants (as at 1/9/99) who joined as trainees	80%
% of partners (as at 1/9/99) who joined as trainees	50%

MACFARLANES

10 Norwich Street London EC4A 1BD
Tel: (020) 7831 9222 Fax: (020) 7831 9607
Email: GS@MACFARLANES.COM
Website: www.macfarlanes.com

Firm Profile

A leading City firm serving national and international commercial, industrial, financial and private clients.

Main Areas of Work

Company, Commercial and Banking 49%; Property 22%; Litigation 16%; Tax and Financial Planning 13%.

Trainee Profile

Any degree discipline. Actual or predicted 2:1 or better.

Training Environment

Macfarlanes divides the training contract into four six-month periods. You will usually spend time in each of the firm's four main departments (Company, Commercial and Banking; Litigation; Property; Tax and Financial Planning). There is an extensive in-house training programme. Trainees have responsibility for real work and make a contribution that is acknowledged and appreciated.

Benefits

Twenty-one working days holiday in each calendar year (rising to 26 days upon qualification); profit related pay; interest free season ticket loans; free permanent health insurance*; free private medical insurance*; subsidised conveyancing; subsidised health club/gym; subsidised firm restaurant; subscription paid to the City of London Law Society or the London Trainee Solicitors' Group.

*After 12 months service.

Vacation Placements

Places for 2000: 40; Duration: 2 weeks; Remuneration: £200 p.w.; Closing Date: 29 February 2000 but applications considered and places offered from 2 January 2000.

Sponsorship & Awards

CPE and LPC full fees and £4,500 maintenance for courses studied in London and Guildford and £4,000 for courses studied elsewhere. Prizes for those gaining distinction and commendation.

Partners	55
Assistant Solicitors	105
Total Trainees	39

Contact
Graham Stoddart

Method of Application
Application form and letter

Selection Procedure
Interview and practical assessment

Closing date for 2002
31 July 2000

Application

Training contracts p.a.	20
Applications p.a.	1,500
% interviewed p.a.	16%
Required degree grade	2:1

Training

Salary: 1st year(2000)	£21,500
Salary: 2nd year(2000)	£24,000
Holiday entitlement	21 days
% of trainees with a non-law degree p.a.	40%

Post-Qualification

Salary (1999)	£33,000
% of trainees offered job on qualification (1999)	92%
% of assistants (as at 1/9/99) who joined as trainees	53%
% of partners (as at 1/9/99) who joined as trainees	65%

Overseas Offices
Brussels

MARTINEAU JOHNSON

St. Philips House St. Philips Place Birmingham B3 2PP
Tel: (0121) 200 3300 Fax: (0121) 200 3330
Email: diane.price@martjohn.com
Website: www.martineau-johnson.co.uk

Firm Profile
Martineau Johnson is regarded as one of the most innovative and progressive commercial law firms in Birmingham and offers an unrivalled diversity of experience. There are 6 departments which are divided into specialist teams. The firm is also a member of Multilaw, an association of law firms covering 38 countries in Europe, America and the Pacific Rim.

Main Areas of Work
Corporate 11%; Property 16%; Litigation 18%; Private Client 14%; Education 5%; Intellectual Property 6%; Employment 5%; Banking and Insolvency 7%; Finance and Tax 6%; Trade and Energy 12%.

Trainee Profile
The firm seeks trainees who have commercial flair, are capable of originality and have the desire to succeed within a progressive firm. Ambition, enthusiasm, commercial acumen and the ability to exploit opportunities are just some of the qualities that the firm is looking for in a potential trainee.

Training Environment
The firm is committed to ensuring that trainees receive in-depth coaching and supervision throughout their training contract. Trainees have their own personal mentor which provides them with an additional point of contact to discuss their career progression. Trainees follow a unique system of seat rotation. Seats are of four months duration and can be combined so that you spend time in six different seats or longer if desired. During the last eight months, trainees receive priority to experience whichever area(s) of specialisation they choose. In addition to the above, all trainees follow a structured training programme. Trainees are encouraged to take part in the firm's varied sporting activities, and there is an active social life both within the firm and with the Birmingham Trainee Solicitors' group.

Benefits
Pension, Life Assurance, Private Medical Insurance, PHI & Travel Loans.

Open Days
Places for 2000: 60; Duration: 1day; Closing Date: 25 Feb 2000.

Sponsorship & Awards
CPE and LPC funding; £3,500 maintenance for LPC.

Partners	35
Assistant Solicitors	71
Total Trainees	18

Contact
Diane Price

Method of Application
Application form

Selection Procedure
Assessment centre - half day

Closing date for 2002
28 July 2000

Application

Training contracts p.a.	10/12
Applications p.a.	500
% interviewed p.a.	10%
Required degree grade	2:1

Training

Salary: 1st year(2000)	£15,500
Salary: 2nd year(2000)	£17,000
Holiday entitlement	23 days
% of trainees with a non-law degree p.a.	38%

Post-Qualification

Salary (2000)	£26,500
% of trainees offered job on qualification (1999)	100%
% of assistants (as at 1/9/99) who joined as trainees	56%
% of partners (as at 1/9/99) who joined as trainees	61%

MASONS

30 Aylesbury Street London EC1R 0ER
Tel: (020) 7490 4000 Fax: (020) 7490 2545
Email: info@masons.com
Website: www.masons.com

Firm Profile

Masons is not a traditional law firm. It is entrepreneurial and highly reponsive to change. It is also driven by a strategic vision aimed at strengthening its reputation as one of the most highly regarded and successful law firms in Europe and the Far East.

Main Areas of Work

A training contract with Masons will give you access to first class resources combined with hands on experience in a highly focused and exciting enviroment. You will be part of an expanding international team that is well known for its advice in the areas of Information and Technology, Major Projects, Engineering and Construction. Masons also provides Property, Commercial, Enviromental, Employment, Pension, Tax and Financial Planning legal services.

Trainee Profile

Applications are welcome from individuals with quality legal or non-legal degrees, a minimum of 2:1.

Training Environment

In London, trainees spend four months in six seats. You will receive early exposure to the day to day work of the firm. You will learn at first hand what it takes to deal with clients, resolve complex problems and deliver consistent results. This invaluable experience will be underpinned by a comprehensive training programme designed around a range of formal training.

Benefits

PRP, life assurance, private health care, subsidised restaurant and season ticket loan (London).

Vacation Placements

Places for 2000: 36 (London), 5 (Manchester); Duration: 2 weeks in 2 different departments, June–end of August; Closing Date: 11 Feb 2000.

Sponsorship & Awards

All fees paid for CPE and LPC, plus a bursary of up to £4,000 for the year.

Partners	84*
Assistant Solicitors	167*
Total Trainees	40

** denotes world-wide figures*

Contact

Melanie Hilton

Method of Application

Firm's own application form

Selection Procedure

Assessment day followed by an interview

Closing date for 2002

31 July 2000

Application

Training contracts p.a.	23-25
Applications p.a.	900
% interviewed p.a.	10%
Required degree grade	2:1

Training

Salary: 1st year(1999)	£22,000 (London)
Salary: 2nd year(1999)	£24,000 (London)
Holiday entitlement	21 days

Post-Qualification

Salary (1999)	£34,000 (London)
% of trainees offered job on qualification (1999)	85%
% of partners (as at 1/9/99) who joined as trainees	29%

Overseas Offices

Brussels, Dublin, Guangzhou (PRC), Hong Kong, Singapore

MAY, MAY & MERRIMANS

12 South Square Gray's Inn London WC1R 5HH
Tel: (020) 7405 8932 Fax: (020) 7831 0011
Email: mmm@link.org

Firm Profile

May May & Merrimans is an old established Inns firm with a broad based practice which has a particularly strong reputation for its work with private clients, including landed estates and their related trusts.

Main Areas of Work

Private client including tax and estate planning for UK and offshore clients, Wills, Settlements and Probate; Charity law; agricultural, commercial and residential property; civil litigation and family law; business law for private clients and unquoted companies.

Trainee Profile

The firm welcomes applications from law and non-law graduates with a first class academic record. The qualities it looks for in its trainees are initiative, enthusiasm, a practical turn of mind and good communication skills.

Training Environment

The firm's approach to training is to offer active involvement in good quality work and to maintain a careful balance between exercising surpervision and encouraging trainees to accept as much responsibility as possible. The firm is not strictly departmentalised and trainees normally spend the first few months of their training contract concentrating on litigation and family law and the remainder working on a variety of non-contentious matters, principally private client and property.

Sponsorship & Awards

Discretionary loans for LPC.

Partners	11
Assistant Solicitors	7
Total Trainees	2

Contact

Alexandra Sarkis

Method of Application

Letter and CV

Selection Procedure

Interview

Closing date for 2002

31 July 2000

Application

Training contracts p.a.	1
Applications p.a.	200
% interviewed p.a.	3%
Required degree grade	2.1

Training

Salary: 1st year(2000)
Competitive with similar size/type firms

Holiday entitlement 20 days

Post-Qualification

% of trainees offered job on qualification (1997-99) 100%

% of assistants (as at 1/9/99) who joined as trainees 70%

% of partners (as at 1/9/99) who joined as trainees 55%

MAYER, BROWN & PLATT

Bucklersbury House, 3, Queen Victoria Street,
London EC4N 8EL
Tel: (020) 7246 6200 Fax: (020) 7329 4465
Email: rrogers@mayerbrown.com
Website: www.mayerbrown.com

Firm Profile

Mayer, Brown & Platt is an international law firm headquarted in Chicago, with offices and associated offices across the United States, Mexico and Europe. MBP's London office, established in 1974, has approximately 40 lawyers and is the flagship of MBP's European and CIS network. Worldwide there are 800+ lawyers.

Main Areas of Work

The principal practice areas of the firm's London offices: Conventional finance; Project finance; Leasing and asset finance; Capital markets, Securities and derivatives; Mergers and acquisitions; General corporate matters.

Trainee Profile

The firm seeks outstanding candidates with academic excellence and a flexible attitude with business acumen, along with a sense of humour, good judgement, common sense and motivation.

Training Environment

Trainees are inducted into the firm's culture and environment. Training seats are offered in the following departments: Civil litigation; Commercial; Company; and Banking. The litigation seat is covered by secondment for three months to a City law firm. Trainees usually move from seat to seat, sharing an office with a supervising senior associate or partner. The Professional Skills Course is run externally, and monthly in-house lectures are run for lawyers that trainees are encouraged to attend. At least three formal appraisals are carried out during the training contract, and ongoing progress is monitored at all times. MBP has a friendly, sociable environment with an open door policy. It regularly holds evening social events for all members of staff.

Benefits

Private medical insurance, season ticket loan, life assurance (4x basic salary).

Vacation Placements

Places for 2000: Not offered at present.

Sponsorship & Awards

50% funding for CPE and LPC plus maintenance grant.

Partners	9
Assistant Solicitors	20
Total Trainees	2

Contact

Ricia Rogers

Method of Application

CV and covering letter

Selection Procedure

Two interviews with partners, associates and often a current trainee

Closing date for 2002

Not yet specified

Application

Training contracts p.a.	2
Applications p.a.	600
% interviewed p.a.	2%
Required degree grade	High 2:1

Training

Salary: 1st year(2000)	£25,000
Salary: 2nd year(2000)	£26,000
Holiday entitlement	20 days
% of trainees with a non-law degree p.a.	50%

Post-Qualification

Salary (2000)	£42,500
% of trainees offered job on qualification (1999)	100%

Overseas Offices

Chicago, Berlin, Charlotte, Houston, Köln, Los Angeles, New York, Washington.
Representative offices: Ashgabat, Bishkek, Tashkent
Independent correspondent offices: Mexico City and Paris

McCORMICKS

Britannia Chambers 4 Oxford Place Leeds LS1 3AX
Tel: (0113) 246 0622 Fax: (0113) 246 7488
Email: mccormicks@btinternet.com
Wharfedale House 37 East Parade Harrogate HG1 5LQ
Tel: (01423) 530630 Fax: (01423) 530709

Firm Profile
McCormicks is a high profile, progressive and highly regarded firm offering a full range of legal services to both corporate and private clients. It is regarded as one of the leading firms in the North of England and has been described by the Yorkshire Post as 'a law firm in the top rank' and by Yorkshire Television as 'one of the Region's top law firms.' The average age of the partners is 35 and the firm has a reputation for a vibrant and dynamic atmosphere.

Main Areas of Work
(alphabetically) Charities; Commercial Litigation; Company and Commercial; Corporate Crime including VAT and Inland Revenue Investigation work and tribunals; Debt Collection and Mortgage Repossessions; Defamation; Employment; Family; General Crime (especially Road Traffic); Insolvency; Intellectual Property; Media/ Entertainment; Sports Law; Personal Injury; Private Client – the firm is regarded as one of the leading commercial, litigation, fraud, media and sports law practices in the North.

Trainee Profile
A McCormicks trainee will combine intellectual achievement, sense of humour, commitment to hard work and a pro-active disposition to achieving the best possible outcome for the firm and its clients.

Training Environment
Trainees are recruited with the sincere expectation that they will be future partners. You will be assigned to the appropriate department and will be supervised by a mentor. Your work and development will be constantly reviewed by your mentor together with regular file and progress reviews both by your team supervisor and by the Training Partner. This framework provides for your maximum development within a friendly, progressive and supportive environment. There is an open-door policy and a great team spirit.

Vacation Placements
Places for 2000: Available throughout all student vacations – as many students as possible are accommodated.

Partners	8
Assistant Solicitors	12
Total Trainees	7

Contact
Mark Burns, Training Partner

Method of Application
Letter and CV

Selection Procedure
Minimum of one interview with Training Partner

Closing date for 2002
31 July 2000

Application

Training contracts p.a.	4
Applications p.a.	1000
% interviewed p.a.	10%
Required degree grade	2:1

Training

Salary: 1st year (2000)	Highly competitive

Post-Qualification

Salary (2000)	Highly competitive
% of trainees offered job on qualification (1999)	75%
% of partners (as at 1/9/99) who joined as trainees	70%

MCDERMOTT, WILL & EMERY

7 Bishopsgate London EC2N 3AQ
Tel: (020) 7577 6900 Fax: (020) 7577 6950
Website: www.mwe.com

Partners	465*
Assistant Solicitors	372*
Total Trainees	1

** denotes world-wide figures*

Contact
Human Resources Manager

Method of Application
Hand-written letter and C.V.

Closing date for 2002
31 July 2000

Training
Salary: 1st year(2000) £24,000

Firm Profile

Founded in 1934 in Chicago, McDermot, Will & Emery is an international law firm with over 850 lawyers in 12 offices worldwide. The Firm's legal practice in London encompasses a broad range of practice groups, including corporate and commercial, mergers and acquisitions, securities and finance, restructuring and workouts, tax, arbitration, employment, intellectual property and environmental. The London office, which opened in November of 1998, is growing rapidly and, as at December 1999, was 43 lawyers strong. New lawyers join almost weekly.

Main Areas of Work

International and Commercial; Mergers and Acquisitions; Corporate Finance; International Taxation; Litigation; Telecoms; Employment and Banking and Finance.

Trainee Profile

Applications are invited from commercially aware candidates who have an outstanding academic record and who possess a high degree of initiative and confidence.

Training Environment

Four seats over a two year period of traineeship. Comprehensive in-house training in Corporate and Litigation, plus 2 of the Firm's other practice areas will enable you to experience hands-on work in each of these departments. The trainee will share an office with an experienced solicitor and will be formally reviewed at the end of each period. MW&E aims to provide trainees with a high level of responsibility and work related experience, thereby allowing the trainee to fully understand the scope of the work carried out by the Firm. Trainees participate in training lectures and seminars with other solicitors to further acquaint themselves with the Firm's culture and expectations. Scope does exist for the trainee to work on U.S. secondment and on secondment to UK clients. MW&E is proud of its friendly and open working environment, whilst maintaining the highest levels of professional responsibility to clients.

Benefits

Private Medical and Dental Insurance, Life Assurance, Permanent Health Insurance, Non-Contributory Pension, Interest-Free Season Ticket Loan, Gym Membership.

Sponsorship & Awards

CPE and LPC funding; Tuition for relevant courses.

MILLS & REEVE

Francis House 112 Hills Road Cambridge CB2 1PH
Tel: (01223) 364422 Fax: (01223) 355848
Email: s.trowbridge@mills-reeve.com
Website: www.mills-reeve.com

Partners	55
Assistant Solicitors	170
Total Trainees	27

Firm Profile
Mills & Reeve is one of the largest UK law firms outside London. They operate throughout England and Wales from offices in Birmingham, Cambridge, Cardiff and Norwich.

Main Areas of Work
The firm offers a full range of corporate, commercial, property, litigation and private client services to a mix of regional and national businesses. They are regional leaders in corporate and commercial work, and national specialists in the sectors of Health, Insurance, Higher Education and Agriculture.

Trainee Profile
Lively personalities who listen and communicate effectively. Accuracy, attention to detail and a solid academic background are also important to the firm.

Training Environment
Trainees are offered four five-month seats followed by a final seat of four months. This final seat allows the trainees to revisit the area of law into which they are going to qualify, or experience a new area of law. During each seat, trainees sit with a partner or experienced solicitor. Early responsibility is encouraged and performance is reviewed via a mix of formal appraisals and informal reviews. Staff at all levels are friendly and approachable. The firm operates a full induction programme to integrate trainees immediately. Practical training is complemented by a series of in-house lectures and the PSC.

Benefits
Life assurance at two times pensionable salary and a contributory pension scheme.

Vacation Placements
Places for 2000: 25; Duration: 2 weeks; Remuneration: £100 p.w.; Closing Date: 1 March 2000.

Sponsorship & Awards
The firm pays the full costs of the LPC fees and offers a maintenance grant for the LPC year. Funding for the CPE is discretionary.

Contact
Stephen Trowbridge
Graduate Recruitment Officer

Method of Application
Firm's application form

Selection Procedure
A 2:1 degree in any discipline.
Computer skill required.

Closing date for 2002
15 August 2000

Application
Training contracts p.a.	15-20
Applications p.a.	500
% interviewed p.a.	16%
Required degree grade	2:1

Training
Salary: 1st year(2000)	£15,000
Salary: 2nd year(2000)	£16,000
Holiday entitlement	25 days
% of trainees with a non-law degree p.a.	Approx 25%

Post-Qualification
Salary (2000)	£25,500
% of trainees offered job on qualification (1999)	92%
% of assistants (as at 1/9/99) who joined as trainees	48%
% of partners (as at 1/9/99) who joined as trainees	30%

MISHCON DE REYA

21 Southampton Row London WC1B 5HS
Tel: (020) 7440 7198 Fax: (020) 7404 5982
Email: postmaster@mishcon.co.uk
Website: www.mishcon.co.uk

Firm Profile

An expanding commercial practice based in Central London. As well as being known for its commercial litigation, defamation and media work, there has been a conscious expansion of its non-contentious departments including company commercial and commercial property. The majority of partners are under 40.

Main Areas of Work

Litigation 42%; Company Commercial 23%; Property 22%; Family 9%; Private Client 4%.

Trainee Profile

Those who read nothing but law books are probably not the right trainees for this firm. They want people who can meet the highest intellectual and business standards, while maintaining outside interests. Candidates should be cheerful, enterprising and ambitious - they should see themselves as future partners.

Training Environment

Trainees have four six-month seats. Three of these are usually in the litigation, property and company commercial departments, with an opportunity to specialise in the fourth seat. Trainees share a room with an assistant solicitor or a partner and the firm style is friendly and informal. Computer literacy is encouraged and access to on-line legal and business databases is available. Trainees are encouraged to participate in voluntary work at Law Centres.

Benefits

Health cover, subsidised gym membership, season ticket loan, permanent health insurance, life assurance.

Vacation Placements

Places for 2000: 8; Duration: 4 weeks; Remuneration: £150 p.w. Closing Date: 28th April 2000.

Sponsorship & Awards

LPC funding and bursary.

Partners	27
Assistant Solicitors	32
Total Trainees	20

Contact
Human Resources Department

Method of Application
Application form

Selection Procedure
Assessment Day and Interview

Closing date for 2002
31 July 2000

Application

Training contracts p.a.	8
Applications p.a.	1,000+
% interviewed p.a.	10%
Required degree grade	2:1

Training

Salary: 1st year(2000)	£19,500
Salary: 2nd year(2000)	£21,000
Holiday entitlement	22 days
No. of seats available abroad p.a.	Occasional secondments available

Post-Qualification

% of trainees offered job on qualification (1999)	75%
% of assistants (as at 1/9/99) who joined as trainees	38%
% of partners (as at 1/9/99) who joined as trainees	30%

MORGAN COLE

Bradley Court Park Place Cardiff CF1 3DP
Tel: (029) 2038 5385 Fax: (029) 2038 5331
Buxton Court 3 West Way Oxford OX2 0SZ
Tel: (01865) 262 600 Fax: (01865) 262 670
Email: info@morgan-cole.com
Website: www.morgan-cole.com

Firm Profile
Morgan Cole is one of the leading independent law practices in the country, providing a full range of legal services to both individual and corporate clients in both the public and private sectors. The firm has a reputation for excellence and therefore attracts the highest quality of staff from all fields. The firm is a founder member of the Association of European Lawyers, one of the five leading UK law firms responsible for establishing a network of English speaking lawyers throughout Europe, thus ensuring that clients with business interests in Europe are provided with expert legal advice. The practice consists of five main divisions: business services, property, litigation, insurance litigation and specialist insurance services. As a modern practice, it strives to meet the legal needs of clients in all sectors of industry and commerce, and as a result, the firm has specialist units including banking, construction, debt recovery, employment, energy, European, environmental, healthcare, information technology, insolvency, leisure, licensing, intellectual property law, media, PFI, planning, professional indemnity and sport.

Trainee Profile
Successful candidates should be commercially aware, proactive, outgoing and able to apply a logical and common-sense approach to solving client problems. The firm is keen to recruit trainees who will stay on once they have qualified. The firm is seeking applications from graduates/undergraduates in both law and non-law subjects, preferably with a 2:1 degree.

Training Environment
Trainees spend not less than six months in at least three different divisions, and since each division handles a wide variety of work within its constituent teams, there is no danger of over-specialisation. Every effort is made to accommodate individual preferences and qualifications, and trainees will have the opportunity to work in different offices as the practice needs dictate.

Vacation Placements
Places for 2000: Available

Sponsorship & Awards
Full funding of fees for attendance on the LPC for those trainess who will commence training with the firm.

Partners	104
Assistant Solicitors	235
Total Trainees	39

Contact
Paul Rippon

Method of Application
Firm's application form available from the HR department in your preferred location

Selection Procedure
Assessment Centre and interview

Closing date for 2002
31 July 2000

Application
Required degree grade 2:1

Training
Salary: 1st year(2000)
competitive and reviewed annually
Salary: 2nd year(2000)
competitive and reviewed annually

Offices
London, Reading, Swansea

NABARRO NATHANSON

Lacon House, Theobald's Road, London WC1X 8RW
Tel: (020) 7524 6000 Fax: (020) 7524 6524
Graduate Recruitment Freephone: 0800 056 4021
Website: www.nabarro.com Email: j.squire@nabarro.com

Firm Profile
One of the UK's largest commercial practices with offices in London, Reading and Sheffield. The atmosphere in all its offices is friendly and informal, yet highly professional.

Main Areas of Work
Commercial Property; Planning; Pensions & Employment; Corporate Finance; Health & Safety; Commercial Litigation; Intellectual Property; IT; Insolvency; Construction; PFI; Venture Capital; Energy; Health; Charities; Local Government; Environmental Law.

Trainee Profile
Nabarro Nathanson welcomes applications from law and non law undergraduates. Candidates will usually be expecting a minimum 2:1 degree. As well as strong intellectual ability our graduates need exceptional qualities. These include: enthusiasm, drive and initiative, common sense and strong interpersonal and teamworking skills.

Training Environment
They are a friendly, unstuffy firm with a first-name and open door culture. You will spend six months in each of four seats with supervision provided by a Partner and Solicitor. The seats are: Company Commercial, Commercial Property, Litigation, and a specialist area. The firm is keen to encourage responsibility and high quality work as soon as you are ready for it. By the fourth seat your work will approach the level of a newly qualified solicitor. Nabarro Nathanson is well known for its coherent and integrated training strategy.

Benefits
Trainees are given private medical health insurance, 25 days' holiday entitlement per annum, a season ticket loan and access to a subsidised restaurant. Trainee salaries are reviewed annually.

Vacation Placements
Places for 2000: Places available; Duration: 3 weeks – between mid-June and end of August; Closing Date: 25 February 2000.

Sponsorship & Awards
CPE and LPC sponsorship and a maintenance grant.
London and Guildford: £4,500. Elsewhere: £4,000.

Partners	113
Assistant Solicitors	199
Total Trainees	56

Contact
Jane Squire

Method of Application
Application form

Selection Procedure
Interview and assessment day

Closing date for 2002
31 July 2000

Application

Training contracts p.a.	30
Applications p.a.	1,500
Required degree grade	2:1

Training
Salary: 1st year(2000)

London & Reading	£21,000
Sheffield	£16,000

Salary: 2nd year(2000)

London & Reading	£24,000
Sheffield	£17,500
Holiday entitlement	25 days

Post-Qualification
Salary (2000) London £33,000 (reviewed annually)

Overseas Offices
Brussels. Associated offices – Dubai, Hong Kong, Paris

NICHOLSON GRAHAM & JONES

110 Cannon Street London EC4N 6AR
Tel: (020) 7648 9000 Fax: (020) 7648 9001
Email: info@NGJ.co.uk
Website: www.ngj.co.uk

Firm Profile
A successful mid-sized practice, offering strength across a number of key disciplines to a broad range of corporate clients.

Main Areas of Work
Company, Commercial, Litigation, Property, Construction & Engineering, Banking & Insolvency, Private Client, Intellectual Property, Planning & Environmental, Employment, Sport, Travel.

Trainee Profile
The firm recruits both law and non-law graduates with excellent degrees and a practical approach.

Training Environment
Training is broad-based with six months in each of the main departments: Company/Commercial, Litigation and Property and a six month seat of your choice. The emphasis is on-the-job training with personal supervision from partners. There is also a comprehensive induction and in-house training programnme for each department and on a firmwide basis. The firm encourages individual development through early responsibility and client contact. Trainees participate in all activies including business development and marketing. The atmosphere is genuinely friendly and supportive and trainees' contributions are valued.

Vacation Placements
Places for 2000: 26 June and 10 July 2000. 4 students per fortnight; Remuneration: £180 p.w.;

Sponsorship & Awards
LPC Fees and expenses paid. CPE fees.

Partners	54
Assistant Solicitors	50
Total Trainees	20

Contact
Gail Harcus/Sophie Leman

Method of Application
Application form

Selection Procedure
Interview and assessment

Closing date for 2002
28 July 2000

Application
Training contracts p.a.	10
Applications p.a.	1000
% interviewed p.a.	4%
Required degree grade	2:1

Training
Salary: 1st year(2000)	£21,000
Salary: 2nd year(2000)	£23,000
Holiday entitlement	25 days
% of trainees with a non-law degree p.a.	Varies

Post-Qualification
Salary (2000)	£34,000
% of trainees offered job on qualification (1999)	80%

Overseas Offices
Brussels

NORTON ROSE

Kempson House Camomile Street London EC3A 7AN
Tel: (020) 7283 6000 Fax: (020) 7283 6500
Email: grad.recruitment@nortonrose.com
Website: www.nortonrose.com

Firm Profile

A leading City and international law firm specialising in large-scale corporate and financial transactions. Strong in asset, project and ship finance. More than two thirds of the firm's work has an international element.

Main Areas of Work

Corporate Finance 27%; Banking 27%; Litigation 26%; Property, Planning & Environmental 9%; Taxation 5%; Competition 3%; Employment, Pensions + Incentives 2%; Intellectual Property + Technology 1%.

Trainee Profile

Successful candidates will be commercially aware, focused, ambitious and team-orientated. High intellect and international awareness are a priority, and language skills are appreciated.

Training Environment

Norton Rose's seat system is innovative. In the first 16 months of the 24-month training contract, trainees will have a seat in each of the core departments of banking, commercial litigation and corporate finance, plus one in a more specialist area. The remaining time can be spent in one of three ways: all eight months in one chosen seat; or four months in one department and four months in the department in which they want to qualify; or six months abroad and two in their chosen department. In-the-field experience is considered as important as formal training at Norton Rose, and trainees are expected to learn by observing experienced lawyers at work, interacting with clients and solicitors, handling sensitive issues and organising their time as well as attending external courses. Internal competition among trainees is discouraged, as great store is placed on team-working.

Benefits

Life assurance (25+), private health insurance (optional), season ticket loan, subsidised gym membership.

Vacation Placements

Places for 2000: 45 Summer, 15 Christmas; Duration: Summer: 3 weeks, Christmas: 2 weeks; Remuneration: £200 p.w.; Closing Date: 25 February 2000 for Summer, 3 November 2000 for Christmas. 5-6 open days per year are also held.

Sponsorship & Awards

£1,000 travel scholarship, £500 loan on arrival, 4–6 weeks unpaid leave on qualification.

Partners	131*
Assistant Solicitors	365*
Total Trainees	103

** denotes world-wide figures*

Contact

Brendan Monaghan

Method of Application

Employer's application form

Selection Procedure

Interview and group exercise

Closing date for 2002

4 August 2000

Application

Training contracts p.a.	60–70
Applications p.a.	2,500+
% interviewed p.a.	10%
Required degree grade	2:1

Training

Salary: 1st year(2000)	£21,000
Salary: 2nd year(2000)	£24,000
Holiday entitlement	22 days
% of trainees with a non-law degree p.a.	35%
No. of seats available abroad p.a.	12

Post-Qualification

Salary (2000)	£33,500
% of trainees offered job on qualification (1999)	97%

Overseas Offices

Athens*, Bahrain, Bangkok*, Brussels, Jakarta*, Moscow, Paris, Piraeus*, Prague*, Singapore

**Associate Office*

ORCHARD

99 Bishopsgate London EC2M 3YU
Tel: (020) 7392 0200 Fax: (020) 7392 0201

Firm Profile

Established in 1995, Orchard has quickly made its name as one of the newest, most vibrant firms in London. Built on the expertise of a highly experienced team, it is just one of the reasons why Orchard has already won the business of many major banks and international corporations. The firm is committed to working in partnership with its clients.

Main Areas of Work

Commercial Litigation, Corporate Finance, Mergers & Acquisitions, Banking, Financial Services and Markets, Commercial Contracts, Commercial Property, Employment and Employee Benefits, IT/IP, Corporate Insolvency.

Trainee Profile

Successful candidates are self motivated individuals with excellent interpersonal skills. High standards of academic achievement are important, but so too are commercial awareness and enthusiasm. Essential qualities are flexibility of approach and a sense of humour. All potential trainees should be computer literate.

Training Environment

Trainees will spend six months in four of the firm's main practice areas. They will sit with a Partner or Senior Solicitor and are actively involved in quality work at a very early stage. Trainees will benefit from a system which will allow them to work both independently and as part of a team. Each trainee is assigned a personal mentor to assist them throughout their contract period and regular appraisals are conducted on both an informal and formal basis with either their work supervisor and/or the partner responsible for trainees. Continuing education is supplemented with both in house seminars and video training. The phrase 'work hard, play hard', could have been written for this firm!

Benefits

Under review.

Partners	9
Assistant Solicitors	10
Total Trainees	4

Contact

Patricia Hart

Method of Application

Application form

Selection Procedure

Two interviews

Closing date for 2002

July 2000

Application

Training contracts p.a.	4–6
Applications p.a.	600
% interviewed p.a.	5%
Required degree grade	2:1

Training

Salary: 1st year	market rate
Salary: 2nd year	market rate
Holiday entitlement	20 days
% of trainees with a non-law degree p.a.	50%

OSBORNE CLARKE

50 Queen Charlotte St Bristol BS1 4HE
Joanne Moody, Recruitment Officer
Tel: (0117) 917 4298 Fax: (0117) 917 4299
Email: joanne.moody@osborneclarke.com
Website: www.osborneclarke.com

Firm Profile
Osborne Clarke is widely held to be one of the dominant commercial law firms in the South of England – and one of the fastest growing. It is a major force in its chosen national practice areas – corporate finance, employment, venture capital, IT, telecoms and media – where it competes head on with the largest City and national firms. With 59 partners and over 200 lawyers, the firm is particularly well-endowed with prominent sector specialists in litigation, commercial property, corporate banking, insolvency, tax, environmental and pensions. It also has a growing international client base in the US and Europe particularly in Denmark and in Germany, and is a founding member of the European alliance – Osborne Westphalen International.

Main Areas of Work
Corporate finance, employment, venture capital, IT, telecoms and media.

Trainee Profile
The firm values personality, enthusiasm, the ability to provide practical commercial solutions and the communication skills to deal with clients at all levels. A non-law degree and/or time spent travelling are viewed positively.

Training Environment
Trainees will spend six months in three core departments, either in Bristol, London or Thames Valley or in Europe, before choosing to specialise in a particular area. They are expected to take on responsibility at an early stage. There is a structured timetable of external and internal training, with three and six monthly reviews. The firm encourages a wide variety of social and sports activities.

Benefits
None until qualified.

Vacation Placements
Places for 2000: 20; Duration: 1 week; Remuneration: £80 p.w.; Closing Date: 26 February 2000.

Sponsorship & Awards
LPC fees paid.

Partners	59
Assistant Solicitors	141
Total Trainees	31

Contact
Joanne Moody

Method of Application
Application form and brochure available on request.

Selection Procedure
Individual interviews and group exercises.

Closing date for 2002
31 July 2000

Application

Training contracts p.a.	14–16
Applications p.a.	800–900
% interviewed p.a.	10%
Required degree grade	2:1

Training

Salary: 1st year(2000)	£15,000–£15,500 + location allowance
Salary: 2nd year(2000)	£16,000–£16,500
Holiday entitlement	21 days
% of trainees with a non-law degree p.a.	30%
No. of seats available abroad p.a.	3

Post-Qualification

Salary (2000)	£27,000
% of trainees offered job on qualification (1999)	90%

Overseas Offices
Barcelona, Brussels, Copenhagen, Cologne, Frankfurt, Hamburg, Lyon, Milan, Paris, Rotterdam.

PAISNER & CO

Bouverie House 154 Fleet St London EC4A 2JD
Tel: (020) 7353 0299 Fax: (020) 7583 8621
Email: personnel@paisner.co.uk
website: www.paisner.co.uk

Partners	52
Assistant Solicitors	64
Total Trainees	17

Firm Profile
Based in the City, Paisner & Co is a broadly-based commercial firm handling all aspects of legal work for commercial clients both national and international. Clients include UK and international listed and smaller companies from a wide range of industry sectors, in particular leisure, retail and mail order, health, communications, manufacturing, high-technolgy, property development, insurance and financial services.

Main Areas of Work
The firm's three core practice areas are corporate/commercial, commercial property and commercial litigation. Specialist areas include: computer, media and intellectual property; asset and consumer finance; charities; construction and engineering; corporate tax; employment and pensions; EU/UK competition; property litigation; regulatory law; reinsurance/insurance; trusts and estate planning. Company/Commercial 36%; Commercial Property 24%; Litigation 18%; Trusts & Estate Planning 9%; Insurance/Reinsurance 8%; Employment 5%.

Trainee Profile
Intelligent, energetic, positive and hard working team players. Individuals who gain a sense of achievement from finding solutions and providing services.

Training Environment
Trainees spend six months in four of the following departments- company and commercial, commercial litigation, commercial property, employment and trusts. You will often work in cross-departmental teams, but will have one-to-one supervision from a partner or senior solicitor. Development is monitored with an assessment every six months. Internal and external lectures, carrying Law Society Continuing Education Points, are given twice a day. Trainees are given library research and Lexis induction courses. Staff are encouraged to get to know each other- partners and senior solicitors are accessible and willing to teach. The office environment is relaxed and informal. Social and sporting events are organised and there is a daily internal e-bulletin.

Vacation Placements
Places for 2000: 10; Duration: 4 weeks; Remuneration: £150 p.w.; Closing Date: 30 April 2000.

Sponsorship & Awards
LPC Funding: Yes; CPE Funding: No.

Contact
Personnel Manager

Method of Application
Handwritten letter and CV

Selection Procedure
CV and interview

Closing date for 2002
31 July 2000

Application

Training contracts p.a.	10
Applications p.a.	2,000
% interviewed p.a.	3%
Required degree grade	2:1

Training

Salary: 1st year(2001)	£22,500
Salary: 2nd year(2001)	£24,000
Holiday entitlement	21 days
% of trainees with a non-law degree p.a.	3%

Post-Qualification

Salary (2000)	£34,000
% of trainees offered job on qualification (1999)	80%
% of assistants (as at 1/9/99) who joined as trainees	7%
% of partners (as at 1/9/99) who joined as trainees	8%

PALSER GROSSMAN

Discovery House Scott Harbour Cardiff Bay CF10 4HA
Tel: (029) 2045 2770 Fax: (029) 2045 2328
Email: law@palser-grossman.co.uk

Partners	18
Assistant Solicitors	26
Total Trainees	7

Firm Profile

Founded in 1992 as a specialist litigation practice and expanded rapidly in response to client demand, to encompass non-contentious high calibre commercial and property work. Offices are at Birmingham, Bristol, Cardiff, Southampton and Swansea. The firm is a progressive, modern firm and invests considerably in state of the art technology.

Main Areas of Work

Personal Injury Litigation; Commercial Litigation; Company & Commercial; Employment and Commercial Property.

Trainee Profile

Candidates need to demonstrate excellent intellectual capabilities, interpersonal skills and resourcefulness. IT skills and a current driving license are essential.

Training Environment

Training consists of six-month seats in four of the following departments: Personal Injury Litigation; Commercial Litigation; Company & Commercial; Employment and Commercial Property. Trainees are placed within departments as an integral part of the team and day to day supervision is the responsibility of designated partners. In addition a partner with overall responsibility for trainees will conduct quarterly reviews both with the trainee and the supervising partner. The firm considers staff at all levels to be partners of the firm and there are various social events and charitable sponsorship events that staff are encouraged to participate in.

Sponsorship & Awards

The firm supports one trainee annually in relation to LPC fees. This is awarded on the basis of examination results, other achievements and interview performance.

Contact

Karen Phillips
Practice Manager

Method of Application

CV and covering letter

Selection Procedure

2 Interviews - the first with a mixed panel and the final interview with partners

Closing date for 2002

31 July 2000

Application

Training contracts p.a.	4
Applications p.a.	200
% interviewed p.a.	10%
Required degree grade	2:1 preferred

Training

Salary: 1st year(1999)	£14,000
Salary: 2nd year(1999)	£15,000
Holiday entitlement	20 days

PANNONE & PARTNERS

123 Deansgate Manchester M3 2BU
Tel: (0161) 909 3000 Fax: (0161) 909 4444
Email: julia.hearn@pannone.co.uk
Website: www.pannone.com

Firm Profile
A high profile Manchester firm continuing to undergo rapid growth. The firm prides itself on offering a full range of legal services to a diverse client base which is split almost equally between personal and commercial clients. The firm was the first to be awarded the quality standard ISO9001 and is a founder member of Pannone Law Group - Europe's first integrated international law group.

Main Areas of Work
Commercial Litigation 28%; Personal Injury 22%; Corporate 13%; Commercial Property 7%; Family 10%; Clinical Negligence 12%; Private Client 8%.

Trainee Profile
Selection criteria include a high level of academic achievement, teamwork, organisation and communication skills, a wide range of interests and a connection with the North West.

Training Environment
An induction course helps trainees adjust to working life, and covers the firm's quality procedures and good practice. Regular trainee seminars cover the work of other departments within the firm, legal developments and practice. Additional departmental training sessions focus in more detail on legal and procedural matters in that department. Four seats of six months are spent in various departments and trainees' progress is monitored regularly. Trainees have easy access to support and guidance on any matters of concern. Work is tackled with gusto here, but so are the many social gatherings that take place.

Vacation Placements
Places for 2000: 20; Duration: 1 week; Remuneration: 0; Closing Date: 10 March 2000.

Partners	55
Assistant Solicitors	37
Total Trainees	18

Contact
Julia Hearn

Method of Application
Application form and CV

Selection Procedure
Individual interview, second interview comprises a tour of the firm and informal lunch

Closing date for 2002
11 August 2000

Application

Training contracts p.a.	8
Applications p.a.	600
% interviewed p.a.	10%
Required degree grade	2:1

Training

Salary: 1st year(2000)	£15,500
Salary: 2nd year(2000)	£17,500
Holiday entitlement	20 days
% of trainees with a non-law degree p.a.	50%

Post-Qualification

Salary (2000)	£24,500
% of trainees offered job on qualification (1999)	80%
% of assistants who joined as trainees	35%
% of partners who joined as trainees	37%

PAYNE HICKS BEACH

10 New Square Lincoln's Inn London WC2A 3QG
Tel: (020) 7465 4300 Fax: (020) 7465 4400
Email: a-palmer@payne-hicks-beach.co.uk

Firm Profile
Payne Hicks Beach is a medium-sized firm based in Lincoln's Inn. It primarily provides specialist tax, trusts and probate advice to individuals and families. It also undertakes corporate and commercial work.

Main Areas of Work
Private Client 33%; Commercial Litigation 13%; Commercial Property 12%; Matrimonial and Family Law/ Litigation 10%; Residential/Agricultural Property 10%; Tax (business and corporate) 10%; Corporate/Commercial 10%; General, Miscellaneous 2%.

Trainee Profile
The firm looks for law and non-law graduates with a good academic record, a practical ability to solve problems, enthusiasm and an ability to work hard and deal appropriately with their colleagues and the firm's clients. French or German may be an advantage.

Training Environment
Following an initial induction course, trainees usually spend six months in four of the firm's departments. Working with a partner, they are involved in the day to day activities of the department, including attending conferences with clients, counsel and other professional advisers. Assessment is continuous and you will be given responsibility as you demonstrate ability and aptitude. To complement the PSC, the firm runs a formal training system for trainees and requires them to attend lectures and seminars on various topics. Sports/social activities including an active arts society are popular.

Benefits
Season travel ticket loan, life assurance 4 x salary, permanent health insurance.

Sponsorship & Awards
Fees for the CPE and LPC are paid.

Partners	19
Assistant Solicitors	11
Total Trainees	5

Contact
Mrs Alice Palmer

Method of Application
Handwritten letter and CV

Selection Procedure
Interview

Closing date for 2002
11 August 2000

Application
Training contracts p.a.	2
Applications p.a.	1,000
% interviewed p.a.	3%
Required degree grade	2:1

Training
Salary: 1st year(2000)	£19,500
Salary: 2nd year(2000)	£21,000
Holiday entitlement	4 weeks
% of trainees with a non-law degree p.a.	50%

Post-Qualification
Salary (2000)	£31,000
% of trainees offered job on qualification (1999)	50%
% of assistants (as at 1/9/99) who joined as trainees	35%
% of partners (as at 1/9/99) who joined as trainees	20%

PENNINGTONS

Bucklersbury House 83 Cannon Street London EC4N 8PE
Tel: (020) 7457 3000 Fax: (020) 7457 3240

Firm Profile

An international law firm, with offices in the City, Basingstoke, Godalming, Newbury and Paris. There are four main departments. Specialist units cover industry sectors and key overseas jurisdictions.

Main Areas of Work

Property 33%; Litigation (including Shipping and Family) 29%; Corporate/Commercial 21%; Private Client 17%.

Trainee Profile

Penningtons is looking for bright, enthusiastic, highly motivated and well rounded individuals with a keen interest in the practice of law.

Training Environment

Six-month seats are provided in three or four of the following departments: corporate/commercial, property, litigation, and private client. Individual preference is usually accommodated in the second year. Trainees are given a thorough grounding in the law. International opportunities do arise. There are in-house lectures and reviews and appraisals occur regularly. The firm aims to utilise trainees' talents to their full, but is careful not to overburden them. All staff are supportive and the atmosphere is both professional and informal.

Benefits

Subsidised sports and social club, life assurance, season ticket loan.

Vacation Placements

Places for 2000: 60 on London Open Days at Easter; Remuneration: expenses; Closing Date: 15 February 2000. Some summer vacation placements out of London. Closing date 31 May 2000.

Sponsorship & Awards

LPC Funding is available. Awards are given for commendation or distinction in LPC.

Partners	38*
Assistant Solicitors	65*
Total Trainees	22

** denotes world-wide figures*

Contact

Lesley Lintott

Method of Application

Handwritten letter, CV and application form

Selection Procedure

1 interview with a partner and director of studies

Closing date for 2002

15 August 2000

Application

Training contracts p.a.	10/11
Applications p.a.	2,000
% interviewed p.a.	5%
Required degree grade	2:1

Training

Salary: 1st year (1999)	£20,000 (London)
Salary: 2nd year (1999)	£21,000 (London)
Holiday entitlement	22 days
% of trainees with a non-law degree p.a.	40%

Post-Qualification

Salary (1999)	£31,000 (London)
% of trainees offered job on qualification (1999)	60%
% of assistants (as at 1/9/99) who joined as trainees	45%
% of partners (as at 1/9/99) who joined as trainees	49%

Overseas Offices

Paris

PINSENT CURTIS

Dashwood House 69 Old Broad Street London EC2M 1NR
Tel: (020) 7418 7097 Fax: (020) 7418 7050
3 Colmore Circus Birmingham B4 6BH
Tel: (0121) 626 5731 Fax: (0121) 626 1040
41 Park Square Leeds LS1 2NS
Tel: (0113) 294 5246 Fax: (0113) 244 8000
Email: nimisha.gosrani@pinsent-curtis.co.uk
Website: www.pinsents.com

Firm Profile

Pinsent Curtis is a major national commercial firm. It has a first class reputation based on its work for a substantial list of quality corporate clients. The firm also has strong contacts with merchant banks, underwriters and insurers, and has the largest tax department outside London.

Main Areas of Work

Litigation & Professional Indemnity; Corporate; Commercial; Property; Tax; Employment.

Trainee Profile

The firm seeks applications from both law and non-law graduates with a good honours degree. However, not only is a good academic background required, but also personality, commitment and common sense. Given that the bulk of work is business oriented, trainees need to communicate with the business community, be interested in its problems and have the ability to give positive commercial advice.

Training Environment

Trainees sit in four seats of six months ranging from corporate, property, litigation, commercial, tax and employment. Hands-on experience is seen as an essential part of the learning process, so early responsibility and contact with clients are encouraged. Partners or associates oversee your work and are on hand to help and advise. The PSC is taught in-house, and there is an internal structured development programme to broaden your knowledge. The firm has an open-door policy and informal atmosphere, and there are many social and sporting activities for its staff.

Vacation Placements

Easter and Summer schemes.
Places for 2000: 140; Duration: 1 week;
Closing Date: 28 February 2000.

Sponsorship & Awards

CPE/ LPC fees are paid. In addition to this, maintenance grants of £2,500 for CPE and £4,500 for LPC are offered.

Partners	130
Assistant Solicitors	130
Total Trainees	66

Contact

Miss Nimisha Gosrani
Recruitment Hotline:
(020) 7418 7097

Method of Application

Application form

Selection Procedure

Assessment centre including interview

Closing date for 2002

31 July 2000

Application

Training contracts p.a.	25-30
Applications p.a.	4000
Required degree grade	2:1

Training

Salary: 1st year(1999)	£21,500
Salary: 2nd year(1999)	£24,000
Holiday entitlement	20 days
No. of seats available abroad p.a.	1

Overseas Offices

Brussels

PRITCHARD ENGLEFIELD

14 New St London EC2M 4HE
Tel: (020) 7972 9720 Fax: (020) 7972 9722
Email: po@pritchardenglefield.co.uk

Firm Profile

A medium-sized City firm practising a mix of general commercial and non-commercial law with many German and French clients. Despite its strong commercial departments, the firm still undertakes family and private client work and is known for its medical negligence and PI practice and its strong international flavour.

Main Areas of Work

All main areas of commercial practice including litigation, company/commercial (UK, German, French and some Italian), employment also private client/probate, personal injury, medical negligence and some family.

Trainee Profile

Normally only high academic achievers with a second European language (especially German and French) are considered. However, a lower second degree coupled with exceptional subsequent education or experience could suffice.

Training Environment

An induction course acquaints trainees with the computer network, library and administrative procedures and there is a formal in-house training programme. Four six-month seats make up most of your training. You can usually choose some departments, and you could spend two six-month periods in the same seat. Over two years, you learn advocacy, negotiating, drafting and interviewing, attend court, use your language skills and meet clients. Occasional talks and seminars explain the work of the firm, and you can air concerns over bi-monthly lunches with the partners comprising the Trainee panel. PSC is taken externally over two years. Quarterly drinks parties, musical evenings and ten-pin bowling number amongst popular social events.

Benefits

Some subsidised training, luncheon vouchers.

Sponsorship & Awards

£2,000.

Partners	22
Assistant Solicitors	17
Total Trainees	8

Contact

Marian Joseph

Method of Application

Standard application form available from Graduate Recruitment

Selection Procedure

1 interview only in September

Closing date for 2002

31 July 2000

Application

Training contracts p.a.	4
Applications p.a.	300–400
% interviewed p.a.	10%
Required degree grade	generally 2:1

Training

Salary: 1st year(2000)	£18,000
Salary: 2nd year(2000)	£18,250
Holiday entitlement	25 days
% of trainees with a non-law degree p.a.	Approx 50%

Post-Qualification

Salary (2000)	Approx £30,000
% of trainees offered job on qualification (1999)	75%
% of assistants (as at 1/9/99) who joined as trainees	75%
% of partners (as at 1/9/99) who joined as trainees	50%

Overseas Offices

Frankfurt, Hong Kong

RADCLIFFES

5 Great College Street Westminster London SW1P 3SJ
Tel: (020) 7222 7040 Fax: (020) 7222 6208
Email: marie.o'shea@radcliffes.co.uk
Website: www.radcliffes.co.uk

Firm Profile

A distinctive, highly accomplished law firm, Radcliffes combines traditional values like integrity and prompt response with a client-focused approach to everything it does. From its offices in the heart of Westminister, the firm handles commercial matters and private client work with equal skill, empathy and understanding of clients' individual needs.

Main Areas of Work

The firm is organised into five departments: Company/Commercial, Litigation and Dispute Resolution, Commercial Property, Tax and Private Client, and Family Law. Experts within these departments integrate their knowledge in the firm's specialist groups: Growing Businesses, Property Investment and Development, Private Client, Charity and Health.

Trainee Profile

Its aim is to recruit trainee solicitors who have a real prospect of becoming future partners. The firm seeks not just academic but also extra curricular activities, self-confidence, determination and a sense of humour.

Training Environment

Trainees are introduced to the firm with a full induction week.

Benefits

Health insurance, season ticket loan, life assurance, PHI.

Vacation Placements

Places for 2000: 10; Duration: 2 weeks;
Remuneration: £130 p.w.;
Closing Date: 31 March 2000.

Partners	33
Assistant Solicitors	20
Total Trainees	8

Contact
Marie O'Shea
Administration Secretary

Method of Application
CV and covering letter or EAF

Selection Procedure
2 Interviews with partners

Closing date for 2002
28 July 2000

Application

Training contracts p.a.	4
Applications p.a.	1016
% interviewed p.a.	9%
Prefered degree grade	2:1

Training

Salary: 1st year(1999)	£19,000
Salary: 2nd year(1999)	£21,000
Holiday entitlement	22 days p.a.

Post-Qualification

Salary (1999)	£29,500
% of trainees offered job on qualification (1999)	67%
% of assistants (as at 1/9/99) who joined as trainees	50%
% of partners (as at 1/9/99) who joined as trainees	50%

REYNOLDS PORTER CHAMBERLAIN

Chichester House 278-282 High Holborn London WC1V 7HA
Tel: (020) 7306 3509 Fax: (020) 7242 1431
Email: pt1@rpc.co.uk
Website: www.rpc.co.uk

Firm Profile
Reynolds Porter Chamberlain is a leading commercial law firm with over 170 lawyers. In addition to its main offices in Holborn, the firm has an expanding office at Leadenhall Street in the City which serves its insurance clients. Best known as a major litigation practice, particularly in the field of professional negligence, RPC also has thriving corporate, commercial property, private client and construction departments. Another rapidly expanding part of the firm is its media and technology unit. This handles major defamation actions and has dealt with some of the biggest internet deals to date.

Main Areas of Work
Litigation 60%; Corporate 10%; Commercial Property 10%; Construction 10%; Media & Technology 5%; Family/Private Client 5%.

Trainee Profile
The firm appoints seven trainees each year from law and non-law backgrounds. Although proven academic ability is important (they require a 2.1 or above), RPC also values flair, energy, business sense, commitment and the ability to communicate and relate well to others.

Training Environment
As a trainee you will receive first rate training in a supportive working environment. You will work closely with a Partner and be given real responsibility as soon as you are ready to handle it. At least six months will be spent in each of the three main areas of the practice and they encourage trainees to express a preference for their seats. This provides a thorough grounding and the chance to develop confidence as you see matters through to their conclusion. In addition to the externally provided Professional Skills Course they provide a complimentary programme of in-house training.

Benefits
Four weeks' holiday, two bonus schemes, private medical insurance, season ticket loan, subsidised gym membership, four office parties per year.

Vacation Placements
Places for July 2000: 12; Duration: 2 weeks; Remuneration: £175 p.w.; Closing Date: 29 February 2000.

Sponsorship & Awards
CPE Funding: Fees paid + £4,000 maintenance.
LPC Funding: Fees paid + £4,000 maintenance.

Partners	48
Assistant Solicitors	75
Total Trainees	16

Contact
Sally Andrews
Head of Personnel

Method of Application
Hand-written covering letter and application form

Selection Procedure
Assessment Days held in September

Closing date for 2002
14 August 2000

Application

Training contracts p.a.	7
Applications p.a.	600
% interviewed p.a.	6%
Required degree grade	2.1

Training

Salary: 1st year(1999)	£21,000
Salary: 2nd year(1999)	£23,000
Holiday entitlement	20 days
% of trainees with a non-law degree p.a.	25%

Post-Qualification

Salary (1999)	£33,000
% of trainees offered job on qualification (1999)	66%
% of assistants (as at 1/9/99) who joined as trainees	50%
% of partners (as at 1/9/99) who joined as trainees	35%

RICHARDS BUTLER

Beaufort House 15 St. Botolph Street London EC3A 7EE
Tel: (020) 7247 6555 Fax: (020) 7247 5091
Email: law@richardsbutler.com

Firm Profile

Established in 1920, Richards Butler is noted for the exceptional variety of its work. It has acknowledged strengths in shipping, commodities, company/commercial, litigation, property, insurance, media/ entertainment, competition and energy law, in each of which it has international prominence.

Main Areas of Work

Corporate/ Commercial/ Banking/ Finance 43%; Shipping/ International Trade & Commodities/ Insurance 23%; Commercial Litigation 20%; Commercial Property 14%.

Trainee Profile

Candidates should be players rather than onlookers, work well under pressure and be happy to operate as a team member or team leader as circumstances dictate. Candidates from diverse backgrounds are welcome, including mature students with commercial experience and management skills.

Training Environment

Richards Butler provides practical experience across as wide a spectrum of the law as possible. Training is divided into four periods of five months and one period of four months. Trainees start in general corporate, litigation and commercial property seats, however there are opportunities to work in other additional specialised areas such as shipping, media law, or international trade in later seats.

Benefits

Life insurance, Private Patients' Plan, interest free season ticket loan, subsidised staff restaurant.

Vacation Placements

Places for 2000: 45; Duration: 2 weeks; Remuneration: £200 p.w.; Closing Date: 31 March 2000. In addition, the firm offers overseas scholarships to 4 students.

Sponsorship & Awards

CPE and LPC fees and maintenance paid.

Partners	94*
Assistant Solicitors	166*
Total Trainees	59*

** denotes world-wide figures*

Contact

Jill Steele

Method of Application

Firm's application form

Selection Procedure

1 interview

Closing date for 2002

31 July 2000

Application

Training contracts p.a.	20
Applications p.a.	1,500
% interviewed p.a.	7.5%
Required degree grade	n/a

Training

Salary: 1st year(2000)	£21,500
Salary: 2nd year(2000)	£24,000
Holiday entitlement	22 days
% of trainees with a non-law degree p.a.	33%
No. of seats available abroad p.a.	10

Post-Qualification

Salary (2000)	£33,000
% of trainees offered job on qualification (1999)	100%
% of assistants (as at 1/9/99) who joined as trainees	65%
% of partners (as at 1/9/99) who joined as trainees	33%

Overseas Offices

Abu Dhabi, Beijing, Brussels, Doha, Hong Kong, Islamabad, Muscat, Paris, Piraeus, São Paulo, Warsaw.

ROWE & MAW

20 Black Friars Lane London EC4V 6HD
Tel: (020) 7248 4282 Fax: (020) 7248 2009
Email: roweandmaw@roweandmaw.co.uk
Website: www.roweandmaw.co.uk

Firm Profile

Founded 100 years ago, Rowe & Maw is a leading commercial firm, with offices in London, including one at Lloyds, and in Brussels. Its strength lies in advising companies and businesses on day-to-day work and special projects.

Main Areas of Work

Corporate 35%, Litigation 22%, Property 9%, Pensions 8%, Intellectual Property 8%, Construction 7%, Banking and Projects 7%, Employment 4%.

Trainee Profile

The firm is interested in students with a good academic record and a strong commitment to law. Commercial awareness gained through legal or business work experience is an advantage. Extra-curricular activities are taken into consideration. The firm wants trainees to become future partners. The current senior partner trained with the firm.

Training Environment

There are September and March intakes. Training divides into four six-month seats. All trainees spend time in the corporate, litigation and property departments, frequently working for blue chip clients. Secondments to Brussels or to clients in the UK or abroad are an option for some. The firm has a professional development and training programme which covers subjects like EU law and the workings of the City. Advocacy and drafting skills are also taught. Trainees are encouraged to join in the sports and social life.

Benefits

Interest free season ticket loan, subsidised membership of sport clubs, private health scheme.

Vacation Placements

Places for 2000: 25; Duration: 2 weeks; Remuneration: £200 p.w.; Closing Date: 29 February 2000.

Sponsorship & Awards

CPE and LPC fees paid and £4,000 maintenance p.a.

Partners	73
Assistant Solicitors	125
Total Trainees	45

Contact

Vicky Barnbrook

Method of Application

Application form

Selection Procedure

Selection workshops including an interview and a business exercise

Closing date for 2002

31 August 2000

Application

Training contracts p.a.	25
Applications p.a.	1,250
% interviewed p.a.	10%
Required degree grade	2:1

Training

Holiday entitlement	21
% of trainees with a non-law degree p.a.	50%
No. of seats available abroad p.a.	2

Post-Qualification

Salary (1999)	£34,000
% of trainees offered job on qualification (1999)	80%
% of assistants (as at 1/9/99) who joined as trainees	50%
% of partners (as at 1/9/99) who joined as trainees	36%

RUSSELL-COOKE

2 Putney Hill London SW15 6AB
Tel: (020) 8789 9111 Fax: (020) 8785 4286
Email: thorntonj@russell-cooke.co.uk

Firm Profile

A medium-sized practice with three offices in the London area. The City office deals primarily with commercial property. The Putney office has a range of specialist departments including company/commercial, crime, judicial review, commercial litigation, matrimonial, domestic and commercial conveyancing, personal injury litigation and private client. The Kingston-upon-Thames office is a general practice with a specialist child-care department.

Main Areas of Work

Commercial Property/General Commercial 30%; Litigation (Commercial, PI and Property) 20%; Private Client 10%; Domestic Conveyancing 10%; Matrimonial 10%; Crime 20%.

Trainee Profile

Trainees will need at least two A grades and a B grade at A Level and a 2:1 degree, though not necessarily in law. You will also need to be good at the practical business of advising and representing clients. Intellectual rigour, adaptability and the ability, under pressure, to handle a diverse range of people and issues efficiently and cost-effectively are vital attributes.

Training Environment

Trainees are offered four seats lasting six months each. Photocopying and researching points of law will not take up all your time in the firm. You will have the chance to manage your own case work and deal directly with clients, with supervision suited to your needs and the needs of the department and clients. Internal training and an annual executive staff conference supplement the externally provided PSC. Social events include quiz nights, wine tasting, summer and Christmas parties, and thriving cricket and netball teams.

Partners	20
Assistant Solicitors	25
Total Trainees	8

Contact
J.M. Thornton

Method of Application
Application form

Selection Procedure
First and second interviews.

Closing date for 2002
13 August 2000

Application

Training contracts p.a.	3–4
Applications p.a.	500
% interviewed p.a.	7%
Required degree grade	2:1

Training

Salary: 1st year(2000)	£17,500
Salary: 2nd year(2000)	£18,500
Holiday entitlement	22 days
% of trainees with a non-law degree p.a.	50%

Post-Qualification

Salary (2000)	Market
% of trainees offered job on qualification (1999)	75%
% of assistants (as at 1/9/99) who joined as trainees	30%
% of partners (as at 1/9/99) who joined as trainees	50%

RUSSELL JONES & WALKER

Swinton House 324 Gray's Inn Road London WC1X 8DH
Tel: (020) 7837 2808 Fax: (020) 7837 2941
Email: enquiries@rjw.co.uk
Website: www.rjw.co.uk

Firm Profile

Russell Jones & Walker was founded in London in the 1920s but has expanded in recent years to become one of the largest litigation practices in the country with more than 440 lawyers and support staff and offices in London, Leeds, Birmingham, Bristol, Manchester, Sheffield, Newcastle-upon-Tyne and Cardiff.

Main Areas of Work

Personal Injury 66%; Criminal 13%; Commercial Litigation 12%; Employment 5%; Family/Probate 2%; Commercial and Domestic Conveyancing 2%.

Trainee Profile

They are looking for candidates who are motivated and hard-working with a sense of humour and the ability and confidence to accept responsibility in fee earning work and client care.

Training Environment

Each trainee will spend six months in four of the following departments under the supervision of a partner or senior solicitor - personal injury; commercial litigation, family and probate; clinical negligence; criminal and investigation; employment/trade union regulation and commercial conveyancing. Your supervisor will conduct a three-month assessment and six-month review. The PSC is taught externally at present. The firm is extremely sociable and trainees are encouraged to participate in social and sporting events. There is a comprehensive in-house education timetable. Liz Dux, the training partner, supervises all aspects of the training contract. IT training and an induction progamme are provided.

Benefits

Season ticket loan, pension, private healthcare, permanent health.

Vacation Placements

No structured scheme in place.

Sponsorship & Awards

CPE/LPC Funding: interest free loan to assist with fees available (£1,000).

Partners	45
Assistant Solicitors	61
Total Trainees	11

Contact

Lorraine Hunt
Training Officer

Method of Application

Application form

Closing date for 2002

28 July 2000

Application

Training contracts p.a.	8
Applications p.a.	1,000–1,500
% interviewed p.a.	5-7%
Required degree grade	2:1

Training

Salary: 1st year(2000)	£19,000
Salary: 2nd year(2000)	£21,000
Holiday entitlement	4 weeks
% of trainees with a non-law degree p.a.	50%

Post-Qualification

Salary (2000)	£27,000
% of trainees offered job on qualification (1999)	50%
% of assistants (as at 1/9/99) who joined as trainees	c.25%
% of partners (as at 1/9/99) who joined as trainees	10%

SALANS HERTZFELD & HEILBRONN HRK

Clements House 14–18 Gresham Street London EC2V 7NN
Tel: (020) 7509 6000 Fax: (020) 7726 6191
Email: london@salans.com

Firm Profile

Salans Hertzfeld & Heilbronn ('SHH') is a multinational law firm with full-service offices in the City of London, Paris and New York, together with further offices in Moscow, St Petersburg, Warsaw, Kiev, Almaty and Baku. The firm has currently over 365 fee-earners, including 100 partners.

Main Areas of Work

Banking & Finance/Corporate 50%; Litigation 25%; Employment 15%; Commercial Property 10%.

Trainee Profile

Candidates need to have high academic qualifications and the ability to approach complex problems in a practical and commercial way. The firm looks to recruit those who demonstrate an ability and a willingness to assume responsibility at an early stage, possess common sense and good judgement. Language and IT skills are also valued.

Training Environment

The firm operates an in-house training scheme for both trainees and assistant solicitors. In addition, trainees will be offered the opportunity to attend external courses wherever possible. Trainees are at all times supervised by a partner and encouraged to take an active part in the work of their department. The caseload of the trainee will, in each case, depend on the trainee's level of expertise and experience. Where possible the firm seeks to recruit its trainees at the end of the training periods.

Partners	100
Assistant Solicitors	260
Total Trainees	7

Contact

Alison Gaines
Partner

Method of Application

Handwritten Letter and CV

Selection Procedure

2 interviews with partners

Closing date for 2002

31 July 2000

Application

Training contracts p.a.	3 or 4
Applications p.a.	500+
% interviewed p.a.	5%
Required degree grade	2:1

Training

Salary: 1st year (1999)	£20,000
Salary: 2nd year (1999)	£21,500
Holiday entitlement	20 days
% of trainees with a non-law degree p.a.	Variable
No. of seats available abroad p.a.	None at present

Post-Qualification

Salary (1999)	Variable
% of trainees offered job on qualification (1999)	3 out of 3
% of assistants (as at 1/9/99) who joined as trainees	not available
% of partners (as at 1/9/98) who joined as trainees	not available

Overseas Offices

Almaty, Baku, Kiev, Moscow, New York, Paris, St Petersburg, Warsaw.

SHADBOLT & CO

Chatham Court Lesbourne Road Reigate RH2 7LD
Tel: (01737) 226277 Fax: (01737) 226165
Email: sally_thorndale@shadboltlaw.co.uk
Website: www.shadboltlaw.co.uk

Firm Profile

Established in 1991, Shadbolt & Co is a specialist firm servicing business clients in the UK and internationally. Well known for its strengths in major projects, construction and engineering and more recently for its company commercial practice. All partners have City backgrounds.

Main Areas of Work

Corporate and Commercial Disputes 40%; Projects/non-contentious Construction and engineering 30%; Company and Commercial 30%.

Trainee Profile

Mature self-starters with a strong academic background and outside interests. They should be able to take responsibility, have good interpersonal skills and be able to play an active role in the future of the firm. Linguists (especially French) are particularly welcome. Travel is favourably viewed.

Training Environment

Four six-month seats from: corporate, commercial, commercial property, projects/non contentious construction, and litigation. Where possible, individual preference is noted. Work has an international bias. French speaking trainees work temporarily in an associated Paris office. Trainees are seconded to major plc construction/engineering clients. As a small firm, trainees are rapidly integrated and immediately take active roles and early responsibility. All trainees sit with partners/senior solicitors who monitor progress. One appraisal is held per seat. In certain seats trainees may be given their own files. Lunch time lectures occur frequently, and trainees participate in publishing a construction law and other updates. The PSC is taught externally. The firm's atmosphere is young and informal, and there are various social and sporting activities.

Benefits

Permanent health insurance.

Vacation Placements

Places for 2000: 6; Duration: 2 weeks; Remuneration: £120 p.w.; Closing Date: 17 March 2000.

Sponsorship & Awards

LPC fees partly payable when trainee commences work.

Partners	15
Assistant Solicitors	18
Total Trainees	9

Contact

Sally Thorndale

Method of Application

Handwritten letter and CV

Selection Procedure

Interview(s)

Closing date for 2002

31 August 2000

Application

Training contracts p.a.	6
Applications p.a.	200
% interviewed p.a.	10%
Required degree grade	2:1

Training

Salary: 1st year(2000)	£19,000
Salary: 2nd year(2000)	£21,000
Holiday entitlement	20 days
% of trainees with a non-law degree p.a.	50%
No. of seats available abroad p.a.	1/2

Post-Qualification

Salary (2000)	£28,000
% of trainees offered job on qualification (1999)	100%
% of assistants (as at 1/9/99) who joined as trainees	20%
% of partners (as at 1/9/99) who joined as trainees	0%

Overseas Offices

Hong Kong, Paris

SHARPE PRITCHARD

Elizabeth House Fulwood Place London WC1V 6HG
Tel: (020) 7405 4600 Fax: (020) 7831 1284
Email: abadcock@sharpepritchard.co.uk
Website: www.sharpepritchard.co.uk

Firm Profile
Sharpe Pritchard is best known for its work with the public sector. It has strong litigation, public procurement and parliamentary departments. It has expanding commercial, property and planning departments.

Main Areas of Work
Litigation 40%; Commercial/Procurement 20%; Parliamentary 15%; Property and Planning 25%.

Trainee Profile
Trainees will need to show good intellectual capabilities, effective communication skills, resourcefulness and an ability to work as part of a team.

Training Environment
The firm's training consists of seats normally between four and six months in length in the following areas: Administrative law and judicial review, general litigation, employment law, contracts and commercial, property work. There is also a prospect of undertaking parliamentary and planning work. You would normally share an office with the solicitor responsible for supervising your work. A review of progress is carried out at the end of each seat. In addition you will have regular meetings throughout your training period with the training partner. The firm has an in-house series of seminars taking the form of both skills training and updates in the law and you are encouraged to attend these.

Benefits
Season ticket loan.

Sponsorship & Awards
Possible financial assistance with LPC.

Partners	11
Assistant Solicitors	12
Total Trainees	8

Contact
Ashley Badcock Senior Partner

Method of Application
Letter and CV

Selection Procedure
Interview with the Senior Partner

Application
Training contracts p.a. 4

Training
Salary: 1st year(2000)c.£20,000
Salary: 2nd year(2001) c.£21,000
Holiday entitlement 25 days

SHERIDANS

14 Red Lion Square London WC1R 4QL
Tel: (020) 7404 0444 Fax: (020) 7831 1982
Email: general@sheridans.co.uk

Firm Profile

A Holborn firm specialising in litigation and the entertainment and media industry, and offering private client and commercial services including property and company work.

Main Areas of Work

Commercial and other litigation including Media, Family and Crime 35%; Entertainment and Media 40%; Property and Planning 15%; Company/Commercial 10%.

Trainee Profile

Candidates should be intelligent, ambitious and self-confident with excellent communication and interpersonal skills.

Training Environment

Trainees spend six to eight months in each department (litigation, company/commercial, property and planning). Working alongside senior partners or solicitors, you will be involved with a whole variety of work. There are regular trainee and department meetings. In the second year, trainees may be given a limited number of their own files. Early responsibility is encouraged. Trainees are not usually placed in media and entertainment (at least not until their last six months, due to its particularly specialised nature). The training programme is being expanded to include in-house seminars and video assisted learning schemes. Full computer and technology training is provided. Trainees are expected to work hard and think on their feet. The firm is friendly and informal and organises a range of social/sporting activities.

Benefits

Life assurance.

Sponsorship & Awards

LPC funding is variable for those who have accepted training contracts.

Partners	16
Assistant Solicitors	8
Total Trainees	7

Contact

Cyril Glasser

Method of Application

Letter and CV

Selection Procedure

2 interviews

Application date for 2002

1–31 August 2000

Application

Training contracts p.a.	3
Applications p.a.	700
% interviewed p.a.	8%
Required degree grade	2:1

Training

Salary: 1st year(2000)	£18,800
Salary: 2nd year(2000)	£20,000
Holiday entitlement	20 days
% of trainees with a non-law degree p.a.	28%

Post-Qualification

Salary (2000)	£27,000
% of trainees offered job on qualification (1999)	67%
% of assistants (as at 1/9/99) who joined as trainees	77%
% of partners (as at 1/9/99) who joined as trainees	31%

SHOOSMITHS

The Lakes Bedford Road Northampton NN4 7SH
Tel: (01604) 543000 Fax: (01604) 543543
Email: Northampton@shoosmiths.co.uk
Website: www.shoosmiths.co.uk

Firm Profile
A leading national commercial firm with private client department. The firm has in excess of 1,000 members of staff and 74 partners.

Main Areas of Work
Insurers 39.9%; Business Services, Property & Banking 41.4%; Financial Institutions 10%; Private Client 8.7%.

Trainee Profile
Candidates must show academic and personal achievement and commitment to work and the firm.

Training Environment
The training contract is divided into four seats of six months. Occasionally a trainee may choose to specialise and spend two seats in one department. It is compulsory for trainees to sit in either the commercial/corporate or in the litigation department. Trainees may move around the regional offices. Trainees sit with a partner who is responsible for giving hands-on training. Lectures are held internally for trainees and staff and the PSC is also taught in-house. All the staff in the firm are accessible and happy to give assistance. The firm has invested over four million pounds in IT over the past year and trainees will develop IT skills. Social and sporting activities are organised by every office and the practice as a whole.

Benefits
Life assurance, contributory pension after 3 months.

Vacation Placements
Places for 2000: 25; Duration: 2 weeks; Remuneration: £120 p.w.; Closing Date: 29 February 2000.

Sponsorship & Awards
Funding up to £6,500 maximum plus £1,500 maintenance grant.

Partners	74
Assistant Solicitors	104
Total Trainees	29

Contact
Donna Hanlon

Method of Application
Application form

Selection Procedure
Assessment centre – one day

Closing date for 2002
31 July 2000

Application

Training contracts p.a.	16
Applications p.a.	1,000
% interviewed p.a.	10%
Required degree grade	2:1

Training

Salary: 1st year(2000)	£15,500
Salary: 2nd year(2000)	£16,750
Holiday entitlement	23 days

Post-Qualification

Salary (2000)	£24,500

Offices
Northampton, Nottingham, Reading

SIDLEY & AUSTIN

1 Threadneedle Street London EC2R 8AW
Tel: (020) 7360 3600 Fax: (020) 7626 7937
Email: zzell@sidley.com
Website: www.sidley.com

Partners	14
Assistant Solicitors	36
Total Trainees	11

Firm Profile
Founded in Chicago in 1866, Sidley & Austin is now one of the largest law firms in the world, with approximately 900 lawyers practising on three continents. They have nearly 50 lawyers in London and are expanding fast.

Main Areas of Work
Banking, Capital Markets, Banking Regulation, Structured Finance and Securitisation, Corporate and Commercial Law, Corporate Tax, Property Finance, the Information Industries (Telecoms, Information Technology, Internet, Media, Networks etc.) and Intellectual Property.

Trainee Profile
Sidley & Austin is looking for focused, intelligent and enthusiastic individuals with personality and humour who have a real interest in practising law in the commercial world. Trainees normally have at least a 2.1 degree (not necessarily in law) and three A-levels at A and B grades. Trainees would normally be expected to have passed the CPE (if required) and the LPC at the first attempt.

Training Environment
Sidley & Austin are looking to recruit 6-8 trainee solicitors to start in September 2002/March 2003. It is not a typical City firm or a 'legal factory' - so there is no risk of you being just a number. The team at Sidley & Austin in London is young, dynamic and collegiate. Everyone is encouraged to be proactive and to create their own niche when they are ready to do so. Trainees spend a period of time in the firm's five specialist groups: International Finance, Information Industries, Corporate, Tax and Property. Sidley & Austin in London does not have a separate litigation department, although some litigation work is undertaken. In each group you will sit with a partner or senior associate to ensure that you receive individual training that is both effective and based on a real caseload. In addition, there is a structured timetable of training on a cross-section of subjects and an annual training weekend.

Benefits
Healthcare, disability cover, life assurance, contribution to gym membership, interest free season ticket loan.

Sponsorship & Awards
CPE and LPC fees paid and maintenance p.a.

Contact
Zoe Zell

Method of Application
Covering letter and employee application form - Please call 0800 731 5015

Selection Procedure
Interview(s)

Closing date for 2002
21 July 2000

Application

Training contracts p.a.	6-8
Applications p.a.	300
% interviewed p.a.	35
Required degree grade	2:1

Training

Salary: 1st year(1999)	£22,750
Salary: 2nd year(1999)	£24,750
Holiday entitlement	22 days
% of trainees with a non-law degree p.a.	50%

Overseas Offices
Chicago, Dallas, Hong Kong, Los Angeles, New York, Shanghai, Singapore, Tokyo, Washington D.C.

SIMMONS & SIMMONS

21 Wilson Street London EC2M 2TX
Tel: (020) 7628 2020 Fax: (020) 7628 2070
Email: recruitment@simmons-simmons.com
Website: www.simmons-simmons.com

Firm Profile

Simmons & Simmons is one of the major international law firms. It has developed an increasingly international practice to serve the needs of its clients and has ten offices in different locations across the globe. An extensive network of overseas contacts enables the firm to extend its reach far beyond those countries in which it has offices and offers clients a multi-jurisdictional service of the highest quality.

Main Areas of Work

Corporate/Corporate Finance/M&A 41%; Commercial/ IP/EC 14%; Property 13%; Litigation 12%; Banking and Capital Markets 10%; Tax 6%; Employment 3%; Environment 1%.

Trainee Profile

While a good academic record and sound commercial judgement are important, strength of character and outside interests are also taken into consideration.

Training Environment

Trainees are involved in the firm's work from the start of their contract. Simmons & Simmons allocate each trainee a training principal to oversee their training and career development. Each move to a new department is accompanied by a structured series of seminars on relevant areas of law. Simmons & Simmons supports the Battersea Legal Advice Centre and provides advice on a *pro bono* basis to prisoners on 'death row' in Jamaica.

Benefits

Season ticket loan, fitness loan, PRP, group travel insurance, group accident insurance, group health insurance.

Vacation Placements

Places for 2000: 30; Duration: 2 weeks; Remuneration: £200 p.w.; Closing Date: 25 February 2000.

Sponsorship & Awards

In the absence of Local Authority funding the firm will pay LPC fees and, where necessary, CPE fees and offer a maintenance allowance of £4,500 for those at Law School in London or Guildford and £4,000 elsewhere.

Partners	141
Assistant Solicitors	348
Total Trainees	132

Contact

Katharyn White

Method of Application

Application form, CV and covering letter

Selection Procedure

Assessment day: document exercise, interview and written excercise

Closing date for 2002

25 August 2000

Application

Training contracts p.a.	50-60
Applications p.a.	2,700
% interviewed p.a.	10%
Required degree grade	2:1

Training

Salary: 1st year(1999)	£21,000
Salary: 2nd year(1999)	£24,000
Holiday entitlement	22 days
% of trainees with a non-law degree p.a.	50%
No. of seats available abroad p.a.	18

Post-Qualification

Salary (1999)	£33,000
% of trainees offered job on qualification (1998)	91%

Overseas Offices

Abu Dhabi, Brussels, Hong Kong, Lisbon, Milan, New York, Paris, Rome, Shanghai.

SINCLAIR ROCHE & TEMPERLEY

Royex House 5 Aldermanbury Square London EC2V 7LE
Tel: (020) 7452 4000 Fax: (020) 7452 4001

Firm Profile

They are a major international law firm, founded in 1934. Over two thirds of the work handled in their London office is for non-UK clients. Their particular expertise is in shipping, aviation, international trade and energy, also emerging markets. Areas of work include shipping and commercial litigation and arbitration, collision, salvage and marine insurance, ship finance, aviation, oil and gas, company commercial and tax, commercial property, project, asset and trade finance and EC law.

Main Areas of Work

Shipping and Commercial; Litigation; Ship and Project Finance; Company/Commercial; Marine Casualty and Insurance; Commercial Property; Aviation; EU; Tax.

Trainee Profile

An employer offering equal opportunities looking for motivated trainees with a strong personality and good academic record. Commitment and interest in the firm's and their clients' businesses are essential.

Training Environment

Four six month seats. Trainees sit with a partner or senior assistant. As well as gaining the requisite legal skills, business development and management skills will be covered. Client contact is encouraged. A thorough programme of continuing professional training through lectures, seminars and external courses is provided.

Benefits

Private health cover, discretionary bonus, PHI, accident insurance, subsidised sports club membership.

Vacation Placements

Places for 2000: 12; Duration: 2 weeks; Remuneration: £160 p.w.; Closing Date: 28 February 2000, subject to availability.

Sponsorship & Awards

CPE and LPC fees paid and £4,000 maintenance p.a.

Partners	31
Assistant Solicitors	68
Total Trainees	22

Contact

Dawn Morgan

Method of Application

CV and covering letter

Selection Procedure

Interview

Closing date for 2002

31 October 2000 subject to availability

Application

Training contracts p.a.	8
Applications p.a.	1,750
% interviewed p.a.	6%
Required degree grade	2:1

Training

Salary: 1st year(2000)	£21,000
Salary: 2nd year(2000)	£22,000
Holiday entitlement	20 days
% of trainees with a non-law degree p.a.	Varies
No. of seats available abroad p.a.	Varies

Post-Qualification

Salary (2000)	£33,000
% of trainees offered job on qualification (1999)	82%
% of assistants (as at 1/9/99) who joined as trainees	50%

Overseas Offices

Bucharest, Hong Kong, Shanghai

SLAUGHTER AND MAY

35 Basinghall Street London EC2V 5DB
Tel: (020) 7600 1200 Fax: (020) 7600 0289
Website: www.slaughterandmay.com

Firm Profile

One of the leading law firms in the world, Slaughter and May enjoys a reputation for quality and expertise. The corporate and financial practice is particularly strong and lawyers are known for their business acumen and technical excellence. International work is central to the practice and lawyers travel widely. No London partner has ever left the firm to join a competing practice.

Main Areas of Work

Corporate and Financial 66%; Commercial Litigation 11%; Tax 7%; Property (Commercial) 6%; Pensions and Employment 5%; EC and Competition Law 3%; Intellectual Property 2%.

Trainee Profile

The work is demanding and the firm looks for intellectual agility and the ability to work with people from different countries and walks of life. Common sense, a mature outlook and the willingness to accept responsibility are all essential. The firm expects to provide training in everything except the fundamental principles of law, so does not expect applicants to know much of commercial life. Trainees are expected to remain with the firm on qualification.

Training Environment

Four or five seats of three or six months' duration. Two seats will be in the corporate and financial department and one seat in either Litigation, Intellectual Property, Tax or Pensions and Employment. In each seat, a partner is responsible for monitoring your progress and reviewing your work. There is an extensive training programme which includes the PSC. There are also discussion groups covering general and specialised legal topics.

Benefits

BUPA, STL, pension scheme, membership of various sports clubs, 24 hour accident cover.

Vacation Placements - Summer 2000

Places: 60; Duration: 2 weeks; Remuneration: £225 p.w.; Closing Date: ASAP from December but before 18 February 2000 for penultimate year (of first degree) students only.

Sponsorship & Awards

CPE and LPC fees and maintenance grants are paid; some grants are available for postgraduate work.

Partners	109
Assistant Solicitors	380
Total Trainees	132

Contact

Neil Morgan

Method of Application

Covering letter and CV to include full details of all examination results.

Selection Procedure

Interview

Application

Training contracts p.a. approx 75
Applications p.a. 3,000
% interviewed p.a. 20%
Required standard Good 2:1 ability

Training

Salary: 1st year(2000) £21,000
Salary: 2nd year(2000) £24,000
Holiday entitlement 25 days on qualification
% of trainees with a non-law degree p.a. 50%
No. of seats available abroad p.a. approx 30

Post-Qualification

Salary (2000) £33,000
% of trainees offered job on qualification (1999) 95%

Overseas Offices

Brussels, Hong Kong, New York, Paris, Singapore.

SPEECHLY BIRCHAM

6 St Andrew Street, London EC4A 3LX
Tel: (020) 7427 6400 Fax: (020) 7427 6600
Email: speechlys@speechlys.co.uk
website: www.speechlybircham.co.uk

Firm Profile

Based in the City of London, this commercial firm specialises in the following areas: corporate, tax, financial services, property, construction, employment, private client and charities, commercial and property litigation. Operating on a UK and an international basis, it has strong links with Europe, North America, the Caribbean and South Africa.

Main Areas of Work

Corporate 30%; Property 20%; Litigation 25%; Private Client 25%.

Trainee Profile

The firm looks for a consistently high level of academic achievement, self-motivation, a commitment to and interest in the profession (notably work experience), and an ability to work in a team. Candidates should be articulate, confident, responsible and reliable with good social and organisational skills.

Training Environment

Trainees have four six-month seats, supervised by a partner or senior assistant. You will have responsibility for the daily management of your files and the opportunity to contribute to planning your own career development within the firm. The training partner regularly reviews your progress and oversees your training. There is also a trainee liaison representative. In addition to the formal PSC, there are monthly talks and in-house workshops on technical and management topics. A sports and social committee organises outings and sporting activities.

Benefits

Season ticket loan, private medical insurance, life assurance.

Vaccation Placements

Places for 2000: 8; Duration: 3 weeks; Renumeration: £160pw; Closing Date: end February 2000.

Sponsorship

CPE and LPC Funding: Fees paid + £3,00 maintenance.

Partners	36
Assistant Solicitors	39
Total Trainees	10

Contact

Jane Henry
Partner

Method of Application

Application form

Selection Procedure

Interview

Closing date for 2002

15 August 2000

Application

Training contracts p.a.	5
Applications p.a.	1,000
% interviewed p.a.	5%
Required degree grade	2:1

Training

Salary: 1st year(1999)	£21,000 £22,000
Salary: 2nd year(1999)	£23,000 £24,000
Holiday entitlement	20 days
% of trainees with a non-law degree p.a.	50%

Post-Qualification

Salary (1999)	£34,000
% of trainees offered job on qualification (1999)	75%
% of assistants (as at 1/9/99) who joined as trainees	50%
% of partners (as at 1/9/99) who joined as trainees	30%

STEELE & CO

2 Norwich Business Park Whiting Rd Norwich NR4 6DJ
Tel: (01603) 627107 Fax: (01603) 625890
Email: ca@steele.co.uk
Website: www.steele.co.uk

Firm Profile

Steele & Co is an innovative and progressive commercial firm with an increasingly national client base. It is recognised in particular for the strength of its commercial practitioners and for the range and quality of its services to local authorities and the commercial sector.

Main Areas of Work

The firm offers a full range of corporate, property, litigation and public sector services. The firm is dedicated to delivering high quality value for money services to its clients regardless of location.

Trainee Profile

Candidates will be highly motivated, with a strong academic record and previous legal work experience.

Training Environment

The aim is to ensure that every trainee will wish to continue their career with the firm. The training programme consists of four six-month seats in the following departments: company commercial, commercial property, civil litigation, commercial disputes, employment, family and public sector.You will have some choice in the order of you seats. Trainees are encouraged to get involved and gain hands on experience early on in their training contract. Bi-monthly meetings provide a forum for discussion of topical issues. The offices are open-plan providing a supportive and learning environment which reflects our accreditation to both ISO 9001 and Investor in People. Trainee Solicitors are appraised at the end of each seat and are part of the firm's mentor scheme. There is an active sports and social life.

Benefits

Permanent health insurance, accident insurance, legal services.

Vacation Placements

Places for 2000: Places offered throughout the Easter and Summer vacation.

Partners	14
Assistant Solicitors	16
Total Trainees	8

Contact

Ann Chancellor
Human Resources Manager

Method of Application

Handwritten letter and CV

Selection Procedure

Interview

Application

Training contracts p.a.	6
Applications p.a.	300-400
Required degree grade	2:1

Post-Qualification

% of trainees offered job on qualification (1999)	100%

STEPHENSON HARWOOD

One, St Paul's Churchyard London EC4M 8SH
Tel: (020) 7329 4422 Fax: (020) 7606 0822
Email: info@stephensonharwood.com

Firm Profile

Established in the City of London in 1828, Stephenson Harwood has developed into a large international practice, with a commercial focus and a wide client base.

Main Areas of Work

Corporate; Banking; Litigation; Property; Private Client.

Trainee Profile

The firm looks for high calibre graduates with excellent academic records and an outgoing personality.

Training Environment

As the graduate intake is relatively small, the firm gives trainees individual attention, coaching and monitoring. Your structured and challenging programme involves four six-month seats in either corporate or banking, litigation, property and another seat of your choice. These seats include "on the job" training, sharing an office and working with a partner or senior solicitor. In-house lectures complement your training and there is continuous review of your career development. You will have the opportunity to spend six months abroad and have language tuition where appropriate. You will be given your own caseload and as much responsibility as you can shoulder. The firm plays a range of team sports, has its own gym, subsidised membership of a city health club and has privileged seats for concerts at the Royal Albert Hall and the London Coliseum and access to private views at the Tate Gallery.

Benefits

LVs, subsidised membership of health club, season ticket loan and 22 days paid holiday per year.

Vacation Placements

Places for 2000: 21; Duration: 2 weeks; Remuneration: £175 p.w.; Closing Date: 18 February 2000.

Sponsorship & Awards

£6,700 fees paid for CPE and LPC and £4,500 maintenance p.a.

Partners	72*
Assistant Solicitors	115*
Total Trainees	41

** denotes world-wide figures*

Contact

Ms Alison Warner, Legal and Graduate Recruitment Manager

Method of Application

Application form

Selection Procedure

Interview with 2 partners

Closing date for 2002

31 July 2000

Application

Training contracts p.a.	20
% interviewed p.a.	10%
Required degree grade	2:1

Training

Salary: 1st year(1999)	£21,500
Salary: 2nd year(1999)	£24,000
Holiday entitlement	22 days
% of trainees with a non-law degree p.a.	46%
No. of seats available abroad p.a.	8

Post-Qualification

Salary (1999)	£34,000
% of trainees offered job on qualification (1999)	100%
% of assistants (as at 1/9/99) who joined as trainees	37%
% of partners (as at 1/9/99) who joined as trainees	46%

Overseas Offices

Brussels, Guangzhou, Hong Kong, Madrid, Piraeus, Singapore.

TARLO LYONS

Watchmaker Court 33 St. John's Lane London EC1M 4DB
Tel: (020) 7405 2000 Fax: (020) 7814 9421
Email: info@tarlo-lyons.com
Website: www.tarlo-lyons.com

Partners	26
Assistant Solicitors	30
Total Trainees	6

Firm Profile

Tarlo Lyons was founded in 1927 and undertakes increasingly specialised and highly sophisticated work for commercial clients. The firm has particular expertise in Information Technology and Telecommunications Law (including a significant e-commerce practice), Entertainment Law (specifically live stage, TV and film), Commercial Litigation and Gaming and Licensing Law. It recently acquired Investor in People accreditation, and has nearly doubled in size in the past two years.

Main Areas of Work

Information Technology, Telecommunications and E-commerce; Dispute Resolution; Company/Commercial; Property; Entertainment.

Trainee Profile

Candidates need to demonstrate intellectual capacity combined with common sense, resourcefulness and a sense of humour. Basic IT skills essential; languages valued. A well spent gap year or commercial experience can be an advantage.

Training Environment

Trainees are introduced to the firm during a two day induction course. Training consists of six month seats in four of the following five departments: property, litigation, IT/telecoms, company/commercial and entertainment. You will be allocated to a Supervisor in each Department, who will monitor your workflow and training. In addition you will meet with the Training Partner every 2-3 months for a formal review. Some in-house training, especially on skills eg., IT, personal management, client care etc. Trainees are encouraged to attend relevant external courses on technical matters. The PSC is taught externally. The firm has a friendly, open door policy and trainees take part in a wide range of marketing, sporting and social events.

Benefits

Contribution to private health insurance and season ticket loan.

Contact

Robert Carolina
Partner

Method of Application

Letter and CV

Selection Procedure

2 Interviews with partners

Closing date for 2002

15 August 2000

Application

Training contracts p.a.	3
Applications p.a.	400+
% interviewed p.a.	5%
Required degree grade	2:1

Training

Salary: 1st year(2000)	£20,000 on average
Salary: 2nd year(2000)	£22,000 on average
Holiday entitlement	20 days
% of trainees with a non-law degree p.a.	50%

Post-Qualification

Salary (2000)	£30,000
% of trainees offered job on qualification (1999)	100%

TAYLOR JOYNSON GARRETT

Carmelite 50 Victoria Embankment Blackfriars
London EC4Y 0DX
Tel: (020) 7300 7000 Fax: (020) 7300 7100
Website: www.tjg.co.uk

Firm Profile
Taylor Joynson Garrett is a major City and international law firm, with an impressive UK and international client base. The firm, which has offices in London, Brussels and Bucharest, has recognised expertise in its corporate and intellectual property practices, as well as strength in depth across the full range of commercial disciplines.

Main Areas of Work
Corporate 25%; Litigation 21%; Intellectual Property 19%; Private Client 9%; Commercial Property 13%; Banking 7%; Employment 6%.

Trainee Profile
Academic achievement is high on the firm's list of priorities, and a 2:1 or better is expected. It wants individuals who have good communication skills and will flourish in a competitive environment. Strength of character, determination and the ability to think laterally are also important.

Training Environment
Trainees will have six-month seats in four different departments, with the possibility of a placement in Brussels. You will be supervised by a partner or assistant and appraised both two months into, and at the end of, each seat. There will be plenty of opportunity to take early responsibility. The firm works closely with external training providers to meet the needs of the PSC. The course is tailored to suit the firm's needs, and most of the training is conducted in-house. A full sports and social calendar is available.

Benefits
Private medical care, permanent health insurance, STL, subsidised staff restaurant, non-contributory pension scheme on qualification.

Vacation Placements
Places for 2000: 30; Duration: 2 weeks; Remuneration: £200 p.w.; Closing Date: 25 February 2000.

Sponsorship & Awards
CPE and LPC fees paid and £4,000 maintenance p.a.

Partners	76
Assistant Solicitors	116
Total Trainees	43

Contact
Trainee Solicitors' Recruitment Department

Method of Application
Firm's application form

Selection Procedure
2 interviews, 1 with a partner.

Closing date for 2002
11 August 2000

Application
Training contracts p.a.	22
Applications p.a.	2,500
% interviewed p.a.	6%
Required degree grade	2:1

Training
Salary: 1st year(2000)	£21,000
Salary: 2nd year(2000)	£23,500
Holiday entitlement	25 days
% of trainees with a non-law degree p.a.	40%
No. of seats available abroad p.a.	4

Post-Qualification
Salary (2000)	£33,500
% of trainees offered job on qualification (1999)	80%
% of assistants (as at 1/9/99) who joined as trainees	51%
% of partners (as at 1/9/99) who joined as trainees	31%

Overseas Offices
Brussels, Bucharest

TAYLOR VINTERS

Merlin Place Milton Rd Cambridge CB4 0DP
Tel: (01223) 423444 Fax: (01223) 423486
Email: pt@taylor-vinters.co.uk
Website: www.taylor-vinters.co.uk

Firm Profile
One of the largest firms in East Anglia, based in the University City of Cambridge. The largest single office firm in Cambridge.

Main Areas of Work
Company Commercial; Commercial Litigation; Commercial Property; Claimant Personal Injury.

Trainee Profile
Candidates should have energy, enthusiasm, intelligence, common sense, a friendly nature and a good sense of humour. Non law degree graduates are welcomed.

Training Environment
The training contract comprises four seats; commercial, property/planning, claiment personal injury and commercial litigation. Opportunities exist for exchanges with European Network firms. Trainees' progress is reviewed and assessed every three months. There is an extensive in-house training programme within all departments and firmwide. The PSC is also organised in-house.

Benefits
Benefits are currently under review but are likely to include private medical insurance, life insurance and a choice of other benefits. Full details will be available on application. Many social activities are actively encouraged, from a theatre club to karaoke. Cambridge of course now has the largest pub in Europe.

Vacation Placements
Places for 2000: Places available; Duration: 1 week.

Partners	22
Assistant Solicitors	45
Total Trainees	8

Contact
Paul Tapner

Method of Application
Application form

Selection Procedure
Single interview with two partners

Closing date for 2002
15 September 2000

Application

Training contracts p.a.	4
Applications p.a.	300
Required degree grade	2(ii)

Training

Salary: 1st year(1999)	£14,535
Salary: 2nd year(1999)	£16,050
Holiday entitlement	23 days
% of trainees with a non-law degree p.a.	40%

Post-Qualification

Salary (1999)	£25,000

plus benefits

TAYLOR WALTON

36-44 Alma Street Luton LU1 2PL
Tel: (01582) 731161 Fax: (01582) 457900
Email: luton@taylorwalton.co.uk
Website: www.taylorwalton.co.uk

Firm Profile

Strategically located in Luton, Harpenden, St Albans and Hemel Hempstead, Taylor Walton is a major regional law practice advising both businesses and private clients. Its strengths are in commercial property, corporate work and commercial litigation, whilst maintaining a strong private client side to the practice. It has a progressive outlook both in its partners and staff and in its systems, training and IT.

Main Areas of Work

Company/Commercial 15%; Commercial Property 20%; Commercial Litigation 15%; Employment 5%; Personal Injury 5%; Family 5%; Private Client 10%; Residential Property 20%; Relocation 5%.

Trainee Profile

Candidates need to show excellent intellectual capabilities, coupled with an engaging personality so as to show that they can engage and interact with the Firm's clients as the practice of law involves the practice of the art of communication. Taylor Walton sees its partners and staff as business advisers involved in clients businesses, not merely stand alone legal advisers.

Training Environment

The training consists of four six month seats. The training partner oversees the structural training along side a supervisor who will be a partner or senior solicitor in each department. The Firm does try to take trainees' own wishes in relation to seats into account. In a regional law practice like Taylor Walton you will find client contact and responsibility coupled with supervision, management and training. There is an in-house training programme for all fee earning members of staff. At the end of each seat there is a post seat appraisal conducted by the training partner, the trainee and the supervisor. The PSC is taught externally. The Firm is friendly with an open door policy and there are various sporting and social events.

Vacation Placements

Places for 2000: 2-3; Duration: up to 4 weeks; Remuneration: agreed with trainee; Closing Date: 30 April 2000.

Partners	20
Assistant Solicitors	27
Total Trainees	6

Contact
Jim Wrigglesworth

Method of Application
CV with covering letter

Selection Procedure
First and second interview with opportunity to meet other partners

Closing date for 2002
31 July 2000

Application
Required degree grade 2:1 or above.

TEACHER STERN SELBY

37–41 Bedford Row London WC1R 4JH
Tel: (020) 7242 3191 Fax: (020) 7242 1156
Email: bl@tsslaw.co.uk
Website: www.tsslaw.co.uk

Firm Profile

A central London-based general commercial firm, with clientele and caseload normally attributable to larger firms. It has a wide range of contacts overseas.

Main Areas of Work

Commercial Litigation 36%; Commercial Property 37%; Company and Commercial 13%; Secured Lending 8%; Residential Conveyancing/Probate 3%; Personal Injury/Education/Judicial Review 3%.

Trainee Profile

Emphasis falls equally on academic excellence and personality. The firm looks for flexible and motivated individuals, who have outside interests and who have demonstrated responsibility in the past. Languages an advantage.

Training Environment

Trainees spend six months in three departments (Company Commercial, Litigation and Property) with, where possible, an option to return to a preferred department in the final six months. Most trainees are assigned to actively assist a partner who monitors and supports them. Trainees are expected to fully immerse themselves and take early responsibility. After a short period you will conduct your own files. Trainees are welcome to attend in-house seminars and lectures for continuing education. The atmosphere is relaxed and informal.

Vacation Placements

Places for 2000: Possibly to those that have accepted training contracts.

Sponsorship & Awards

CPE Funding: none; LPC Funding: unlikely.

Partners	13
Assistant Solicitors	19
Total Trainees	6

Contact

Barbara Lombardi

Method of Application

Letter and application form

Selection Procedure

2 interviews

Closing date for 2002

31 October 2000

Application

Training contracts p.a.	3
Applications p.a.	500
% interviewed p.a.	5%
Required degree grade (not absolute)	2:1

Training

Salary: 1st year(2002)	£20,000 minimum
Salary: 2nd year(2002)	£22,250
Holiday entitlement	4 weeks
% of trainees with a non-law degree p.a.	50%

Post-Qualification

Salary (2000)	£31,000
% of trainees offered job on qualification (1999)	100%
% of assistants (as at 1/9/99) who joined as trainees	47%
% of partners (as at 1/9/99) who joined as trainees	46%

THEODORE GODDARD

150 Aldersgate Street London EC1A 4EJ
Tel: (020) 7606 8855 Fax: (020) 7606 4390
Email: recruitment@theodoregoddard.co.uk
Website: www.theogoddard.com

Partners	57
Total Fee-earners	190
Total Trainees	35

Firm Profile
Theodore Goddard is a long-established, unstuffy City firm. It has a particular reputation for work in the fields of banking & finance and media & communications as well as offering a wide range of well developed specialisations. The firm has offices in Brussels and Paris (where it has an associated office). International work is central to the firm's business and it works with a well-established network of international firms.

Main Areas of Work
Corporate, corporate finance and corporate tax, banking & finance, commercial litigation, commercial property and media & entertainment.

Trainee Profile
Graduates of all disciplines should apply. In an increasingly global, technology driven market, the firm is looking for graduates who think they will enjoy a fast paced, intellectually demanding work environment. Individuals with drive, commercial acumen and an approachable manner will thrive in its distinctive culture.

Training Environment
Theodore Goddard has been nominated for five and won four awards for the quality of its training. Much of the PSC is delivered in-house. Trainees sit with either a partner or assistant solicitor. Trainees spend six months in four practice areas with the option of three months in Paris or Brussels and are consulted about seat choices.

Benefits
Permanent employment offered from the outset. Contributory pension, permanent health insurance, private medical insurance, death in service benefit, subsidised sports club membership and staff restaurant.

Vacation Placements
Places for 2000: 20 in the Summer vacation (with 70 open day places in the Easter vacation); Duration: 2 weeks; Remuneration: £200 p.w.; Closing Date: End February 2000 for both vacation placements and open days.

Sponsorship & Awards
CPE and LPC fees paid in full. £4,200 maintenance paid for London and South East, £3,750 elsewhere.

Contact
Fiona Jones
Recruitment Manager

Method of Application
Firm's application form

Selection Procedure
Initial interview followed by second interview

Closing date for 2002
31 August 2000

Application

Training contracts p.a.	20
Applications p.a.	4000
% interviewed p.a.	c5%
Required degree grade	2:1+

Training

Salary: 1st year(1999)	£22,000
Salary: 2nd year(1999)	£25,000
Holiday entitlement	22 days
% of trainees with a non-law degree p.a.	50%
No. of seats available abroad p.a.	8

Post-Qualification

Salary (2000)	£33,500
% of trainees offered job on qualification (1999)	100%

Overseas Offices
Brussels, Paris (associated offices worldwide)

TITMUSS SAINER DECHERT

2 Serjeants' Inn London EC4Y 1LT
Tel: (020) 7583 5353 Fax: (020) 7775 7322
Email: info@titmuss-dechert.com
Website: www.titmuss-sainer-dechert.com

Firm Profile

Titmuss Sainer Dechert is the combination of Titmuss, Sainer & Webb and US firm, Dechert Price and Rhoads. Together they are a world-wide commercial practice with over 600 lawyers. The London office majors in business law, commercial property, litigation and investigations. Additionally, it has a number of specialist areas (all of them recommended in Chambers' clients' guide to Law Firms). These include Customs & Excise; insurance; intellectual property; tax; private client and financial services.

Main Areas of Work

Business, Insurance & Financial services 40%; Property 35% Litigation 20%; Tax and Private Client 5%.

Trainee Profile

Candidates should be able to empathise with a wide range of people, as their clients come from all walks of life. TSD looks for enthusiasm, intelligence, an ability to find a practical solution to a problem and for powers of expression and persuasion. Also wanted are those with a desire and ability to promote the firm's business at every opportunity. TSD want people who will remain on qualifying and make their careers with the firm. They take fewer trainees than comparable firms because they regard as paramount the quality of training and opportunities for individual progression and those believed to be the best are guaranteed by keeping their intake relatively small.

Training Environment

Unusually training is divided into six periods of four months, giving trainees the chance to sample a wide range of work. Your supervisor will participate with you and a Trainee Panel Partner (who will be responsible for your wellbeing throughout your training contract) in a formal oral and written assessment of your work towards the end of each seat. Trainees have the opportunity to spend four months at Dechert Price & Rhoads' Brussels office. The greater number of seats makes it easier for us to fit in with any special requests to work in specific areas of the firm. Titmuss Sainer Dechert was the first English firm to appoint a training director in the early 1980s and their most recent appointee is a senior educator and the former director of the College of Law in London. The PSC is provided in a tailored format by the firm, with some modules taking place in-

Partners	47
Assistant Solicitors	84
Total Trainees	22

Contact

Lynn Muncey

Method of Application

Letter and application form

Selection Procedure

1 interview with at least 2 partners

Closing date for 2002

18 August 2000

Application

Training contracts p.a.	10-15
Applications p.a.	over 1,000
% interviewed p.a.	12%
Required degree grade	2:1

(or capability of attaining a 2:1)

Training

Salary: 1st year(2000)	£22,000
Salary: 2nd year(2000)	£24,000

(to be reviewed in October 2000)

Holiday entitlement	20 days
% of trainees with a non-law degree p.a.	Varies
No. of seats available abroad p.a.	3

Post-Qualification

Salary (2000)	£34,000

(to be reviewed October 2000)

% of trainees offered job on qualification (1999)	70%
% of partners (as at 1/9/99) who joined as trainees	30%

house. That apart there is an extensive training programme in which trainees are encouraged to participate (numerous aspects being particularly aimed at trainees).

Benefits

Free permanent health and life assurance, subsidised membership of a local gym and interest-free season ticket loans.

Vacation Placements

Places for 2000: 8; Duration: 10 July to 21 July; Remuneration: £190 per week; Applications considered between: 1 November 1999 and 25 February 2000.

Open day

Places for 2000: 20-30; Date: 25 April 2000. Applications considered between 1 November 1999 and 25 February 2000. We will also be holding a special event for CPE students in the Summer/Autumn (details will be available nearer the time).

Sponsorship & Awards

LPC fees paid and £4,000 maintenance p.a. for those living in London and £3,750 for those outside (where local authority grants unavailable).

Trainee Comments

"Having expressed an early interest in the area of commercial litigation, and having done one seat in contentious Intellectual Property, my wish to gain further experience in other contentious fields of practice was readily and easily granted within our unique "six seat" framework.

I managed to get a full year of training in two areas of litigation, whilst also trying seats in property and business law. This has put me in good stead for the daily challenges that I now meet as a newly qualified in the contentious Insurance department". (Laura Abbott, newly qualified solicitor, read law at Cambridge)

"The Brussels office with a mix of American, Belgian and English lawyers provides a rewarding environment for solving client matters which often have legal implications on both an international and national level. Indeed, competition policy is never as exciting as when discussed over Belgian waffles in the conference room overlooking the Palais de Justice." (Danny Brower, newly qualified solicitor, read law at Manchester)

TSD is renowned for its friendly and supportive atmosphere and the wealth of sports and social activities within the firm are a reflection of this.

Titmuss Sainer Dechert

2 Serjeants' Inn, London EC4Y 1LT Telephone 0171-583 5353

TRAVERS SMITH BRAITHWAITE

10 Snow Hill London EC1A 2AL
Tel: (020) 7248 9133 Fax: (020) 7236 3728
Email: Graduate.Recruitment@TraversSmith.co.uk
Website: www.traverssmith.co.uk

Firm Profile
A leading medium-sized corporate, financial and commercial law firm with the capability to advise on a wide range of business activities. The practice offers small, closely-knit teams providing consistent service to clients.

Main Areas of Work
Corporate 38%; Litigation 15%; Property 15%; Finance 14%; Tax 8%; Pensions 5%; Employment 5%.

Trainee Profile
Candidates should have a strong academic background and show ambition and determination. A sense of humour is vital.

Training Environment
Training consists of four six-month seats taken from the corporate, commercial, banking/insolvency, employment, litigation, property, pensions and tax departments. There is no crowd to get lost in; trainees quickly get to know each other and everyone else in the firm. They are treated as individuals and given immediate responsibility for handling deals and clients. Formal training includes a comprehensive programme of in-house training and seminars, a weekly technical bulletin to keep staff abreast of changes in the law, a good library, and a computerised information centre. The office is designed to ensure there is close contact between staff members at all times. Social and sporting activities are enjoyed by the whole firm.

Benefits
Private health insurance, season ticket loans, luncheon vouchers, subsidised sports club membership.

Vacation Placements
Places for 2000: 45; Duration: 3 weeks; Remuneration: £200 p.w.; Closing Date: End March 2000.

Sponsorship & Awards
LPC and CPE fees paid and £4,000 maintenance p.a.

Partners	46
Assistant Solicitors	89
Total Trainees	39

Contact
Christopher Jon Carroll

Method of Application
Handwritten letter and CV

Selection Procedure
Interviews

Closing date for 2002
September 2000

Application

Training contracts p.a.	20
Applications p.a.	1,600
% interviewed p.a.	15%
Required degree grade	2:1

Training

Salary: 1st year(2000)	£21,000
Salary: 2nd year(2000)	£24,000
Holiday entitlement	20 days
% of trainees with a non-law degree p.a.	Approx 50%

Post-Qualification

Salary (2000)	£33,000
% of trainees offered job on qualification (1999)	86%
% of assistants (as at 1/9/99) who joined as trainees	75%
% of partners (as at 1/9/99) who joined as trainees	33%

TROWERS & HAMLINS

Sceptre Court 40 Tower Hill London EC3N 4DX
Tel: (020) 7423 8000 Fax: (020) 7423 8001
Email: gradrecruitment@trowers.com
Website: www.trowers.com

Firm Profile
Trowers & Hamlins is a substantial international firm. A leader in housing and public sector law, the firm also has a strong commercial side. The firm has regional offices in the UK, offices in the Middle East and links with Jordan, Yemen, Singapore, USA and Europe.

Main Areas of Work
Property (Housing, Public Sector, Comm.) 35%; Company and Commercial/Construction 32%; Litigation 27%; Private Client 6%.

Trainee Profile
Personable, enthusiastic candidates with a good academic record and wide-ranging outside interests. The ability to work under pressure and with others, combined with versatility are essential characteristics.

Training Environment
Trainees will gain experience in four seats from: company/commercial, construction, property, international, litigation, employment and private client. Trainees are encouraged to learn from direct contact with clients and to assume responsibility. The training programme is flexible and, with reviews held every three months, individual preferences will be considered. A training officer assists partners with the training programme and in-house lectures and seminars are held regularly. There are opportunities to work in Manchester, Exeter and the Middle East. The firm encourages a relaxed atmosphere and blends traditional qualities with contemporary attitudes. Activities are organised outside working hours.

Benefits
Season ticket loan, private health care after one year's service, Employee Assistance Programme & discretionary bonus.

Vacation Placements
Places for 2000: 25-30; Duration: 3 weeks;
Remuneration: £175 p.w.; Closing Date: 31 January (Easter); 1 March (Summer).

Sponsorship & Awards
CPE and LPC fees paid and £4,000 – £4,250 maintenance p.a.

Partners	63
Assistant Solicitors	85
Total Trainees	25

Contact
Graduate Recruitment Office

Method of Application
Letter, application form and CV

Selection Procedure
Interview(s), essay and practical test

Closing date for 2002
1 August 2000

Application
Training contracts p.a. 12–15
Applications p.a. 1,600
% interviewed p.a. 4%
Required degree grade 2:1+

Training
Salary: 1st year(2000) £21,500
Salary: 2nd year(2000) £23,500
Holiday entitlement 20 days (year 1)
22 days (year 2)
% of trainees with a non-law degree p.a. 40%
No. of seats available abroad p.a. Between 4 and 6

Post-Qualification
Salary (2000) £35,000
% of trainees offered job on qualification (1999) 90%
% of assistants (as at 1/9/99) who joined as trainees 40%
% of partners (as at 1/9/99) who joined as trainees 45%

Overseas Offices
Abu Dhabi, Dubai, Oman, Bahrain, Cairo.

UK Branch Offices
Manchester, Exeter.

WALKER MORRIS

Kings Court 12 King Street Leeds LS1 2HL
Tel: (0113) 283 2500 Fax: (0113) 245 9412
Email: info@walkermorris.co.uk
Website: www.walkermorris.co.uk

Firm Profile

Based in Leeds, Walker Morris is one of the largest commercial law firms in the North, providing a full range of legal services to commercial and private clients. It is increasingly gaining an international reputation.

Main Areas of Work

Commercial Litigation 32%; Commercial Property 30%; Company and Commercial 22%; Building Societies 12%; Private Clients 4%.

Trainee Profile

Bright, articulate, highly motivated individuals who will thrive on early responsibility in a demanding yet friendly environment.

Training Environment

Trainees commence with an induction programme, before spending four months in each main department (commercial property, corporate and commercial litigation). Trainees can choose in which departments they wish to spend their second year. Formal training workshops and seminars complement what is largely a hands-on learning style. The PSC is covered internally. Individual IT training is provided. An option exists for a four-month trainee exchange programme with a leading Parisian law firm. Emphasis is placed on teamwork, inside and outside the office. The firm's social and sporting activities are an important part of its culture and are organised by a committee drawn from all levels of the firm. A trainee solicitors committee also organises events and liaises with the Leeds Trainee Solicitors Group.

Vacation Placements

Places for 2000: 30-40 – over 3 weeks; Duration: 1 week; Remuneration: £100 p.w.; Closing Date: 28 February 2000.

Sponsorship & Awards

CPE Funding: Fees + £1,000; LPC Funding: Fees + £1,000.

Partners	33
Assistant Solicitors	61
Total Trainees	20

Contact

Nick Cannon

Method of Application

Application form and covering letter

Selection Procedure

Telephone and face to face interviews

Closing date for 2002

31 July 2000

Application

Training contracts p.a. 10
Applications p.a. approx 500
% interviewed p.a.
Telephone: 16%
Face to face: 10%
Required degree grade 2:1

Training

Salary: 1st year(2000) £16,798
Salary: 2nd year(2000) £18,000
Holiday entitlement 24 days
% of trainees with a non-law degree p.a. 30% on average
No. of seats available abroad p.a. 1

Post-Qualification

Salary (2000) £26,000
% of trainees offered job on qualification (1999) 90%
% of assistants (as at 1/9/99) who joined as trainees 60%
% of partners (as at 1/9/99) who joined as trainees 47%

WARNER CRANSTON

Pickfords Wharf Clink St London SE1 9DG
Tel: (020) 7403 2900 Fax: (020) 7403 4221
Email: Joy-Iley@Warner-Cranston.com
Website: www.warner-cranston.com

Partners	17
Assistant Solicitors	35
Total Trainees	8

Firm Profile

A London and Coventry based firm formed in 1979 with an international reputation for handling all types of commercial transactions. Its underlying principle is one of big firm expertise, coupled with a personal service.

Main Areas of Work

Company Commercial and Finance 37%; Commercial Litigation 20%; Employment 15%; Construction and Arbitration 7%; Property 14%; Personal Injury 4%; Debt Recovery 3%.

Trainee Profile

Proactive, commercially-minded graduates with a practical hands-on approach, who welcome responsibility.

Training Environment

The firm invests heavily in training, with in-house seminars (including advocacy course), drafting programmes and vital business skills courses. The firm aims to provide an informal but fast-paced working environment, where trainees are immediately given demanding work. A fine balance between supervision and responsibility is observed. There are four seats available, in company commercial, litigation, employment and property. Progress is reviewed regularly by a senior partner. An entrepreneurial atmosphere is encouraged, allowing trainees to flourish in what the firm calls the 'Warner Cranston Alternative'. The firm is located in attractive offices near London Bridge, overlooking the Thames.

Benefits

BUPA, IFSTL, life assurance, permanent health insurance, pension contributions (after qualifying period).

Vacation Placements

Places for Summer 2000: 12; Duration: 2 weeks; Remuneration: £400; Closing Date: 31 March 2000.

CV ?

Sponsorship & Awards

CPE/LPC fees and maintenance grant plus interest-free loan.

Contact

Joy Iley
Human Resources Manager

Method of Application

Application form and covering letter

Selection Procedure

Assessment Day: 2 interviews, aptitude test and presentation.

Closing date for 2002

31 July 2000

Application

Training contracts p.a.	4
Applications p.a.	1000
% interviewed p.a.	3%
Required degree grade	2:1

Training

Salary: 1st year(1999)	£21,500
Salary: 2nd year(1999)	£23,000
Holiday entitlement	25 days
% of trainees with a non-law degree	25%

Post-Qualification

Salary (1999)	£34,000

WATSON, FARLEY & WILLIAMS

15 Appold Street London EC2A 2HB
Tel: (020) 7814 8000 Fax: (020) 7814 8141/2
Website: www.wfw.com

Firm Profile

Established in 1982, Watson, Farley & Williams has its strengths in corporate, banking and asset finance, particularly ship and aircraft finance. The firm aims to provide superior service in specialist areas and to build long-lasting relationships with its clients.

Main Areas of Work

Shipping; Ship Finance; Aviation; Banking; Asset Finance; Corporate; Litigation; Intellectual Property; EC and Competition; Taxation; Property; Insolvency.

Trainee Profile

Outgoing graduates who exhibit energy, ambition, self-assurance, initiative and intellectual flair.

Training Environment

Trainees are introduced to the firm with a comprehensive induction course covering legal topics and practical instruction. Seats are available in at least four of the firm's main areas, aiming to provide trainees with a solid commercial grounding. There is also the opportunity to spend time abroad, working on cross-border transactions. Operating in an informal, friendly and energetic atmosphere, trainees will receive support whenever necessary. You will be encouraged to take on early responsibility and play an active role alongside a partner at each stage of your training. The practice encourages continuous learning for all employees and works closely with a number of law lecturers, producing a widely-read 'digest' of legal developments, to which trainees are encouraged to contribute. All modules of the PSC are held in-house. The firm has its own sports teams and organises a variety of social functions.

Benefits

Life assurance, PHI, BUPA, STL, pension, subsidised gym membership.

Vacation Placements

Places for 2000: 30; Duration: 2 weeks; Remuneration: £200 p.w.; Closing Date: 31 March 2000. CV ?

Sponsorship & Awards

CPE and LPC Fees paid and £4,000 maintenance p.a. (£3,600 outside London).

Partners	53
Assistant Solicitors	142
Total Trainees	22

Contact

Graduate Recruitment Officer

Method of Application

Handwritten letter and application form

Selection Procedure

Interview and assessment

Closing date for 2002

31 July 2000

Application

Training contracts p.a.	10–12
Applications p.a.	1,500
% interviewed p.a.	5%
Required degree grade	2:1 ideally

Training

Salary: 1st year(1999)	£23,000–£25,000
Salary: 2nd year(1999)	£24,000–£26,000
Holiday entitlement	22 days
% of trainees with a non-law degree p.a.	50%
No. of seats available abroad p.a.	8

Post-Qualification

Salary (1999)	£35,000
% of trainees offered job on qualification (1999)	90%
% of assistants (as at 1/9/99) who joined as trainees	35%
% of partners (as at 1/9/99) who joined as trainees	4%

Overseas Offices

Copenhagen, Moscow, New York, Paris, Piraeus, Singapore.

WEDLAKE BELL

16 Bedford Street Covent Garden London WC2E 9HF
Tel: (020) 7395 3000 Fax: (020) 7836 9966
Email: legal@wedlakebell.co.uk

Firm Profile
Based in Covent Garden, this medium-sized friendly firm, offers corporate, litigation, property and private client advice. It has an office in Guernsey, and links with the European Union through TELFA and Russia and with the United States.

Main Areas of Work
Corporate/Commercial 33%; Property 24%; Litigation 23%; Private Client 20%.

Trainee Profile
In addition to academic excellence, Wedlake Bell looks for flexibility, enthusiasm, a personable nature, confidence, mental agility and computer literacy in their candidates. Languages are not crucial.

Training Environment
Trainees have four seats of six months. You will be encouraged to meet clients and accept responsibility as soon as possible. Wedlake Bell prides itself on its training programme and aims to retain its trainees post-qualification. Seats available in corporate finance, banking, construction, IP & media, pensions/employment, litigation, property and private clients.

Benefits
On qualification: life assurance, medical insurance, PHI, subsidised gym membership and travel loan.

Vacation Placements
Places for 2000: 4; Duration: 3 weeks in July;
Remuneration: £150 p.w.; Closing Date: End of February.

Partners	32*
Assistant Solicitors	34*
Total Trainees	8

** denotes world-wide figures*

Contact
Natalie King

Method of Application
CV and covering letter

Selection Procedure
Interviews in September

Closing date for 2002
End August 2000

Application
Training contracts p.a.	4
Applications p.a.	800
% interviewed p.a.	3%
Required degree grade	2:1

Training
Salary: 1st year(2000)	Not known
Salary: 2nd year(2000)	Not known
Holiday entitlement	20 days
% of trainees with a non-law degree p.a.	25%

Post-Qualification
% of trainees offered job on qualification (1999)	66%
% of assistants (as at 1/9/99) who joined as trainees	50%

Overseas Offices
Guernsey

WEIL, GOTSHAL & MANGES

One South Place London EC2M 2WG
Tel: (020) 7903 1000 Fax: (020) 7903 0990
Email: weil.london@weil.com
Website: www.weil.com

Firm Profile

The London office of the New York firm Weil, Gotshal & Manges LLP was established in January 1996. It now houses over 170 staff and was, in only its second year, voted "Best London Office of an Overseas Law Firm" by Legal Business magazine.

Main Areas of Work

Acquisition and asset financing, banking, debt and equity capital markets, litigation, public and private mergers and acquisitions, corporate finance, telecommunications and securitisation. Also, given the firm's innate dual capability to practice both UK and US law, it undertakes a variety of US securities work.

Trainee Profile

Notwithstanding its emphasis on academic ability, the firm is looking for trainees with personality, commitment and drive who would feel comfortable in this young, dynamic office.

Training Environment

Trainees who join the firm in 2001/2002 will complete four six-month seats, one of which may be undertaken in the firm's New York office. In order to ensure its trainees receive adequate support and on-the-job training they each work closely with a senior associate or partner. The practical experience gained through exposure to client work is enhanced by regular internal seminars and attendance at external conferences. Weil, Gotshall & Manges aims to keep all trainees on qualification.

Benefits

Pension, Permanent Health Insurance, Private Health Cover, Life Assurance, subsidised gym membership, season ticket loan.

Vacation Placements

Places for 2000: Paid four week placement on being offered a training contract.

Sponsorship & Awards

The firm will pay tuition fees and a maintenance allowance for CPE/LPC.

Partners	18
Assistant Solicitors	63
Total Trainees	4

Contact

Elizabeth Sanderson
Graduate Recruitment

Method of Application

Letter and CV

Closing date for 2002

31 August 2000

Application

Training contracts p.a.	8
Required degree grade	2:1

Training

Salary: 1st year(1999)	£24,000
Holiday entitlement	23 days

Overseas Offices

Brussels, Budapest, Dallas, Houston, Menlo Park (Silicon Valley), Miami, New York, Prague, Warsaw, Washington DC

WHITE & CASE LLP

7-11 Moorgate London EC2R 6HH
Tel: (020) 7600 7300 Fax: (020) 7600 7030
Email: trainee@london.whitecase.com
Website: www.whitecase.com

Firm Profile

White & Case is a global law firm with over 1000 lawyers in 25 countries. It works with financial institutions, multi-national corporations and governments on major international corporate and financial transactions and complex disputes.

Main Areas of Work

In the London office: Project finance; Corporate finance; M&A; Joint ventures; Company/commercial; Capital markets; Construction; Litigation, arbitration and ADR; European and UK competition law; Intellectual property.

Trainee Profile

Trainees should be enthusiastic, be able to show initiative and have a desire to be involved with innovative and high profile legal matters. You should have an understanding of international commercial issues.

Training Environment

The firm's English law trainees are important and valued members of the London office and often work on multi-jurisdictional matters requiring close cooperation with lawyers throughout the firm's established overseas network. You will spend six months in each seat, and cover the majority of work dealt with in the London office during the course of the two-year contract. You will be sitting with an associate or partner, and experience gained from working with your supervisor and other lawyers will be backed up with more formal legal knowledge training sessions. You are encouraged to spend six months in one of our overseas offices to gain a fuller understanding of the global network. The Professional Skills Course is run throughout the contract.

Benefits

BUPA, gym membership contribution, life insurance, pension scheme, permanent health scheme, season ticket loan.

Vacation Placements

Places for 2000: 20; Duration: 2 weeks; Remuneration: £250; Closing Date: end of February 2000.

Sponsorship & Awards

CPE and LPC fees paid and £4,000 maintenance p.a. Prizes for commendation and distinction in the LPC.

Partners	12
Assistant Solicitors	33
Total Trainees	13

Contact

Ms Elizabeth Normand

Method of Application

Covering letter and cv

Selection Procedure

Interview

Closing date for 2002

End of July 2000

Application

Training contracts p.a.	10
Applications p.a.	1300
% interviewed p.a.	2.5%
Required degree grade	2:1

Training

Salary: 1st year(2000)	£24,000
Holiday entitlement	22 days

All trainees are encouraged to spend a seat abroad

Post-Qualification

Salary (2000)	£45,000

Overseas Offices

Almaty, Ankara, Bangkok, Bratislava, Bombay, Brussels, Budapest, Hanoi, Helsinki, Ho Chi Minh City, Hong Kong, Istanbul, Jeddah, Johannesburg, London, Los Angeles, Mexico City, Miami, Moscow, New York, Palo Alto, Paris, Prague, Riyadh, São Paulo, Singapore, Stockholm, Tokyo, Warsaw, Washington DC.

WHITEHEAD MONCKTON

72 King St Maidstone ME14 1BL
Tel: (01622) 698000 Fax: (01622) 690050
Email: Enquiries@Whitehead-Monckton.co.uk

Firm Profile

Whitehead Monckton traces its roots to 1780 and is now one of the largest legal practices in Kent. From these beginnings the firm has developed a modern, progressive practice with a substantial and diverse client base. The firm offers a first-rate legal service and is able to do so by delivering specialist skills to the highest professional standards. Its principal office is at Maidstone and it has a branch office at Tenterden. Within the firm there are four main departments which provide a focus for specialist skills. The four departments are commercial, litigation, private client and property. The work of each department is complex, demanding and varied.

Trainee Profile

Whitehead Monckton looks to engage new trainee solicitors each year. The firm seeks graduates from any discipline who have an interest in applying their skills to the law. There is no mimimum qualification but good academic results are often a guide to ability and it is ability the firm seeks.

Training Environment

Whitehead Monckton provides a friendly yet demanding working environment and much is expected of those who work with us. If the standard is attained it will be a rewarding experience. It is, however, a two-way relationship and the extent to which any trainee benefits will always depend upon his or her attitude, willingness to learn and initiative. The firm aims to provide trainee solicitors with experience in most areas of its work and in each department during their training period. Sometimes this is modified to suit individual interests or particular needs. The wish is that trainees will become part of the firm and develop his or her own skills. The firm aims to foster those skills through increasing responsibility during the training period. The extent and speed of this process depends upon the individual and the skill he or she demonstrates. The trainee can usually expect to undertake most of the tasks performed in a department. The prospects of any trainee after completion of the training period depend entirely upon their demonstrated ablility.

Partners	12
Assistant Solicitors	6
Total Trainees	4

Contact
The Training Partner

Method of Application
Firm's application form accompanied by a handwritten letter and a full CV

Selection Procedure
Interviews (in December of year of application)

Closing date for 2002
1 November 2000

Application
Training contracts p.a. 2

WIGGIN AND CO

The Quadrangle Imperial Square Cheltenham GL50 1YX
Tel: (01242) 224 114 Fax: (01242) 224223
Email: law@wiggin.co.uk

Firm Profile
Based in Cheltenham, with offices in London and Los Angeles, Wiggin and Co is a 'city-type' practice. It has strengths in the tax, company/commercial, media, communications, technology and entertainment fields.

Main Areas of Work
Private Client 40%; Media and Entertainment 40%; Litigation 12%; Property 8%.

Trainee Profile
Candidates will have a strong academic background, be personable and show a willingness to work hard individually or as part of a team.

Training Environment
The training is divided into four six-month seats. Trainees will spend time in four out of five departments, namely the company/commercial, media, property, litigation and private client departments. In each department you will sit with a partner or a senior solicitor. You will be encouraged to take an active role in transactions, assume responsibility and deal directly with clients. In-house lectures and seminars are held regularly and training reviews are held every three months. The firm offers the attraction of Cheltenham combined with technical ability and experience akin to a large City firm. Its relatively small size encourages a personal approach towards staff and client relations.

Benefits
Life assurance, private health cover, pension scheme, permanent health insurance.

Sponsorship & Awards
CPE and LPC Fees and £3,000 maintenance p.a. Brochure available on request.

Partners	12
Assistant Solicitors	14
Total Trainees	4

Contact
Sean James

Method of Application
Letter and CV

Selection Procedure
2 interviews

Closing date for 2002
21 August 2000

Application
Training contracts p.a.	2/3
Applications p.a.	1,700
% interviewed p.a.	2%
Required degree grade	2:1

Training
Salary: 1st year(2000)	£21,600
Salary: 2nd year(2000)	£25,200
Holiday entitlement	20 days
% of trainees with a non-law degree p.a.	50%

Post-Qualification
Salary (2000)	£31,600
% of trainees offered job on qualification (1999)	100%
% of assistants (as at 1999) who joined as trainees	15%
% of partners (as at 1999) who joined as trainees	17%

Overseas Offices
Los Angeles

WILDE SAPTE

1 Fleet Place London EC4M 7WS
Tel: (020) 7246 7000 Fax: (020) 7246 7777
Email: njg@wildesapte.com
Website: www.wildesapte.com

Firm Profile
Founded in 1785, Wilde Sapte is a commercial City firm handling a wide range of work for UK and international clients, with a particular emphasis on banking, finance and insurance markets.

At the time of going to press it was announced that City firms Wilde Sapte and Denton Hall are to merge in February 2000. Please consult the firm website or Nicola Graham for more information.

Main Areas of Work
Banking & Finance 46%; Litigation 24%; Property 11%; Company & Commercial 11%; Taxation 7%; Misc.1%.

Trainee Profile
Law graduates or graduates with a highly developed second language (ideally French, Spanish, German, Russian, Japanese or Mandarin). Non-law graduates should expect to achieve a first class degree.

Training Environment
Training consists of four six month seats. The third or fourth seat is either spent abroad in one of Wilde Sapte's Paris, Brussels or Tokyo offices or in a chosen specialist area, subject to availability. Trainees complete the PSC in the first year. Language training is available throughout the 2 year training contract.

Benefits
Subsidised gym, interest free season ticket loan, death in service benefit, PPP, PRP, contributory pension at age 28 after qualification, staff restaurant.

Vacation Placements
Places for 2000: 75; Duration: 1 week; Remuneration: £160 p.w.; Closing Date: 17 March 2000.

Sponsorship & Awards
CPE and LPC fees paid and £4,000 maintenance p.a.

Partners	62*
Assistant Solicitors	290*
Total Trainees	62*

world-wide figures as of October 1999

Contact
Nicola Graham

Method of Application
Application form
(available from February 2000)

Selection Procedure
Interviews and testing. Details to be confirmed in February.

Closing date for 2002
Law/Non-Law: mid-August

Application
Training contracts p.a.	30
Applications p.a.	2,500
% interviewed p.a.	10%
Required degree grade	2:1

Training
Salary: 1st year(2000)	£21,500
Salary: 2nd year(2000)	£24,000
Holiday entitlement	20 days
% of trainees with a non-law degree p.a.	25%
No. of seats available abroad p.a.	8

Post-Qualification
Salary (2000)	£34,000
% of trainees offered job on qualification (1999)	95%
% of assistants (as at 1/9/99) who joined as trainees	40%
% of partners (as at 1/9/99) who joined as trainees	25%

Overseas Offices
Brussels, Hong Kong, Paris, Tokyo.

WITHERS

12 Gough Square London EC4A 3DW
Tel: (020) 7936 1000 Fax: (020) 7936 2589
Email: mailto@withers.co.uk
Website: www.withers.co.uk

Firm Profile
A thriving, medium-sized practice, based between the High Court and the City. Half the firm's work is for corporate clients and institutions, the balance is for individuals and families. Withers has specialist practices ranging from an agriculture department to an Alternative Investment Market sector.

Main Areas of Work
Private Client and Charities 40%; Litigation 19%; Corporate, Company and Commercial 17%; Property (Agricultural, Commercial and Residential) 13%; Family 11%; International 5%.

Trainee Profile
As well as a keen intellect, trainees should have the confidence and social skills to interact successfully with clients and colleagues, and the determination and ambition to do well. They should show business acumen, entrepreneurial flair and commercial awareness. A genuine international outlook and foreign languages, particularly Italian, would be an advantage.

Training Environment
After a two week induction period, trainees spend six months in four of the main departments (corporate, family law, private client, property, litigation), sitting with senior assistants or partners. You will work as part of a small team within each department and be given responsibilities at an early stage.

Benefits
Interest free season ticket loan, private medical insurance, life assurance, social events, cafe facilities.

Vacation Placements
Places for 2000: 16; Duration: Easter (3 weeks), summer (3 weeks); Remuneration: £130 p.w.; Closing Date: 18 February 2000.

Sponsorship & Awards
LPC and CPE fees paid and £4,000 maintenance p.a. and cash prize for distinction or commendation in CPE and LPC.

Partners	48*
Assistant Solicitors	80*
Total Trainees	23

** denotes world-wide figures*

Contact
Graduate Recruitment Officer

Method of Application
Application form

Selection Procedure
2 interviews

Closing date for 2002
2 August 2000

Application

Training contracts p.a.	10
Applications p.a.	1,500
% interviewed p.a.	5-10%
Required degree grade	2:1

Training

Salary: 1st year(2000)	£20,500
Salary: 2nd year(2000)	£22,600
Holiday entitlement	20 days
% of trainees with a non-law degree p.a.	40%

Post-Qualification

Salary (2000)	£32,000
% of trainees offered job on qualification (1999)	90%
% of assistants (as at 1/9/99) who joined as trainees	8%
% of partners (as at 1/9/99) who joined as trainees	36%

Overseas Offices
Paris and Associate Italian office

WITHY KING

5 & 6 Northumberland Buildings Queen Square
Bath BA1 2JE
Tel: (01225) 425731 Fax: (01225) 315562
Email: withyking.solicitors

Partners	12
Assistant Solicitors	14
Total Trainees	4

Contact
Mrs Lin Clark

Method of Application
Download application form from website and return by post together with a recent photograph

Closing date for 2002
31 August 2000

Training
Salary: (2000)

1st six months	£12,200
last six months of training contract	£14,000

Offices
Bath and West Wilts.

Firm Profile
Withy King prides itself on an inclusive approach to law. It has developed expertise in the areas of: Plaintiff PI, Clinical Negligence, Company Commercial, Construction CDR, Commercial Property and Private Client. The firm has opened its first retail shop for the sale of conveyancing services and other packaged products. A customer centred stategic focus provides clear direction for the future of the firm. A wide variety of social activities and meetings promote communication and build relationships between all those working in the business.Team and individual development linked with good communication are considered the cornerstone of the firm's practice. They were awarded Investors in People in 1996, an achievement in which the firm takes great pride.

Main Areas of Work
Corporate, commercial property, commercial dispute resolution, construction and employment, probate, trust, residential conveyancing, financial services, personal injury, clinical negligence, matrimonial, crime.

Trainee Profile
Committed lawyers with lively outside interests.

Training Environment
Trainees' wishes are taken into account when deciding seats. As a trainee, you will spend some time working in different areas of the practice giving the widest possible range of experience during your training contract. You will be encouraged to show initiative and shoulder responsibility by dealing with clients as you gain experience. The firm seeks to retain trainees on qualification, viewing them as the firm's future. The PSC is taught externally.

WRAGGE & CO

55 Colmore Row Birmingham B3 2AS
Tel: (0121) 233 1000 Fax: (0121) 214 1099
Email: lucy_gibson@wragge.com
Website: www.wragge.com

Firm Profile
Wragge & Co is the largest single UK office law firm outside London. Its rapid growth and success are a result of a distinctive strategy to develop a national law firm from Birmingham. Wragge & Co's clients continue to appreciate the benefits of its consistent and integrated approach to client service, whilst its people enjoy working in a strong and cohesive culture.

Main Areas of Work
As a full service commercial law firm, Wragge & Co provides a comprehensive range of legal services to large companies, public authorities and financial institutions, in the UK and overseas, including over 165 listed companies. Wragge & Co enjoys a national reputation in areas such as corporate, litigation, property, employment, tax, pensions, IP, transport and logistics, utilities, project finance, PFI and EC/competition law.

Trainee Profile
Graduates should show commercial acumen as well as academic excellence. Adaptability, ambition and enthusiasm are valued and candidates should be problem solvers and clear communicators.

Training Environment
Wragge & Co places considerable emphasis on transforming trainees into high quality, commercially-minded lawyers. You will spend six months in four different practice areas (usually property, corporate and litigation, with a chance to specialise in a final seat of your choice). From day one, you will work on live files with direct client contact. The more aptitude you show, the greater the responsibility you will be given. You will be supported by a monitoring partner and a second year trainee who will be assigned to 'mind' you. Introductory courses are provided at the start of each seat in addition to the Professional Skills Course training requirements. This formal training complements 'on the job' learning. There is a 'hyperactive' sports and social club, and the Birmingham Trainee Solicitors Group is equally dynamic. It is hoped that trainees will work hard and play hard!

Benefits
Life assurance, permanent health scheme, pension, interest free travel loans.

Partners	81
Assistant Solicitors	258
Total Trainees	40

Contact
Lucy Gibson

Method of Application
Application form

Selection Procedure
Assessment day and interview

Closing date for 2002
18 August 2000

Application

Training contracts p.a.	25
Applications p.a.	1,000
% interviewed p.a.	10%
Required degree grade	2:1 (preferred)

Training

Salary: 1st year(1999)	£15,500
Salary: 2nd year(1999)	£17,500
Holiday entitlement	23 days
% of trainees with a non-law degree p.a.	varies

▶

WRAGGE & CO *continued*

Vacation Placements

Places for Easter 2000: 20 places (1 week £125pw)
Places for Summer 2000: 48 places (2 weeks £125pw)
Closing date for both schemes: 11 February 2000
Apply by Application Form

Sponsorship & Awards

CPE and LPC fees paid £3,500 maintenance grant for LPC students, and £3,000 per year for CPE students.

Trainee Comments

"I was accepted for a training contract at Wragge & Co in September 1994, just before I started to study for the CPE. I chose Wragge & Co because of its excellent reputation both regionally and nationally, and I was made to feel very welcome on the day of my interview. I started at Wragge & Co in Septemer 1996 and commenced my training in the Commercial Litigation Department. This was a good first seat not least of all because I was well supervised, and not exposed to too much too quickly. Nevertheless, towards the end of this seat, I was running files of my own.

I then moved to the Property Department for my second seat where I experienced planning and general development work. From the outset, I was running files of my own, and was again supervised on larger scale work.

My third seat was in the Corporate Department where I was involved in general PLC work. Such work does not lend itself to individual files for trainees, and so I worked as part of a team on larger projects, with considerable client contact.

As a fourth seat trainee, I was given as much client contact and responsibility as I wanted and was given several files to run on my own, particularly in the run up to qualification.

My option seat was spent in the Employment and Pensions teams. Now that I have qualified into the Employment team, my experience of pensions work has proved invaluable. Socially, I have always found Wragge & Co a friendly firm, with each department holding social events to help you to get to know new members of the team. Birmingham itself is regenerating fast, and with the decision to knock down the Bull Ring, it may one day shake off the bad reputation it has earned itself. In the meantime, it is a well kept secret which can only be good for those of us in the know!"
(Selwyn Blyth, studied French and Spanish at Cambridge University, completed the CPE at Birmingham University and did the LPC at the College of Law in York)

Post Qualification

Salary (1999)	£27,000
% of trainees offered job on qualification (1999)	100%
% of assistants (as at 1/9/99) who joined as trainees	28%
% of partners (as at 1/9/99) who joined as trainees	47%

Training as a Barrister

TIMETABLE FOR TRAINING AS A BARRISTER

Second Year Law Students and Third Year Non-Law Students

Autumn Term:	Compile information about sets of chambers. Obtain chambers' literature. Attend law fairs on campus. Look into funding possibilities for the conversion course and/or BVC.
Spring Term:	Apply for mini-pupillages and other work experience. Apply for the conversion course before February closing date if necessary. Attend law fairs on campus.
Summer Term:	Obtain application details for BVC from CACH (Centralised Applications Clearing House). Find out about pupillage application. Attend pupillage fairs.

Final Year Law Students and Students on the conversion course

Autumn Term:	Apply for BVC. Sort out funding if possible. Research the Inns of Court and join one. Make further pupillage enquiries.
Spring and Summer Terms:	Attend pupillage fair in London and pick up copy of Chambers Pupillages and Awards Handbook, complete with application disk. Make PACH (Pupillage Applications Clearing House) and non-PACH pupillage applications. Closing date for PACH is in July. Non-PACH chambers all have their own application methods and closing dates.

BVC Students

Autumn Term:	Attend pupillage interviews. In mid-November offers of pupillage are made through PACH. Applicants must accept or reject offers within seven days. The PACH pool system begins in December. Candidates will be informed of any remaining pupillage places.

THE BAR SYSTEM

Definition of terms

Brief: document by which a solicitor instructs a barrister in court

Chambers: the offices occupied by a barrister or group of barristers; the collective name for the barristers practising from that set of chambers

Clerk: administrator/manager for barristers who organises diaries, payment of fees etc

Counsel: barrister, or barristers collectively

Junior: a barrister who is not a QC, however senior in age or experience (a 'senior junior')

PACH: Pupillage Applications Clearing House, through which many applications for pupillage are received

Pupil master/mistress: barrister who supervises the training of a pupil in chambers

Set: set of chambers

Silk: a Queen's Council(QC), so called because s/he is entitled to wear silk robes

Tenant: a barrister who is a member of Chambers

The majority of barristers in England and Wales are in independent practice as tenants of sets of chambers. Essentially, they are self-employed, running individual practices within a support network of other barristers, clerked by increasingly commercial and professional managers. The London Bar is the largest, but nationally the six court circuits are served by chambers throughout the country.

Members of the 'employed bar' work in industry and finance and for a range of government bodies from the Crown Prosecution Service to the armed forces. For further information on the employed bar refer to the 'Options' section.

Each set of chambers will have its own reputation and specialist practice areas. The following sections of the book expand on just some of these practice areas. When applying to chambers through PACH (The Pupillage Applications Clearing House) or to sets that take direct applications, it is essential to select those that specialise in the practice area to which you are best suited. Consider carefully whether you have an interest and an aptitude for their practice area before applying to a niche set. The choice of pupillage is one of the most significant career decisions you will make - so get it right. Have you always pictured yourself in court defending the defenceless from a criminal charge or are you intent on making money and a name for yourself as a commercial counsel?

Mini pupillages are a great way of gauging which sort of practice you are most in tune with and the opportunity to work for one or more sets for a few weeks can really make a difference. It will ensure that you move forward to the next stage of training with your eyes wide open and a feeling of greater confidence in what can, at first, be an unfamiliar world. Per Laleng of 42 Castle Street in Liverpool told us that "the deep division between the theory and practice isn't emphasised enough at university or bar school. You're really ignorant in the early stages of training and you start to pick up the secret language and understand things during pupillage. Students could help themselves by going out and gaining experience doing mini-pupillages. Try to decide quite early which area to specialise in and make sure you really want to do it."

So what do barristers actually do? Their role is twofold; as advisor and advocate. Solicitors have always turned to barristers for second opinions on complex issues, such as whether or not a scheme or contract clause is lawful or valid or whether or not their client has a viable claim against another party. This advisory capacity seems set to continue unhindered by the changes that are now affecting the profession. The other role of the barrister is that of advocate. Solicitors enlist the services of proficient and practised court performers, who know the judges, know how to present a case and how to maximise the chances of victory in court.

Is there still a need for two branches of the profession and are solicitors really a threat to the Bar? The Bar is staring at two very significant issues at the moment, each posing at the least a challenge to the profession and at worst a threat to the livelihood of individual barristers. First, the increase in solicitor advocates who can take a case through from start to finish without recourse to the Bar. The Access to Justice Act 1999 contains the latest in a series of measures which have had the effect of removing the exclusivity of the Bar's rights of audience in most courts. Increasingly during the research for the Chambers Guide to the Legal Profession the response to questions as to which barristers are instructed by leading solicitors brings the response "We don't really use counsel, we do the advocacy ourselves." Then consider the impact on court procedure and case management brought about by the Woolf reforms. The overriding theme of the changes to civil litigation procedures is the requirement to keep costs to a reasonable minimum and to use all means to avoid trial. Solicitors now think twice about instructing counsel for advice, and may completely avoid using them for advocacy.

Barristers remain specialists, however, and solicitors will continue to seek their assistance whilst the two branches of the profession remain distinct entities. It's a long, tough and winding road to make it through the first few years of practice. The journey is an expensive and often precarious one, but once there the financial and professional rewards have the potential to be huge. If you have strength of character and a tenacious, independent nature; if you can marshall your thoughts and present concise and clear advice with confidence; if you can hold the attention of all and be persuasive in your argument then this may be the career for you.

The Inns of Court

The bar of England and Wales is comprised of four Inns of Court - Inner Temple, Middle Temple, Lincoln's Inn and Gray's Inn. Physically they are Oxbridge-like oases of gardens, squares, staircases, cobbles and chapels around the Royal Courts of Justice in London. Historically all barristers would have lived and worked within one or other of these Inns. Practically only the Inns have the power to make new barristers. Students who successfully complete the Bar Vocational Course are "called to the Bar" by them.

In order to qualify as a barrister you must join an Inn before the end of June in the year that you start your BVC. Choice of Inn is completely personal and does not dictate the subsequent choice of chambers. Most people choose their Inns for practical or social reasons. All provide broadly the same services: a library, lunching and dining facilities, a collegiate support network, common rooms, training, social activities and beautiful gardens in the centre of London. Importantly they also provide the opportunity to network with qualified barristers in your chosen area of practice. However, for many students the first role of the Inn is as a funding body for the BVC. [See funding pages]

"At the time," one new tenant told us, " I based my decision as to the choice of Inn solely on the likelihood of getting an award. But now I wish I had taken other factors such as the quality of their advocacy training into account. Some Inns are definitely better than others for training." At over £7,000 for tuition fees alone, finding some sort of scholarship or award is a must for many bar hopefuls. Many chambers do not fund their pupils and aside from the potential to earn small amounts during the second six of pupillage, times can be extraordinarily lean for a couple of years. The Inns of Court do, however, provide over £2 million in bursaries and scholarships. Students, nonetheless clearly require an additional source of funds.

Dining

One of the peculiarities of qualifying as a barrister is the requirement to dine in hall at your Inn. Dining is divided between education dinners (includes lectures and talks), domus dinners (when students and seniors dine together) and social dinners (such as Grand Night or nights when students may bring guests). Most students are at best ambivalent about the whole question of dining, feeling it is an old-fashioned and daunting process. Daunting because part of the process is for barristers to pick on new faces and challenge them to make a speech or raise a toast for example. However, it does give students a chance to meet and talk with other prospective pupils and with the barristers and judges themselves. It is also a chance to become acquainted with a number of old traditions and customs of the Inn. One pupil who recently left Bar School advises against caution; "You have to do it, so make the most of it." You won't get very far in your quest to become a barrister if you are put off by a bit of tradition, embarrassment or laddism!

Some pupils and junior tenants feel that there is still an 'ivory tower' feel to the bar and that nepotism was still a factor. As with any profession, you will come across individuals of all types and views. Your choice of set will be the most crucial factor in determining the cultural environment in which you will find yourself. Some sets are more 'pc' than others; some more set in their ways. After speaking with black and Asian barristers there appears to be no overt culture of racism in the profession although some women barristers considered gender to be of relevance in the eyes of some sets. The most prominent cultural influence was that of educational background. Whilst an Oxbridge degree is not a guaranteed passport to acceptance by the Bar, it is believed by many to be of great assistance.

PUPILLAGE & TENANCY

Pupillage structure

This is an apprenticeship in chambers normally of two six month slots called 'sixes.' Adding a third six is increasingly more common, allowing for a second bite at the cherry of tenancy (a permanent place within chambers). First and second sixes can be served at two different chambers. Indeed, with the prior consent of the Master of the Bench of their Inn there are several options open to pupils during their second six, including:

- working with a solicitor or other practising lawyer in an EU country for three months

- undertaking a 'stage' in the legal departments of the European Commission in Brussels or Luxembourg or a placement at the European Commission in London for 5 months

- working with a registered pupil master in the employed bar

- marshalling with a judge of the High Court or a Circuit Judge for up to six weeks

- working with a solicitor or other professional person whose work is relevant to the practice of your pupil master for up to four weeks

However, the harsh fact is that completing pupillage is absolutely no guarantee of tenancy.

Pupils are assigned to a pupilmaster/mistress who they shadow during the first six. Performance assessment is on-going and the pupil becomes introduced to 'real work' via the practice of the master or mistress. As time goes by other members of chambers will seek the pupil's assistance, thus adding to their workload. "You're being assessed the whole time," Claire Weir of Blackstone Chambers told us. "It's a fairly impressive year - you learn so much. However it can be stressful." As you progress through the second six, more opportunities arise to take on cases and earn fees for yourself although this is unlikely to be a significant amount.

Applying for pupillage

There are two methods of getting pupillage and most students are likely to use both. Around 70% of chambers are members of PACH (Pupillage and Applications Clearing House), a system which operates rather like UCAS and is monitored by the Bar Council. You will need to obtain a copy of the Chambers Pupillages & Awards Handbook, together with the application form which is on disk. The handbook covers both PACH and non-PACH chambers giving details of the types of work undertaken and very useful statistical information as to the numbers of pupils taken on and the numbers of tenancies granted in recent years. The book will also indicate whether or not an award is paid by the set to the pupil.

Students may select and apply for 12 PACH chambers plus three reserves. There is no limit to the number of separate applications that can be made to non-PACH chambers. Adhere closely to the timetables set out in the handbook which in past years has been produced in April before the year to which it applies. Applications to PACH have, to date, had a July deadline.

Tenancy

This is the final cut. The lucky will be offered a tenancy in chambers. Competition is fierce and performance over the previous year will be crucial. But do not despair if you find yourself without that elusive place. Try to get a third and even a fourth six or look elsewhere, to the employed bar for example or to the public sector. A training at the bar will never be time wasted. It is a highly respected training which will have equipped you with transferable skills invaluable for other legal careers or careers outside the law.

For those that make it there are some practical considerations. You will be self employed within chambers and responsible for your own computer equipment and furniture. You will have to think about tax returns and chambers fees. You will have to have the right wardrobe for court and of course there's the *pièce de resistance*: the wig! All of this can be quite costly. Once again, those with a separate source of funds will be at an advantage.

A final word

Most of you reading this will not become barristers in independent practice. Competition is probably tougher than you imagine. It is a long, stressful and expensive process battling your way to the independent bar. Only the academically strong, the career-driven and the most organised will make it. If you intend to apply to bar school then you must prepare yourself for the struggle ahead. Be smart. Plan your strategy and arm yourself with the best information that you can. Seek experience widely. Evaluate yourself and understand what it is that you have to offer. Try to strengthen weak areas. Be clear about where you want to go and be focused. Disregard factors over which you have no control, such as nepotism, and find your own strategy to compensate. Only you are responsible for maximising your own individual potential.

ALTERNATIVE CAREERS

Its harsh, but the statistics show just how difficult it is to become a part of the independent bar. Take ten law undergraduates, hearts set on becoming barristers. Each makes an application for the BVC course. Two will be refused a place. Of the eight that complete (and pass) the BVC only four will obtain pupillage. Four will need to consider other career options at this stage. Of this lucky four, there is a 60-70% chance of securing a tenancy. Only two of these can guarantee a role in independent practice, a third will have a good chance and the fourth will find that they have to consider other options.

This year we have considered the alternatives to independent practice.

The employed bar

Banks, insurance companies, industry and commerce all offer employment to those with a legal training. Law graduates are regarded favourably. In order to practise as a barrister, you will have to have completed pupillage. Alkan Shenyuz did a first six in chambers and then moved into commerce to complete his pupillage with a registered pupil master at an international bank. "Its a small gateway but once you're in its a huge world" he enthuses. There's an ever growing number of barristers practising outside of chambers now. "The culture was a revolution for me and my business acumen and legal skills had to be re-tuned to a business environment. The employed bar is all about quick thinking and true independence of mind. I had the option of going for tenancy but I realised there were more exciting options." Information about the opportunities in industry and commerce are available through BACFI (the Bar Association for Commerce Finance and Industry).

Contact: Lesley Whitlow Tel: (01344) 868752.

Training as a solicitor

A viable option, particularly in the light of an apparent increase in the availability of training contracts. Successfully completing the BVC will allow you to by-pass the LPC and apply to firms of solicitors for the two year contract necessary in order to qualify as a solicitor. Alternatively, switching after the first or second six months of pupillage should allow you to reduce the length of time required to complete a training contract.

Contact: The Education department of the Law Society. Tel: (020) 7242 1222

The Crown Prosecution Service

This organisation has offices throughout England and Wales with more than 2000 lawyers whose role is to review police case files and to initiate and conduct criminal prosecutions. Crown Prosecution lawyers work in one of 42 national areas, where they will prosecute a wide variety of crimes, or in one of the central directorates. The Casework Directorate deals with bigger and more complex cases involving such issues as extradition and terrorism. The Policy Directorate looks at the implications of legislation on the work of the CPS. There are many opportunities for advocacy in the CPS as Crown Prosecutors have rights of audience in Magistrates Courts, and accredited higher court advocates can now speak in the Crown Courts. The CPS only recruits qualified lawyers, and it is no longer possible to take a training contract or pupillage there. For details see the website at www.CPS.gov.uk.

Contact: Personnel Branch 2 Crown Prosecution Service, 50 Ludgate Hill London EC4M 7EX. Tel: (020) 7796 8000.

The Magisterial Service

Trainee positions for court clerks are available. The organisation maintains a register of applicants (who must have passed either the BVC or the LPC) and forwards names for interview as and when a vacancy is notified to it by any of the magistrates courts around the country. The training lasts two years and includes a professional skills course. Court Clerks advise magistrates on the law and sentencing issues as well as the conduct of proceedings in court, dealing with criminal, family, youth and licensing cases. "It's a job with real responsibility" says Sue Matthews of the service. "You need a good knowledge of the law and it is important to know how to deal with all types of members of the public"

Contact: The Association of Magistrates Courts, 79 New Cavendish Street, London W1M 7RB. Tel (020) 7723 1975.

The Law Commission

Research positions are available each year to law graduates or those who have passed the BVC or LPC. It is not uncommon for practising solicitors and barristers to apply in order to take a break from private practice. Fixed term contracts of 12 months, with the possibility of extension up to three years are generally offered. Researchers assist in the process of the Commission's work to make recommendations for changes in the law. There is also the chance to work with eminent judges, practising lawyers and university professors.

Contact: The Law Commission, Conquest House, 37/38 John Street, Theobalds Road, London WC1N 2BQ. Tel: (020) 7453 1210

Judicial Assistants

There are around 25 judicial assistants working in the Court of Appeal. All have completed 12 months either of a training contract or of pupillage. This is a rare opportunity to observe the life of the court at close quarters and to observe quality advocacy at close range. Judicial assistants work with a Justice assisting in the organisation and consideration of paperwork. Further, they will be asked to analyse the pertinent points of a case and ensure that the Justice can focus on the key information and issues. A top notch CV is essential as there is heavy competition for these roles.

Contact: the Clerk to the Master of the Rolls. Tel (0207) 936 6371.

Specialist Practice Areas

CHANCERY

Area of law

If you don't already know anything about Chancery work then you are effectively unaware of a fascinating area of the law. Take the time to investigate it further and you may find that you uncover the place at the bar that is everything you imagined the law to be. Concepts such as "equity" and "justice" are coins in the everyday currency of the Chancery Division of the High Court, together with hard legal principles and a rigorous examination of facts.

Chancery barristers are a different breed to their common law and commercial counterparts. Whilst the facts of a case are crucial, there is a definite emphasis on the application of the law and its principles. Members of this part of the bar are sometimes described as "lawyers' lawyers"- the tools of their trade are legal principles and arguments. The skill in Chancery work is applying these tools to real situations.

As with other sections of the bar, sets are becoming increasingly specialised, sophisticated and commercial in the way they interact with solicitors and the business world. Typically, you would remain a generalist for the first few years but would then aim to develop a reputation for having specific expertise. It is this that becomes attractive to your clients. Barristers at the premier end of the Chancery bar have a reputation for being quite expensive and maybe a "cut above." This is, indeed, an area in which only the highest quality of advice is viable.

Type of work

Chancery work comes in two varieties which are most often referred to as 'traditional' (trusts, probate, real property, charities, mortgages, partnerships) and 'commercial'(company cases, shareholdings, banking, pensions, financial services, insolvency, media and IP, professional negligence). The division between traditional Chancery and commercial Chancery is vanishing in that most sets will do both types of work.

There are some fine brains at the Chancery bar and it has a reputation for producing highly respected QCs and judges; but don't labour under the illusion that it's all paperwork and lofty academia. Rupert Reed, a junior tenant at Wilberforce Chambers told us how real and relevant Chancery work felt. "After six months at the commercial bar, focused largely on dry reinsurance matters, I switched to the Chancery bar to complete my pupillage. There is enormous human interest in contentious probate work and even corporate work, involving shareholder disputes in small companies for example."

You'll have plenty of opportunity to spend time in court developing your advocacy style, although it is true to say that the volume of court work is higher in other practice areas. As a junior led by seniors you'll be introduced to the specialist work of your set. You'll probably cut your teeth on County Court landlord and tenant actions, winding up applications and insolvency cases allowing you to hone those courtroom skills. After a few years you may find that you have ended up with a fascinating overseas practice. The offshore tax havens provide plenty of high value work for Chancery barristers. Rupert Reed has already gained a fair share of overseas experience. He has been called to The Cayman Bar for a case in the Grand Court, travelled regularly to Switzerland and has acted in cases to be heard in Hong Kong, Bermuda and the Channel Islands.

Skills needed

There's no escaping the fact that you need to be pretty bright to succeed within the Chancery Bar. More importantly, you must also be an excellent communicator. Solicitors will sometimes come to you with extremely complex and puzzling cases which will need to be pulled apart and analysed. You must adore research and get a buzz from getting to the crux of often very interesting and intellectual questions. You then need to be able to interpret and communicate these conceptual ideas to your client and feel confident in your findings.

You can tell pretty quickly when someone's right for the Chancery bar according to Brian Green QC at Wilberforce Chambers. "It's a spark of inventiveness and imagination; a light behind the eyes" that singles someone out. "It takes more than being persuasive on paper, you need to have life in the way you communicate."

The Sets

The leading commercial sets include 13 Old Square, Serle Court Chambers and 4 Stone Buildings. Leading traditional sets encompass 5 Stone Buildings, 3 New Square and 11 New Square.

However, with a foot on the medal winners' podium in both commercial and traditional work is Wilberforce Chambers.

Possibly the most noteworthy Chancery case at present is a dispute over vast family trusts called "Thyssen-Bornemisza v Thyssen-Bornemisza" involving assets valued at over £1.2 bn. Members of chambers at Serle Court and Wilberforce will be battling it out in the Bermuda courts for many months.

Outside London, leading Chancery sets include Guildhall Chambers in Bristol, 9 Park Place in Cardiff, St Philip's Chambers in Birmingham and 40 King Street in Manchester. There are a number of other good chambers which are referred to in the main edition of the *Chambers Guide to the Legal Profession.*

▶

Leading Sets

	Traditional Chancery	Commercial Chancery	Pensions	Property	Tax
Barnards Inn Chambers (Saggerson)				****	
4 Breams Buildings (Lockhart-Mummery QC)				*****	
Enterprise Chambers (Mann QC)		****		****	
One Essex Court (Grabiner QC)					***
35 Essex Street (Inglis-Jones QC)			***		
Falcon Chambers (Gaunt QC & Lewison QC)				******	
8 Gray's Inn Square (Soares)					**
Gray's Inn Tax Chambers (Grundy)					*****
1 New Square (Hamilton QC)	***	****			
3 New Square (Goodhart QC)	****				
11 New Square (Crampin QC)	****				
11 New Square (Gardiner QC)					***
12 New Square (Mowbray QC)	***	***			
24 Old Buildings (Bretten QC)					***
24 Old Buildings (Mann QC & Steinfeld QC)		****			
9 Old Square (Driscoll QC)		*****		*****	
10 Old Square (Price QC)	***				
11 Old Square (Crawford & Simpkiss)	***				
13 Old Square (Lyndon-Stanford QC)	***	******		****	
Pump Court Tax Chambers (Thornhill QC)					******
Serle Court Chambers (Sparrow QC)	***	******		****	
3-4 South Square (Crystal QC)		***			
3 Stone Buildings (Vos QC)	***	****	***		
4 Stone Buildings (Heslop QC)		******			
5 Stone Buildings (Harrod)	*****		**		
7 Stone Buildings (Aldous QC)		*****	**		
9 Stone Buildings (Ashe QC)	***				
11 Stone Buildings (Beckman QC)		***			
3 Temple Gardens (Bramwell QC)					**
Wilberforce Chambers (Nugee QC)	******	******	******	*****	

Sets and their star ratings are based on Chambers' Directory 1999–2000. Six stars represent a top-ranked set, five stars a second-ranked set, etc.

COMMERCIAL

Area of law

The work handled by the commercial bar will cover a broad range of business disputes and problems, for a variety of industry sectors. A barrister may be asked to advise on the breakdown of a contract between a supplier and its customer or maybe a dispute between a record company and its artist. There are as many different types of case as there are different types of business relationship. In fact, there are more opportunities to get a diverse selection of work at the commercial bar than one would think.

Practitioners and sets as a whole may develop a niche area in work such as shipping, banking or construction, for example. Increasingly, specialisation is seen as the way forward by some, whilst for others, a more general practice can be maintained in one of the top league of commercial sets. There is certainly an overlap of work between the Chancery bar and the common law bar, but that merely reflects the fact that commercial work is an umbrella term and not a rigidly defined practice area.

Commercial work, in its purest sense, is dealt with by the Commercial Court or one of the County Court Business Courts. However, a large amount of work is also heard by the High Court (both Queen's Bench and Chancery Divisions) or dealt with by way of arbitration. Alternative Dispute Resolution is an increasingly common way to conclude business disputes and at the same time allow for the possibility of the commercial relationship continuing without the damage inflicted upon it by full blown litigation.

Type of work

Instructions are generally paper – and fact – intensive and often involve huge sums of money. The cases may involve multiple parties (for example, in a construction case where any number of contractors, subcontractors, suppliers or professionals could have contributed to a defect in a building or a delay in its completion). As commerce becomes ever more international, so the commercial barrister will find that he or she will be advising increasingly on cross-border issues. This will include EU/competition, international public and trade law and conflicts of laws.

Do you have business acumen? You'll certainly need it to feel comfortable advising lay clients in conference, such as the reinsurance head of department who comes to you with a highly complex point, or the shipping company that wants your opinion on how an international trade treaty impacts on its liability on a certain dispute.

Prepare yourself for a career which is mainly advisory. You won't be on your feet in court every day like a criminal advocate, for example. However, there is likely to be a steady flow of arbitrations and County Court hearings during the first few years. In any case, as one pupil in a leading construction set notes, even drafting pleadings in the early stages of your career can be exciting "when you have a case looming and, as a pupil, it's one of the few times when you are on the cusp of litigation. Although you don't have the fear of having to stand up in court, you know that the stuff you're drafting is going to be used." In terms of the big high profile cases, initially you can aspire to a role as second or third junior. Although this is unlikely to provide many opportunities for oral advocacy, it will certainly allow you to be a vital member of the team. You will, however, gain valuable advocacy experience in interlocutory applications and through deployment in a range of tribunals.

Skills needed

"It's a fiercely practical area of the law," states Deepak Nambisan, new tenant at Fountain Court. "Often it's less about black letter law and more about being a business adviser. You're always trying to gear towards the business solution. You need an eye for detail and to be fully on top of the facts."

As so much of the contact with your clients will be by way of written advice, you need to be a skilled paper advocate. You need to absorb yourself in the world of commerce and have a genuine interest in it. If you become specialised (and many believe that this is essential) the requirement to be steeped in your particular niche is paramount. Some previous industry experience could be the thing that marks you out from the rest of the pack. Competition for pupillage at the commercial bar is fought out by some of the very best candidates. You will need to prove you have what it takes.

The Sets

The following tables give an indication of the variety of work at the commercial bar. Traditionally seen as leading for general commercial work are Brick Court Chambers, One Essex Court, Essex Court Chambers and Fountain Court. You'll see these and a few other names feature prominently in many of the niche areas and you'll find other leaders which feature at the top in only one or two practice areas.

For media cases, Blackstone Chambers and 8 New Square lead, for construction work it is Atkin Chambers and Keating Chambers. Brick Court Chambers share the top position with Monckton Chambers for EC/Competition work whilst for insolvency, 3-4 South Square, Erskine Chambers, 24 Old Buildings and 4 Stone Buildings lead the pack.

On the circuits, Guildhall Chambers and St John's Chambers lead the west; St Philip's Chambers, 5 Fountain Court and 3 Fountain Court in Birmingham are top in the Midlands. Enterprise Chambers and Park Court Chambers stand out in the north east and Byrom Street Chambers lead the field on the northern circuit.

The table should assist you to gauge the direction and breadth of the different sets.

Leading Sets

Arbitration

Atkin Chambers (Blackburn QC)	*****	20 Essex Street (Milligan QC)	*****
Brick Court Chambers (Clarke QC)	****	Fountain Court (Boswood QC)	****
Essex Court Chambers (Pollock QC)	******	Keating Chambers (Fernyhough QC)	*****
One Essex Court (Grabiner QC)	*****	7 King's Bench Walk (Tomlinson QC)	****
4 Essex Court (Teare QC)	****		

Aviation

Brick Court Chambers (Clarke QC)	*****	Fountain Court (Boswood QC)	******
Essex Court Chambers (Pollock QC)	****	Monckton Chambers (Swift QC)	****
4 Essex Court (Teare QC)	*****		

Banking

Brick Court Chambers (Clarke QC)	******	Fountain Court (Boswood QC)	******
Erskine Chambers (Sykes QC)	*****	4-5 Gray's Inn Square (Appelby/Beloff)	*****
Essex Court Chambers (Pollock QC)	*****	3-4 South Square (Crystal QC)	*****
One Essex Court (Grabiner QC)	*****	3 Verulam Buildings (Simons/Jarvis)	******
20 Essex Street (Milligan QC)	*****		

Leading Sets

Company

Set	Rating
Enterprise Chambers (Mann QC)	****
Erskine Chambers (Sykes QC)	******
One Essex Court (Grabiner QC)	****
3 New Square (Goodhart QC)	****
13 Old Square (Lyndon-Stanford QC)	****
Serle Court Chambers (Sparrow QC)	****
3-4 South Square (Crystal QC)	****
4 Stone Buildings (Heslop QC)	*****
7 Stone Buildings (Aldous QC)	****

Construction

Set	Rating
Atkin Chambers (Blackburn QC)	******
39 Essex Street (Glasgow QC)	****
Keating Chambers (Fernyhough QC)	******
12 King's Bench Walk (Stow QC)	***
Monckton Chambers (Swift QC)	***
Four New Square (Powell QC)	*****
One Paper Buildings (Spencer QC)	***
4 Pump Court (Mauleverer QC)	*****
3 Serjeants' Inn (Naughton QC)	***
2 Temple Gardens (O'Brien QC)	***

Energy

Set	Rating
Atkin Chambers (Blackburn QC)	***
Essex Court Chambers (Pollock QC)	*****
One Essex Court (Grabiner QC)	******
Fountain Court (Boswood QC)	*****
Keating Chambers (Fernyhough QC)	***
7 King's Bench Walk (Tomlinson QC)	****
2 Mitre Court Buildings (FitzGerald QC)	*****
1 Serjeants' Inn (Read QC)	***

European Union

Set	Rating
Brick Court Chambers (Clarke QC)	******
Monckton Chambers (Swift QC)	******

Financial Services

Set	Rating
Blackstone Chambers (Baxendale/Flint)	*****
Brick Court Chambers (Clarke QC)	*****
Erskine Chambers (Sykes QC)	******
One Essex Court (Grabiner QC)	****
3-4 South Square (Crystal QC)	****
4 Stone Buildings (Heslop QC)	*****
3 Verulam Buildings (Symons/Jarvis)	****

General Commercial (London)

Set	Rating
Blackstone Chambers (Baxendale/Flint)	***
Brick Court Chambers (Clarke QC)	******
Essex Court Chambers (Pollock QC)	******
One Essex Court (Grabiner QC)	******
4 Essex Court (Teare QC)	**
Fountain Court (Boswood QC)	******
One Hare Court (Neill/Southwell)	**
7 King's Bench Walk (Tomlinson QC)	****
11 King's Bench Walk (Tabachnik/Goudie)	***
Littleton Chambers (Kallipetis QC)	****
4 Pump Court (Mauleverer QC)	***
Serle Court Chambers (Sparrow QC)	**
3 Verulam Buildings (Symons/Jarvis)	*****

Sets and their star ratings are based on Chambers' Directory 1999–2000. Six stars represent a top-ranked set, five stars a second-ranked set, etc. The table shows London sets unless otherwise stated.

Leading Sets

General Commercial (Regions)

3 Fountain Court (Treacy QC), Birmingham	***	St. John's Chambers (Denyer QC), Bristol	***
5 Fountain Court (Barker QC), Birmingham	***	St Philip's Chambers (Tedd QC), Birmingham	***
Guildhall Chambers (Palmer QC), Bristol	****		

Insolvency

Enterprise Chambers (Mann QC)	****	13 Old Square (Lyndon-Stanford QC)	*****
Erskine Chambers (Sykes QC)	*****	Serle Court Chambers (Sparrow QC)	****
One Essex Court (Grabiner QC)	****	3-4 South Square (Crystal QC)	******
1 New Square (Hamilton QC)	****	4 Stone Buildings (Heslop QC)	*****
24 Old Buildings (Mann/Steinfeld)	****	11 Stone Buildings (Beckman QC)	****

Insurance

Brick Court Chambers (Clarke QC)	*****	Fountain Court (Boswood QC)	****
Essex Court Chambers (Pollock QC)	******	7 King's Bench Walk (Tomlinson QC)	******
One Essex Court (Grabiner QC)	***	4 Pump Court (Mauleverer QC)	***
20 Essex Street (Milligan QC)	****	3 Verulam Buildings (Symons/Jarvis)	***

IT

Atkin Chambers (Blackburn QC)	***	19 Old Buildings (Wilson QC)	*****
Three New Square (Young QC)	*****	11 South Square (Floyd QC)	******
8 New Square (Fysh QC)	******		

Intellectual Property

One Essex Court (Grabiner QC)	***	19 Old Buildings (Wilson QC)	***
Three New Square (Young QC)	******	One Raymond Buildings (Morcom QC)	***
8 New Square (Fysh QC)	******	11 South Square (Floyd QC)	******

Media

Blackstone Chambers (Baxendale/Flint)	******	8 New Square (Fysh QC)	******
Brick Court Chambers (Clarke QC)	*****	5 Raymond Buildings (Milmo QC)	*****
Doughty Street Chambers (Robertson QC)	****	3 Stone Buildings (Vos QC)	****
Essex Court Chambers (Pollock QC)	*****	3 Verulam Buildings (Symons/Jarvis)	****
5 New Square (Rayner James QC)	*****		

Sports

Blackstone Chambers (Baxendale/Flint)	******	4-5 Gray's Inn Square (Appelby QC)	*****
Brick Court Chambers (Clarke QC)	****		

COMMON LAW

Area of Law

The body of common law has developed through precedents set in previous cases rather than from statutes. The majority of these cases are dealt with in the Queen's Bench Division (QBD) of the High Court and the County Courts. Most cases turn on tort and contract claims. However the work handled by the common law bar is very broadly based and its edges blur into both chancery and commercial law.

Certain factors have reduced the volume of instructions currently available to junior barristers. Solicitor advocates are definitely on the increase. Coupled with legal aid cutbacks and the growth in ADR and mediation this has cut down the number of available cases. The Woolf reforms have certainly changed the adversarial nature of claims and many preliminary hearings simply no longer take place. One set told us "We're waiting to see the real impact of Woolf but 50% of the smaller end diary work is no longer there." Competition for the sort of work that juniors cut their teeth on is fierce and rumours circulate about brief fees tumbling to uneconomic levels.

Type of work

The variety of work at the common law bar is huge and many sets will offer a mix of other types of work such as crime, family or personal injury which forms a significant part of the junior's common law caseload. In the early years, much of the work will involve drafting pleadings and attending hearings. These could be on anything ranging from RTA's and consumer credit debts to criminal hearings at the magistrates court and arbitrations, employment tribunals and family cases. The more general the profile of the set, the more general your experience. The opportunities for advocacy are fewer than at a specialist criminal set but greater than with a Chancery or commercial set. Your work load will be a blend of drafting, advice and court work.

Skills needed

You'll need to be a quick learner and have a good short term memory for facts and the law. This is particularly true during the initial stages of your tenancy when your practice will probably leap-frog between many different types of case. Perseverance is essential if you are to get to the stage where routine matters become familiar and straightforward and you can, perhaps, begin to specialise in a chosen area. If work really is scarce in the early years you'll have to be impressive to justify your next instruction and part of that boils down to personality and how well you interact with your client. "Clearly we look for someone who's pretty bright," said Practice Director Joanna Poulton at 9 Gough Square, "but personability is the key. You've almost got to have a sixth sense about people. The common law bar needs people who can get on with clients, be prepared to listen but not get taken in."

You'll probably be doing a mixture of written advice and presentation in court. There will be less client contact than in criminal law, but probably more more than in commercial or chancery practice, so you'll need good people skills and an ability to adapt to a range of clients. As Philip Naughton QC points out, "This area involves many different types of litigant, so the demeanour of the barrister is very important."

The Sets

In London the top sets for personal injury include 2 Crown Office Row, 39 Essex Street, Farrar's Buildings, 12 King's Bench Walk, Old Square Chambers and 2 Temple Gardens. For clinical negligence those with the strongest reputations are 1 Crown Office Row, 6 Pump Court and 3 Sergeants' Inn. For professional negligence, the market leaders are Brick Court Chambers, 2 Crown Office Row, Fountain Court, Four New Square, 4 Pump Court and 2 Temple Gardens.

For employment matters, leading sets include Blackstone Chambers, 11 King's Bench Walk, Littleton Chambers and Old Square Chambers.

The top sets on defamation cases are 1 Brick Court and 5 Raymond Buildings whilst New Court Chambers is headed by famous silk George Carman. For consumer work Gough Square Chambers leads the field and for product liability Fountain Court, Doughty Street Chambers, 2 Harcourt Buildings and One Paper Buildings are the most respected sets.

In the regions there are a large number of sets with good reputations for general common law work but fewer sets have gained niche reputations. 17 Carlton Crescent in Southampton has built up a fantastic reputation for consumer work however, so when considering the regional sets it is certainly worth your while trying to ascertain which specialisms they offer.

Leading Sets

London	Employment	Defamation	Product Liability	Consumer
Blackstone Chambers (Baxendale/Flint)	*****			
1 Brick Court (Hartley QC)		******		
Cloisters (Cox QC)	***			
Devereux Chambers (Burke QC)	****			
Doughty Street Chambers (Robertson QC)		***	******	
Essex Court Chambers (Pollock QC)	***			
Fountain Court (Boswood QC)	***			
Gough Square Chambers (Philpott)				******
2-3 Gray's Inn Square (Scrivener QC)				****
4-5 Gray's Inn Square (Appelby/Beloff)	****			
2 Harcourt Buildings (Henderson QC)			******	
11 King's Bench Walk (Tabachnik/Goudie)	******			
Littleton Chambers (Kallipetis QC)	*****			
Old Square Chambers (Hendy QC)	*****			
One Paper Buildings (Spencer QC)			******	
5 Raymond Buildings (Milmo QC)		******		
Regional				
17 Carlton Crescent (Gibbons QC), S'hampton				******

London	Personal Injury	Clinical Negligence	Professional Negligence
9 Bedford Row (Goldring QC)	***	***	
29 Bedford Row Chambers (Ralls QC)	**		
Brick Court Chambers (Clarke QC)			*****
Cloisters (Cox QC)	**	***	
1 Crown Office Row (Seabrook QC)		*****	
1 Crown Office Row (Strachan QC)	**		
2 Crown Office Row (Purchas QC)	******	***	*****
Devereux Chambers (Burke QC)	****		
Doughty Street Chambers (Robertson QC)		****	
35 Essex Street (Inglis-Jones QC)	**	***	
39 Essex Street (Glasgow QC)	******	***	***
Farrar's Building (Elias QC)	*****		
Fountain Court (Boswood QC)			*****
9 Gough Square (Roberts QC)	****		
2 Harcourt Buildings (Henderson QC)	**		
Keating Chambers (Fernyhough QC)			****
7 King's Bench Walk (Tomlinson QC)			***
12 King's Bench Walk (Stow QC)	******		
Littleton Chambers (Kallipetis QC)			***
Four New Square (Powell QC)			******
Old Square Chambers (Hendy QC)	*****		
9 Old Square (Driscoll QC)			***
One Paper Buildings (Spencer QC)	**	****	****
4 Paper Buildings (McGregor QC)		****	*****
Plowden Buildings (Lowe QC)	***		
4 Pump Court (Mauleverer QC)			*****
6 Pump Court (Coonan QC)		*****	
3 Serjeants' Inn (Naughton QC)		******	
199 Strand (Andrews QC)	***	***	
1 Temple Gardens (Carlisle QC)	***		
2 Temple Gardens (O'Brien QC)	*****		*****
3 Verulam Buildings (Jarvis/Symons)			***
Wilberforce Chambers (Nugee QC)			***

Regional	Personal Injury	Clinical Negligence	Professional Negligence
Byrom Street Chambers (Hytner QC), Manchester			***
14 Castle Street (Lyon), Liverpool	*		
Deans Court Chambers (Goddard QC), Manchester	**		
Exchange Chambers (Waldron QC), Liverpool	*		
5 Fountain Court (Barker QC), Birmingham	***		
Iscoed Chambers (Davies), Swansea	*		
Old Square Chambers (Hendy QC), Bristol	**		
Oriel Chambers (Sander), Liverpool	*		
Park Court Chambers (Stewart/Smith), Leeds	*		
Park Lane Chambers (Brown QC), Leeds	*		
9 Park Place (Murphy QC), Cardiff	**		
30 Park Place (Jenkins QC), Cardiff	*		
33 Park Place (Rees QC), Cardiff	**		
Ropewalk Chambers (Maxwell QC), Nottingham	***		
St. John's Chambers (Denyer QC), Bristol	**		
9 St. John Street (Hand QC), Manchester	**		
18 St. John Street (Foster), Manchester	*		
28 St. John St (Goldstone QC), Manchester	**		
St Philip's Chambers (Tedd QC), Birmingham	*		

Sets and their star ratings are based on Chambers' Directory 1999–2000. Six stars represent a top-ranked set, five stars a second-ranked set, etc.

CRIMINAL

Area of law

There's certainly plenty of courtroom drama in films and on TV and its pretty hard to avoid reading the odd John Grisham novel. Those fictional criminal advocates are portrayed in an exciting and dynamic environment, but is your perception of the reality anywhere near accurate? In terms of the buzz you can get from the work, the sense of being involved in something of key social importance and utility and the adrenaline levels, then yes, it probably is. When you speak to a criminal barrister, there's a genuine feeling that this is a really challenging and rewarding area of the law. We suspect that you probably already know if you want to be a criminal advocate.

David Fisher QC at 6 King's Bench Walk, told us that you simply never lose interest because the cases become more interesting and more challenging as you acquire seniority. "It's a good life; you're out there in the fray! I would find it very boring settling papers all the time, but after 27 years at the criminal bar I still love coming through the door of chambers. No two cases are alike."

On the whole, the criminal bar fears no shortage of work. Whilst that may be a sad indictment of our society, it is encouraging for those in the early stages of a career. Despite talk of an assault on traditional bar work from solicitor advocates and the Crown Prosecution Service there is still plenty of work keeping the junior bar busy.

Type of work

The first year or so will be a continual round of magistrates' court appearances on petty matters like motoring offences, committals to the Crown Court, sentencing, pleas in mitigation and directions hearings. This, however, is where you'll learn to develop court skills, confidence and client handling techniques. With just a little time you'll progress to trying cases themselves, initially on smaller crimes such as common assault and the taking of motor vehicles, then graduating to ABH, robbery, indecent assault, and possession of drugs with intent to supply. You may get the opportunity to be a junior working with more senior members of chambers on white collar crime, kidnapping, rape or murder for example.

During your first six in pupillage you'll shadow your pupil master or mistress and see first hand how a criminal advocate operates. The seriousness of the crimes you'll be involved with will be a taste of what is to come in the long term future. It's a time to observe how an experienced barrister interacts with all the other participants in the case; the instructing solicitor, the defendant, the prosecution barrister, the witnesses, the judge and the jury. You'll be of assistance in researching points of law and helping to prepare skeleton arguments. Many chambers will also send you out to court with juniors to give you a more immediate experience of the work you'll be handling following pupillage.

Almost immediately after pupillage you may apply to be included on the CPS List, which will enable you to receive instructions to prosecute as well as defend private clients. There will be opportunities to appear in the Crown Court on sentencing and pre-trial review and gradually you will move towards your own trials in that venue. Some juniors also advise on Criminal Injuries Compensation and do voluntary work for legal advice centres or organisations such as Victim Support.

The criminal bar is no different to any other area of the law in that the volume of work available to you (and potential earnings) in the early years depend on the reputation and fortunes of your chambers. Some barristers at less well known sets pointed out the unpredictability of criminal bar work. You may be kept busy for weeks and then suddenly have nothing for days on end. At the leading sets, however, it is not uncommon for you to be in court almost every day and in any set you must be prepared for action at any time and often on no notice.

Skills needed

The work of a criminal barrister centres on people. Those who commit crimes, the victims and witnesses of those crimes, the juries that must reach verdicts and the professionals who administer justice. You need to be a good judge of character and to exercise good judgement yourself. You will be in the spotlight and it's important that you enjoy this. You will be responsible for your victories and for your defeats, so a balanced outlook will assist. As an advocate, your audience includes lay members of the public and you must speak their language and not just that of the other lawyers.

As a junior you may be asked to do unappealing work. You will often be required to travel a great deal with papers you have had little or no time to prepare. One junior tenant related the time his train ticket to a hearing cost more than the brief fee. "You just have to grin and bear it - you need the experience."

It's hard work, so stamina is essential and as instructions will often come to you on short notice you'll need to be flexible and quick thinking. In court too, you need to think quickly on your feet; you can't just turn round to the judge and ask him for half an hour to figure out how to deal with a witness's response to a question in your cross-examination.

The job requires immense sensitivity at times, especially in cases of child sex abuse and rape. It is vital that you take great care with some witnesses. At the same time you do need to be thick skinned in order to deal with often very dislikeable clients or defendants who have committed serious crimes. You don't have to be a hard person but sometimes you have to be tough in court.

The Sets

There are many superb sets in London and around the country. We mention just a few of the London élite sets.

In London, for general crime, 3 Hare Court, 6 King's Bench Walk, Queen Elizabeth Buildings, 3 Raymond Buildings and 18 Red Lion Square are at the top of the pile.

In the regions we highlight Albion Chambers and St John's Chambers in Bristol, 3 Fountain Court in Birmingham, Park Court Chambers in Leeds and Exchange Chambers and Peel House in Liverpool.

For white collar crime look to both the leading general crime sets and to sets at the commercial bar such as Blackstone Chambers, Brick Court Chambers, Fountain Court and others.

Readers should note that our table of leading sets is limited in scope, and reflects the élite chambers. There are many sets at the bar which provide an excellent service and have very good criminal advocates yet it would be impossible to rank them all here.

▶

Leading London Sets

	General	Fraud
Atkinson Bevan Chambers *(Atkinson QC / Bevan QC)*	****	
9 Bedford Row *(Goldring QC)*	*****	
36 Bedford Row *(Hunt QC)*	***	
9-12 Bell Yard *(Evans QC)*	**	***
Blackstone Chambers *(Baxendale QC & Flint QC)*		******
Brick Court Chambers *(Clarke QC)*		******
Cloisters *(Cox QC)*	***	
Doughty Street Chambers *(Robertson QC)*	*****	
One Essex Court *(Grabiner QC)*		******
23 Essex Street *(Lawson QC)*	**	*****
35 Essex Street *(Inglis-Jones QC)*		***
Farrar's Building *(Elias QC)*	*	
Fountain Court *(Boswood QC)*		******
Furnival Chambers *(Mitchell QC)*	****	
Two Garden Court *(Macdonald QC)*	*****	
3 Gray's Inn Square *(Tansey QC)*	*****	
1 Hare Court *(Kramer QC)*	*****	
3 Hare Court *(Clegg QC)*	******	*****
6 King's Bench Walk *(Worsley QC)*	******	*****
10 King's Bench Walk *(Khayat QC)*	*	
1 Middle Temple Lane *(Dines QC & Trollope QC)*	*	***
5 Paper Buildings *(Carey QC & Caplan QC)*		****
Queen Elizabeth Building *(Bevan QC & Whiteman QC)*	******	******
3 Raymond Buildings *(Nicholls QC)*	******	******
18 Red Lion Court *(Arlidge QC)*	******	****
Serle Court Chambers *(Sparrow QC)*		******
3 Temple Gardens *(Goldberg QC)*	**	
14 Tooks Court *(Mansfield QC)*	**	
2-4 Tudor Street *(Ferguson QC)*	****	
3 Verulam Buildings *(Symons QC & Jarvis QC)*		******

Sets and their star ratings are based on Chambers' Directory 1999-2000. Six stars represent a top-ranked set, five stars a second-ranked set, etc.

FAMILY

Area of law

The popular image of family law conjures up feuding couples and desperately bitter child custody battles. It is certainly a demanding practice area for a barrister, who will only be involved in the most complex or combative cases.

In truth, a large amount of court time in England & Wales is allotted to divorce, separation, adoption, child residence and contact orders, financial provision and domestic violence. Family barristers cut their teeth on simpler County Court matters and progress over time to more complex matters which might be heard in the Family Division of the High Court. Some practitioners see this area of the law as a market for legal services that won't shrink; that people will always end up in messy matrimonial and family situations that need sorting out in court. In the last ten years or so, there has been an increase in the profile of mediation between parties to attempt to resolve disputes instead of requiring the court to hear lengthy arguments in order to decide what is essentially the stuff of interpersonal relationships (albeit ones with legal definitions).

At one stage the family bar worried about a wave of mediation and surge of new solicitor advocates leading to a sharp downturn in the amount of work available, but it appears to have continued unabated. One senior barrister told us that "the family law bar definitely has a future because there will always be family disputes and people who want to go to court. There are surprisingly few specialist solicitors and most solicitors don't have the time to take cases all the way to court."

Type of work

Typically in pupillage and in the early period of tenancy your caseload will include a lot of private law children work. At first this will be minor appointments, directions hearings and timetabling but then you'll begin to receive more substantive work, including final hearings. The ancillary relief work (financial arrangements between the parties) can be more complex and thus it takes a little longer to become proficient at it. To do well on the financial side it helps to have a flair for things like pensions and shares and to have a grounding in the basics of trusts and property. After a few years of experience, and having built up a reputation amongst instructing solicitors, a barrister would often find herself or himself specialising either in the field of work relating to children, their custody, access and adoption or in the field of matrimonial finance following the breakdown of marriage. Despite the fact that the two specialisms draw on different skills some barristers manage to build up excellent reputations for both areas of work.

Whilst conflict is often deeply embedded in a case, the law requires an attempt at resolution through mediation. A tough adversarial approach is generally not appropriate and practitioners need to focus on client contact and genuine discussion and to bear in mind that at the heart of child cases is the paramount consideration of the child's best interests.

Skills needed

Sometimes it can feel like everyone concerned is in a no win situation, particularly where children are concerned. The talented barrister will sift through the facts of a case and find something worthwhile rather than merely assuming that there is little prospect of any sensible solution. The ability to maintain an even keel when dealing with distressing matters and to remain positive towards clients is essential. A genuine empathy for your lay client and his or her position is a must; no solicitor would wish to instruct a barrister perceived to be aloof or disinterested in the specifics of the client's case. At the same time, it is not the barrister's role to issue soothing words and paper handkerchiefs.

Omar Yaqub, a new tenant at specialist family law set One Garden Court Family Law Chambers, feels that you must really know yourself before embarking on a career at the family bar. "Inevitably you'll be affected by the work sometimes, especially on difficult cases such as child abuse. But because you do it every day and the issues are often the same you don't have the time to become over-involved. It's not your job to get emotional; it's to help your client. You're the one who knows the system and it doesn't serve a purpose to get emotional. Sometimes you have to be forceful because clients in the midst of a crisis often lose sight of things, including the welfare of the child."

Perhaps the thing to remember is that in family cases the ruling made or the settlement reached can have a massive impact on each of the human lives touched by it. As a consequence, it is vital that the barrister recognise the appropriate course of action in each case and work with the solicitor in managing the case from an early stage.

The sets

There are a number of very good sets throughout the country handling family work, both relating to children and financial settlements.

In London, 1 Mitre Court Buildings has increased its standing and is now regarded by many in the profession as joint leading set with Queen Elizabeth Building which handles some very high profile cases, such as the Picasso divorce. Also most highly ranked by the legal profession are 29 Bedford Row Chambers and One King's Bench Walk.

Around the country there are a wealth of sets packed with quality silks and juniors. Some of the most well known are East Anglian Chambers in Ipswich; Albion Chambers in Bristol; Southernhay Chambers in Exeter; 30 Park Place in Cardiff; 5 Fountain Court, King Charles House and St Mary's Chambers all in Birmingham; India Buildings Chambers in Liverpool and 37 Park Square and No.6 Park Square in Leeds.

Leading London Sets

Set	Rating	Set	Rating
29 Bedford Row Chambers *(Ralls QC)*	*****	1 Mitre Court Buildings *(Blair QC)*	******
One Garden Court *(Platt/Ball)*	***	4 Paper Buildings *(Swift QC)*	**
One King's Bench Walk *(Hacking QC)*	*****	Queen Elizabeth Building *(Coleridge QC)*	******

Sets and their star ratings are based on Chambers' Directory 1999-2000. Six stars represent a top-ranked set, five stars a second-ranked set, etc.

PUBLIC LAW

Area of law

A decision made by a publicly accountable body is subject to question by an affected party. For example, the decision of the Home Office to deny a non-national the right to remain in the country, or the decision of a Local Planning Authority to refuse permission for an out of town supermarket. One of the most notable recent public law cases has been that concerning the extradition procedings of General Pinochet to Spain.

Indeed, the new Human Rights Act is expected to have a marked affect on numerous areas of law. Practitioners predict a increasing amount of work over the next few years dealing with issues thrown up by the act.

As public bodies operate within statutory constraints, so their decisions may be challenged. Have they considered the relevant facts in reaching decisions? Have the officers acted strictly in accordance with the correct procedure? Did the body or officer in question have the authority to make the decision in the first place? If these questions interest you and you are passionate about principles of justice and the advancement of the law, then read on.

Type of work

A public law barrister will receive instructions to act on a case by case basis. Those building up a Local Authority clientele, for example, may find themselves acting for a number of different departments on a range of work, but often leaning heavily towards decisions concerning planning, housing or environmental matters and education, health and children.

By far the most common of public law matters is the judicial review of an immigration decision. About half of the Crown Office List is comprised of immigration cases and consequently this work is likely to feature prominently in a junior barrister's practice.

Not all public law sets limit themselves to this practice area; many combine the work with a general common law or competition or employment. Additionally, many sets which do not hold themselves out as specialist public law sets carry out judicial review work.

Public Inquiries are raised where an event or series of events is deemed to be of great significance to society as a whole. The Bloody Sunday Inquiry, the BSE Inquiry and the inquiry following the death of Stephen Lawrence are examples of the very different types of issues under scrutiny.

Alex MacQueen, a pupil at local government and planning set 4 Breams Buildings, particularly enjoys the developing nature of public law. With new grounds for judicial review emerging through case law, "there's a lot of room for creative thought." He is also enthusiastic about the variety of clients; "your contact could range from dealings with Customs Officers to Secretaries of State, from Police Constables to the Football Association, from the local City Council to the new National Assemblies."

Pupillage at a public law set will often consist of drafting opinions and shadowing your pupil master, with some advocacy in the second six such as applying for urgent injunctions. As applications for judicial review are heard in the High Court, it is not usual for the most junior barristers to provide advocacy in this area, but after a few years you should have a highly interesting practice with a good balance of advice and advocacy.

Skills needed

Its all about understanding red tape and having the desire to battle through it for your client. You have to really care about the development of the fundamental laws by which we live.

Remember though that the work doesn't necessarily involve close contact with your lay client. In many cases the client does not attend the hearing in person at all.

You must develop a comprehensive knowledge of administrative and constitutional law and be familiar with the inner workings of central and local government generally. As with so many areas of the law, a deep appreciation for EU and international law will be of increasing importance.

The courts deal with such a high volume of cases that you need to develop an efficient style of advocacy. This is not an area in which long and dramatic performances are well received. You'll have to learn how to cut to the chase and deliver the pertinent information, draw on the relevant case law or statutory regulations and present your arguments promptly. An inquiring and analytical mind is essential.

The Sets

The following table highlights four leading sets in the field of administrative and public law generally; 4-5 Grays Inn Square, Blackstone Chambers, 4 Breams Buildings and 39 Essex Street. A number of the silks and juniors at these sets are regularly instructed by the Crown.

For civil liberties work and immigration two sets stand out above a number of other strong players. Doughty Street Chambers has played a leading role in many human rights issues including those of prisoners. Head of chambers Geoffrey Robertson QC has acted in the Pinochet case and is probably the first name for civil liberties at the bar. Two Garden Court also benefits from a leading profile in criminal work and has had involvement in some high profile miscarriage of justice cases. Michael Mansfield of 14 Tooks Court was involved in the Stephen Lawrence enquiry and the Bridgewater appeal.

For planning and local government work the top names are 4 Breams Buildings, 4-5 Grays Inn Square, 2 Mitre Court, 2 Harcourt Buildings and 1 Sergeants' Inn.

In Manchester, 40 King Street is the leading northern set and the Midlands' front runner is 5 Fountain Court in Birmingham.

Leading London Sets

	Administrative and public	Civil Liberties	Immigration	Planning
Blackstone Chambers (*Baxendale/Flint*)	*****	****	**	
4 Breams Buildings (*Lockhart-Mummery QC*)	****			******
Brick Court Chambers (*Clarke QC*)	*			
Cloisters (*Cox QC*)		***		
Doughty Street Chambers (*Robertson QC*)	***	******	***	
Enfield Chambers (*Gillespie*)			*	
39 Essex Street (*Glasgow QC*)	****		**	
Two Garden Court (*Macdonald/Davies*)	***	*****	******	
2-3 Gray's Inn Square (*Scrivener QC*)	***			*****
4-5 Gray's Inn Square (*Appelby/Beloff*)	******	**		******
2 Harcourt Buildings (*Ryan QC*)	*			*****
6 King's Bench Walk (*Kadri QC*)		**	**	
11 King's Bench Walk (*Tabachnik/Goudie*)	****			****
2 Mitre Court Buildings (*FitzGerald QC*)				*****
Mitre House Chambers (*Gilbert*)		**		
Plowden Buildings (*Lowe*)			*	
1 Pump Court (*Hoyal*)		**		
1 Serjeants' Inn (*Read QC*)				*****
14 Tooks Court (*Mansfield QC*)		****	**	

Sets and their star ratings are based on Chambers' Directory 1999-2000. Six stars represent a top-ranked set, five stars a second-ranked set, etc.

a-z of Barristers' Chambers

BLACKSTONE CHAMBERS (P Baxendale QC and C Flint QC)

Blackstone House Temple London EC4Y 9BW DX: 281
Tel: 020 7583 1770 Fax: 020 7822 7350
Email: clerks@blackstonechambers.com
Website: www.blackstonechambers.com

Chambers Profile

Established at its old site 2 Hare Court for many years, Blackstone Chambers recently moved to new purpose built fully networked premises in the Temple.

Type of Work Undertaken

Chambers' formidable strengths lie in three principal areas of practice of commercial, employment and public law. Commercial law including financial/business law, international trade, conflicts, media and entertainment, intellectual property and professional negligence. All aspects of Employment law, including discrimination, are covered by Chambers' extensive employment law practice. Public law incorporates judicial review, acting both for and against central and local government agencies and other regulatory authorities, human rights and other aspects of administrative law.

Pupil Profile

Chambers looks for articulate and intelligent applicants who are able to work well under pressure and demonstrate high intellectual ability. Successful candidates usually have at least a 2:1 honours degree, although not necessarily in law.

Pupillage

Chambers offers 4 12 month pupillages to those wishing to practice full time at the Bar normally commencing in October each year. Pupillage is divided into 3 or 4 sections and every effort is made to ensure that pupils receive a broad training. The environment is a friendly one; pupils attend an induction week introducing them to the Chambers working environment, Chambers prefers to recruit new tenants from pupils wherever possible.

Mini Pupillages

Assessed mini-pupillages are available and are an important part of the application procedure. Applications for mini-pupillages and for pupillages must be made by 30th June; earlier applications are strongly advised and are preferred in the year before pupillage commences. Application forms for pupillages or mini-pupillage are available on request.

Funding

Awards of £23,000 per annum are available. The pupillage committee has a discretion to consider applications for up to £4,000 of the pupillage award to be advanced during the BVC year.

No of Silks	21
No of Juniors	35
No of Pupils	6 (current)

Contact

Ms Julia Hornor
Practice Manager

Method of Application

Chambers' own application form

Pupillages (p.a.)

12 months: 4
Required degree grade
Minimum 2.1 (law or non-law)

Income

Award: £23, 000
Earnings not included

Tenancies

Junior tenancies offered in last 3 years 100%
No of tenants of 5 years call or under 10

1 CROWN OFFICE ROW (Mark Strachan QC)

1 Crown Office Row (3rd Floor) Temple
London EC4Y 7HH DX: 212
Tel: (020) 7583 9292 Fax: (020) 7353 9292

No of Silks	4
No of Juniors	20
No of Pupils	4

Contact
James Dingemans
Michael Oliver
(Chambers Manager)

Method of Application
PACH

Pupillages (p.a.)
12 months: 3

Tenancies
Junior tenancies offered in last 3 years 2
No of tenants of 5 years call or under 4

Chambers Profile

Whilst individual practices within Chambers differ significantly, most members of Chambers specialise in the field of commercial and business law. This includes everything from international arbitration to sale of goods and employment law. Members of Chambers frequently appear in the Privy Council undertaking constitutional, human rights cases and other appellate work. The work of Chambers also includes most areas of non-specialist civil litigation such as personal injury and landlord and tenant work. There is also work in the field of public and administrative law.

Pupil Profile

Chambers seeks to have 3 or 4 pupils at any time and offer 12 month pupillages. Chambers are well aware that the aim of most pupils is to secure a tenancy and to this end seek to recruit one tenant of sufficient calibre every year. Pupils will be reviewed after 5 months and given an indication of whether they have any prospect of becoming a tenant at the end of the year.

Mini Pupillages

Mini-pupillages and student visits are available. Application by letter and CV to Michael Oliver.

Funding

It is Chambers' policy to offer finance to two pupils for 12 months. There are two awards of up to £25,000, being £12,500 for the first six months and £12,500 from earnings and/or Chambers' funds in the second six months.

ESSEX COURT CHAMBERS (Gordon Pollock QC)

24 Lincoln's Inn Fields London WC2A 3ED DX: 320
Tel: (020) 7813 8000 Fax: (020) 7813 8080
Email: clerksroom@essexcourt-chambers.co.uk
Website: www.essexcourt-chambers.co.uk

No of Silks	15
No of Juniors	42
No of Pupils	4

Contact
Pupillage Secretary

Method of Application
PACH (pupillage); Letter and CV (mini-pupillage)

Pupillages (p.a.)

12 months:	4
Required degree grade	2:1

Income
£25,000 p.a.

Tenancies

Junior tenancies offered in last 3 years	7

Chambers Profile

Essex Court Chambers is one of London's leading commercial sets. In Chambers Directory 1999, Essex Court Chambers appeared in eight categories as a "leading set": Arbitration, Commercial Litigation; Insurance & Reinsurance; Shipping; Banking; Energy & Utilities; Media & Entertainment and Aviation, and was "highly regarded" for Employment. Twelve of its silks were recognised as "leading" in one or more fields with Head of Chambers Gordon Pollock QC leading the "Stars at the Bar". 25 Juniors were recommended; 13 in two or more areas of specialisation.

Type of Work Undertaken

Barristers at Essex Court Chambers advise on a wide range of international and domestic commercial law and appear as Counsel in litigation and commercial arbitration world-wide. In addition to the "leading" areas of specialisation above, Essex Court Chambers has expertise in the following areas of law: Administrative/Judicial Review, Agriculture/Farming; Chinese; Company/Insolvency; Construction; Engineering; Commodities; Computer; Employment; Sports; Environmental; European; Financial Services; Human Rights; Injunctions/Arrests; Fraud; International Trade and Transport, Professional Negligence; Public International; Product Liability and VAT. For further information see the website; a detailed brochure is also available on request.

Pupil Profile

The best candidates are required for this set's intellectually demanding work. (2:1 or higher preferred)

Pupillage

Up to 4 12 month funded pupillages are offered each year for an October start. Applications are welcomed through PACH in 2000 for pupillage in October 2001 and for deferred pupillage in October 2002.

Mini Pupillages

Application by letter and CV to the Pupillage Secretary for funded places for those already embarked on legal studies.

Funding

£25,000 per annum, payable in two instalments. Applications to advance part are considered for the BVC year; interest free loans are also available.

4 ESSEX COURT (Nigel Teare QC)

4 Essex Court Temple London EC4Y 9AJ
DX: 292 London (Chancery Lane)
Tel: (020) 7797 7970 Fax: (020) 7353 0998
Email: clerks@4essexcourt.law.co.uk

Chambers Profile

4, Essex Court is one of the foremost and longest-established sets of Chambers specialising in commercial law. Chambers has remained in Essex Court although it moved from No 2 to No 4 some 6 years ago. Chambers has kept abreast of the latest technological advances in Information and Computer Technology. 4, Essex Court offers a first class service at sensible fee rates and has a staff renowned for their openness and fairness.

Type of Work Undertaken

The challenging and rewarding work of Chambers encompasses the broad range of commercial disputes embracing Arbitration, Aviation, Banking, Shipping, International Trade, Insurance and Re-insurance, Professional Negligence, Entertainment and Media, Environmental and Construction Law. Over 70% of Chambers' work involves international clients.

Pupil Profile

4, Essex Court seeks high calibre pupils with good academic qualifications (at least a 2:1 degree) who exhibit good written and verbal skills.

Pupillage

Chambers offers a maximum of 4 funded pupillages of either 6 or 12 months duration. 12 months pupillages are reviewed after 6 months. Pupils are normally moved amongst several members of Chambers and will experience a wide range of high quality commercial work. Outstanding pupils are likely to be offered a tenancy at the end of their pupillage.

Mini Pupillages

Mini - pupillages are encouraged in order that potential pupils may experience the work of Chambers before committing themselves to an application for full pupillage.

Funding

Awards of up to £28,000 p.a. (£14,000 per 6 months) are available for each funded pupillage - part of which may be forwarded during the BVC, at the Pupillage Committee's discretion.

No of Silks	7
No of Juniors	28

Contact

Ms Michelle Dean
Secretary to Pupillage Committee

Method of Application

PACH

Pupillages (p.a.)

1st 6 months:	4
2nd 6 months:	4
12 months: (reviewed at 6 months)	
Required degree	good 2.1+

Income

1st 6 months:	up to £14,000
2nd 6 months:	up to £14,000

Earnings not included

Tenancies

Current tenants who served pupillage in chambers	18
Junior tenancies offered in last 3 years	9
No of tenants of 5 years call or under	4
Income (1st year):	c£40,000

20 ESSEX STREET (Iain Milligan QC)

20 Essex Street London WC2R 3AL DX: 0009 (Ch.Ln.)
Tel: (020) 7583 9294 Fax: (020) 7583 1341
Email: clerks@20essexst.com
Website: www.20essexst.com

Chambers Profile
20 Essex Street is the address of one of the country's longest established sets of commercial chambers. Chambers moved from its former address at 3 Essex Court to its current address in 1994.

Type of Work Undertaken
The practising members of 20 Essex Street specialise in Commercial and EC Law. Most members of Chambers specialise in Commercial Law, in particular shipping, international sales, carriage by land, sea and air, insurance and reinsurance, and every type of domestic and international commercial agreement, appearing in the High Court (principally the Commercial Court), Court of Appeal and House of Lords as well as in arbitrations. A part of Chambers' work comprises EC Law, with certain members of Chambers appearing before the European Court of Justice.

Pupil Profile
Chambers look for candidates with a good academic background who seek to practise at the commercial bar. Chambers usually require a First or a strong 2:1 honours degree, though not necessarily in law.

Pupillage
Pupillage begins in October and is for twelve months. Usually Chambers take between three and five pupils each October. All applications must be made though PACH, in accordance with the deadlines set by PACH.

Mini Pupillages
Although not essential we strongly encourage those who may wish to apply for a pupillage here to apply for a mini-pupillage first. Write to Michael Coburn enclosing a CV and indicating the dates on which you would like to come. Write before Easter for summer mini-pupillages and before Christmas for Easter mini-pupillages.

Funding
Three funded pupillages with awards of £25,000 for twelve months are generally offered.

No of Silks	13
No of Juniors	24
No of Pupils	3

Contact:
Write to Andrew Baker about pupillage or Michael Coburn about mini-pupillage.
Other enquiries: write to Neil Palmer, Senior Clerk.

Method of Application
For pupillage, through PACH

Pupillages (p.a.)
12 months: 3–5

Income
Three pupillage awards of £25,000 p.a.

20 Essex Street

FALCON CHAMBERS (Jonathan Gaunt QC & Kim Lewison QC)

Falcon Court London EC4Y 1AA DX: 408
Tel: (020) 7353 2484 Fax: (020) 7353 1261
Website: www.falcon-chambers.co.uk

No of Silks	7
No of Juniors	21
No of Pupils	3
Pupillages (p.a.)	
1st 6 months:	2/3
2nd 6 months:	0/1
Required degree grade	2.1
Income	
1st 6 months:	£12,000
2nd 6 months:	£12,000

Chambers Profile

Falcon Chambers is regarded (and regularly described in reviews) as the leading set of chambers for property litigation and landlord and tenant law. Chambers work primarily in litigation, from the House of Lords down to county courts and valuation tribunals. Members are often briefed in arbitrations, and sometimes act as arbitrators, experts and legal assessors. Chambers also have substantial advisory and drafting practices, and have written most of the leading text books in our specialist fields of practice. Chambers is modern and friendly, demanding in the standards it sets, and very successful.

Type of Work Undertaken

All Members of Chambers specialise in litigation in the real property and property-related fields, including some non-specialist commercial litigation. Apart from commercial and residential property work, Chambers has a strong speciality in agricultural, and agricultural tenancy law, and in general property law, including easements, restrictive covenants, mortgages and options. Chambers are regularly involved in solicitors and surveyors professional negligence cases, and in cases involving insolvency and more general chancery law.

Pupil Profile

Chambers looks for intelligent and enthusiastic pupils with a real interest in property law and the potential to become a good advocate. The minimum academic requirement is a 2:1 degree, not necessarily in law.

Pupillage

Up to three six-month pupillages are available each year. Chambers has a preference for first six-month pupils. Pupils have two pupilmasters, for three months each. All pupils sit in their pupilmaster's room, and accompany them to court. Pupils also have the opportunity to work with other Members of Chambers, and will go to court with the most junior tenants. It is Chambers' policy to seek to recruit annually. Mini pupillages are available, and prospective applicants for pupillage are encouraged to apply in writing enclosing a CV, to Emily Windsor in Chambers.

Funding

Each six month pupillage carries an award of £12,000. It is sometimes possible to receive part of this award in advance during the Bar Finals year.

FURNIVAL CHAMBERS (Andrew Mitchell QC)

32 Furnival Street London EC4A 1JQ DX: 72
Tel: (020) 7405 3232 Fax: (020) 7405 3322
Email: clerks@furnivallaw.co.uk
Website: www.furnivallaw.co.uk

Chambers Profile

Since its formation in 1985, Furnival Chambers has provided a comprehensive and specialist criminal law service. Chambers, with leading and junior counsel of considerable experience and ability, is experienced in dealing with cases of more serious and complicated nature. Chambers' building is well suited to the traditions of the Bar, yet is able to offer those services which are essential in the modern Bar including a communications system of the highest and latest specification, equipped to send and receive information through an integrated computer system.

Type of Work Undertaken

The work of Chambers ranges from the most involved commercial fraud to the simplest road traffic matter. Expertise is therefore available in all areas of criminal law. Members specialise in cases of white collar fraud, drugs related offences, cases of a sexual nature including rape and child abuse, and crimes of violence including murder and terrorism. In addition, Furnival Chambers has a specialist team which deals with confiscation, asset forfeiture and money laundering. Members of the team have appeared in the vast majority of the leading cases in the High Court and Court of Appeal.

Pupil Profile

Chambers is an equal opportunity and multi-racial set. Chambers' aim is to ensure that all that is good in the traditional and independent Bar thrives in a modern environment.

Pupillage

Pupils will see a great deal of court work and undertake a certain amount of paperwork. Second six pupils will conduct a substantial amount of their own work whilst being monitored and assisted by their pupilmaster/mistress. Chambers offer excellent experience and run a continuing education programme for pupils including an in-house advocacy training course of approximately forty hours.
Applications will be considered for pupillage from students in their final undergraduate or CPE year as well as those in their BVC year with a view to offering pupillages 2 years in advance.

Mini Pupillages

Mini-pupillages and student visits are available.

Funding

Our funding policy is under review following the recent High Court decision but will obviously meet the legal requirements of the minimum wage.

No of Silks	3
No of Juniors	40
No of Pupils	4

Contact
Giles Cockings
Pupillage Secretary

Method of Application
PACH

Pupillages (p.a.)

12 months:	4

Tenancies

Current tenants who served pupillage in chambers	26
Junior tenancies offered in last 3 years	3
No of tenants of 5 years call or under	6

OLD SQUARE CHAMBERS (Hon. John Melville Williams QC)

1 Verulam Buildings Gray's Inn London WC1R 5LQ
DX: 1046 Chancery Lane/London
Tel: (020) 7269 0300 Fax: (020) 7405 1387
Email: moor@oldsquarechambers.co.uk
Website: www.oldsquarechambers.co.uk

Chambers Profile
A highly specialised, forward thinking set committed to expansion.

Type of Work Undertaken
Employment, personal injury, product liability and environmental law, Public law and human rights issues are encompassed within these areas. There is some business and mercantile work and some medical negligence. There is much use of European jurisprudence. In employment law, members of chambers have been involved in many of the ground-breaking cases of the past 20 years. Our profile in personal injury law is excellent, particular strengths are disaster and multi-party litigation. Environmental law work is predominantly on large 'toxic tort' litigation - damage caused by pollution. Fields of practice are organised around Special Interest Groups in chambers enabling the sharing of information and effective marketing.

Pupil Profile
Chambers look for intelligent candidates who have the potential to be excellent advocates. You must be motivated to come to the bar and practise in at least one of Chambers' specialist fields. You must have ability to cope with hard work and deal with many different people. Chambers is committed to equal opportunities. Our recruitment methods are designed to prevent any discrimination on the grounds of race, gender, disability, sexuality or religion.

Pupillage
Chambers offer high quality training, generously funded. Pupils spend 3 months with each pupil supervisor. Preferences for fields of work will be considered. There is the opportunity to undertake work for silks on complex and sometimes high profile work.

Mini Pupillages
Mini pupillages are available but in demand. Preference is given to final year students. Send Philip Mead your CV and a letter explaining your interest in chambers.

Funding
2001 grant: between £17,000 and £20,000 for 12 months in London, £14,000 in Bristol. 2nd six pupils undertake work on their own account, fees are retained without any deduction.

No of Silks	7
No of Juniors	33
No of Pupils	3

Contact
Sarah Moor

Method of Application
PACH

Pupillages (p.a.)

12 months:	3

Tenancies

Junior tenancies offered in last 3 years	4

For more information see our Website or write to Sarah Moor

Annexes
Hanover House
47 Corn Street
Bristol BS1 1HT
Tel: (0117) 927 7111
Fax: (0117) 927 3478

OLD SQUARE CHAMBERS

10 OLD SQUARE (Leolin Price CBE QC)

10 Old Square Lincoln's Inn London WC2A 3SU DX: 306
Tel: (020) 7405 0758 Fax: (020) 7831 8237

Chambers Profile
10 Old Square is a specialist Chancery set of chambers with 28 full-time tenants and a number of eminent academic members. The Head of Chambers, Leolin Price CBE QC, is a renowned Chancery silk and the set is well known for its high-quality trust and probate specialists.

Type of Work Undertaken
Chambers undertake the entire range of work which falls within the commercial and traditional Chancery fields. Their brochure, which is available upon request, provides further information.

Pupil Profile
Chambers seek to recruit pupils with excellent academic records; in the absence of exceptional circumstances, applicants should have attained a degree at class 2:1 or higher. Candidates should also have a proven ability to formulate complex arguments and to express them clearly, both orally and in writing.

Pupillage
Pupils are usually assigned to two pupil masters during the course of a six month pupillage, spending 3 months with each. In addition, pupils are encouraged to undertake occasional work for other tenants. Chambers aim to provide pupils with a thorough grounding for practice at the Chancery bar.

Mini Pupillages
Mini pupilllages are available. Successful applicants will usually have completed at least one year of a law degree course, or will be in the process of completing their CPE. Applications (by handwritten covering letter with a CV enclosed) should be made to Robert Arnfield.

Funding
Up to two funded six month pupillages are available every year; each carries an award of £8,000. In addition Chambers may offer up to two unfunded six month pupillages.

No of Silks	2
No of Juniors	25
No of Pupils	4

Contact
Mr Nicholas Harries
Pupillage Secretary

Method of Application
PACH

Pupillages (p.a.)
1st 6 months:	2
2nd 6 months:	2
Required degree grade	2:1 or higher

Income
Awards up to 2 funded pupillages each carrying up to £8,000.

10 OLD SQUARE

4 PAPER BUILDINGS (Lionel Swift QC)

4 Paper Buildings Temple London EC4Y 7EX DX: 1035
Tel: (020) 7583 0816 Fax: (020) 7353 4979
Email: clerks@4pb.com

Chambers Profile

4 Paper Buildings has a reputation as one of the friendliest sets in which to do your pupillage. An informal atmosphere is combined with high-profile work of the highest calibre in both civil law (especially professional negligence and employment) and all aspects of family law.

Type of Work Undertaken

Family law: Adoption care proceedings (for local authorities, families and guardians ad litem), child abduction, Children Act cases, cohabitees, divorce, inheritance and family provision, judicial review, matrimonial finance and wardship.
Civil: Arbitration, banking and securities, construction, contract (commercial and general), employment, judicial review, landlord and tenant, personal injury, professional negligence, sale of goods and consumer credit.

Pupil Profile

4 Paper Buildings follows the Equality Code for the Bar and aims to select the best, irrespective of race, ethnic origin, sex, sexual orientation, marital status, disability or religion.

Pupillage

If your application is successful, you will enjoy effective training with 3 different pupil masters and mistresses and will be encouraged to go to court with every member of Chambers. Current trends indicate that you will be extremely busy during your second 6 months.

Mini Pupillages

Please write to Alexander Schofield at 4 Paper Buildings or e-mail him at ags@4pb.com

Funding

Both awards are for £12,000 per annum, payable quarterly in advance. You will keep all your earnings, save for a small clerking percentage, in addition to your award.

No of Silks	4
No of Juniors	30
No of Pupils	2

Contact
Sam Neaman
Pupillage Secretary

Method of Application
PACH

Pupillages (p.a.)
12 months: 2

Income
1st 6 months: £6,000
2nd 6 months: £6,000
Earnings not included
Income (1st year): £30,000

Tenancies
Current tenants who served pupillage in chambers 21
Junior tenancies offered in last 3 years 3
No of tenants of 5 years call or under 4

5 PAPER BUILDINGS (G. Carey QC & J. Caplan QC)

5 Paper Buildings Temple London EC4Y 7HB DX: 365
Tel: (020) 7583 6117 Fax: (020) 7353 0075
Email: clerks@5-paperbuildings.law.co.uk

Chambers Profile

5 Paper Buildings are a leading, well established set of Chambers specialising in all areas of criminal law. Members undertake a broad range of work with an emphasis on commercial fraud. Members of Chambers have appeared in some of the largest fraud cases in recent years: Guinness, BCCI, Maxwell etc. Other tenants undertake civil and commercial litigation including contempt, restraint of trade, civil actions against the police.

Pupillage

When Chambers recruit pupils they look for candidates who have the abilities to become successful advocates. When interviewing, Chambers are looking at applicants as potential tenants. Chambers offer 12 month pupillages, as well as 2nd and 3rd six pupillages. Pupils can look forward to a variety of work in and around London. Chambers also offer an education programme for all pupils.

Mini Pupillages

Mini pupillages are available - contact Senior Clerk, Stuart Bryant. Student visits are not available.

Funding

Twelve month pupils will receive an award of approximately £6,000 in their first 6 months and with 2nd six pupils are guaranteed earnings of £7,500. On successful completion of Bar Finals, up to £1,000 may be claimed in advance, for guaranteed earnings.

No of Silks	8
No of Juniors	25

Contact

Emma Deacon
Pupillage Committee

Method of Application

12 months and 2nd six months via PACH. 3rd six months by application form only available from Chambers

Pupillages (p.a.)

1. Chambers offer 3 pupillages a year through PACH: a combination of 2nd six and 12 months pupillages.
2. In addition, Chambers offer 3 3rd six pupillages in October

Tenancies

Junior tenancies offered in last 3 years	5
No of tenants of 5 years call or under	3

33 PARK PLACE (John Charles Rees QC)

33 Park Place Cardiff CF10 3TN DX: 50755 Cardiff 2
Tel: (029) 2023 3313 Fax: (029) 2022 8294

Chambers Profile

33 Park Place is a well known set of Chambers with an established reputation. It has a wide ranging area of practice, both geographically and in subject matter. Accommodation is in a recently refurbished building occupying a prominent and convenient location with a full range of up to date facilities. Informal but business like the approach is forward looking whilst building upon past strengths.

Type of Work Undertaken

A broad based common law Chambers, there is a flexible division into criminal, civil and family practitioner groups. In addition to extensive criminal, family and personal injury work, there is particular experience in specialist areas including chancery, planning, licensing, commercial, employment, professional negligence and local government law.

Pupil Profile

Chambers is looking for pupils who are committed to success and able to take advantage of the significant opportunities for rapid progress that circuit work offers. Academic and all round ability will be recognised and rewarded.

Pupillage

Twelve month pupillage, ordinarily providing experience in each of the three principal areas of practice, it is nevertheless responsive to individual preferences. All members of Chambers welcome the opportunity to train and help pupils.

Mini Pupillages

Application by letter with CV to the Clerk to Chambers, Graham Barrett.

Funding

£6,000 p.a.

No of Silks	3
No of Juniors	35
Door Tenants	3 silks
	4 juniors

Contact

Graham Walters
(Head of Pupillage)

Method of Application

To Head of Pupillage

Pupillages (p.a.)

12 months: 2
Required degree grade
2:1 degree strongly preferred

Income

£6,000

Tenancies

Junior tenancies offered in last 3 years: 6
No of tenants of 5 years call or under: 12

18 RED LION COURT (Anthony Arlidge QC)

18 Red Lion Court London EC4A 3EB DX: 478 LDE
Tel: (020) 7520 6000 Fax: (020) 7520 6248/9
Email: chambersofarlidgeclerks@18rlc.co.uk

Chambers Profile

Chambers operate from a spacious listed building off Fleet Street near the Temple. Comprising 19 silks and 44 juniors, we offer one of the most comprehensive cross-sections of expertise in the field of criminal law.

Type of Work Undertaken

18 Red Lion Court covers the whole range of crime, defending and prosecuting at all levels. Particular strengths are commercial fraud, Inland Revenue and VAT offences, money laundering, corruption, drugs and drug trafficking and sex cases, including child abuse and obscene publications. Individual members are involved in international human rights cases from Rwanda to Santa Monica. Others have written well respected practitioners texts on a wide range of topics. Chambers' work is centred primarily on the South Eastern circuit with an emphasis on London and East Anglia. Much of the East Anglian work is serviced by our annexe in Chelmsford. A few practitioners undertake civil and administrative law work.

Pupil Profile

Chambers look for pupils with potential to develop into first class advocates. Pupils are selected for a combination of marked intellectual ability, together with good judgement and independent personalities.

Pupillage

Chambers offer 3 funded twelve months pupillages and three unfunded first six months. Funding is currently under review, however for entry in 2000, funded pupils will receive £15,000, made up of half award, half guaranteed earnings. All first six month pupillages will be subject to the minimum wage. Our pupils receive excellent training. In addition to experiencing a broad range of work, all pupils participate in our in-house advocacy programme. Nearly all of our pupils get tenancies with us or elsewhere. Pupillage applications should be made through PACH. Chambers do not offer 2nd or 3rd six pupillages. Sponsored pupils are accepted.

Mini Pupillages

Applications should be made to Tom Forster.

No of Silks	19
No of Juniors	44
No of Pupils	6

Contact

Elizabeth Webster
Pupillage Secretary

Method of Application

Through PACH

Pupillages (p.a.)

1st 6 months:	3
12 months:	3

Income

1st 6 months: minimum wage
12 months: £15,000
(made up of awards and guaranteed earnings)

Tenancies

Junior tenancies offered in last 3 years: 5

Annexes

Chelmsford

3 VERULAM BUILDINGS (Christopher Symons QC/John Jarvis QC)

3 Verulam Buildings Gray's Inn London WC1R 5NT
DX: LDE 331
Tel: (020) 7831 8441 Fax: (020) 7831 8479
Email: clerks@3verulam.co.uk
Website: www.3verulam.co.uk

Chambers Profile

3 Verulam Buildings is a large commercial set with a history of expansion by recruitment of tenants from amongst pupils. Over the past ten years at least two of its pupils have become tenants every year. Chambers occupies recently refurbished, spacious offices overlooking Gray's Inn Walks with all modern IT and library facilities. Chambers prides itself on a pleasant, friendly and relaxed atmosphere.

Type of Work Undertaken

A wide range of commercial work, in particular banking and financial services, insurance and reinsurance, commercial fraud, professional negligence, company law, entertainment, insolvency, public international law, EU law, arbitration/ADR, environmental law, building and construction as well as other general commercial work. Members of Chambers regularly appear in high profile cases and a substantial amount of Chambers' work is international.

Pupil Profile

Chambers looks for intelligent and ambitious candidates with strong powers of analysis and reasoning, who are self confident and get on well with others. Candidates should normally have at least a 2.1 grade in an honours subject which need not be law.

Pupillage

Chambers takes 3–5 funded twelve months pupils every year through PACH. Each pupil spends three months with four different members of Chambers to gain experience of different types of work. Chambers also offers unfunded pupillages to pupils who do not intend to apply for a tenancy in Chambers. There is a discretionary fund available for the purposes of the minimum wage legislation.

Mini Pupillages

Mini pupillages are available for one week at a time for university, CPE or Bar students who are interested in finding out more about Chambers' work. Chambers considers mini-pupillage to be an important part of the recruitment process. Candidates should have, or expect to obtain, the minimum requirements for a funded 12 month pupillage. Applications are accepted throughout the year and should be addressed to Natalie Baylis.

Funding

In the year 2000-2001 the annual award will be £25,000 payable monthly.

No of Silks	12
No of Juniors	38
No of Pupils	6

Contact

Ms Natalie Baylis
Pupillage Committee

Method of Application

PACH/CV and handwritten letter to Chambers.

Pupillages (p.a.)

1st 6 months:	2
12 months:	3-5
Required degree grade	2.1

Income

£25,000 per annum.
Earnings not included

Tenancies

Current tenants who served pupillage in chambers	37
Junior tenancies offered in last 3 years	7
No of tenants of 5 years call or under	12

Funding

charities

2000

FUNDING

TRAINEE SOLICITORS

Both the CPE and LPC are deemed to be full time courses of higher education and as such, you will not be entitled to claim social security benefits. Many firms, however, not only pay for the course fees but also provide a moderate living allowance which keeps the wolf from the door, if not allowing for much luxury. For details of the sponsorship and awards available from individual firms see the A-Z of firms in this book and firms' own literature. Working in the college vacations or picking up evening work will help financially, although both courses require a degree of commitment which might mean that extra-curricular work could damage your academic prospects. The question of whether to work or not is one that you will have to consider carefully.

Leaning on the generosity of parents and getting into debt with banks are the most common approaches to that element of the cost of the academic training which cannot be resourced from scholarships or grants. A majority of LPC students are in debt by thousands of pounds.

The major banks are willing to advance up to £10,000 per year to those on CPE and LPC courses. It is the security of a guaranteed income from the training contract which makes the student such an attractive lending proposition. At the time of going to press, typical interest rates were set at 1% over base rate and repayments were commonly delayed until part way through the training contract.

Once you have actually started your training contract you may also find that a number of the major banks will lend to you on quite favourable terms. Loan terms may include low interest rates, no arrangement fees and repayments deferred until after qualification. You may wish to consider whether you should transfer your existing loan debt to such a new arrangement.

Don't be surprised if your new lifestyle as a trainee costs you much more than you had anticipated. Most people are surprised how they manage to get through their trainee salary without trying. You're lifestyle takes a dramatic change on several fronts; your new work wardrobe will set you back an initial several hundred pounds, you may find yourself socialising with colleagues in more expensive bars and restaurants and you may find your eating habits take an expensive turn. Just don't be surprised that you get through a salary that would have felt like a fortune 12 months earlier.

Useful Names and Addresses

Local Education Authority Contact them for a publication currently titled Financial Support For Students In 1999/2000: A Guide For Those Starting In Higher Education After 1998

Career Development Loans
Freepost, Newcastle upon Tyne, NE85 1BR **Tel:** 0800 585505

Barclays Bank 147 High Holborn, London, EC1N 2NU or 19 Fleet Street London EC4P 4DR **Tel:** 0345 550088

Lloyds TSB Law Courts, 222 The Strand, London WC2R 1BB
Tel: 0345 300004

HSBC Chancery Lane & Fleet Street Branch, 123 Chancery Lane, London WC2A 1QH
Attn: David Pappa/Lee Church
Tel: (020) 7599 6740

NatWest Law Courts, Temple Bar Legal Centre, PO Box 11052, 217 The Strand, London WC2R 1AR
Tel: (020) 7664 9113

TRAINEE BARRISTERS

The issue of funding for Bar students and pupils has long been of concern to most individuals considering a career as a barrister. Not only do they have to deal with the idea that embarking on this route by no means ensures qualification, they also have to consider the financial implications of the decision. Many law firms offer trainee solicitors financial support and course fees whilst they are completing their LPC and even the CPE. At the end of the academic stage a reasonably healthy salary awaits them. For trainee solicitors, it is possible to guarantee solvency at a fairly early stage in their careers; not so for the majority of aspiring barristers. The average cost of completing the CPE and/or BVC is estimated at over £15,000, including living expenses.

The Inns of Court

Between them, the four Inns of Court distribute over £2 million a year in funding to those studying for BVC and/or CPE and in pupillage. Some awards are merit based, others take into account financial hardship. Students can only apply to their own Inn for an award and our interviews with pupils and junior tenants confirmed that the volume and size of awards is a key factor in choosing an Inn whilst a student. Some Inns opt for fewer larger awards whilst others offer a greater number of more modest ones. An outline of the awards available from each Inn are set out in the table overleaf. Contact the Inns for further information on how and when to apply.

Chambers

Very few sets provide any financial assistance for the CPE or the BVC. It is not unusual for chambers to provide some sort of funding during pupillage and in the second six one has always been able to earn some sort of income from fee paying work. The practice of "devilling" (earning money by carrying out work for more senior members of chambers) is a feature at some sets. However, in the Autumn of 1999, a pupil barrister, Rebecca Edmonds, won a High Court victory over her employer to establish that the Minimum Wage Act 1998 applied to pupillages. Rebecca Edmonds and her employer had agreed to be parties to the test case in order that the principle be established. What does this mean for the future? It is likely that some sets that cannot afford to pay pupils will simply cease to offer pupillage. In the academic year 1997/98, up to a third of pupillages were unpaid. Until the Bar Council is able to formulate a policy on the matter each set will have to respond to the High Court ruling as it sees fit. At this time it is too early to assess the full impact of the case.

Work

The Education and Training Department of the Bar Council discourages students from taking a job whilst studying for the BVC full time. The reality, however, is that some students find it necessary to undertake some Saturday and limited part time work in this period. The Bar Council's regulations do allow for pupillage to be broken down into smaller chunks of time, but in the second six, no break in the time spent with the pupil master may be more than one month in duration and the second six should not be more than nine months in duration. A second six must be commenced within 12 months of the completion of the first six.

Benefits

The CPE and BVC are both classed as full time courses of higher education. It is not possible to state that you are actively seeking work and are immediately available for work during your BVC.

Loans

Banks provide loan packages for trainee barristers with repayments delayed until between six and 12 months following the completion of pupillage. The branches of the major banks located close to the law courts are well set up for dealing with requests for funding from BVC students and pupils. Up to £10,000 is commonly on offer for each of the BVC year and the pupillage year. It is more difficult to come by loans for the CPE year however. Career Development Loans are another option.

The Bar Council

The Bar Scholarship Trust provides a small number of loans of up to £4,000 for pupillage.

Stages in Brussels

Six-month secondments with the European Commission count towards pupillage. Each candidate receives £5,000.

Other Sources

Charities and educational foundations are a further source of funds.

Name of Inn	Total funds available	CPE/BVC Awards	Pupillage Awards	Contact Details
Inner Temple	£616,950	£15,000 x 3 £12,500 x 4 £10,000 x 20 £272,000 split into awards of up to £10,000 £13,000 Benefactors Scholarships £160 x 50 Admission/Call fees £15,000 Disabililty Grants		Sophie Found Tel: 0207 797 8210 sfound@innertemple.org.uk
Middle Temple	£520,000	£1,000 - £15,000 x 80 - 100 (20 of which are allocated to CPE)	Pupillage awards under review	Students Department Tel: 0207 427 4800 student_enquiries@middletemple.org.uk
Gray's Inn	£553,000	For CPE: £46,500 split into separate awards For BVC: £15,000 x 3 £12,500 x 12 £10,000 x 6 £5,000 x 22 £3,000 x 19 £85 Admission Fees x 25 Up to £10,000 x 1	£59,800 split between various awards £15,500 split between various awards for the 1st year of practice	Margaret Chadderton - Deputy Under Treasurer (Students) Tel: 0207 458 7900
Lincoln's Inn	£654,000	For CPE: Admission/Call/Dining charges x 100 Up to £8,000 x up to 15 For BVC: £8 - 15,000 x up to 32 £7,000 x up to 25 £8,000 x 2 15 Rooms in Self Contained Flats (7 at £5,500, 8 at £4,350) £2,000 sundry exam prizes	£46,000 split between various awards	Judith Fox Tel: 0207 405 0138 judith.fox@lincolnsinn.org.uk

All figures are accurate at the time of going to press

HSBC

HSBC Bank plc, formerly Midland Bank, is the pre-eminent provider of financial services to students. There is a wide range of services available to students and graduates from all of our 1700 branches across the country.

The professional studies loan is available to law students who intend to be a solicitor or barrister, taking one of the following courses: Common Professional Exam, Legal Practice Course, Postgraduate Diploma in Law, or the Bar Vocational Course.

The facility can be used to cover living expenses, tuition costs or books, and the rate of interest charged is extremely competitive at 1% over our Base Rate. There are no repayments made during the period of study and for aspiring barristers the repayment moratorium may be extended until 12 months into tenancy. The loan can be drawn down in tranches as you need the funds to keep the interest charged to a minimum.

In addition to the Professional Studies Loan you will be eligible for a student banking package if you are continuing your studies without a break. This includes an interest-free overdraft and fee-free MasterCard credit card and tailored insurance for your belongings.

Professional Studies Loans are available at all branches but, if you are aiming to become a barrister, the Chancery Lane & Fleet Street branch is the one with the most expertise to be able to give you specialist advice.

For further information, call the branch or 0800 130 130 and ask for an information pack on Professional Studies Loans. Written quotations are also available. To help improve our service and in the interests of security, we may monitor and/or record your telephone calls with us.

Details of funding available
Professional Studies Loan

Loan Amount
All course fees and living expenses up to the greater of £5000 or two thirds of any salary you earned in the 12 months before starting the course.

Repayment schedule
No repayments are made during your studies. Repayments will start at a time agreed with you but usually no earlier than 6 months after you complete your studies. Generous repayment periods are available.

No. of branches
Approx 1700 nationwide

Contact address
Chancery Lane & Fleet Street Branch
123 Chancery Lane
London
WC2A 1QH
Tel: 020 7599 6740
Fax: 020 7599 6741

Universities and Law Schools

BPP LAW SCHOOL

67-69 Lincoln's Inn Fields, London WC2A 3JB
Tel: (020) 7430 2304 Fax: (020) 7404 1389

College Profile

BPP Law School is based in London and offers postgraduate law courses for students intending to become barristers or solicitors. As part of the BPP Professional Education Group, the Law School is extremely well-resourced and is amongst those with the best teaching facilities in the country. The teaching team comprises practitioners and academics and the school has a reputation for being professional and friendly, providing well-taught and well-organised courses.

LPC full-time or part-time

Designed for those intending to practice as solicitors, emphasis is on the application of legal knowledge in practice. As well as the core subjects of Business, Litigation and Conveyancing, a wide range of city, commercial and private client options is on offer. The Law Society has awarded a "Good" rating to this course since October 1995.

BVC full-time only

This course is designed both for those who intend to practice at the Bar and for those who intend to pursue a career in commerce and industry or the Civil Service. The course is skills-based and practical, demanding a high level of commitment and work from the student. Instruction is given by an experienced team, the majority of whom remain in practice or have had recent experience at the Bar.

Postgraduate Diploma in Law full-time or part-time

The Diploma is intended to provide a stimulating course in itself as well as a positive foundation for the professional courses and practice thereafter. All foundation subjects required by the CPE Board are included. The Diploma presents the substance of these subjects in a form which reflects the economic and social context in which the law operates.

Contact Name
Christine Taylor

Address for application and course information:

BVC:
Central Applications Clearing House (CACH),
General Council of the Bar,
2/3 Cursitor Sreet,
London EC4A 1NE

LPC & PGDL
(full-time courses):
Central Applications Board,
PO Box 84, Guildford,
Surrey GU13 1YX

LPC & PGDL
(part-time courses):
Course Registrar,
Administration Department,
BPP Law School,
67-69 Lincoln's Inn Fields,
London WC2A 3JB

CARDIFF LAW SCHOOL

Centre For Professional Legal Studies PO Box 294 Cardiff CF10 3UX
Tel: (029) 2087 4964 Fax: (029) 2087 4984
Email: Selley@Cardiff.ac.uk
Website: www.cf.ac.uk/uwc/claws/cpls

University Profile

Cardiff Law School is long established, well-resourced and enjoys an international reputation for its teaching and research. In the most recent assessment of research quality conducted by the Higher Education Funding Council, Cardiff achieved a grade 5 rating, placing it in the top dozen law schools in the country. Cardiff offers opportunities for students to pursue postgraduate study by research leading to the degrees of M.Phil and Ph.D. In addition, taught Masters degrees in the areas of canon, commercial, criminal justice and medical law are offered in full and part-time mode.

Within the Law School, the Centre for Professional Legal Studies is validated to offer both the Legal Practice Course and the Bar Vocational Course. Students are taught by experienced solicitors and barristers who have been specifically recruited for this purpose. All students pursuing the vocational courses are guaranteed placements with solicitors' firms or sets of chambers, while students studying the Bar Vocational Course additionally enjoy a one week placement with a Circuit or District Judge. Cardiff's Legal Practice Course has twice been rated "Excellent" by the Law Society; one of only five out of the 30 providers of this course to achieve the top ranking.

Recent developments within the Law School include extensive IT provision together with dedicated accommodation for the vocational courses which house a practitioner library, courtroom facilities, fixed and movable audio visual equipment for recording interactive practitioner skills activities. In addition, the main law library contains a substantial collection of primary and secondary material.

The Law School is housed in its own building at the heart of the campus, itself located in one of the finest civic centres in Britain and only a short walk from the main shopping area. The University has its own postgraduate centre, together with a full range of sporting and social facilities.

Contact Name
Mrs Zoe Selley

UNIVERSITY OF CENTRAL ENGLAND

Franchise Street Perry Barr Birmingham B42 2SU
Tel: (0121) 331 5640 Fax: (0121) 331 6438
Email: Iss@uce.ac.uk
Website: www.uce.ac.uk

College Profile

Based in Birmingham, the School of Law has been a major centre for postgraduate and undergraduate legal education for over 30 years. A wide range of high quality courses is taught by experienced and well qualified staff. Our facilities include a legal practice resource centre, fully-equipped IT workrooms, a court room and solicitor's office both with audio-visual links.

Legal Practice

Legal practice today is demanding. Our LPC course is designed to give you an advantageous start to your career as a solicitor in a competitive professional environment. We offer a wide range of commercial and private client options. The interactive teaching and learning methods replicate the typical transactions which take place in a solicitor's office and are designed to develop the self-sufficiency and confidence necessary when embarking on your training contract. The course can be studied by 4 days' attendance over one year or by two evenings' attendance over two. The University's award of Postgraduate Diploma in Legal Practice is made to those completing the course.

Postgraduate Diploma in Law/CPE (Full Time and Part Time)

This is the University's academic stage course for non-law graduates seeking to qualify as solicitors or barristers. Our course places emphasis on the development of legal skills by use of interactive teaching and learning methods and problem solving techniques. Successful students are guaranteed a place on our LPC.

Masters Degree in Legal Practice (Part Time)

This course is designed for students who have completed the LPC or are qualified solicitors and wish to acquire further specialisation in an aspect of legal practice. It is a research based course that can be completed in substantial part by distance learning.

Contact Name

Please apply to Admissions Officer,
Faculty of Law & Soc Sciences, Perry Barr, Birmingham B42 2SU.

Tel: (0121) 331 6610
Fax: (0121) 331 6622
E-mail: Iss@uce.ac.uk
Website: www.uce.ac.uk

CITY UNIVERSITY

The Law Department Northampton Square London EC1V 0HB
Tel: (020) 7477 8301 Fax: (020) 7477 8578
Website: www.city.ac.uk/law

College Profile

City University was granted a Royal Charter in 1966. The University is located within walking distance of the Law Society, the major City firms of solicitors, the Bar Council, the Inns of Court, the Royal Courts of Justice and the Central Criminal Court. Almost half the students at the University are studying for a postgraduate qualification. The Law Department has close ties with the professions and the Inns of Court School of Law is affiliated to the University. City Law Department graduates currently have a guaranteed Legal Practice Course place available to them.

Diploma in Law / Common Professional Examination (Full-time or part-time)

The original CPE, City's Diploma in Law is the largest University Diploma/CPE course and benefits from specialist staff with unrivalled experience, including visiting academics from Oxford, Cambridge and other established Universities. Unashamedly academic in the way it is taught, the City Diploma can be converted into an LLB by completing additional course units on a part-time basis and may be converted into an MA by thesis. There is an annual mooting competition sponsored by the Inns of Court and a departmentally organised Careers Fair attended by City solicitors.

Graduate-entry LLB Honours degree

City's graduate-entry LLB is a programme designed for non-law graduates who want a broader two-year course leading to a qualifying law degree. The course is designed to provide both a general knowledge of the central areas of the law and to allow special interests to be developed. In addition to completing the seven foundation subjects students choose two additional subjects from a range of options. The academic work and examinations are of first degree standard and the course is taught jointly with the Department of Law's three year undergraduate LLB degree. Separate tutors and tutorials give this course its own special identity within the Department.

LLM Environmental Law

This new taught Masters course provides an opportunity to study environmental law at an advanced level. It comprises three taught modules and a dissertation and may be studied full-time or part-time.

Contact Name

Diploma in Law/CPE

Applications for the full-time course should be made to the Central Applications Board by February. Part-time applications direct to City University by 30 April.

Course Director (Admissions):
Katherine Reece Thomas
Tel: 020 7477 8312
Fax: 020 7477 8578
E-mail: CPE@city.ac.uk

Graduate-entry LLB

Applications should be made to City University preferably by 30 April.

Course Director:
Dr Yvonne Jacobs
Tel: 020 7477 8306
Fax: 020 7477 8578
E-mail: Y.JACOBS@city.ac.uk

LLM Environmental Law

Applications should be made to City University. No specific closing date.

Course Director:
Professor Mike Purdue
Tel: 020 7477 8311
Fax: 020 7477 8578
E-mail: h.m.purdue@city.ac.uk

Northampton Square
London EC1V 0HB

THE COLLEGE OF LAW

Braboeuf Manor Portsmouth Road Guildford GU3 1HA
Tel: 0800 3280153 Fax: (01483) 460 494
Email: info@lawcol.co.uk
Website: www.lawcol.org.uk

College Profile

The College of Law, the largest legal training establishment in Europe, has branches in Guildford, London, Chester and York. The College has an excellent reputation with law firms and chambers and its teaching staff are professionally qualified as solicitors or barristers. The College's specialist knowledge and extensive contacts are coupled with its careers advisory service, specifically geared towards law students, to help students gain training contracts and pupillages. It offers the following courses:

Postgraduate Diploma in Law (Full-time, Part-time or Distance Learning) - formerly CPE

The PgDL is the law conversion course for graduates of disciplines other than law who wish to become solicitors or barristers. Students will receive in-depth tuition in seven foundation subjects from tutors with a proven track record in providing legal education. Successful students receive a Diploma in Law and are guaranteed a place on the College's Legal Practice Course.

Legal Practice Course (Full-time, Part-time, or Block Learning)

The LPC is the vocational stage of training for prospective solicitors. The College's LPC has been developed in consultation with both City and provincial firms to address the real needs of today's legal profession, and ensure the course meets the demands of life in practice.

Bar Vocational Course (Full-time)

The BVC is the vocational stage of training for prospective barristers and is available at the College's site in Chancery Lane, London. It has been developed in conjunction with practising barristers to prepare students for life in their early years at the Bar. Practitioners from highly respected sets of chambers also contribute to the delivery of the course.
For further information about courses at any of the College's branches please contact Admissions.

Contact Name
Freephone: 0800 3280153
Email: info@lawcol.co.uk

INNS OF COURT SCHOOL OF LAW

4 Gray's Inn Place Gray's Inn London WC1R 5DX
Tel: (020) 7404 5787 Fax: (020) 7831 4188
Email: bvc@icsl.ac.uk or 1pc@icsl.ac.uk or llm@icsl.ac.uk
Website: www.icsl.ac.uk

College Profile

The Inns of Court School of Law (ICSL) is a leading provider of postgraduate legal skills training. Best known as 'The Bar School' for its pre-eminent role in training barristers, it has for a long time provided training for soliciters as part of its in-house CPD training programmes. When the Law Society set up the LPC it drew on the strengths the school had in devising the BVC in 1989.

Please apply to Admissions for further details or to request a prospectus.

Bar Vocational Course (Full-time or Part-time)

The ICSL is launching a new revamped BVC 2000 course that seeks to provide lawyers for the future with flexible training that will help then cope with change and to provide a high quality of service for clients. The course provides training in seven skill areas: Advocacy (where students are continously videoed and assessed); conference skills; negotiation; opinion writing; drafting; fact management and legal research. Training manuals for the course are written by staff and provided free, so no additional books are required to be purchased for the course. Places offered: 750 Full-time; 100 Part-time

Legal Practice Course (Full-time)

The ICSL has been newly validated to run this newly designed LPC course. In designing the course the school conducted extensive research amongst leading firms of solicitors, especially with City firms and is offering a course that is highly tailored to meeting future needs in practice, with a heavy emphasis on learning via the use of IT resources. The foundation course consists of: Ethics; Skills, The European Context and Taxation, followed by compulsory subjects of Business Law and Practice; Litigation and Advocacy and Conveyancing, with a choice of three out of six electives encompassing the necessary training for City and high street solicitors. Places offered: 100 Full-time

LLM in Criminal Litigation (Full-time or Part-time)

Run in association with City University, it is the only postgraduate degree course in the country to be devoted exclusively to Criminal Litigation. It allows students to examine critically the four key subjects that underpin the criminal justice system. The course takes a broad look at criminal procedure, sentencing, criminal evidence and criminal advocacy, and makes a comparative reference to other legal systems. There is a great deal of practical work where students are videoed and given feedback.

KEELE UNIVERSITY

Law Department Keele ST5 5BG
Tel: (01782) 583229 Fax: (01782) 583228
Website: www.keele.ac.uk

College Profile

Keele University is a friendly campus community located in attractive surroundings in the Midlands, with easy access to Manchester and Birmingham. The Law Department is dynamic, lively and research-active, with a strong emphasis on interdisciplinary studies, and is firmly committed to graduate study. The campus offers excellent IT facilities, a sports centre and thriving students' union.

Diploma in Legal Studies/CPE Course (Full-time or Part-time)

Enables non-law graduates to complete the first stage of professional training at an established university with small group teaching. Students are taught by experienced law staff; there are modules on mooting and client interviewing, and a chance to upgrade to a Master's degree. A link with Chester College of Law provides guaranteed places on the LPC.

LLM in Child Law/MA in Child Care Law & Practice

These courses concentrate upon issues concerned with children, parents, human rights, the professions and the state. The LLM is offered full-time or part-time; the MA is taught part-time only in four teaching blocks per year. The MA is accredited for Law Society CPD points.

LLM in General Legal Studies & Research (Full-time or Part-time)

Offers an opportunity to study a variety of different areas of law in depth, together with a research training course. Assessment is by a variety of methods, including a research dissertation.

M.Phil/Ph.D supervision

Research supervision is offered in many fields. Areas of expertise include; professional negligence; criminal law; health care law; civil liberties; constitutional & administrative law; European Union law; legal history; gender, sexuality and law; property & taxation; planning; legal theory; child & education law; international human rights.

Contact Name

Eileen Farne
Department of Law,
Keele University, Keele,
Staffordshire ST5 5BG
Tel: 01782 583229
Fax: 01782 583228
E-mail: lab07@law.keele.ac.uk
Website: www.keele.ac.uk/depts/la/home.htm

KINGSTON UNIVERSITY LAW SCHOOL

Kingston Hill Kingston upon Thames KT2 7LB
Tel: (020) 8547 7323 Fax: (020) 8547 7038
Website: www.kingston.ac.uk

College Profile

The Law School has been in existence for more than thirty years, the last twenty at the Kingston Hill campus, attractively situated adjacent to Richmond Park and with easy access to London.

The Law School Courses

Undergraduate

LLB (Hons) and a number of "LLB (Hons) with..." pathways; with French or German Law, French, German or Spanish Studies, European Studies and Business. All these degrees, which give students choice of subject and flexibility of study, are fully recognised by the legal professional bodies.

Postgraduate

LLM

The LLMs in Business Law and the General LLM require the completion of ten modules in either one or two years, the year one course effectively being full-time. All assessment is by supervised dissertation.

The LLM in Dispute Resolution is delivered over two years. All assessment is by supervised dissertation.

The MA in Legal Studies, gained by submission of a supervised dissertation, is open to those who have completed the CPE course or are qualified lawyers.

The Postgraduate Diploma

A one year full-time or two year part-time course open to non-law graduates who, on successful completion, may go on to take the professions' qualifying examinmations.

Contact Name

LLB courses:
P.Ford@kingston.ac.uk
LLM:
Alan.Clark@kingston.ac.uk
Diploma:
S.Caird@kingston.ac.uk

MANCHESTER METROPOLITAN UNIVERSITY

School of Law Elizabeth Gaskell Campus Hathersage Road Manchester M13 OJA
Tel: (0161) 247 3050 Fax: (0161) 247 6309
Email: law@mmu.ac.uk

College Profile
The School of Law is one of the largest providers of legal education in the UK, and enjoys an excellent reputation for the quality and range of its courses. The School's courses are well designed and taught, combining rigorous academic standards with practical application. Giving you the best possible start for your career.

Bar Vocational Course (Full-time)
This course provides the vocational stage of training for intending practising barristers. Adopting a Syndicate Group approach, the BVC is activity based and interactive. Extensive IT and audio visual facilities combine with dedicated, well equipped premises to provide an enjoyable and stimulating experience. Excellent student support is provided including mentoring by practising barristers and an Additional Professional Programme which is designed to bridge the gap betweeen student and professional life.

Legal Practice Course (Full-time or Part-time)
This course is for those wishing to qualify as a solicitor. Offering a full range of commercial and private client electives the Legal Practice Course, taught by professionally qualified staff, prepares you for every day practice. There is a dedicated Resource Centre and an excellent pastoral care programme for LPC students. Consistently recognised by the Law Society for its high quality.

Postgraduate Diploma in Law/CPE (Full-time or Part-time)
An increasing number of graduates enter the legal profession this way, with employers attracted by the applicant's maturity and transferable skills. The course places emphasis on the acquisition of legal research and other relevant legal skills. The School guarantees a place on the LPC, subject to satisfactory performance, and gives favourable treatment for the BVC.

Contact Name
Contact the Admissions Tutor for the relevant course.

UNIVERSITY OF NORTHUMBRIA AT NEWCASTLE

School of Law University of Northumbria
Sutherland Building Newcastle-upon-Tyne NE1 8ST
Tel: (0191) 227 4494
Fax: (0191) 227 4557
Email: muriel.theillere@unn.ac.uk
Website: www.unn.ac.uk

College Profile

The School of Law at the University of Northumbria is known for its excellence in the provision of academic and professional legal education. Situated in central Newcastle the School has over 60 full-time teaching staff and is one of the largest departments in the University. Full-time, part-time and distance learning modes of study are available. The School is validated to run the Bar Vocational Course, the Legal Practice Course and the Common Professional Examination/Diploma in Law Course. It also offers the Professional Skills Course and an extensive LLM programme, including courses in Mental Health Law, Commercial Law and newly validated courses in Medical Law and EU Law. The Law School has dedicated lecture and workshop accommodation together with its own Law Skills Centre which includes a large practitioner library, court room and offices with full CCTV facilities plus open access IT equipment.

Contact Name
Ms. M. Theillere

LPC (full-time or part-time)

- the vocational training course for students who wish to qualify as solicitors
- a wide range of corporate and private client electives
- practical workshops

BVC (full-time)

- the vocational training course for students who wish to qualify as barristers
- practical skills training in dedicated accommodation
- strong practitioner participation

CPE

- the academic stage of training for non-law graduates who wish to qualify as solicitors or barristers
- structured study materials
- opportunity to obtain a law degree with an additional study programme
- guaranteed places for successful students either on our Legal Practice Course or, subject to the requirements of the General Council of the Bar, on our Bar Vocational Course.

NOTTINGHAM LAW SCHOOL

Nottingham Law School
Belgrave Centre Nottingham NG1 5LP
Tel: (0115) 948 6871 Fax: (0115) 948 6878

Bar Vocational Course

The Bar Vocational Course (BVC): Nottingham Law School has designed their BVC to develop to a high standard a range of core practical skills, and to equip students to succeed in the fast-changing environment of practice at the Bar. Particular emphasis is placed on the skill of advocacy, utilising the Law School's expertise as a leading provider of advocacy training. The BVC is taught entirely by recently practising barristers, and utilises the same integrated and interactive teaching methods as all of the school's other professional courses. Essentially, students learn by doing and Nottingham Law School provides a risk-free environment in which students are encouraged to realise, through practice and feedback, their full potential.

Legal Practice Course

The LPC is offered by full-time and part-time block study. This course has been designed to be challenging and stimulating for students and responsive to the needs of firms, varying from large commercial to smaller high street practices.

Nottingham Law School's LPC features: integration of the transactions and skills, so that each advances the other, whilst ensuring the transferability of skills between different subject areas. Carefully structured inter-active group work which develops an ability to handle skills and legal transactions effectively, and in an integrated way. A rigorous assessment process that nevertheless avoids 'assessment overload', to maintain a teaching and learning emphasis to the course. A professionally qualified team, retaining substantial links with practice. A top rating from The Law Society's Assessment Panel in every year of its operation.

The Postgraduate Diploma in Law (full-time):

The Nottingham Law School PGDL is a one year conversion course designed for any non-law graduate who intends to become a solicitor or barrister in the UK. The intensive course effectively covers the seven core subjects of an undergraduate law degree in one go. It is the stepping stone to the LPC or the BVC at Nottingham Law School, and a legal career thereafter. It is a postgraduate Diploma (Dip Law) in its own right, which can be presented to employers. It operates on a similar basis to the LPC (see above), though inevitably it has a more academic bias.

Contact Name
Nottingham Law School
Belgrave Centre
Chaucer Street
Nottingham
NG1 5LP

OXFORD BROOKES UNIVERSITY

School of Social Sciences and Law Gipsy Lane Headington Oxford OX3 OBP
Tel: (01865) 484901 Fax: (01865) 484930
Email: sebannister@brookes.ac.uk
Website: www.brookes.ac.uk/school/social/law

College Profile

Oxford Brookes University enjoys a well-established position as one of the top new universities. It combines the advantages of its location in an ancient university city with excellent IT, library and sporting facilities. The Law Department has been rated 'excellent' by the HEFCE for the quality of its teaching and has been placed in high positions in recently published league tables of university law departments. The sixteen lecturers have a wide range of research interests which complement the work of the Centre of Legal Research and Policy Studies. In addition to providing a CPE qualification with its advanced Diploma in Law, the postgraduate portfolio includes two taught LLMs, with further programmes planned.

Both LLMs are available in full-time (one year) or part-time (two years) mode. Students receive a grounding in research methods, have a range of options from which to select their course of study and submit a dissertation. Students benefit from an individual approach to learning.

LLM - Criminal Justice

A taught master's programme with emphasis on the human rights aspects of criminal justice. Options include criminal law, criminology, policing and punishment.

LLM - International Law

A taught master's programme in which students can choose to focus on Public, Private or General International Law. Options include banking, trade and human rights law.

Contact Name
Mrs Samantha Bannister
Law Administrator

SEMPLE PIGGOT ROCHEZ

Lower Ground 62 Blenheim Crescent Notting Hill London W11 1NZ
Tel: (020) 7833 4306 Fax: (020) 7837 7322
Website: www.spr-law.com

College Profile

Semple Piggot Rochez acquired the legal division of Wolsey Hall in 1998. Working with their partner, The Law Group at Middlesex University, SPR delivers a two year part-time distance learning Postgraduate Diploma in Law (CPE) accredited by the CPE Board - the first CPE in the UK to be fully supported online on the internet.

First CPE to be supported fully on the internet

While it is not necessary to have internet access to do the course - as the course is self contained - those with access will be able to use the purpose designed website (www.spr-law.com). Students will be given free online access over the net to LAWTEL, The Official Law Reports, All England Law Reports, Weekly Law Reports, Haslbury's Laws, Legislation Direct, Law Direct, Law Reports Digest, PLC Magazine and European Counsel magazine. The Virtual Workstation on the SPR website provides a range of additional services; mail service, notice boards, conferencing, text based real time communication channels, SPR 'netcasts', online debate forum, links to over 4500 legal and other resources on the net.

Two Centres: Oxford and London

SPR is accredited by the CPE board to enrol 100 students in each year. The programme held over 4 extended study weekends (Friday-Sunday) is fully supported by detailed course manuals written by members of the lecturing team. Teaching will be held in two centres: Oxford and London. Students may choose either the Oxford Centre on the London Centre to suit their convenience. Students attending the Oxford course will be given access to the Bodleian Library. Students attending the London Centre will be provided with reader cards to a London Library.

SPR reverses the fees trend by reducing the tuition fees

The fee for the course is now £1850, reduced from £2262 last year. If you are interested in joining this innovative net supported course, please visit the website. You will be able to down load a prospectus and review the many services online. SPR also provides, free of charge to all students, some 2000 pages of legal course notes and other materials - online. Alternatively call Jane O'Hare, the Course Director on 01865 201546 or Linda Guererro or Mike Semple Piggot on 020 7833 4306. SPR is always pleased to meet students who wish to make an appointment to see them at their London office.

Contact

Jane O'Hare Course Director
01865 201546
Mike Semple Piggot
Linda Guerrero
0207 833 4306

Prospectus

Online
www.spr-law.com

Printed
Semple Piggot Rochez
Lower Ground
62 Blenheim Crescent
Notting Hill
London
W11 1NZ
(020) 7833 4306

Email
msp@spr-law.com

SEMPLE PIGGOT ROCHEZ

UNIVERSITY OF WOLVERHAMPTON

School of Law Molineux Street Wolverhampton WV1 1SB
Tel: (01902) 321000 Fax: (01902) 321570

College Profile

Based in Wolverhampton and offers courses for students intending to become solicitors. The law school has been offering these courses for over 20 years. Their LPC programme has had consistently good ratings. The lecturers are drawn from ex-solicitors, barristers, academics and individuals from business and industry. There are excellent IT facilities, a well-stocked library and a sports centre.

Legal Practice Course (full/part-time)

The vocational training course for those intending to practise as solicitors. The core subjects of Business, Litigation and Conveyancing are taught, together with a range of commercial and private client options. Professional skills courses, practical workshops and seminars are all part of the training. Close links with local practitioners, mentoring, and CV distribution. Purpose built courtroom. Exclusive LPC resources room.
Group social activities.

Common Professional Examination (full/part-time)

The academic stage of training for non-law graduates wishing to become solicitors or barristers. A full programme of lectures and tutorials is offered on this demanding course. Students are taught by ex-solicitors and barristers. Places on the LPC are guaranteed for successful students. Flexible studying choices are under review.

Contact Name

Lynn Leighton-Johnstone
Recruitment and Admissions
(01902) 321 999

ANGLIA POLYTECHNIC UNIVERSITY

The Admissions Office Victoria Road South Chelmsford CM1 1LL
Tel: (01245) 493131 Fax: (01245) 490835
Email: admissions@anglia.ac.uk
Website: www.anglia.ac.uk
Contact: Ms Margie Freeman
Course Information:
CPE (full-time); LPC (full-time); LLM (Cambridge campus only) in International and European Business Law; LLM - MA International Sports Law; LLB (2 year Graduate Entry).

UNIVERSITY OF BIRMINGHAM

The Faculty of Law Edgbaston Birmingham B15 2TT
Tel: (0121) 414 6290 Fax: (0121) 414 3585
Contact: Mr David Salter
Course Information:
CPE full-time (contact Mrs D Lees); LPC (through De Montford University, contact Rachel Bathers); taught LLM full-time (contact Bernadette Lynch); LLM by research; MJur by research. (contact Stephen Shut); PhD by research full or part-time (contact Sally Lloyd-Bostock)

BOURNEMOUTH UNIVERSITY

School of Finance and Law Talbot Campus Dorset House Poole BH12 5BB
Tel: (01202) 595 187 Fax: (01202) 595 261
Email: fandl@bournemouth.ac.uk
Website: www.bournemouth.ac.uk
Course Information:
LPC (full-time); MA/Postgrad Diploma in Law (formerly CPE), full and part-time; MA/LLM Intellectual Property Management (full and part-time); LLM International Commerce Law (full and part-time); MA Media Law & Practice (full and part-time).

UNIVERSITY OF BRISTOL

Department of Professional Legal Studies Wills Memorial Building Queens Road Bristol BS8 1HR
Tel: (0117) 954 5361 Fax: (0117) 925 6717
Contact: Mr Maurice Cook
Course Information:
PhD; LLM (both taught and by research 2 years); MA in Legal Studies (2 years); LPC (1 year); Diploma in Intellectual Property Law and Practice (part-time for recently qualified solicitors); weekend certificate courses.

DE MONTFORT UNIVERSITY

Department of Professional Legal Studies The Gateway Leicester LE1 9BH
Tel: (0116) 257 7177 Fax: (0116) 257 7186
Website: www.dmu.ac.uk
Course Information:
LPC (full-time and open learning run at Leicester, Birmingham and Bristol in association with the University of Bristol); CPE (Postgrad Diploma in Law, full-time or distance learning); LLM in Advanced Legal Practice.

UNIVERSITY OF DURHAM

The Law Department 50 North Bailey Durham DH1 3ET
Tel: (0191) 374 2033 Fax: (0191) 374 2044
Website: www.dur.ac.uk/law
Contact: Postgraduate Admissions Secretary
Course Information:
LLM International and European Legal Studies; MA International Boundaries; research degrees: PhD, MJur and MPhil.

UNIVERSITY OF EAST ANGLIA

The Norwich Law School Norwich NR4 7TJ
Tel: (01603) 592 520 Fax: (01603) 250 245
Email: law@uea.ac.uk
Website: www.uea.ac.uk/law
Contact: Mrs Heather Reynolds
Course Information:
LLM Family Law and Family Policy; LLM Family Justice Studies; LLM International, Commercial and Business Law; Post Graduate Diploma in Legal Studies; Post Graduate Degrees by research LLM/MPhil and PhD.

UNIVERSITY OF ESSEX

The Department of Law Wivenhoe Park Colchester CO4 3SQ
Tel: (01206) 872587 Fax: (01206) 873428
Email: fsceats@essex.ac.uk
Contact: Kirstie Sceats
Course Information:
LLM International Human Rights; LLM European Community Law; LLM International Trade; LLM Public Law; LLM Law in Transition in the New Europe; Doctoral programme in Legal Theory; PhD and MPhil research programmes.

UNIVERSITY OF EXETER

The Centre for Legal Practice Amory Building Rennes Drive Exeter EX4 4RJ
Tel: (01392) 263157 Fax: (01392) 263400
Email: Jenny.L.Cook@exeter.ac.uk
Website: www.exeter.ac.uk/clp/
Contact: Professor Vivienne Shrubsall
Course Information:
Pg Dip Law; LPC.

UNIVERSITY OF GLAMORGAN

Law School Pontypridd CF37 1DL
Tel: (01443) 483007 Fax: (01443) 483008
Website: www.glam.ac.uk
Contact: Mr Bryn Lloyd
Course Information:
CPE (full and part-time); LPC (full and part-time); LLM European Community Law; LLM Commercial Dispute Resolution.

UNIVERSITY OF HERTFORDSHIRE

Central Admissions Hatfield Campus College Lane Hatfield AL10 9AB
Tel: (01707) 285197 Fax: (01707) 284870
Email: m.temple@herts.ac.uk
Website: www.herts.ac.uk/business/division/law/pages
Contact: Mrs Margaret Temple
Course Information:
PG Dip LPC (P/T), LLM (various subjects), LPC, CPD Short Courses for Barristers, Research degrees in various subjects.

UNIVERSITY OF HOLBORN

Registry 200 Greyhound Road London W14 9RY
Tel: (020) 7385 3377 Fax: (020) 7381 3377
Email: HLT@holborncollege.ac.uk
Website: www.holborncollege.ac.uk
Contact: Karen Clifton
Course Information:
LLM in conjunction with the University of Wolverhampton; Bar course (full-time) for non U.K. Practitioners; New York Bar course; LDip/CPE.

UNIVERSITY OF HUDDERSFIELD

The Department of Law Queensgate Huddersfield HD1 3DH
Tel: (01484) 472192 Fax: (01484) 472279
Website: www.hud.ac.uk
Contact: The Secretary at the Department of Law
Course Information:
PgDip in Law (CPE) (full and part-time, open and distance learning); LPC (full and part-time); LLM (distance learning); LLM European Business Law; MA Legal Studies; MA Health Care Law.

ILEX TUTORIAL COLLEGE LTD

College House Manor Drive Kempston Bedford MK42 7AB
Tel: (01234) 841010 Fax: (01234) 841373
Email: itslaw@ilex-tutorial.ac.uk
Website: www.ilex-tutorial.ac.uk
Contact: Jenine Marshall
Course Information:
Distance-Learning Post-Graduate Diploma in Law (formerly the CPE); Distance-Learning LPC; Fast-track Professional Skills Course (PSC); Distance-Learning LL.M/Post-Graduate Diploma in Business Law.

THE LANCASHIRE LAW SCHOOL

University of Central Lancashire Preston PR1 2HE
Tel: (01772) 893060 Fax: (01772) 892972
Email: l.studies@uclan.ac.uk
Contact: Law Admissions Officer
Course Information:
CPE (full and part-time); LPC (part-time and full-time subject to validation); LLM Employment Law (full and part-time); LLM Environmental Law (full and part-time); MA International Law and Business (full-time); MPhil/PhD.

LEEDS METROPOLITAN UNIVERSITY

The School of Law Cavendish Hall Beckett Park Campus Leeds LS6 3QS
Tel: (0113) 283 7549 Fax: (0113) 283 3206
Contact: Mrs Jane Larkin
Course Information:
PG Dip Law (full and part-time); PG Dip Legal Practice (full and part-time); LLM.

UNIVERSITY OF LEICESTER

The Faculty of Law University Road Leicester LE1 7RH
Tel: (0116) 252 2753 Fax: (0116) 252 5023
Email: jmg16@le.ac.uk
Contact: Mrs J Goacher
Course Information:
LLM or MA Criminal Law and Justice; LLM European and International Trade Law; LLM European Higher Legal Studies; LLM or MA Human Rights and Civil Liberties; LLM or MA Legal Studies.

LIVERPOOL JOHN MOORES UNIVERSITY

School of Law, and Applied Social Studies Josephine Butler House 1 Mertle Street Liverpool L7 4DN
Tel: (0151) 231 3951 Fax: (0151) 231 3908
Email: lswdmage@livjm.ac.uk
Contact: Deborah Magee
Course Information:
LLM in European Business Studies (part-time); LPC (part-time).

LONDON GUILDHALL UNIVERSITY

Department of Law 84 Moorgate London EC2M 6SQ
Tel: (020) 7320 1616 Fax: (020) 7320 3462
Email: enqs@lgu.ac.uk
Website: www.lgu.ac.uk
Contact: Course Enquiry Unit
Course Information:
LLM International and Comparative Business Law; Legal Practice Course; CPE.

MIDDLESEX UNIVERSITY

Middlesex University Business School The Burroughs Hendon London NW4 4BT
Tel: (020) 8362 5000 Fax: (020) 8202 1539
Email: C.Chang@mdx.ac.uk
Website: mubs.ac.uk
Contact: Mr Chris Chang
Course Information:
CPE (full-time and distance learning); LLM Employment Law.

UNIVERSITY OF NEWCASTLE-UPON-TYNE

Newcastle Law School Newcastle-upon-Tyne NE1 7RU
Tel: (0191) 222 7558 Fax: (0191) 212 0064
Email: law-staff@newcastle.ac.uk
Contact: Ms I. Cheyne
Course Information:
LLM International Legal Studies; LLM International Trade; LLM Environmental Legal Studies; MPhil or PhD by research; MA Environmental Law and Policy.

UNIVERSITY OF NORTH LONDON

School of Law Ladbroke House 62-66 Highbury Grove London N5 2AD
Tel: (020) 7607 2789 Fax: (020) 7753 5403
Email: cpedulla@unl.co.uk
Contact: Christine Pedulla
Course Information:
CPE (full and part-time); LPC (part-time) - Contact Janet Loveless.

OXFORD INSTITUTE OF LEGAL PRACTICE

King Charles House Park End Street Oxford OX1 1JD
Tel: (01865) 722 619 Fax: (01865) 722 408
Email: oilp@brookes.ac.uk
Website: www.oxilp.ac.uk
Contact: Mr Nick Johnson
Course Information: LPC.

QUEEN MARY AND WESTFIELD COLLEGE UNIVERSITY OF LONDON

Centre for Commercial Law Studies London E1 4NS
Tel: (020) 7975 5127 Fax: (020) 8980 1079
Email: admissions-ccls@qmw.ac.uk
Contact: The LLM Administrator
Course Information:
LLM Commercial Law (wide range of modules available) full and part-time; MSc Management of Intellectual Property; Diplomas in Advanced Commercial Law; Certificate in Intellectual Property Law; research degrees: MPhil and PhD.

UNIVERSITY OF SHEFFIELD

The Law Department Crookesmoor Building Conduit Road Sheffield S10 1FL
Tel: (0114) 222 6752 Fax: (0114) 222 6832
Email: lpc@sheffield.ac.uk
Contact: The Central Applications Board
Course Information:
LPC (full-time) plus others. Information on application.

SOUTH BANK UNIVERSITY

Post Graduate Admissions 103 Borough Road London SE1 0AA
Tel: (020) 7815 8158 Fax: (020) 7815 6130
Email: enrol@sbu.ac.uk
Website: www.sbu.ac.uk
Contact: General Enquiries
Course Information:
PG Dip Legal Studies (CPE); PG Dip Legal Practice (LPC); Certificate in applied advice work.

STAFFORDSHIRE UNIVERSITY

Staffordshire University Law School Leek Road Stoke on Trent ST4 2DF
Tel: (01782) 294550 Fax: (01782) 294335
Contact: Ms Pat Hopkins
Course Information:
LLM (27 modules available); CPE; LPC; LLM in Legal Practice; MA Legal Studies; Postgraduate MPhil by dissertation.

UNIVERSITY OF STRATHCLYDE

Centre for Professional Legal Studies The Law School 141 St. James' Road Glasgow G4 0LT
Tel: (0141) 548 2745 Fax: (0141) 552 4264
Email: linda.iron@strath.ac.uk
Contact: Mrs Linda Iron
Course Information:
Pg Dip Legal Practice (full-time); Postgraduate Diploma/LLM in Construction Law and in Information Technology Law (full and part-time); Masters Programme Information Technology (distance learning); research degrees (variety of subjects); LLM Commercial Law.

UNIVERSITY OF SUSSEX

School of Legal Studies Art Block E Falmer Brighton BN1 9SN
Tel: (01273) 678 562 Fax: (01273) 678 466
Email: L.O-Meara@sussex.ac.uk
Website: www.susx.ac.uk
Contact: Ms Lynn O'Meara
Course Information:
LLM International Criminal Law; LLM International Commercial Law; LLM; CPE; MA in Criminal Justice.

THAMES VALLEY UNIVERSITY

Thames Valley University St Mary's Road Ealing London W5 5RF
Tel: (020) 8231 2592 Fax: (020) 8231 2553
Email: LPC@tvu.ac.uk
Website: www.tvu.ac.uk
Contact: Mary Johnstone or Sally Blakesey
Course Information:
CPE (full and part-time); LPC (full-time).

UNIVERSITY OF THE WEST OF ENGLAND

Faculty of Law Frenchay Campus Coldhabour Lane Bristol BS16 1QY
Tel: (0117) 976 2171 Fax: (0117) 976 3841
Email: law@uwe.ac.uk
Contact: Ms Louise Barks
Course Information:
CPE (full-time and open learning); LPC (full-time and open learning); BVC; PSC (full and part-time); modular MA/LLM.

UNIVERSITY OF WESTMINSTER

School of Law 4-12 Little Titchfield Street London W1P 7FW
Tel: (020) 7911 5088 Fax: (020) 7911 5175
Email: regent@wmin.ac.uk
Website: www.wmin.ac.uk
Contact: Law Admissions Officer
Course Information:
LPC (full or part-time); CPE (full-time); LLM International Law; LLM International Commercial Law; LLM Women and Law; LLM Entertainment Law; LLM Dispute Prevention and Resolution; LLM Venture Capital; Grad Dip Law.

WORCESTER COLLEGE OF TECHNOLOGY

Deansway Worcester WR1 2JF

Tel: (01905) 725 582 Fax: (01905) 289 06

Email: law@wortech.ac.uk

Contact: John Duddington

Course Information: CPE (part-time); MA Legal Studies.